STRATEGIC SELLOUT

Indian-U.S. Nuclear Deal

STRATEGIC SELLOUT

Indian-U.S. Nuclear Deal

P.K. Iyengar

A.N. Prasad

A. Gopalakrishnan

Bharat Karnad

PENTAGON PRESS

Strategic Sellout: Indian-U.S. Nuclear Deal / P.K. Iyengar, A.N. Prasad,
A. Gopalakrishnan, Bharat Karnad

ISBN 978-81-8274-432-5

First Published in 2009

Published by

PENTAGON PRESS
206, Peacock Lane, Shahpur Jat,
New Delhi-110049
Phones: 011-64706243, 26491568
Telefax: 011-26490600
email: rajan@pentagon-press.com
website: www.pentagon-press.com

Printed at
Syndicate Binders
A-20, Hosiery Complex, Noida Phase-II Extn., Noida-201305, U.P.

Acknowledgements

We wish to thank Mr. Yash Gopal Chauhan, Assistant Librarian in the Centre for Policy Research, New Delhi, for help in collating the material for this compilation.

P.K. Iyengar
A.N. Prasad
A. Gopalakrishnan
Bharat Karnad

Contents

PUBLIC LETTERS AND APPEALS BY NUCLEAR SCIENTISTS CRITICAL OF THE NUCLEAR DEAL

CHAPTERS IN BOOKS AND ARTICLES IN PROFESSIONAL JOURNALS

Heading into Nuclear Oblivion

BHARAT KARNAD©

With Manmohan Singh securing a second term in office, the Congress Party coalition government is pressing ahead with the nuclear deal. Consequently, there will be no dearth of books and commentaries in India and the West finding great virtue and new reasons why this deal is a bargain for India. This book is an antidote to such flummery, revealing what is fundamentally wrong with the deal in terms of grand strategy, strategy, and nuclear science and technology development. It is a compilation of writings by specialist authors who sounded the tocsin well before the deal was mooted and who continued to do so long after it was formalized. There was also warning that in the Barack Obama presidency, the nuclear deal would become a garrote for India. That prediction will come true with the triumvirate of Robert J. Einhorn, Ellen Tauscher, and Rose Gotmoeller installed in the State Department and dictating US nonproliferation policy.

The concern of the authors is not what happens in Washington, DC but what motivates the Indian Government and animates Indian policy. Prime Minister Manmohan Singh is at the centre of this deal. Having unwisely expended a lot of his personal capital on it, he is loath other than to push on with the deal. Apparently, it matters little to him that the benchmarks mentioned in the July 18, 2005 Joint Statement, which he repeatedly iterated in his *suo moto* statements in Parliament in defence of the deal, have not been met by the United States. India was to enjoy the basic "rights and privileges" of a country with "advanced nuclear technology"—a phrase, the Indian government has insisted is a synonym for nuclear weapon state status, and parity of treatment with the United States in the nuclear realm. Alas, the supposedly friendly George W. Bush Administration flatly rejected this reading of the Joint Satement and the successor regime of President Barack Obama has entirely ignored it in mounting pressure on the Indian Government to sign the 1968 Non-Proliferation Treaty (NPT) as a non-nuclear weapon state along with Pakistan and North Korea.[1]

Worse, while India fulfilled its obligations—submitting a "separation plan" acceptable to the International Atomic Energy Agency (IAEA) in Vienna that cleaved its nuclear energy programme into separate and uneconomical civilian and military spheres and, in good faith, negotiated the "123 Agreement", for example, the enabling US law—the "Henry J. Hyde United States-India Civilian Atomic Energy Cooperation Act of 2006", besides emphasizing the "no testing" predicate for nuclear cooperation, banned transfer of any technology relating to uranium enrichment, plutonium re-processing and heavy water manufacture, enjoined India to get its Iran policy to "converge" with that of the US policy, forbade the reprocessing of the foreign origin spent fuel from imported reactors and, vide the so-called "Obama Amendment", prevented India from stockpiling either imported natural uranium used in two-thirds of all the indigenous CANDU/INDU reactors that, as a result of the deal, have gone under IAEA safeguards or the enriched uranium fuel for light water reactors beyond what is required for immediate "operational" needs of the power plants. These requirements fly in the face of contrary declarations by the Indian Government.

Such and other developments are not a surprise, however, and along with the other problems that may arise in the future, were foretold by the four authors in the articles they wrote for various newspapers, websites, and periodicals which are here compiled in chronological order (in the first section), and in the longer analyses published in professional journals or as chapters in anthologies (grouped in the second section). The Annexure section adds value by reproducing the documents—July 18, 2005 Joint Statement, 123 Agreement, the Hyde Act, etc—mentioned in the articles as reference, so that the reader may better appreciate the arguments made.

Three of the authors—P.K. Iyengar, A.N. Prasad, and A. Gopalakrishnan, are stalwarts of the Indian nuclear establishment and had stellar roles in making India a nuclear weapons state. All the authors wrote knowledgably, relentlessly, and with urgency and foresight and, for the first time on a public issue of import, in an uncoordinated but sustained "campaign mode", in the hope that the Indian Government would see the light and withdraw from the nuclear deal. We feared, in the main, that it would undermine the integrity of the Indian nuclear programme, hurt independent nuclear technology development, compromise the nuclear security interests of the country and its strategic independence, and lead to the loss of India's sovereignty. The views especially of the scientist-authors evolved over time, from being supportive of nuclear cooperation with the United States and members of the Nuclear Suppliers Group if it ended up providing India access to advanced technology to getting progressively more disturbed as the negotiations proceeded, the deal unfolded, and they became aware of the compromises made at the expense of national security and the indigenous nuclear energy programme.

The articles (compiled in this book) dilate on the larger strategic themes and the foreign policy and military implications, and the economic costs to

India, and throw light on the technological aspects, disclosing just how ephemeral many of the promised benefits are or may turn out to be. Indeed, the authors were usually ahead of the curve, reacting to new developments and anticipating outcomes at every turn in terms of the US actions and policies and the inevitable Indian concessions. (Siddharth Varadarajan reporting in *The Hindu* and Brahma Chellaney, did yeoman work mainly filling in the details—the former using his official contacts, disclosed information about the ongoing negotiations and the state of play at the Delhi, Washington and the International Atomic Energy Agency, Vienna ends, and the latter deconstructed documents such as the Hyde Act, and the "123 Agreement", almost as soon as the texts became available and otherwise kept up a ceaseless patter iterative of criticism.) In fact, so effective was the public campaign against the deal, that included open letters by the nuclear scientists in 2006 to the Prime Minister and to the Members of Parliament in July 2008 on the eve of the confidence vote (and included here), it got up the government's nose. A worried Manmohan Singh regime resorted to illiberal measures, among them "persuading" the majority owner of the only newspaper to feature the writings of the four authors, to desist from doing so. Having succeeded in this censorship mission, Sanjaya Baru, the then Media Adviser to the Prime Minister crowed "We have silenced *The Asian Age*!".[2] During that period the daily was edited by M.J. Akbar.

The articles published in the period 2004-2009 and reproduced in this book are important because the arguments made in them continue to remain valid, providing the criteria to judge the downstream and long-term effects of the deal as and when it is implemented. The repeated warnings by the authors on numerous aspects can be juxtaposed against the optimistic statements in support of it by its chief promoter, Manmohan Singh. Specifically, as the writings show, the authors anticipated correctly the ground that was ceded by India in the negotiations and the dangers involved in doing so, the indistinct nature of the American *quo* compared to the substantive Indian *quid*, of fluffy US inducements in the form of promised transfers of advanced technology, which was only a euphemism for selling reactor technology to revive the US nuclear industry. It is another matter that this reactor design— the Westinghouse AP 1000—has repeatedly failed safety tests and denied certification by the US Nuclear Regulatory Commission.[3] Further, the prospect of an Indian role in international nuclear technology development projects that apparently so dazzled Dr. Manmohan Singh are, as the authors predicted, of the "pie in the sky" variety such as the International Thermonuclear Experimental Reactor (ITER), or the kind the US itself is abandoning such as the Global Nuclear Energy Partnership (GNEP).[4]

The worrisome question is why did the Prime Minister swallow such bare-faced baits? Why did he want India to join GNEP, considering that this programme favours design and development of proliferation-resistant "once through" thermal reactors that "burn" more of the fissile material, when India long ago embarked on the alternative track, of going in for reactors that "breed" it? Utilizing India's vast Thorium reserves requires breeder reactors, as the nuclear visionary and first chairman of the Indian Atomic Energy Commission, Homi J. Bhabha's 1955 three stage plan recognized, to produce feedstock for Thorium-fueled power plants, which will become the engines of genuine energy security and economic prosperity for the country. In the event, doesn't subscribing to GNEP seem in conflict with, and subversive of, the Bhabha plan that the Indian Government continues to swear by?

The authors, additionally, sounded the alarm, among other things, over the "separation plan" even as it was being hatched, pointing out that it was configured to weaken the country's weapons capability and the integrity, coherence, and the economic viability of the dual-purpose Indian nuclear energy programme painstakingly put together by Dr. Bhabha. And, generally, they foresaw the major turn of events in the underway process to hammer out, what in retrospect appears to be a bad "bargain". It thus transpired that the negotiations progressed in parallel with the rise in the demands by Washington coupled with subtle or substantial changes in positions it had originally taken. The gullible or, alternatively, beleaguered Manmohan Singh, feeling the heat, caught in the tightening US nonproliferation policy tourniquet, and finding himself out on a limb politically at home, but determined to save face and the deal at the same time, heeded Washington more than he did the national interest. Thus, in the crucial "123 Agreement", for instance, the authors pointed out, that India was compelled to accept only in the preamble of the document a mention of the "corrective measures" India would feel free to take if the United States and the other 44 members of Nuclear Suppliers Group (NSG) failed to deliver on their commitments and nuclear trade and commerce did not materialize because of official obstacles. Without spelling out in detail elsewhere in the document just what India meant by "corrective measures"—such as withdrawing its nuclear facilities from the IAEA safeguards regime, for instance, it amounted to little and offers India no legal protection. With more and more indigenous reactors and imported power plants constructed and going on grid, a progressively larger portion of its nuclear energy programme will come under international supervision and oversight, as will its nuclear research projects, which the scientists feared would lead to proprietary information becoming available to the IAEA and through this agency, to the US. For example, Brazil has designed and developed more efficient and effective horizontal rotor for centrifuges (instead of the standard vertical rotor) used in uranium enrichment but has prevented IAEA from accessing it because it expects the US will get hold of the details and the data.

Moreover, with the number of dedicated military use reactors frozen at eight, in a crisis or under pressure to sign the FMCT, the surge capacity for production of weapon grade plutonium and of tritium (a by-product of the functioning of the heavy water moderated natural uranium CANDU reactors] separable by the indigenously developed multi-phase "detritiation technology"[5] will be unavailable to India. The country, as a result, will find itself hamstrung nuclear weapons capability-wise, strategically constrained, and slipping slowly into the international nonproliferation net. These negatives are what—as the articles in this book show—the authors, Cassandra-like, kept wailing about.

Are there any positives to the nuclear deal? One potential geopolitical gain the Prime Minister probably was influenced by was the US' professed goal to help India become, in Secretary of State Condoleeza Rice's words, a "major power in the world in the 21st century". The Prime Minister seemingly did not stop to wonder how the country could achieve such status if the US, at the same time, insisted that India not test again nor acquire reliable and credible thermonuclear weapons to attain at least "notional [strategic] parity" with China in Asia.[6] Instead, Manmohan Singh, by way of his main justification of the nuclear deal, harped about making up the energy deficit in the country in the shortest possible time by purchasing reactors from abroad. This was necessary, he claimed, to maintain a high economic growth rate. But, as the authors made plain, this energy solution does not measure up. India will have to resume nuclear testing—later if not sooner—because the thermonuclear weapon tested in 1998 was a "fizzle", producing only 7-20 percent of its designed yield. The inherent flaw(s) in the design cannot be corrected by computer simulation alone, and some time or the other will have to undergo physical tests for validation purposes. Testing becomes necessary, as the authors stressed, also because of the limitations of the country's simulation capability based on the twin facts that the explosion physics data is derived from a single, and that too failed, test and the relatively meagre computational speeds available to Indian weapons designers. Indian super computers have speeds in the 1-2 trillion operations per second range compared, say, to the 1000 trillion operations per second capacity super computers in the Los Alamos National Laboratory used in crunching data from 1,800 tests the US has conducted so far. And, unlike the US, India does not have a powerful inertial confinement fusion facility to engineer miniature thermonuclear explosions to aid in designing hydrogen weapons without actually testing. [7]

If and when India tests, nuclear cooperation with the US and the NSG will end. In the period leading up to that eventuality, however, it is likely several foreign reactors will have begun operating and many more would be under construction or in the pipeline. The cutoff in the fuel supply will result in the power plants slowly grinding to a halt, and the construction of newer reactors bought from abroad stopping as well. At a minimum, India will confront a serious dilemma—test and obtain a credible thermonuclear deterrent but absorb the financial losses from a shut-down of imported power plants and half-constructed reactors. Or, stay stuck with strategic forces armed with unproven, untested, unsafe and unreliable hydrogen weapons but continue having a slightly higher quantum of nuclear electricity in the grid than before the deal. And, were a future Indian Government to choose to secure a credible deterrent over additional nuclear power and order nuclear testing, the hard currency reserves expended on the foreign reactors up to that point, will have to be written off, and the plants already paid for will become dead investment. Worse, parts of the economy dependent on nuclear energy from these reactors may have to close down for a while until alternative power is made available. This will create serious economic and industrial dislocations. These were the sorts of risk calculi the authors brought out into the open.

But all this assumes that Manmohan Singh's plan to install 20,000 MW worth of imported reactors by 2020 is practicable in the first place, which the authors have repeatedly asserted it is not. It may take until 2020 just to sort out the differences over the liability clause, completion time and performance guarantees, and other such onerous issues, and bring closure to the contract negotiations. The foreign reactor Companies have learned from recent experiences about the difficulties attending on the construction of reactor complexes and the troubles they have encountered with customers. Areva, the Franco-German firm, for example, is under assault at home, facing a French government mandated breakup, with its Transport and Distribution arms accounting for 15% of the world market for "medium tension electricity grid equipment" being spun off and sold to generate the monies for investment in the Company's core nuclear business.[8] Ann Lauvergeon, the chief executive, has opposed this sale on the basis that retaining these smaller companies enables Areva to more effectively sell the whole package of reactors and associated hardware and services.[9] For India, a splintered French Company will result in negotiations with several corporate entities further ratcheting up the price for the French reactor systems. Areva is facing heavy penalties for time and cost-over runs in the construction of the 1600 MW reactor in Olkiluoto, Finland, costing some $8 billion. While the two parties have agreed on international arbitration, Areva is blaming the Finnish authorities for impeding timely construction of the plant and escalating the cost.[10]

If the relatively efficient Finnish State can be held responsible for the project delays, the horrendously inept and inefficient government system in India will provide Areva and the other foreign Companies with a raft of ready excuses to pushback on the project completion date and to get out from under other contractual obligations, including holding the price line. Indeed, these foreign Firms will insist on passing on to the Indian taxpayer every financial risk, burden and onus for delay and product quality and performance, while minimizing their own exposure. As it is, reactor purchases will translate into massive outlays, financial boondoggles, huge commission-mongering and corruption and, ultimately, unaffordable unit cost of electricity, a 'la Dabhol—the controversial thermal power plant fueled by imported naptha that was erected at great cost, carried tales of enormous corruption, was meant to deal with the energy shortfalls in Maharashtra, but ended up not getting on grid because no consumers could be found to off-take the pricey electricity.

Moreover, it is a roiled world of reactor technology suppliers that the Manmohan Singh-led government faces. The German conglomerate, Siemens, is seeking to end its joint venture with Areva and to combine instead with the Russian vendor, Rosatom.[11] It will complicate India's negotiations with both France and Russia. Considering the problems faced by all the vendors and the difficulties of negotiating a satisfactory contract with the supplier Firms to guarantee electricity by certain date and at reasonable price, the initial plan involving the purchase of two 1,000 plus MW reactors each from France (Areva), Russia (Rosatom), and the United States (Toshiba-Westinghouse), is already in trouble. Were the timeline for the realization of Manmohan Singh's imported nuclear energy plan extended to, say, 2030-2035, then even if deals were struck and foreign reactors start production, the proportion of electricity from nuclear sources would still amount to a miniscule 5-6 percent—up from 2-3 per cent today—of the total energy expected to be produced in the country in those years, according to a Planning Commission Study by one of its members, Kirit Parikh. Whence our argument is strengthened that relying on imported nuclear energy is a recipe for wasteful expenditure and a security boondogle. In this context, the relative value of resuming testing, acquiring a dependable thermonuclear deterrent, and ditching the nuclear deal with the United States (that can only poison bilateral relations and preclude productive strategic military cooperation in the future) will increase compared to the slight energy-cum-economic payoffs from the exorbitantly priced imported nuclear megawatts laced with lots of uncertainty.

What is really vexatious about the deal is that Prime Minister Manmohan Singh, fixated on the supposed civilian benefits that in reality will not pan out, has guilelessly ignored its strategic and military ramifications. The US was resolved to freeze India's progress in the weapons field at the low end of the technology learning curve. In this, Washington has succeeded by getting the Indian Government to agree to not test again. Likewise, the US long ago perceived India's heavy water reactors as proliferation threat that needed to be constrained.[12] With this deal, the bulk of the indigenous heavy water reactors in the Indian nuclear programme will come under international oversight, and become unavailable for military use. These two factors will effectively bottle up the Indian strategic nuclear weapons capability.

Manmohan Singh's willingness to divest the country of its strategic options is in stark contrast to what is happening in the neighbourhood. China's proliferation activity has got more brazen. It has accelerated its material assistance speedily to bring two of the largest weapon plutonium-producing reactors anywhere (Kushab I & II) on line,[13] enabling Pakistan to host the fastest growing nuclear weapons programme in the world.[14] This augmentation of the Pakistani nuclear capability and arsenal is occurring at a time when the danger of a Taliban takeover of the Pakistani State and its strategic weapons inventory has increased dramatically.[15] For Beijing, the policy of complicating an adversary's military calculus outweighs its pragmatism, and pursuing a policy of strategically strengthening Pakistan, its proxy in the region, just so it continues to distract and restrict India to the subcontinent, continues to fetch high returns without incurring any great cost (in terms of a hard "tit for tat" Indian response of, say, passing sensitive nuclear technologies to Vietnam and other states on the Chinese periphery fearful of Beijing's ambitions).[16] In the meantime, China is upgrading its strategic forces with a defence budget in 2008 that the Pentagon reckons was as high as $150 billion and which the US military believes has secured "the most active land-based ballistic and cruise missile program in the world."[17]

In contrast to the nuclear buildup in the neighbourhood, India by opting for the nuclear deal may, in fact, have paved the way for its compliance with ever more stringent US nonproliferation demands. It may not formally sign the NPT but India is already an informal adherent, and as part of its obligations as a de facto member, appears willing to acquiesce in the Comprehensive Test Ban Treaty (CTBT)[18] —a fact inherent in its acceptance of the non-testing clause as the foundation of the nuclear deal. And, it left itself open to be arm-twisted into the Fissile Material Cutoff Treaty (FMCT) because Delhi has left itself no wriggle room.

The strategic security milieu is morphing into something dire, quite literally by the day, and yet the Congress coalition government is doing little to shore up the country's strategic forces. This lack of will to protect vital national interests was shown up by the gutsy and no-nonsense attitude of a small and vulnerable North Korea. In an "in your face" gesture, it not only exploded a second, possibly 20 kiloton yield, nuclear device in May 2009[19] but, for added measure, indulged in a spate of missile firings off its coast and prepared its 4,000 mile range intercontinental ballistic missile capable of hitting Alaska for launch.[20] It left the United States and its regional allies South Korea and Japan fuming impotently,[21] and Washington was reduced to pleading with China to do something about North Korea's provocation.[22] Unlike Pyongyang's act of defiance, the Indian Government renewed its calls for nuclear disarmament as if it were an attainable goal.[23] This, notwithstanding US President Obama's candid admission in Prague that nuclear disarmament was unlikely in his "lifetime".[24] Disarmament per se, it is obvious, is not an American priority. But ratification of CTBT and a "new" FMCT that, as Obama put it, "verifiably ends the production of fissile materials intended for use in nuclear weapons" is.[25] In the event, Obama's pushing disarmament at this time may be nothing more than a *ruse strategique*, as Ambassador Arundhati Ghose, former Indian ambassador to the Conference on Disarmament and a votary for a nuclear weapons free world, laments, to douse the anger of the

NPT signatory states lest the 2010 NPT Review Conference end as dismally as the previous RevCon in 2005 did, leaving an already weakened nonproliferation treaty regime tottering.[26]

The trouble, however, is that Obama's FMCT initiative may hoist India with its own petard because Delhi's reticence about signing an FMCT until now hid behind President George W Bush's rejection of intrusive verification.[27] If the US propels a verifiable treaty through the UN Commission on Disarmament in Geneva, the ground will be sheared from underneath the Indian position. Having such contingent change in US attitude in mind, the more prudent course to follow would have been for the Indian Government to declare that it cannot conceive of signing such a treaty for the foreseeable future, considering that China's growing investment in, and modernization of, its strategic nuclear forces will have to be responded to with a strategic beefing up of its own and because, unlike the other weapons powers, including Pakistan, India neither has numerous dedicated high-capacity military-use weapon grade plutonium reactors—with the CIRUS reactor decommissioned under the "separation plan", India has just one 100 MW military use plutonium reactor in operation—nor as yet a sufficient stockpile of weapons-usable fissile material to meet all contingencies.

In fact, a pattern is discernible in the Indian Government's negotiating strategy during Manmohan Singh's Prime Ministership. India settled for a vague reference to "corrective measures" in the 123 Agreement because it believed that US' reluctance during the George W Bush presidency to ratify the CTBT and, implicitly, to nurse the testing option, afforded India an escape route. If the United States tested, India too could do the same. Similarly as regards the FMCT, Delhi was so certain of Washington's fear and distrust of intrusive international verification, that it promised unconditionally to sign a treaty negotiated by the Conference on Disarmament, in the expectation that the US Senate will not ratify it [28] and, in any case, that it can buy time to add to the country's weapon-plutonium holdings by stretching the negotiation phase in the manner it had done the CTBT in the Nineties. In both cases, India has been made hostage to US policy. Obama may try and make disarmament a priority item on the international agenda, but his proposal is careful to retain for the United States a hefty strategic nuclear clout even as it requires other countries to disarm completely. Delhi will have to reject this self-serving American initiative outright. The question is will Manmohan Singh do so? Very likely not. But he will seek to buy time and traction by reviving the 1988 "Rajiv Gandhi Action Plan". A time-bound disarmament plan will be dismissed by the Obama Administration as unrealistic, and the pressure will be on India to sign the CTBT and FMCT. Moreover, with a strong domestic lobby, including many senior retired military officers, albeit mainly those co-opted into Western "peace" efforts, pitching for India's signature on these treaties as way stations on the road to "global zero",[29] and the bulk of the clue-less media and westernized intelligentsia hurrahing, the Manmohan Singh government may just agree to leave the Indian nuclear weapons arsenal permanently small and weakened.

Such bleak prospects make one wonder just what Manmohan Singh has in mind for the country and the extent to which he is ready to go to hobble India's strategic capability in order to get close to the United States. Does he envision India as an American/Western *gendarme* in the region tasked locally with minor jobs (escorting American ships through the Malacca Straits, fighting off pirates), but generally supporting US security initiatives in Asia? With a truncated, quality-wise questionable, deterrent of its own, cowering under the extended US nuclear deterrence umbrella in case relations with China plummet and military hostilities loom, will becomes unavoidable, something foretold early by this author. This and the other costs of his policy of nuclear appeasement is what Manmohan Singh seems prepared for the country to pay.

Putting the Prime Minister's personal proclivities aside, it in no way helps India's reputation as an emerging independent great power in Asia to be seen as having been conned or coerced into a deal or, worse, having willingly entered into it when it is widely perceived as circumscribing the country's strategic wherewithal, capabilities and options and, more significantly, its sovereignty. Indeed, it is the loss of sovereignty—the most appalling consequence of the nuclear deal with the United States—that the authors most fear and which has animated our opposition to it.

With testing obviated, the basic Indian arsenal with the 20 kiloton yield bomb as the only tested and proven weapon in the armoury and a slew of untested and unproven thermonuclear and other warheads/weapons to fit the varying nose-cone geometries of different missiles on the shelf—all of the latter configured mainly by computer simulation—will suffer attrition and gradually degrade (as the Russian nuclear arsenal has done, in the absence of testing and upgradation of design facilities) until, in realistic terms, what little credibility the Indian nuclear arsenal started out with, will zero out. Beyond a qualitative plunge-point though, the Indian nuclear and thermonuclear weapons will cease to deter. India will by then have slid into nuclear irrelevance and oblivion. If the United States adheres strictly to its own law (the Hyde Act)—and there is no reason to believe it will not, this end-state is what the nuclear deal will entail.

END NOTES

1. Sachin Parashar, "India chafes at Obama pressure to sign NPT", *The Indian Express*, May 7, 2009.
2. Baru said this at a 2007 function at the United Service Institution of India attended by senior military men. Related to the author, on a non-attributable basis, by a retired three star rank naval officer.

3. James Kanter, "In Finland, Nuclear Renaissance Runs Into Trouble", *The New York Times*, May 29, 2009 at www.nyt.com.

4. "US GNEP programme dead, DOE confirms", April 15, 2009, *Nuclear Engineering International* at www.neimagazine.com

5. For more on the indigenously developed "detritiation" technology, see Bharat Karnad, *India's Nuclear Policy* [Newport, CN, and London: Praeger, Oct 2008; special South Asian edition [New Delhi: Pentagon Press, 2nd print, 2009], p. 56.

6. The concept of "notional parity" against China developed in Bharat Karnad, *Nuclear Weapons and Indian Security: The Realist Foundations of Strategy*, 2nd edition [New Delhi: Macmillan India, 2005, 2002]; pp. 614-647.

7. How advanced and complex the technology to construct such a facility is may be gleaned from a report on the National Ignition Facility that has been fired up at the Lawrence Livermore National Laboratory in the US. See William J. Broad, ""In Hot Pursuit of Fusion (or Folly)", *The New York Times*, May 26, 2009 at www.nyt.com.

8. Peggy Hollinger, "Areva division's fate set to be decided", *FT Weekend*, May 24, 2009.

9. Peggy Hollinger and Daniel Schafer, "Nuclear frisson", *Financial Times*, April 28, 2009.

10. Kanter, "In Finland, Nuclear Renaissance Runs Into Trouble".

11. Hollinger and Schafer, "Nuclear frisson".

12. Marvin M. Miller, "Heavy Water and Nonproliferation: Topical Report", *MIT Energy Laboratory Report No. MIT-EL 80-009*, May 1980.

13. Robert Windrem, "Pakistan expanding its nuclear capability", May 12, 2009, www.msnbc.msn.com.

14. Thom Shanker and David E. Sanger, "Pakistan Is Rapidly Adding Nuclear Arms, U.S. Says", *The New York Times*, May 18, 2009 at www.nyt.com.

15. David E. Sanger, "Obama's Worst Pakistan Nightmare", New York Times Magazine, *The New York Times*, January 11, 2009 at www.nyt.com. Also see R. Jeffrey Smith and Joby Warrick, "Nuclear Aims By Pakistan, India Prompt U.S. Congress", *The Washington Post*, May 28, 2009 at www.washingtonpost.com.

16. India's helping Vietnam strategically to arm itself against China discussed in Karnad, *India's Nuclear Policy*, pp. 30-31.

17. Ann Scott Tyson, "China's Defense Tab Sharply Up, U.S. Says", *The Washington Post*, March 26, 2009 at www.washingtonpost.com.

18. "Address bv Special Envoy to the Prime Minister, Mr Shyam Saran, at the Brookings Institution, Washington, DC on Indo-US Civil Nuclear Agreement" , March 23, 2009 at www.indianembassy.org/

19. Demetri Sevastopulo, "Blast signals possibility of further move towards atomic weapon", *Financial Times*, May 26, 2009.

20. "Reports: North Korea prepares long range missile", AP, June 1, 2009 at www.msnbc.msn.com/

21. David E. Sanger,"Tested Early by North Korea, Obama Has Few Options", *The New York Times*, May 26, 2009 at www.nyt.com.

22. Mark Landler and David E. Sanger, "U.S. Presses China for Tough Response to North Korea", *The New York Times*, May 29, 2009 at www.nyt.com.

23. See Shyam Saran's Brookings Speech, fn # 18

24. "Remarks by President Barack Obama, Hradcany Square, Prague, Czech Republic", April 5, 2009 at www.whitehouse.gov/

25. "President Obama's Statement to the Carnegie International Nonproliferation

Conference", [no date, but the Carnegie Conference was held in March 2009] at www.carnegieendowment.org/

26. Arundhati Ghose, "Nuclear Disarmament: Not in Obama's Lifetime?", 12 May 2009 at www.ipcs.org/

27. See Shyam Saran's speech, fn # 18.

28. For a plea that the US should not ratify CTBT, see John R. Bolton, "A Fast Way to Lose the Arms Race", *The New York Times*, May 26, 2009 at www.nyt.com. Bolton was Under-Secretary of State and, later, Ambassador to the UN, 2000-2008.

29. Lieutenant General V.R. Raghavan (Retd.), "Regional Security Dynamics and their Impact on India", *USI Journal*, Vol. CXXXVIII, October-December 2008; pp. 474-477.

Chronology of the Indo-US Nuclear Deal
(adopted from wikipedia.com)

July 18, 2005: President Bush and Prime Minister Singh first announce their intention to enter into a nuclear agreement in Washington.

March 1, 2006: Bush visits India for the first time.

March 3, 2006: Bush and Singh issue a joint statement on their growing strategic partnership, emphasising their agreement on civil nuclear cooperation.

July 26, 2006: The US House of Representatives passes the 'Henry J Hyde United States-India Peaceful Atomic Energy Cooperation Act of 2006,' which stipulates that Washington will cooperate with New Delhi on nuclear issues and exempt it from signing the Nuclear Nonproliferation Treaty.

July 28, 2006: In India, the Left parties demand threadbare discussion on the issue in Parliament.

November 16, 2006: The US Senate passes the 'United States-India Peaceful Atomic Energy Cooperation and US Additional Protocol Implementation Act' to "exempt from certain requirements of the Atomic Energy Act of 1954 United States exports of nuclear materials, equipment, and technology to India."

December 18, 2006: President Bush signs into law congressional legislation on Indian atomic energy.

July 27, 2007: Negotiations on a bilateral agreement between the United States and India conclude.

Aug 3, 2007: The text of the 'Agreement for Cooperation between the Government of the United States of America and the Government of India concerning peaceful uses of nuclear energy' (123 Agreement) is released by both governments.

Aug 13, 2007: Prime Minister Manmohan Singh makes a suo motu statement on the deal in Parliament.

Aug 17, 2007: The CPI(M) General Secretary Prakash Karat says the 'honeymoon (with government) may be over but the marriage can go on'.

Sept 4, 2007: In India, the UPA-Left committee to discuss nuclear deal set up.

Feb 25, 2008: Left parties in India say the ruling party would have to choose between the deal and its government's stability.

March 3–6, 2008: Left parties warn of 'serious consequences' if the nuclear deal is operationalised and set a deadline asking the government to make it clear by March 15 whether it intended to proceed with the nuclear deal or drop it.

March 7–14, 2008: The CPI writes to the Prime Minister Singh, warns of withdrawal of support if government goes ahead with the deal and puts political pressure on the Manmohan Singh government not to go with the deal.o

April 23, 2008: The Indian Government says it will seek the sense of the House on the 123 Agreement before it is taken up for ratification by the American Congress.

June 17, 2008: External Affairs Minister Pranab Mukherjee meets Prakash Karat, asks the Left to allow the government to go ahead with International Atomic Energy Agency (IAEA) safeguards agreement.

June 30, 2008: The Indian Prime Minister says his government prepared to face Parliament before operationalising the deal.

July 8, 2008: Left parties in India withdraw support to government.

July 9, 2008: The draft India-specific safeguards accord with the IAEA circulated to IAEA's Board of Governors for approval.

July 10, 2008: Prime Minister Manmohan Singh calls for a vote of confidence in Parliament.

July 14, 2008: The IAEA says it will meet on August 1 to consider the India-specific safeguards agreement.

July 18, 2008: Foreign Secretary Shivshankar Menon briefs the IAEA Board of Governors and some NSG countries in Vienna on the safeguards agreement.

July 22, 2008: Government is willing to look at "possible amendments" to the Atomic Energy Act to ensure that the country's strategic autonomy will never be compromised, says Prime Minister Singh.

July 22, 2008: The UPA government lead by Manmohan Singh wins trust vote in the Lok Sabha in India.

July 24, 2008: India dismisses warning by Pakistan that the deal will accelerate an atomic arms race in the sub-continent.

July 24, 2008: India launches full blast lobbying among the 45-nation NSG for an exemption for nuclear commerce.

July 25, 2008: IAEA secretariat briefs member states on India-specific safeguards agreement.

Aug 1, 2008: IAEA Board of Governors adopts India- specific safeguards agreement unanimously.

Aug 21-22, 2008: The NSG meet to consider an India waiver ends inconclusively amid reservations by some countries.

Sep 4-6, 2008: The NSG meets for the second time on the issue after the US comes up with a revised draft and grants waiver to India after marathon parleys.

Sept 11, 2008: President Bush sends the text of the 123 Agreement to the US Congress for final approval.

Sept 12, 2008: US remains silent over the controversy in India triggered by President Bush's assertions that nuclear fuel supply assurances to New Delhi under the deal were only political commitments and not legally binding.

Sept 13, 2008: The State Department issues a fact sheet on the nuclear deal saying the initiative will help meet India's growing energy requirements and strengthen the non-proliferation regime by welcoming New Delhi into globally accepted nonproliferation standards and practices.

Sept 18, 2008: The Senate Foreign Relations Committee kicks off a crucial hearing on the Indo-US nuclear deal.

Sept 19, 2008: America's nuclear fuel supply assurances to India are a "political commitment" and the government cannot "legally compel" US firms to sell a "given product" to New Delhi, top officials tells Congressional panel.

Sept 21, 2008: US financial crisis diverts attention from N-deal as both the Bush Administration and the Congress are bogged down over efforts to rescue bankrupt American banks. financial crisis in the country.

Sept 26, 2008: PM Singh meets President Bush at the White House, but were not able to sign the nuclear deal as the Congress did not approve it.

Sept 27, 2008: House of Representatives approves the Indo-US nuclear deal. 298 members voted for the Bill while 117 voted against.

Oct 1, 2008: Senate approves the Indo-US civil nuclear deal with 86 votes for and 13 against.

Oct 4, 2008: Secretary of State Rice visits Delhi. India and the US unable to ink the nuclear agreement with New Delhi insisting that it would do so only after President Bush signs it into a law, an occasion when it expects certain misgivings to be cleared.

Oct 4, 2008: White House announces that President Bush will sign the legislation on the Indo-US nuclear deal into a law on October 8.

Oct 8, 2008: President Bush signs legislation to enact the landmark US-India civilian nuclear agreement.

Oct 10, 2008: The 123 Agreement between India and US is finally operationalized between the two countries after the deal is signed by External Affairs Minister Pranab Mukherjee and his counterpart Secretary of State Condoleezza Rice in Washington D C.

ARTICLES
In Chronological Order

1. When U.S. Talks Nuclear to India

A. GOPALAKRISHNAN

Media reports have been suggesting for sometime that India is about to receive 'civilian nuclear co-operation' from the US. While analysts have been speculating that this might include the supply of foreign reactors and nuclear safety assistance, the Department of Atomic Energy (DAE) and the Ministry of External Affairs (MEA) have been totally silent about the details. In this regard, the central questions we need to ask are these: What concrete assistance does India need from the US to further our civilian nuclear program? What is it that the US wants in return for providing that help? And, what are the short-term and long-term strategic implications of such co-operation?

India today has fourteen operating nuclear power reactors and nine more are under various stages of construction or commissioning. Eighteen of these are pressurized heavy water reactors (PHWRs), two are the US-supplied boiling water reactors (BWRs) at Tarapur, two are pressurized water reactors (PWRs) being built at Kudamkulam, and the last one is a Prototype Fast Breeder Reactor (PFBR) of our own design on which civil work has just started. The US has never had any experience with commercial PHWRs. Tarapur reactors are of 1960 vintage and their US suppliers do not any longer have any spare parts or expertise for them. The PWRs coming up in Kudamkulam are of Russian supply, and here we get adequate help from the Russians. The US has no fast breeder reactors or expertise today to assist us. In short, it is abundantly clear that the US has no worthwhile current expertise in any of the type of reactors involved in the Indian nuclear power program.

The hints that the US is willing to co-operate with us in nuclear safety appears to be an attempt to create some doubt in the minds of the Indian public that perhaps the DAE is not capable of ensuring adequate safety in our installations without some tangible help from the US. In 1995, as Chairman of the Atomic Energy Regulatory Board (AERB), I had submitted a comprehensive report on the status of safety in DAE installations to the government. DAE was aware of most of those safety deficiencies, but had then failed to take corrective steps on their own. However, subsequent to the 1995 AERB report, DAE was compelled by the government to make urgent corrections. Today, I am reasonably assured that most of the critical safety issues pointed out in 1995 have been resolved satisfactorily. Indian engineers and scientists along with the national industries have achieved this, without any foreign assistance and often through the development of indigenous technological solutions. In short, according to several top ranking experts, there is little that we currently need from the US to maintain adequate safety in our civilian nuclear installations. India has just ratified the Convention on Nuclear Safety and what we would welcome is the opportunity for in-depth consultations with international experts, especially with France and Russia, in areas like fast breeder reactor design, operation and safety.

Dr. Homi Bhabha had considerations of energy security and self-reliance in mind when he framed the three-stage nuclear power plan for the country, which envisaged the use of our national resources of uranium and thorium to establish a totally indigenous nuclear technology base. To meet the ambitious nuclear power targets of DAE, we need to build a sufficient number of PHWRs first, so that adequate plutonium is produced for a rapid enough transition to the second stage breeder program. However, at present the DAE is beginning to face a serious shortage of natural uranium, even to fuel the current eighteen reactors on hand. NPCIL is already compelled to reduce the power production in their current PHWRs, in order to stretch out the available fuel for a longer period. Prospects of finding further large deposits of uranium ores in the country are bleek and the starting of mining operations in the few available sites is held up indefinitely due to local opposition. The DAE projection of 10,000 MWe of nuclear power by 2010 is thus unlikely to be met unless there is a substantial improvement in natural uranium availability.

Therefore, if the US is serious about meaningful 'civilian nuclear co-operation' with India, the MEA and the DAE should ask them to assist us in purchasing sufficient quantities of natural uranium or yellow cake from the international market. Today, we are barred from such purchases because of restrictions imposed by the Nuclear Suppliers' Group (NSG). India should initially plan on buying enough uranium to fuel about 5000 MWe of PHWR stations over their entire lifetime. In return, we could offer to place under IAEA safeguards all such PHWRs which will use the imported uranium. For this, the US needs to only make a one-time favourable recommendation to the NSG and exert US influence to get NSG concurrence. After all, the NSG is an entity created by the US, in response to India's 1974 nuclear test, and it is the US which still implicitly controls this group.

The US strategy, however, appears to be deeper than what is projected on the surface. In short, they would like to extract the maximum concessions from India in the nuclear arena, and in return make vague promises about a host of benefits to us in the non-nuclear areas. Certainly, each one of these concessions merits detailed discussions within the country and its parliament, right from the time it is mooted by the US and not just after a government decision is taken.

(The New Indian Express, May 5, 2005)

2. Hasten NPT's End

BHARAT KARNAD

What the great powers have now to consider is whether an inherently leaky system of nuclear non-proliferation is a greater danger to international peace and stability than an overtly nuclear India and Pakistan.

When the issue was so posed by this writer at a round table on non-proliferation held in Islamabad some two months back, it was well received. Even the American representative at the table, George Perkovich from the Carnegie Endowment for International Peace, who has co-authored a new but, not surprisingly, "status quo"-tilting non-proliferation manifesto (*Universal Compliance: A Strategy for Nuclear Security*), conceded that this was a reasonable way to articulate the problem.

The most constructive solution was offered by Josef Goldblat from the United Nations Institute for Disarmament Research, Geneva, who suggested that a "Group of Eight"—the five so-called "Non-Proliferation Treaty recognised" nuclear powers plus India, Pakistan and Israel, be formally constituted to hammer out a safe and secure nuclear non-proliferation regime, but whether as replacement for the prevailing NPT induced order, he tactfully left unsaid.

Goldblat's proposal has many virtues, chief among them being that it accommodates the existing reality and, implicitly, accepts the fact that further proliferation will take place only if one or more of these eight states want it to happen. After all, sustained help and connivance principally by China and, secondarily, the United States, facilitated Pakistan's attainment of nuclear weapons status and, more recently, Pakistan transferred some wherewithal for weaponisation to North Korea and Iran. Proliferation, in other words, was, is and always will be fuelled by the separate national interests of the Haves rather than by their collective assessment of its dangers.

If it is believed expedient and necessary at any time permanently to skew a regional rival or competitor's strategic calculus, what better means than to assist an adjoining state go nuclear? China, with its tradition of strategic foresight and support for the indirect approach to reduce an adversary, nuclear-armed Pakistan and may be considering doing the same with Bangladesh, pace the agreement for nuclear cooperation signed by Premier Wen Jiabao in Dhaka during his recent swing through South Asia.

The weaknesses of the Goldblat proposal, therefore, are many. In particular, there is no guarantee that all these eight nuclear weapon states will undertake to forever eschew nuclear assistance to key partners of the moment. India, with its inane desire to, be seen as a "responsible" nuclear power may, in the circumstances, end up being the only country hewing to this commitment. And, then again, what to do about North Korea and Iran who are readying to climb on board? Make it a "Group of Ten"? If not, why not?

Nevertheless, the Goldblat proposal has real potential, in that it offers substantive benefits for India and a more effective non-proliferation instrument that the US may find acceptable. The nuclear Group of Eight-concept, which has been communicated to officers in the disarmament and international security division in the ministry of external affairs, promises a new non-proliferation management regime in which-India will have its hands on the steering wheel. This means not only a straight-forward recognition of India as a nuclear weapons state but a role in shaping a different nuclear future and world order because, clearly, the present one based on the NPT and the equally defunct Comprehensive Test Ban Treaty, is in its death throes.

Instead of trying to cobble together such a group—on a negotiating track parallel to the ongoing NPT Review Conference (RevCon) in New York—and otherwise setting a new agenda, New Delhi seems content twiddling its thumbs, leaving itself open to pressures. Already, a number of concessions have been mooted by press pundits here premised on the belief that the George W. Bush administration, unlike its predecessor, is ready to ditch its old policy which is incorrect. Washington has not budged an iota from its position of seeking India and Pakistan's signature on the NPT.

It is suggested, for example, that India uphold the extant NPT regime by, among other things, unilaterally putting the country's entire "civilian" nuclear programme under International Atomic Energy Agency safeguards, subscribing to the Additional Protocol to the IAEA it has so far, for very good reasons, stoutly resisted doing, and agreeing to supply enriched uranium and reprocessed plutonium to signatory states who under a stiffened NPT dispensation (which may accrue from the RevCon) will be prevented from acquiring the full nuclear fuel cycle capabilities. These measures are tantamount to being more loyal than the king and an attempt to create a stake in the present system which victimises India. Of course, the US and the other four in the nuclear oligopoly will be thrilled were New Delhi in this manner to concede the game without playing it. It will not be the first time Indian rulers will be complicit in the country's subjugation.

Such recommendations are, in any case, fundamentally flawed. The assumptions that the Indian weapons use fissile material stockpile and production capacity are separate from the civilian programme and can be suitably sequestered and, capacity-wise, is generally on par with its P-5 counterparts, are wrong. India may have just enough reprocessed plutonium stockpiled for a minimally-sized nuclear arsenal. Worse, this proposal fails to factor in the possibility of expending a significant portion of it in future explosive tests (absolutely imperative to validate new weapon designs and verify weapons performance) and of having to respond to an accelerated Chinese strategic build-up which is likely, requiring India quickly to augment its fissile material stock (and its arms inventory) by running civilian power reactors at low fuel burn-up rates to make available plutonium for reprocessing to weapons-grade.

This situation may arise because instead of dedicated purely "military use" straightthrough graphite moderated plutonium producing reactors in its employ, the Department of Atomic Energy opted to build the multi-purpose 100 MW Dhruva with another of the same type under construction, which are incapable of outputting weapon-usable material efficiently and cost-effectively. The distinction between India's "civilian use" and "military use" reactors being spurious, straitjacketing the country's "Janus-faced" nuclear programme in any way and firming up the present nuclear order to win some brownie points, will merely confirm New Delhi's lack of strategic sense and its cluelessness about where India's national security interests really lie.

The NPT-regime is tottering; all it needs is a shove for it to go to pieces. India should provide it rather than be seduced by the US offer of enriched uranium-based "civilian nuclear technology" which is of a different genre and will not advance the state-of-the-art of the "plutonium economy" in India. It should set a deadline for the country's unconditional entry into the Nuclear Suppliers Group, failing which begin marketing its civilian use nuclear wares, including the indigenous INDU reactors in "closed loop" commercial transactions (where India sells and takes back used plutonium fuel), with an export orientation reflecting the *laissez faire* qualities of the Chinese policies. There are no adverse reactions India cannot counter, no sanctions India cannot ride out. The strategic value of unfettered nuclear trade or its threat is something. China in particular has effectively exploited, and Indian policy-makers ought to learn from its experience. And, it should take steps to pay back Beijing by strategically strengthening Vietnam and initiating "peaceful" nuclear cooperation with Taiwan. This two-pronged tack should be in conjunction with exploring the Group of Eight-option with the P-5, which last will show India's earnest in obtaining a stable nuclear order. But this requires nerve and self-confidence.

No-nonsense policies of the kind outlined above will amortise the vast investments India has made Fifties onwards in the nuclear sector and put the country's highly developed and versatile nuclear industry and nuclear energy programme on a sound, financial footing. More importantly it will provide sorely needed evidence that New Delhi has some self-respect and is prepared to play hard-ball.

(The Asian Age, May 9, 2005)

3. India-U.S. Nuclear Mismatch

Civilian nuclear co-operation between India and the US is said to be one of the topics for discussion when our Prime Minister visits Washington in mid-July. The officials of the Ministry of External Affairs (MEA) are quite upbeat about this, the Department of Atomic Energy (DAE) maintains a stoic silence on the matter, and the media analysts in the country anticipate a 'more optimistic outcome than everyone else. But, no official in India or the US is willing to provide a clear picture on what exactly is being discussed.

In this regard, the central questions we need to ask are these: What concrete assistance does India need from the US to further our civilian nuclear program? In relevant areas, are the foreign policy stances of the two countries close enough to warrant the successful initiation of any meaningful nuclear cooperation, without India having to make unacceptable compromises? What is it that the US wants in return from us for this co-operation? And, what are the short-term and long-term strategic implications of such co-operation?

India today has fourteen operating nuclear power reactors and nine more are under various stages of construction or commissioning. A detailed examination reveals that the US has no current experience in any of the types of nuclear reactors India is presently operating or constructing. Therefore, the DAE certainly realizes that the US has no worthwhile knowledge in the design, construction, operation, maintenance or safety of any of the present or future installations of the Indian nuclear power program.

The US and MEA officials keep hinting that the US is willing to cooperate with us in nuclear safety, but the DAE who have the primary responsibility for safety has never asked for any such help. In fact, without any foreign technical assistance, the DAE engineers have rectified almost all the safety deficiencies which I had documented and submitted to the government as Chairman of the Atomic Energy Regulatory Board (AERB) in 1995. Therefore, invoking the need for safety assistance from the US is merely a ploy to indirectly plant a doubt in the minds of the Indian public that DAE's capability to maintain safety in our reactors is inadequate in comparison to US expertise.

With my experience and awareness of nuclear safety in the US and India, I am convinced that neither the US possesses any crucial safety experience of direct relevance to India nor does India badly need their assistance.

The glaring indictment against the advisability of importing nuclear reactors from the US is the predicament in which we find ourselves today in the case of Tarapur reactors. The US having reneged their contractual obligation to supply life-time fuel to these reactors, India finds itself going from country to country to get enriched uranium to keep these reactors running. Contrary to the past DAE expectations, there is also no chance of attracting any foreign investment in conjunction with reactor imports.

Dr. Homi Bhabha had energy security and self-reliance in mind when he framed the three-stage nuclear power plan for the country, which envisaged the use of our natural uranium and the abundant thorium resources we have, to establish a totally indigenous nuclear technology base. Today, some fifty years after Bhabha unveiled his plan, his vision rooted in self-reliance still remains the best approach for India in this increasingly unipolar world.

To meet the nuclear power targets, India needs to build a sufficient number of natural uranium fuelled PHWRs first, so that adequate plutonium is produced for effecting a rapid transition to the second stage breeder program. However, at present the DAE is facing a serious shortage of natural uranium, even to fuel the current eighteen reactors in hand. The Nuclear Power Corporation (NPCIL) is having to deliberately lower the power levels in their operating PHWRs, in order to stretch out the available fuel for a longer period. The known uranium resources in Jaduguda mines are depleting fast and the DAE is unable to start fresh mining in Domiasiat in the Northeast and Nallagunda in AP due to local opposition to uranium mining. DAE may argue that the depleted uranium available from the spent-fuel reprocessing plants will supplement our limited natural uranium stocks, but in reality there will be no substantial alleviation of the problem.

As for ensuring the continued operation of Tarapur reactors, we will need concessions from the Nuclear Suppliers Group (NSG) to obtain additional fuel. All the nations which produce enriched uranium are now members of the NSG, and their current rules will not allow any such fuel sales to India. DAE's comment that we could operate the Tarapur reactors with plutonium-based indigenous fuel is impractical and dangerous, since world-wide studies have established that introducing more than 30-35% plutonium into boiling water reactors could bring about adverse changes in their safety-related physics and kinetics parameters.

The Indian fast breeder reactor experience is limited to operating a test reactor, supplied by France in the early 1970s, at about one-third its rated power level for several years. Based on this limited experience, and some very good R&D work, India is designing and building a large 500 MWe prototype fast breeder reactor (PFBR). France and Russia are two countries which have considerable experience in building and operating commercial size fast breeder reactors, and India is well-advised to initiate detailed technical discussions and consultations with these countries on the PFBR design and our safety philosophy. DAE experts may differ with me on this, but such a step is essential to further ensure public safety. But, again, these countries can openly interact with India only if the NSG does not raise objections.

Therefore, if the seriousness of the US in providing meaningful 'civilian nuclear co-operation' to India is to be tested, the Prime Minister must seek US intervention in the following three subjects. Firstly, request the US to assist India in purchasing sufficient quantities of natural uranium or yellow cake from the international market. In return, we may have to agree to place all reactors which will use that uranium under IAEA safeguards. Secondly, we must ask pointedly how the US is planning to help us meet the enriched uranium requirement for Tarapur reactors. And, thirdly, ask the US to help remove any NSG objections that may come in the way of India, Russia and France having bilateral consultations on the design, construction, operation and safety of our PFBR. Let the US demonstrate the sincerity of their offer through meeting these three genuine needs we face.

India maintains the official position that it is a nuclear weapon State, and considers the NPT and the Comprehensive Test Ban Treaty (CTBT) to be discriminatory. India has decided to maintain a minimum nuclear deterrent and will therefore maintain an active nuclear weapons program. As such, India cannot agree to the IAEA full scope safeguards applicable to non-nuclear weapon states. India is also unlikely to accept IAEA's right for intrusive, short-notice inspections under their Additional Protocol.

The US wants India to eventually join the NPT as a non-nuclear weapon State and has called for India to sign and ratify the CTBT, though they themselves have not ratified it. The US has also formally exhorted the NPT member-States to refrain from having any meaningful nuclear co-operation with non-NPT countries like India. The US Nuclear Non-Proliferation Act, 1978 (NNPA) prohibits nuclear co-operation between the US and India, and the US Congress will have to amend the NNPA if it were to happen. The US were the creators of two multinational nuclear export control groups, the NSG and the Zangger Committee, and both totally preclude any nuclear or dual-use technology cooperation with India. Finally, the US wants the acceptance of the Additional Protocol to be a condition for nuclear co-operation.

Given the above mismatch, one wonders where the MEA's optimism stems from, unless there are discussions going on between the two official sides on certain serious *quid pro quo*, which only the MEA and the Prime Minister's

Office (PMO) are privy to. Therefore, it is high time that the government considers the preparation of a comprehensive white paper on the objectives and status of Indo-US nuclear co-operation and table it in parliament, so that the interim status is known to the nation and an informed debate on the issue can take place in the parliament and outside. The MEA, the DAE and PMO would certainly benefit from such constructive debates and the feedback therefrom in their subsequent pursuit of policy.

(*The Asian Age,* May 31, 2005)

4. India must not be Nuclear Vigilante

A. GOPALAKRISHNAN

On December 9, 2002, based on information provided by the US intelligence agencies, a Spanish warship intercepted the North Korean-owned freighter, *So San,* in the international waters off the coast of Yemen, as an anti-terrorism monitoring action. The Spanish marines boarded the vessel and found 15 Scud missiles and 85 drums of a hazardous precursor for chemical weapons, and handed over the vessel and its cargo to the US navy. Within 24 hours, US was compelled to release the vessel and allow it to transport the cargo to Yemen, because the interdiction action lacked any authority under international laws.

Based on such events, the US and some of its allies recognized the need for more robust and promptly implementable strategies to defeat the proliferation of weapons of mass destruction (WMD) and their delivery systems, and identified interdiction during transport as an area to concentrate on. This led to President Bush on May 31, 2003 announcing the US-led Proliferation Security Initiative (PSI) aimed at stopping shipments of WMD, their delivery systems, and related materials worldwide.

The stated US goal for the PSI is to counter the proliferation to or from 'nation States and non-State actors of proliferation concern' through the use of existing authorities, national and international.

The PSI is a set of activities, which operates through partnerships that establish the basis for co-operation, when a need arises. In effect, PSI is a US-led effort by a "coalition of the willing," much the same way the US fought the war against Iraq in recent years. Both the PSI and the Iraq war are activities outside the formal sanction of the United Nations (UN), having no authorization from its General Assembly or the Security Council. It is to be noted that the PSI interdictions also do not fall within the list of legitimate interventions sanctioned under the UN Convention on the Law of the Sea (UNCLOS). Interestingly, all the countries participating in the PSI efforts are parties to the UNCLOS, except the US which is yet to ratify this Convention. As such, in simple terms, PSI operations are basically US 'unilateralism' in action, for which they are seeking a cloak of 'multilateralism'.

In 2003, the PSI was initiated with the participation of 11 countries including the US. From among the nuclear-weapon States, UK and France joined at the very beginning, Russia joined in May 2004, and China is yet to join. The group of core participants have since grown to 18, with more than 60 other countries currently supporting one or more of the PSI Interdiction Principles announced in September 2003.

In March 2004, during his official visit to India, US Secretary of State Colin Powell expressed his keen interest in India joining the PSI. This interest was once again re-affirmed by the current US Secretary of State, during her visit to India in March 2005. Last month, India's Chief of Naval Staff, Admiral Arun Prakash is reported to have said, "While it will be a political decision whether or not to join the PSI, the Navy has the wherewithal and is also ready and willing."

He stated, "India's status in world affairs warrants that we should be one of the core countries. In all these initiatives, intelligence sharing is the basic tool. We would not like to intercept any vessel without all the intelligence inputs available." Against this backdrop, it is certain that the US will raise the issue of Indian participation in the PSI with Prime Minister Manmohan Singh during his forthcoming US visit in mid-July.

An important criterion for our decision-making will be the accuracy and unbiased nature of the intelligence inputs we are provided with when an interdiction is needed. In the case of Iraq, we have seen how false information on the existence of Iraqi weapons of mass destruction was fabricated and supplied by the US and UK intelligence agencies to persuade other nations to join them in a "coalition of the willing", to support their unilateral invasion. In contrast, though the US had in its possession "actionable intelligence" on the AQ Khan nuclear proliferation network for years, they suppressed those facts and did not act on them because Pakistan was a cold war ally of theirs, whose Inter-Services Intelligence (ISI) agency was helping the US to get the Soviets out of Afghanistan.

The US finally spurted into action only after the September 2001 terrorist attacks, because they directly hurt them, and then it was in their self-interest to rein in Pakistan. If we were to join the PSI and interdict foreign vessels in high seas on the basis of intelligence inputs from others, which we can no way verify, we can never be sure whether or not we are drawn into a conflict to serve as a frontline partner in their motivated political maneuvers. The eventual answerability for such actions, however, will inevitably be on India, irrespective of who provided the intelligence inputs.

The PSI actions are said to be aimed at illicit activities of "nation States and non-State actors of proliferation concern." Who determines which States and organizations come under this category? It is a known fact that the US has labeled a few countries as "rogue nations" on their own, and these States will automatically be in that list. This includes a country like Iran with which India has long-standing friendly relations, while it excludes Pakistan despite its confirmed support to terrorism and its nuclear proliferation and associated black-marketing activities over the years.

Joining the PSI, led by the only major nation which refuses to ratify the UN Convention on the Law of the Sea, and participating in internationally unlawful interdictions at sea will be a disgrace for India. Therefore, we will be well-advised not to join the PSI as a core participant. In case a country does not wish to join as a core participant in PSI and adopt all its interdiction principles, there is the option available for it to assist in one or more of the core activities. If absolutely necessary, we may agree only to assist selectively in a few activities which are consistent with our policies, and totally reject any involvement in the remaining ones. For example, there is no harm in agreeing to board and Search vessels entering, berthing at or leaving our ports, since it is also in the interest of our harbour safety and will be consistent with India's WMD Act, 2005. But, we must avoid participating in any way in the interdiction of foreign vessels in territorial waters or high seas.

Also, we certainly must not sign any bilateral interdiction agreement under which our own flag vessels can be boarded and searched by other PSI States. This would infringe seriously on our sovereignty as an independent nation.

The US would like to use the UN Security Council Resolution No. 1540 (2004) as the legal basis for PSI. Article-10 of the Resolution states, "Further to counter that *(proliferation)* threat, *(the Resolution)* calls upon all States, in accordance with their national legal authorities and consistent with international law, to take co-operative action to prevent illicit trafficking in nuclear, chemical or biological materials." This does not help the US, because this Article insists on actions to be "consistent with international law," and it is quite arguable that PSI operations, certainly in the high-seas, are not in conformity with international law. Of the 190 members of the UN, only about 18 are the core participants of PSI, and about 60 others partially assisting in its operations. This still leaves a sizeable majority who are not volunteering to join the PSI, and India is better off joining that group for the time being. We need to impress on the US that it should seek suitable amendments to Treaties, Conventions or international law to set the PSI operations on a sound legal basis, before India can consider joining the PSI. Let us hope that the Prime Minister, in his demonstrated wisdom, will favourably consider this approach.

(The Deccan Chronicle, June 16, 2005)

5. India's Vision Void—And it looks like Washington is set to exploit it

Few developments are as full of promise and danger for India as its burgeoning relationship with the United States. Had the Indian government configured the right set of "long haul" policies, there was every possibility of the two countries enjoying huge mutual benefits and, colaterally, firming up regional and international peace and stability.

Unfortunately, in apparently seeking only short-term gains and trying to please the US, there is the likelihood of the Manmohan Singh government sacrificing the irreducible Indian national security interests and turning India into a US client state in the region. It is a posture that cannot endure because an economically and militarily hefty India will soon begin to chafe at the bit.

The looming problems could have been avoided had the Congress-led coalition government shown the self-belief and self-confidence to articulate an expansive strategic vision, an "Indian Monroe Doctrine", to mark out an Indian "sphere of responsibility" to match the country's legitimate great power ambitions. New Delhi could have exhumed the idea of "distant defence" popularised by Lord Minto, Governor-General of British India in the 1810s, a concept encompassing the Indian Ocean basin, the Gulf, the Central Asian Republics and the South-East Asian littoral inclusive of Vietnam.

New Delhi could have drawn up a plan, based on the enormous goodwill the Iraqi people have for India, to normalise Iraq minus the US presence and elsewhere, for it to act as a bridge between Iran and Israel/US and between Israel and Palestine. Such attractive options would have created enduring leverage for India in Washington. But, absent an Indian grand strategy or game plan or an alternative design for regional and Asian order, Prime Minister Manmohan Singh will be left exploring with President George W. Bush ways to fit India into the American scheme of things. It is an Indian vision void Washington will exploit. Unlike New Delhi, US has a road-map. It means to emulate the erstwhile Soviet Union and use the sale of military hardware and, especially, the follow-on logistics support requirement to influence Indian politico-military policy—an approach helped by New Delhi's penchant for judging a western country's bonafides by its willingness to sell sophisticated armaments and transfer the latest technology.

The problem the US government is wrestling with is: how to cater to India's conceit as a military and scientific power without augmenting Indian military capabilities to a point where it can upset the "balance" Washington deems necessary to maintain peace and stability in the sub-continent and threaten American strategic interests in the extended region.

The solution the US government has alighted on and reflected in the agreement that Defence Minister Pranab Mukherjee signed in Washington, is to offer pleasing rhetoric and showy combat aircraft—F-16 with "co-production", F-18 probably without it—that are in no way superior to planes already in service with the Indian Air Force, and ballistic missile defence (BMD) systems of questionable worth, in lieu of the advanced "dual use" technologies vaguely promised by the Next Steps in the Strategic Partnership that could enhance India's strategic military prowess and which, therefore, the US is reluctant to part with. A "Procurement and Production Group" has been constituted to facilitate these offers, which are "safe" because other than yanking the supply leash, the US Congress can be prompted at any time to cut-off the sale/transfer deals mid-stride.

The defence accord also tempts India with future augmentation of the ineffective but inordinately expensive terminal phase intercept system (Patriot PAC-2/PAC-3 or Arrow-2)—should India be conned into buying it—with the boost-phase and deep space intercept wherewithal once it is developed. This hardware too, like the Patriot/Arrow, will have to plug into the global American sensor complex and thereby formalise India's dependency status. If the Patriot is useless, this other stuff remains in the realm of science fiction and unlikely to materialise for several decades and, when ready, to bring down more than a score of incoming missiles! Meaning, an adversary can easily defeat the proposed system purchased for thousands of crores of rupees by saturating it with missiles costing between Rs. 80 lakh and Rs. 2 crore each! Indeed, anticipating India's acquisition Pakistan has already constituted its Missile Groups, North and South, in such a way as to undermine any meaningful Indian BMD architecture.

Further, measures to prevent nuclear proliferation, protect sea-lanes in the Indian Ocean basin, cooperate in disaster relief, and to engage in multilateral defence cooperation, mentioned in the agreement are missions the Indian armed forces have been performing for many years now, and do not amount to enlargement of India's activities. relying on "faith-based" intelligence regarding the non-existent WMD in Iraq rather than on "critical analysis". The Manmohan Singh government's national security and science and technology policies seem to be similarly flawed, based as they seem to be on faith in the US's benign intentions when a more skeptical attitude is merited.

How seriously should one take Washington's policy of assisting India to become a "major" power when US maintains pressure on New Delhi to keep its deterrent small and inert and vigorously opposes India's entry into the Security Council with veto rights? It does not help to argue that such doubts are redolent of "Cold War thinking" when it is obvious that national interest alone animates US policy, as it should Indian policy.

There is just too much at stake for New Delhi to agree to initiatives that weaken India's sovereignty and hollow out its national security prerogatives. The US involvement in the critical defence and energy fields is best kept at a minimum level until such time as an equitable relationship can accrue based on mutual trust generated by years of intensive politico-military cooperation and evidence of a more reasonable American stance on Indian nuclear forces and India's place in the emerging international order. This will require modest steps informed by caution, not a series of sprints into a potential minefield.

(*The Indian Express*, July 2, 2005)

6. Snake-Oil Salesmen Smell a Client

BHARAT KARNAD

Those who are suggesting that India rusn headlong into an American strategic embrace are nothing if not ingenuous in their argument. By conflating the imperatives of globalisation and faster-paced economic reforms with the need to climb on to the US global security bandwagon, they are hoping that the Indian government, which they presume is too confused to separate these policy strands, can be pressurised on the globalisation and economic issues enough for it to ignore the perils of the proposed military relationship with the "sole superpower." With the deadline of the Manmohan Singh visit approaching, they are not above using the sales pitch of itinerant hawkers peddling snake-oil to country hicks with their "hurry up and buy it before the stock gets exhausted"—spiel.

Surpassing the so-called "neo-Hindu growth rate of 6%" depends on how quickly the Indian government pushes through economic reforms. It has nothing to do with cooperating with the US in the military and strategic spheres. In this respect, the Congress Party-led regime at the Centre has failed to persuade its ideologically disparate coalition partners. Opposition-ruled states, and even its own party governments in the provinces need to implement economically sensible policies requiring rapid reduction of the government's role in public life, disinvestment in and privatisation of profitable and loss-making public sector units alike, and cuts in government expenditure and subsidies. Surely, such internally generated economic failures cannot be tied to strategic policy choices before the country.

If, on the other hand, a direct causal connection is sought to be made by these advocates between the economic and military relationship with the US, then they are on equally weak ground. American companies outsource software and, growingly, light and; heavy manufactures because of the cost/value advantage, and not because of any Washington diktat to its multinational corporations to cooperate in building up India as a "major" power. Intimacy in the defence field will no doubt have beneficial effect on the economic interactions between the two countries. But it needs to be emphasised that India as one of the few solvent Big Emerging Markets is attracting two-way international trade and commerce in a big way and will continue to do so on a larger scale in the years ahead because this is where the money and the brains are.

The presumed access to high-technology is the pivot for such pleadings. The problem is the US is extremely secretive about and diligently guards its military technology edge. And it makes no concessions even for its closest friends and allies. For instance, the United Kingdom and Italy signed up to co-produce the $300 billion Joint Strike Fighter. But a "special waiver" permitting the British Aerospace Company and an Italian defence combine to "share technology" and access sensitive information to render the production line operational, is not being honoured by Washington. An apoplectic British government and defence industry can apparently do little except hold long futile talks with the Americans and, not that it has helped, threaten to join up with Europe in an alternate military production programme. If London and Rome find it difficult to facilitate contracted technology transfer from the US, New Delhi's belief that it can secure cutting-edge "dual use" technology betrays more hope than hard-headed calculus.

The caution being advised here is also for the reason that military cooperation can always be intensified gradually on a case-by-case basis and in lock-step with rising mutual trust. But diving with the US straightaway into the deep end of the pool of strategic interactions may cost India in terms of clout and leverage as an independent player, one with a reputation for selling its commitment dear and then only because it unambiguously advances Indian national interests. It will mean India's joining the US security consortium geared to realising principally American national interests. The better alternative is for this country to carve out a distinctly Indian geopolitical architecture in which the US can have a role. But this requires a more discriminating policy mindset than being pact of the herd making common cause with the US on American terms.

In other words, aligning so conspicuously with the US, while fetching small dividends, is less likely to pitchfork India into the great power ranks than infect it fatally with that old Indian disease of clientitis. Some worthy in the strategic community has claimed that India need not fear a too close American embrace because it lacks, what he called, the "DNA" to be a client state. This must be a joke, because, as the historical record shows, no nation in the history of the world has been enslaved for as long as India or has so willingly and so often compromised its national security and surrendered its freedom. It led the renowned military sociologist Stanislaw Andreski studying the phenomenon to label India "a land of subjugations."

And, finally, and least convincingly, those wishing to stampede India into the American strategic corral argue that India would be better off striking a deal now when the US is supposedly in need of friends and allies than wait and face a less stretched, strained and attenuated America. If long-term strategies and demographic and productivity trends are considered, it is India's growth as an all-round power that seems inevitable. In the event, it may be wiser for New Delhi to bide its time and concentrate on strengthening its economic, political and military capabilities as much by itself as possible and on its own terms. Hitched to a grand strategic vision for the country, these will provide India with hugely increased bargaining power and leverage, enabling it to negotiate immensely more favourable deals in the strategic and other spheres with America in the future. Moreover, not getting locked into a one-sided strategic engagement with the US will also preserve India's manoeuvring room and options *vis-a-vis* China and Russia and this could be critical if New Delhi means to enter the lists as the great balancer, the so-called "swing state" that can determine the nature of peace and the international order in the 21st century.

(*The Asian Age*, July 14, 2005)

7. Baseless Criticism of the Prime Minister

A. GOPALAKRISHNAN

Ever since the prime minister returned from his recent visit to the US, after agreeing to a tentative framework for civilian nuclear co-operation between the two countries, he has been at the receiving end of a great deal of criticism from the Opposition parties and some of the former senior scientists of our nuclear weapons program.

Both India and the US are democracies, and the legally binding bilateral agreements based on this framework will definitely require legislative approval in both countries. In India, these will have to be discussed and approved by Parliament before they can be internationally binding. No prime minister has any authority under our system to enter into such "agreements" unilaterally and Dr. Manmohan Singh has certainly not done any such thing. So, what is all the clamour about?

The weapon scientists claim that the military and civilian nuclear facilities cannot be delineated separately. This is blatantly wrong, based on what was already done during the Vajpayee government's tenure.

The DAE (Department of Atomic Energy) themselves have done it in 2000, when they wanted to avoid any independent safety regulation of the AERB (Atomic Energy Regulatory Board) on the weapons activities, and there was a Gazette Notification issued in this regard in July 2000. If the DAE could do it then under the previous government, what is the problem in merely updating that exercise in 2005?

Every scientist in the DAE system must remain conscious that India's nuclear program and the DAE itself were not created for conducting nuclear weapons development. Almost all of them have this awareness deeply ingrained in them, except the few privileged ones who work on hush-hush weapons programmes.

The primary purpose of a nuclear program in this developing country, run at an enormous expenditure to the tax payer, is to provide nuclear electricity and other civilian benefits to all of us. Somewhere along the road, in mid-1960s, the nuclear weapon scientists succeeded in relegating this main objective to a lower priority and instead elevated weapon development as DAE's prestigious, but unspoken, first task.

It is time we reverse the priority back to Jawaharlal Nehru's and *[Dr Homi]* Bhabha's original vision of nuclear energy, while we can all still continue to support a modest nuclear weapons programme.

Under the IAEA *[International Atomic Energy Agency]* safeguards which will be applicable to India as per this framework, India can choose and give a list of civilian facilities, on which alone the IAEA safeguards will then be applied. If the weapons group feels strongly that they need to keep under their control certain limited number of extra facilities, by all means exclude them from the civilian list!

The IAEA, under this agreement, certainly cannot demand that India should stop its fast breeder reactor (FBR) work, as alleged by some. Also, any safeguards inspection of a facility can *only be* for the IAEA to ascertain that nuclear materials and support equipment, etc. imported by India under the new arrangement is not being diverted out of the safeguarded facilities. Indian authorities can outright refuse any other inspection or intrusion beyond what is mutually agreed as essential for the IAEA to meet this specific inspection objective.

The ideas of a "minimum nuclear deterrent" and a "voluntary moratorium on nuclear testing" were first put in place by the Vajpayee government after 1998, on the advice of the very same weapon scientists who are now criticising the current prime minister. Once you keep certain installations outside the "civilian" list, the framework has not given any license for the US or the IAEA to probe into what we are doing within those installations.

If these weapon scientists feel, and our government agrees, that they must proceed on to develop megaton thermonuclear weapons, neither the US government nor the IAEA can stop them because of this new framework. But, our weapon developers cannot test any of those new designs, since the moratorium on weapon testing readily agreed to by Mr Vajpayee and these very same scientists in 1998 will still stand binding. What good are such weapons to the armed forces in the country, without their being tested even once?

Healthy and constructive debate of the current issues will be welcomed by all in this country and it is also quite necessary. But, it is politically and professionally unethical to undercut, through misinformation and speculation, a potentially path-breaking initiative which the prime minister has taken, which could be shaped, with constructive co-operation among various factions in the country, into a revised package of national and international policies greatly beneficial to India.

(Rediff.com, July 29, 2005)

8. Indo-US Cooperation in Perspective

A.N. PRASAD

In recent weeks, US has been contemplating a change of attitude towards India as a part of a strategic shift in South Asia policy. Statements coming out from the Bush Administration regarding backing India for a permanent seat in the UN Security Council and helping India to become a major world power in the 21st century seems to have generated a flurry of activity in the Indian bureaucratic circles and many political and defense analysts have started airing their views in the media about the perceptions and implications of these developments. Whatever may be the outcome, self-reliance has been the hallmark of India and it has reached its present stature and is being noticed with respect by the rest of the world largely due to its inherent strength. One cannot become a major global player by others help alone however powerful they may be. In the present day global context, for a stable and sound world order mutual cooperation and interdependence among countries, whether developing or developed, is essential with due mutual respect. For example, Indian brains in the IT sector are making enormous contributions to the economy and advancement of the developed world. As a major shift in the policy towards India, Bush Administration is making statements that it should be helped in the nuclear energy sector. While this is a welcome development and deserves to be fully explored, as a note of caution, the policy-makers should carefully assess if there are any unacceptable conditions that go with the intended change in the US stance which could clash with national security interests, particularly since the experience so far pertaining to the nuclear sector has been far from satisfactory. This is not to suggest that India should start prematurely doubting the US intentions, but give a fair trial to see if anything fruitful could come out of this cooperation for the mutual benefit of both the counties.

Though India started nuclear power generation at Tarapur during the 60's with the US supplied boiling water reactors (BWR), keeping in view the limited uranium resources in the country (about 61,000 tonnes net) and plentiful thorium reserves (2,25,000 tonnes net), went in for mastering the pressurized heavy water reactor technology (PHWR) with great success in the first phase of the now abundantly familiar three stage development programme for nuclear power enunciated by the late Homi Bhabha. Based on such reactors nearly 330 Gwe-yr of electricity can be produced from indigenous uranium resource available, which is equivalent to only about 10,000 MWe installed capacity, assuming a life time of 40 years. Since PHWRs are good plutonium producers, when recycled along with depleted uranium and thorium in fast breeder reactors (FBR) constituting the second stage of nuclear power development could stretch the power generation potential to about 42,200 Gwe-yr equivalent to about 530 Gwe installed capacity with a life time operation of 100 years. This is proposed to be extended further by utilizing the enormous thorium reserves by recycling through appropriate reactor systems in the third stage to a potential of about 150,000 GWe-yr, which can virtually satisfy our energy needs for a long time.

In the short-term it is envisaged that an installed nuclear power generation capacity of 20 Gwe will be set-up by the year 2020 with a mix of PHWRs and FBRs. Construction of the first 500 Mwe prototype FBR has just got under way. While there is considerable confidence in realizing this target, any external participation in setting up power reactors will add to the assurance for realization of the generation target within the time frame. It is in this context the US initiatives for nuclear cooperation in the energy sector could be helpful. However, the experience so far has been disappointing. US has not left any opportunity in the past to impose sanctions and keep extending restrictions, embargoes, controls and what have you on even dual use items ever since the 1974 nuclear test. They unilaterally abrogated the agreement entered into at the time of supply of Tarapur reactors for supply of fuel, by passing the National Nuclear Proliferation Act (NNPA) during the tenure of the agreement. While in spite of all these sanctions and denials India has grown stronger, it could still be open-minded for cooperation but follow a cautious approach without being too optimistic. It should not at any time compromise the basic inherent strength so relentlessly built over the years with grit and determination under heavy odds.

The main stumbling block for any cooperation in the nuclear field at present is the Nuclear Supplier Group (NSG) which has been primarily created to deny India from acquiring any know-how or materials in the pursuit of its nuclear programme as an aftermath of the 1974 Pokhran test, extending to Pakistan and Israel, the three States not party to the discriminatory Non-Proliferation Treaty (NPT). While Israel does not seem to be affected by the NSG guidelines, as it is not having a nuclear power programme, Pakistan which till recently was being helped by China and has now joined NSG is likely to be affected. China and Pakistan will naturally be keenly following any moves by the US to bring about changes in the guidelines to accommodate India which could also benefit them. It will be interesting to see how US will circumvent or go for changing the NSG guidelines which they themselves have been using to prevent even countries willing to help India under international safeguards from cooperating. As though to help US in this task there have been suggestions by some of the analysts in the Indian media that it should place all the civilian nuclear reactors under IAEA safeguards. Some suggestions have gone even to the extent of hinting at demarcation of civilian and military facilities and placing the former under IAEA safeguards. Both these suggestions seem impractical and go against national interests. Let us ponder over them one by one.

In the overall energy context in India, in the long-run, when the conventional resources get depleted and the energy demand increases, contribution from nuclear becomes inevitable. As already pointed out earlier, when once fast breeder reactors and utilization of vast reserves of thorium available in the country reach a stage of maturity, the energy needs can be satisfied for a long time. This calls for considerable R&D efforts to develop technological skills to design, construct and operate complex facilities on our own assuming the present global sanctions continue. India has taken a significant step in starting construction of a 500 MWe prototype fast breeder reactor at Kalpakkam, Tamil Nadu and the national infrastructure is being geared up for successful completion and commissioning of the same with the support of the required fast reactor fuel cycle on an industrial scale, which includes, reprocessing of highly radioactive spent fuel, remote fabrication of separated plutonium for recycle as fuel, and high active waste immobilization among others. Since FBRs will be the mainstay of the nuclear power programme in India for quite some time, and since there is a lot to be established for the first time and improve upon them to achieve a level of maturity required to make it a success, bringing in safeguards at this stage just because they are civil nuclear facilities will seriously hamper efforts and cut into freedom of unhindered pursuit of development of the same. Experience so far in the successful development of technological skills required for the first stage of the nuclear power programme independent of safeguards without the associated distraction bears testimony to this line of thinking. This is an aspect only those who have hands-on experience in operating such facilities and also dealing with intrusive safeguards can fully appreciate and should not be taken lightly. Proponents of the view that all civilian nuclear reactors and the associated nuclear fuel facilities should be put under international safeguards, which almost amounts to acceding to full scope safeguards which India has all along been rejecting, should take particular note of this. In the interest of successful pursuit of the end goals, safeguards option is not worth pursuing in the national interest even if it results in cooperation not going through! However, if any nuclear fuel supply or reactors are forthcoming safeguards could be made applicable to such supplies as has been the case so far.

Regarding the demarcation of civil and military facilities, it is to be noted that India has gone in for a limited nuclear weapons programme more as a deterrent and is not a full time activity. While research reactors are being used as national facilities for science and engineering research could also be used for producing weapons material, dedicating them for single purpose will not only be impractical but also not cost effective. Same is the case with most of the associated costly nuclear fuel cycle facilities which could be used part time for military-related activities. Hence, the suggestion that civil and military facilities should be separated for safeguards purposes is not a feasible option for the scale of military activities involved.

One of the strongest points in favour of India qualifying for international cooperation is its impeccable track record. In spite of being not a party to the NPT India has displayed a very clean record of following non-proliferation norms scrupulously unlike in the case of some countries. In addition, India has voluntarily entered into a number of confidence building measures to make clear its peaceful intentions. This includes, moratorium on tests, no first use of nuclear weapons and an Act recently passed by the government to prohibit unlawful activities, in relation to weapons of mass destruction and their delivery systems.

To sum up, India being a mature and responsible global player in the nuclear field with the know-how and technological capability for building nuclear reactors on its own and also being a *de-facto* nuclear weapons power, is not really expecting any great high level technology transfer from developed countries in the present context, but expects to obtain uranium and participation in the nuclear energy programme on commercial basis to meet the fast growing energy demands of the country in the short-term and perhaps in the medium-term, though indigenous efforts will continue with full vigour. Such cooperation will also benefit the supplier countries through interaction with India, often considered as a nuclear developed country.

(The Hindu, July 2005)

9. Remember the Tritium

BHARAT KARNAD

Washington's powerful "cap-freeze-eliminate" school cutting across party lines may moderate their opposition to the deal US President George W. Bush cut with Prime Minister Manmohan Singh once they are reassured that the core concept of separating the civilian and military facilities in the country's nuclear programme will effectively hamper India's acquisition of reliable hydrogen bombs and, as Atal Behari Vajpayee said in Parliament, hurt "India's capability to decide what kind of credible minimum nuclear deterrent it wants."

Separating the military and civilian streams is easy if the government decides that the national deterrent ought to stay stuck at the low-yield fission weapons level. It becomes a more complex and risky business if the strategic forces are expected to secure thermonuclear heft. This is so for several reasons. The most important material for a thermonuclear arsenal is tritium. Tritium is produced in two ways. It is a byproduct of running CANDU/INDU pressurised heavy water reactors (PHWRs), 11 of which type presently generate electricity in the country. And it is available by irradiating Lithium compounds in the PHWRs. While weapons-grade plutonium once produced can stay on the shelf for a long time and can be stockpiled, tritium has shelf-life of only 12 and a half years and has to be periodically replaced in each "boosted" fission and thermonuclear weapon in the inventory for which reason it has to be continually outputted.

The problem then becomes obvious: all the civilian PHWRs are integrally part of the Indian weapons programme because they all produce tritium by one or the other means. This is what the experts are alluding to when they aver that separating the two streams may be difficult. Worse, in the July 19 joint statement with President Bush, Prime Minister Manmohan Singh reaffirmed the test moratorium. Now it is not clear who else besides Dr R. Chidambaram, science adviser to the PM, actually believes the nonsense he propagated after the 1998 tests that, notwithstanding the thermonuclear design fizzle, India does not need to test again and that it has all the data for simulation purposes in order to scale up the "40 kiloton" dud to a 250 kiloton high-performance weapon. This would require everybody to ignore concrete contrary evidence (crater morphology, large traces of lithium at the site indicating that the lithium deuteride fusion fuel did not fully burn, whence the small, insignificant, yield, etc.), suspend their disbelief and to credit the Indian bomb-makers with the advanced "arrested fusion" technology they do not currently possess.

But this merely highlights the fact that the United Progressive Alliance government has decided that a small, fairly primitive deterrent is all the country need have to meet any and all strategic contingencies in the future. This is a breathtakingly adventurous and risky attitude to adopt where national security is concerned when compared to the policies of almost every other major nuclear weapon state, namely, the US, Russia and China (the United Kingdom and France are, like Germany and Japan, client states of and protected by, the US), each of whom is in the process of modernising and beefing up their strategic thermonuclear forces.

Thermonuclear weaponry is at a premium because fusion devices are cleaner, offer far more bang for the buck, and with megaton yield, create disproportionate political leverage, and the sort of psychological dread that enables deterrence and dissuasion to work even against the most powerful states. It compels big nations hogging the international political and strategic space to cede a good portion of it. And it allows the thermonuclear weapons-owning country to pretty much dictate its own terms for any engagement with the outside world. But the Indian government seems determined to wallow in the shallows, a conclusion buttressed by the fact that the strategic vision and the long-term strategic interests of the country have nowhere been articulated.

Even judged on its own terms the Manmohan Singh-Bush paper comes up short. "Reciprocity" is the hinge of this agreement but the coupling of actions is not explicit. It will permit US officials to pressure the Indian government into taking the first substantial steps of identifying and "islanding" military use and civilian use installations without delivering on their commitments. Further, if India means to be scrupulous about it, the replacement cost of facilities that will need to be duplicated will run into thousands of crores of rupees. More importantly, the bifurcation will result in inefficient use of limited skilled manpower resources. As it is, the supposed organisational reform introduced by the former chairman of Atomic Energy Commission. Chidambaram, with his successor Anil Kakodkar has unfortunately not reversed, is preventing the Physics Group at the Bhabha Atomic Research Centre from working closely with persons in the weapons cell. It has led to little meaningful R&D and no new weapons designs since 1998. It is the sort of *denouement* the late Raja Ramanna, who oversaw the bomb programme for many years, feared and complained about to his former colleagues as early as 2001. A moribund weapons directorate may be an outcome of strict stream separation and critically hurt the country's strategic future.

The many successes the Indian nuclear weapons and strategic programmes have registered may be seen as a series of technological challenges which were overcome by concerned scientists and engineers at BARC and Kalpakkam working in a collegial manner. Indeed, the broad-based capabilities were built up by the visionary Dr Homi Bhabha on the basis of cross-pollination and intense interaction between different disciplines and a defiant attitude typified by Dr A.P.J. Abdul Kalam, who as head of DRDO, stated, "When someone says you cannot do it, we will do it." It reflected the reasonable conviction that India would join the high table by its own efforts and not by looking to some big power to hoist it on to a tall chair. The government needs to understand that great power is not an entitlement but a status India will have to earn by showing the necessary will and acquiring the requisite muscle.

(*The Asian Age*, August 7, 2005)

10. ITER Crumbs and Trojan Horses

Bharat Karnad

The International Atomic Energy Agency (IAEA) decided in June this year to build the ITER (International Thermonuclear Experimental Reactor) in Cadarache, near Marseilles, in France. Environmental concerns about the ravages of greenhouse gases are motivating this project which, in theory, promises virtually endless energy. A kilogram of (deuterium-tritium) thermonuclear fuel, for instance, can produce as much energy as the burning of 10 million kilograms of fossil fuel.

The ITER design is frozen on the inertial confinement fusion (ICF) principle using very powerful magnets to heat up plasma to many times the temperature of the sun to facilitate the fusion of hydrogen molecules. In prototype "tokomak" projects in the Soviet Union-Russia, the United States, Europe and Japan, fusion reaction has been obtained but in very short bursts. However, in the last 50 odd years, virtually no progress has been made in the basic technologies required to first create sustained thermonuclear reaction and then tap the enormous fusion energy so produced.

A sober assessment of the ITER programme by a large number of American scientists involved in fusion research is that a great deal of money will be funnelled into this prestigious international project but few practical technologies are likely to emerge in the foreseeable future, that is, in the next 50 or more years. Indeed, by the late 1990s the expenditure on ITER (originally conceived as a joint USSR-US project by Mikhail Gorbachev and Ronald Reagan during their 1985 summit meeting to highlight the end of the Cold War) was estimated to be so big and the returns on investment so negligible, Washington decided to pare its role in, and financial commitment to, ITER to a point where US funds now constitute less than 10% of the outlays of some $20 billion on this experimental reactor. The ITER project could do with financial support and technological inputs, both of which India, with its growing economic muscle and modest success in laboratory-scale ICF, is in a position to offer. Therefore, the reasons why ITER states would want India in the project, are clear.

What is not clear is how and why the Manmohan Singh regime got into a position wherein in exchange for participation in a technology project with benefits only in the indeterminate future—but portrayed by the US government as the first "tangible and concrete step in nuclear cooperation," New Delhi is ready to be hustled into delivering a plan to separate the civilian and military parts of a wholly integrated Indian nuclear programme that the George W. Bush administration can approve of, but which will permanently undercut India's military nuclear options in the future.

The blame for this fiasco in the making should be laid squarely at the door of Brajesh Mishra, the national security adviser to Bharatiya Janata Party, Prime Minister Atal Behari Vajpayee, who originally made trade in advanced technology with the US the linchpin of bilateral relations, and guided the state into the channel leading to the nuclear shallows it presently finds itself in. In the normal course, a close relationship with the United States would have evolved anyway owing to shared democratic values and the market logic of globalisation. It did not need a one-sided nuclear deal, which is a poison pill and has unnecessarily raised the political stakes for both countries. Should this deal begin to be perceived in the years to come by the Indian polity as having shackled the Indian state strategically, the Congress Party coalition will, of course, be blamed, but there will be bitterness too against the United States. This is bound to have repercussions on the American attitude towards India, and the relations could begin to unravel. The prospects of potentially meaningful and enduring India-US ties, which could be the foundation for an edifice of peace, order and stability in Asia will, as a result, be blighted.

Apprehensions about the nuclear cooperation arrangement may be seeping belatedly into the official establishment as well. This may explain why Dr Manmohan Singh's NSA, M.K. Narayanan, has woken up to the problem of technical commitments negotiated by generalist foreign service officers, and is taking Dr M.R. Srinivasan, former Chairman of the Atomic Energy Commission, with him on his December 12 trip to Washington to, perhaps, try and retrieve the situation for India. While it will benefit Narayanan to have Srinivasan, a nuclear power plant engineer, advising him on the practicability of the Indian separation plan on the anvil, the NSA would gain hugely from having a nuclear physicist with a weapons background to also assist him in his talks with the Americans. Because it is physicists alone who intimately understand weapons designs and weapons performance and can determine how many warheads or weapons and of what quality can be fashioned out of the country's existing fissile material stockpile and how much the stockpile needs safely to be enhanced to ensure that enough nuclear armaments can be tested and fielded in any future contingency or crisis.

This brings the issue back to the *dramatis personae* who have pushed this palpably unfair nuclear deal. The main drivers on the Indian side, it turns out, are not, as in the past, the usual suspects—the NSA and his associates in the Prime Minister's Office. Narayanan, a "nationalist" in these matters, nor the PMO, are the *loci genesis*. Two culprits are identified by insiders, neither of them with the least knowledge of, or responsibility for nuclear policy—Dr

Montek Singh Ahluwalia, the deputy chairman of the Planning Commission, and the Indian ambassador in the US, Ronen Sen. Ahluwalia is a longtime confidant of the Prime Minister's and helped carry out the latter's original economic reforms programme in the 1990s. Dr Singh trusts him implicitly to give him sage advice, apparently even in subject areas in which Ahluwalia knows as little as the PM. Sen served in Rajiv Gandhi's PMO, is supposedly close to Sonia Gandhi, whereof he derives his traction in Delhi, and is regarded by some of his retired colleagues in service as a "Svengali" Sen, standing to acquire reach in Washington, is promoting the American line with gusto.

Incidentally, with his World Bank credentials, Ahluwalia has long been identified as an American 'Trojan Horse" in the Indian policy circles. Ahluwalia's beliefs, it may be safely assumed, are reflected in Dr Manmohan Singh's articulations that India needs to first become an economic powerhouse with US help even if this help is at the cost of India's securing genuine strategic military heft. The danger with such thinking is both that it is anti-historical economic determinism of the worst kind, and that it disregards plain strategic and military common-sense. Washington, always geared to short-term goals, has no reason to cavil at this development. The national security consequences being far more serious for India, the Congress government's strategic short-sightedness is Frightening.

(The Asian Age, December 12, 2005)

11. National Interest is at Stake

A.N. PRASAD

Q: Dr Prasad, since the July 18 agreement was signed you have shown concerns about the separation of India's civilian and military nuclear facilities. Can you please share some of your major concerns?

A: I am misunderstood. Now that the July Statement is in place, for it to proceed further is only legitimate, that the separation process has to go through and be brought to a logical conclusion. With the passage of time since July the whole focus, from the statements emanating from the US side, has been heavily on the separation issue with indications that it should be done by India in a fully transparent and credible manner, perhaps implying that they should be aware of our thinking process in detail, and jointly work with them so that the final list that emerges is to their liking and approval! This, if agreed to, may come in the way of our freedom of our strategic thinking and decision-making.

Q: Importantly, can you tell us as a scientist, at this point in time, how you feel about the entire nuclear debate? Is the Indian nuclear scientists community feeling betrayed by the deal?

A: Frankly, it has been a mixed feeling. On the one hand there is a recognition, though not formal, of our nuclear status and hope of us joining the mainstream of global activities for commercial nuclear power generation and research and development if the agreement comes to fruition. On the other hand, if this agreement is seen by the US as a means to fulfil their long-standing aspiration, which is almost an obsession, to bring us closer to accepting the Nuclear Non-Proliferation Treaty or fullscope safeguards applicable to most of our nuclear facilities and activities, which we have successfully resisted all these years, and leaving only a small portion of facilities and nuclear materials out of safeguards categorizing as for military use, we will be losing a big strategic advantage built over the years. It is too early to say at this point of time whether the Indian nuclear scientific community is feeling betrayed as the whole process is still in the initial stages and much depends on how our negotiators tackle the issue and the US response.

All of us know well that nuclear proliferation is taken seriously by the powerful countries who are in a position to supply fuel to India's nuclear power plants. They are concerned about vertical proliferation in India. If India wants fuel it has to convince the Nuclear Suppliers Group by offering to put civilian research facilities under safeguards along with its power plants. Obviously, for the members of the NSG the issue is not what and how India wants, for them the issue is how to ensure nuclear non-proliferation once India gets fuel.

Also, as you know so well, they are worried about setting of a trend that may be misused by some other countries that are not as credible as India.

The fact is, in spite of the obligations—the nuclear weapon states have entered into under the NPT—in total disregard, they went on increasing their nuclear weapons arsenals which is a clear case of vertical proliferation (though the US and the Russian Federation have taken steps recently to decommission some of the obsolete weapons, thereby showing some reduction), at the same time showing great concerns for horizontal proliferation! As far as proliferation is concerned there is already a double standard. One for the nuclear weapon states and the other for the rest of the world! India has always been saying that it is for total global disarmament which unfortunately has not found takers.

Going by our track record so far, which is impeccable and has been globally recognized, the NSG or anybody else should not doubt our intentions. Our assurance to place all nuclear power reactors and nuclear materials we receive from outside the country under international safeguards should allay the fears of the international supplier community.

Q: What should be the principles behind the separation of Indian nuclear facilities? How should India go about it after agreeing for separation?

A: The ideal situation would be to follow the provisions of the July text of the Joint Statement, which in effect says rights and obligations should be the same as those of the nuclear weapon states and the practices they are following.

Q: We are aware that India's nuclear programs are inextricably interlinked. India's indigenous Fast Breeder Reactors depends on PHWRs [pressurised heavy water-cooled reactors]. But some argue that it is high time Indian nuclear scientists come out in the open and work for the civilian sector without ambiguity. It is said that since long Indian nuclear scientists have been working under secrecy as if they are part of the "unlicensed" industry. After the separation scientists will be freer and will have license to produce energy without remaining under cover. Please comment.

A: This is a complex issue. Since we have been forced to work and develop many of the technologies indigenously in isolation in view of restrictions imposed on us, it is not fair to expect that our R&D facilities which may be used for civilian and strategic purposes be classified as civilian. Similarly, our fast breeder programme is still in the developmental stage and until at least it reaches a level of maturity, the fast reactor fuel cycle is best left outside the civilian list though it can be subject to argument. Reaching the present level of competence has taken a lot of effort and no scientist would like to carry out development activities freely with some international inspectors breathing down his neck. It is not a question of working under secrecy or unlicensed! Issues involved are much more serious.

Q: Once the deal is done and the actual separation process starts, can you envisage how will India deal with 'interlinkages' issue? How will India get fuel for FBRs if they are not put under the fullscope safeguards? And if FBRs are listed on the civilian list what will be the eventual scenario? What will be India's loss?

A: It is premature to talk about this specifically.

Q: Let the negotiations proceed and the separation plan come out. India claims that it has not departed from any of its international commitments of proliferation, but now the world is looking for actual proof and verification mechanism in place for the future. Why should critics object to it when India has nothing to hide?

A: As I have already said, we should be prepared to open out all facilities and subject all nuclear materials which we receive from outside along with our own facilities hitherto not subject to safeguards in which the imported nuclear material will be used, for IAEA safeguards. Others to be negotiated.

Q: Dr Prasad, will you agree that India needs to buy fuel urgently to run its nuclear plants? In a marketplace it's available only under certain conditions. As you are well aware, it's a supplier's market and not a buyer's market. Why are scientists, who are opposing the terms of separation, reluctant to accept the principle of 'give and take'? The supporters of the deal want to know why you don't understand and accept the realities of today's world. How long can India remain away from the mainstream of the nuclear world?

A: Lack of adequate uranium has been our bane of contention, unfortunately. We have lived with this for sometime now and we are trying to come out of it. If this weakness of ours is allowed to be exploited by others, it becomes a question of hard choice between preserving strategic national interests and succumbing to ground realities. It is not a question of simple 'give and take' but national interest is at stake.

Q: Do we really need the nuclear deal with the US? Can you help us to understand the cost of separation? Some bizarre amount was mentioned in one newspaper. What will be an approximate cost to India? Give us just an idea of the expenses.

A: It is foolish to talk quantitatively about cost of separation without arriving at a categorized list of facilities. As I have said earlier, there are many nuclear fuel cycle facilities which are of dual purpose and if they have to be segregated and dedicated facilities need to be built involving duplication, it adds to the cost. So it all depends on the outcome of negotiations.

Q: In the recent past, has the Indian scientific fraternity ever discussed the issue of separation? If yes, when? And if not, why?

A: I don't think the Indian scientific community in general has discussed this issue. Also, it is a complex topic. However, I presume the concerned scientists within the Department of Atomic Energy would have discussed this issue.

Q: Some diplomats privately argue why do Indian scientists not accept that they have collectively failed to deliver cheap and efficient nuclear energy on time? If India is facing stringent conditions for its nuclear facilities it is because our own research is a bit slow and we are behind schedule. No one is doubting the Indian scientists' brilliance or capabilities or achievements, but the fact remains that planning of fuel for plants is less than adequate and research into thorium and construction of new plants are behind schedule.

A: This is a sweeping statement. The nuclear field is relatively young compared to conventional power producing alternatives. It involves complex technologies, safety concerns and public resistance off and on. We are also not allowed to interact globally as in the case of other alternatives using fossil fuels. Still, when the going was good we perhaps missed the opportunity to exploit uranium from our own resources. Now we are facing resistance from the environmentalists.

Q: Sir, it's alleged that you have a grouse against the US because you were denied a visa? When, why and under what circumstances were you denied a visa by the US?

A: This is utter nonsense. I have never been denied a visa. Whatever opinion I express is entirely in the interest of the department. During my entire professional career I was privileged to serve the national interest.

Q: US-based think tanks are hyperactive in publishing data related to separation. Why are Indian thinkers, visionaries and scientists not as forthcoming?

A: Perhaps this has got something to do with our system and practices. Unfortunate. However a set of people who claim to be experts in anything nuclear without any inhibitions keep interacting with the media.

Q: Lastly, keeping in view a balanced picture of the high value attached to the issue of non-proliferation and India's right for sovereign nuclear research, can you tell us what (out of known and declared nuclear energy facilities and R&D centres) India should ideally keep out of the civilian list?

A: I have already answered briefly this question.

Q: It is believed that CIRUS [Canada-India-Research United States, from which the weapons grade plutonium for India's first nuclear tests in 1974 is said to have come] to have commissioned will be included in the civilian list while FBRs will be kept out. Dhruva may be kept out, too. According to one section of scientists two research facilities are enough for future progress. If this news gets confirmed will such a list satisfy experts like you?

A: Though the role of CIRUS reactor for our strategic requirement, being a small reactor, is no big deal, including the same under the civilian list and subjecting it to safeguards in principle is rather disturbing in view of its geographical location.

Q: A lot of arguments are being put forth from Canadian and US sources, that CIRUS built more than 40 years ago under peaceful use commitment by India has been violated and hence needs to be corrected by bringing the same under international safeguards.

A: If one looks from a historical perspective, India is not at fault. If at all India is perceived as a violator, it could be viewed as a reaction to the unilateral abrogation by the US and Canada of legally binding bilateral agreements and obligations. It is a case of the 'pot calling the kettle black'! The reactor has over the years undergone major refurbishing and there is no point in raking up old commitments, particularly when the accuser is actually the accused.

I sincerely hope India will resist the pressure.

(*Rediff.com*, December 26, 2005)

12. A Question of Nuclear Separation

A. GOPALAKRISHNAN

One of the major objectives of the United States in entering into the Indo-US nuclear cooperation agreement is to bring about an early freezing of the Indian weapon-usable nuclear materials stock at the minimum possible level. India, in turn, obviously wants to retain all the accumulated inventory of such materials, as well as the facilities to produce the additional material we consider essential for a minimum deterrence, out of IAEA safeguards. Obviously, each country wants to manoeuvre the separation plan to suit its specific objective.

Despite the facade that the deal is progressing well, it is clear that most of the originally perceived differences between the two sides are very much present even now. It appears that the US side feels that certain facilities, especially reactors, which India has proposed to retain in the strategic group, really belong in the civilian list. In addition, it is clear that the US considers India's time schedule for bringing these facilities in phases into the civilian list as too stretched out, and that we should indeed place them under safeguards at a more rapid pace.

Dhruva and Cirus are the two weapons-grade plutonium producing reactors which are crucial to the Indian strategic programme. It is now known that Canada has formally asked India and the US that Cirus, which was built with Canadian assistance under an agreement that it will be used only for peaceful uses, should now be placed in the civilian list. The US side must have raised this issue with foreign secretary Shyam Saran during his recent visit to Washington, and he perhaps had no option but to reject this demand.

India is using the limited uranium enrichment capacity available at the Rare Materials Plant (RMP) near Mysore for producing the medium enrichment uranium fuel for our nuclear submarine reactors. Since this plant can be upgraded to produce high-enrichment weapons-grade uranium as well, the US could be asking us to place this facility and the submarine reactor(s) under the civilian list.

This, of course, will not be acceptable to India. Similarly, the US may be wanting us to put the laser enrichment programme at the Raja Ramanna Centre for Advanced Technology (CAT), the de-tritiation plants in BARC and

IGCAR where we separate out tritium from irradiated heavy water, the beryllium production facility at Vashi which supports the weapon-core making, the Variable Energy Cyclotron Centre (VECC), Kolkata where the proton-beam bombardment of Lithium-6 could be done for tritium production, etc., under safeguards.

But India should insist on keeping all the facilities under the Bhabha Atomic Research Centre (BARC) and the Indira Gandhi Centre for Atomic Research (IGCAR) within our military list and away from safeguards, since they are all either R&D facilities or meant clearly for the use of the weapons programme.

Of the 15 operating nuclear power reactors in India, four are already under IAEA safeguards. The remaining 11 are pressurised heavy water reactors (PHWRs) which are currently not under safeguards. Of the total eight power reactors under construction, the two Russian units at Koodankulam are already earmarked under safeguards, leaving five PHWRs and the Prototype Fast Breeder Reactor (PFBR) which are currently out of safeguards. When and if the Advanced Heavy Water Reactor (AHWR) is built, we need to keep it outside the civilian list, because of its developmental nature. How many of these 16 un-safeguarded PHWRs will India be agreeable to place under IAEA safeguards, and in what time schedule, is one of the contentious issues in the current Indo-US dialogue.

Closely linked to this issue is the lack of clarity in public mind about our indigenous natural uranium resources. It is true that we may not have enough processed natural uranium to fuel the five PHWRs currently under construction, when they are ready for initial fuelling in 2006-08. But the highest officials of the AEC now reconfirm the view that we have enough natural uranium ores in the country to fuel 10,000 MWe worth of PHWRs, for their lifespan of about 40 years.

The mismatch between production and consumption of uranium has happened because the government approvals for the new PHWRs and their construction process itself have speeded up in the last ten years, while the Department of Atomic Energy (DAE) still continued to lag behind in their minerals exploration and uranium mining tasks. While waiting for these activities to pick up momentum in the coming five years, the DAE should go ahead and place under IAEA safeguards the five PHWRs now in construction, from their dates of initial fuelling with imported natural uranium, so that there need not be any delay in electricity generation.

From the time we enter into this Indo-US nuclear deal, our limited indigenous natural uranium will have to be used judiciously for fuelling the Dhruva and Cirus reactors to the extent we need additional weapons-grade plutonium, and also in the first AHWR developmental unit, while the remaining should be used in the un-safeguarded PHWRs for producing as much reactor-grade plutonium as we can to sustain the operation of the first PFBR(s).

The phased placement of the PHWRs under safeguards can be determined only on the basis of this logic, leaving sufficient room for uncertainties in fresh uranium supplies from our mines. In short, if a PHWR of ours can be run with Indian uranium, there is no hurry in placing it on the civil list, because it is then producing plutonium which will serve as feed material for our unsafeguarded breeder reactor(s).

Thus, the right stand to take at this stage is to keep the Indian fast breeder programme outside the IAEA safeguards, by including it in the strategic facilities group. We may revisit this decision after we have commissioned and operated the first PFBR at full power and also stabilised its associated technology programmes connected with fast reactor fuel fabrication, reprocessing of spent-fuel to extract U-233, and the system improvements we may make on the basis of initial operational experience.

This decision, however, has its consequent repercussions. The initial PFBR(s) in that case will have to rely on the already accumulated reactor-grade plutonium, and the future continued production of similar material from the un-safeguarded PHWRs, for the initial fuel loading and subsequent annual re-fuelling. This would require us to negotiate and keep all the presently available un-safeguarded reactor-grade plutonium in the PHWR spent-fuel out of IAEA safeguards, even while we may agree to put most of these PHWRs under safeguards, in phases, over a stretched period of time.

As and when we wish to put a PHWR into the civilian list and IAEA safeguards, we must first discharge all Indian spent-fuel in it for storage in our strategic group, and re-fuel the reactor entirely with fresh imported fuel. This way we ensure that our limited indigenous uranium resources are not burned up in a safeguarded reactor nor are we giving away part of the earlier unsafeguarded spent-fuel.

In the long-run, whether India can operate enough number of unsafeguarded first-stage breeders based on depleted uranium-plutonium fuel, thereby breeding enough U-233 in their thorium-loaded blanket regions to transition into the ultimate self-sustaining stage of thorium-U-233 breeders, is entirely dependent on how much more indigenous uranium we can find from an aggressive prospecting for minerals.

Indian uranium, thorium and rare metal mining operations, mined ores, and their processing plants have to be kept outside IAEA safeguards. Thus, all facilities of the Uranium Corporation of India Limited (UCIL) and the Indian Rare Earths Limited (IREL) should go into the strategic group. Also, we have to ensure that the required minimum number of production plants for heavy water and reprocessing facilities to extract plutonium or U-233 from the spent-fuel are kept outside the civilian list, to match the requirements of the number of research and power reactors we are keeping in the strategic list at any point in time.

This may not be too difficult because we have nine heavy water plants and four operational spent-fuel reprocessing plants, and some of these could be put under safeguards, while others are kept in the strategic list. But, when it comes to the fuel fabrication facilities, there are different processes and plants involved. Most of these are in the Nuclear Fuel Complex (NFC) at Hyderabad. At NFC, however, a few of the critical plants are not duplicated, and today they serve both the civilian and strategic requirements. Here, India will have no other option but to keep one-of-a-kind facilities at NFC, Hyderabad outside safeguards, until such time that duplicate facilities are planned and constructed.

(*The Asian Age*, January 14, 2006)

13. Desperate for a Nuclear Deal—but why?

BHARAT KARNAD

With the state visit by President George W. Bush looming, the Congress Party-led coalition government seems to be getting increasingly desperate to obtain a deal, any nuclear deal, as long as there is some paper for the US leader and Prime Minister Manmohan Singh to sign. And, apparently, US under-secretary of state, Nicholas Burns' trip offers a last-gasp chance to firm up this transaction. That this will "transform Indo-US relations and consolidate. India's standing as one of the world's major powers" as a media trumpeter breathlessly put it, is doubtful. What it is guaranteed to do, however, is begin firming up India's reputation as a tamed nuclear outlier state, one shorn off its Samson's locks of options and therefore denuded of its political and military leverage.

Ideally, India should be able to fully safeguard both its sources of civilian nuclear energy and its freedom to design and develop its nuclear arsenal and weapons-mix to any qualitative and quantitative specifications necessary to enable it to deal with any conceivable crisis or contingency in the future. But assessments of the future are notoriously tricky. Because these are dogged by uncertainty and risk, it requires a country like India to exercise abundant caution, especially when it comes to negotiating deals, like the one the July 18 Joint Statement promises, which will limit the country's strategic choices.

At the heart of the arguments supportive of a deal is the belief entirely, unsupported by empirical evidence, that India does not require a meaningful deterrent, that a minimally-sized and basic quality of weapons inventory, will do Innocent of the manifold military and political utility of impressive thermonuclear forces or the need to feature tested and proven high-yield, long reach, armaments in the nuclear arsenal and unwilling to factor in the policies of continuous upgradation of strategic forces underway in the US, Russia and China, these worthies are apparently banking on Washington to come to India's aid in an emergency beyond the capacity of the latter's small nuclear arms inventory to handle. The certain, end-state of India as a security dependency of the United States is sought; to be papered over by references to the nuclear civilian technology benefits the country is supposedly set to derive

But if augmenting the nuclear sources of electricity generation is the Indian government's paramount concern, it is not clear why the deal with the US is needed. For one thing there is no real shortage of natural uranium as is propagated by official circles India's publicly touted reserves of uranium worth 10,000 MW equivalent actually do not take into account the "rich" veins of ore with 6-7% uranium content available in Meghalaya and in Nalgonda district of Andhra Pradesh. The government, however, has made no effort whatsoever under enabling provisions of the law to clear out the environmental opposition from the sites and to let the Atomic Minerals' Division in Hyderabad get on with the business of mining the ore found at these locations. Indeed, environmental worries can be got around by having the mined ore trucked to processing plants. Further, even in the depleted uranium mines in Jadugoda, over 30% of the extractable ore has been left unmined owing to the fact that it forms the columns around which the mineral has been dug out. These ore-pillars can be replaced by columns of concrete. Advanced extraction technology enable supposedly exhausted mades and oil fields to once again become productive. It all depends on the current international price of the natural resource. Thus, because of high oil prices. ONGC, for instance, has fond it economical to pump out residual oil from the fields in digbor and elsewhere in Assam by investing some Rs. 3,300 crores. With the price of natural uranium or "yellow cake" sky-rocketing—it has increased by some 300% in just the last couple of years—extraction of uranium from poor quality ore or even sea-water now makes economic sense.

If natural uranium from abroad is not critically needed to fuel the country's indigenous nuclear energy programme, then, let us examine the case for accessing foreign nuclear reactor technology. The US civilian nuclear industry has been in the doldrums for the 35 years with new plant being built in this period. The one new design—Westinghouse 1000 type—Westinghouse Company of America has developed is not yet certified by the US Atomic Energy Commission, meaning India accepts all the safety and other risks in case New Delhi gives in to the arm-twisting and as part of the bargain to get the total deal approved by the US Congress, agrees to buy several of these reactors: Should such certification be expedited, India will thereafter face the threat of a cutoff in fuel supplies. It will be Tarapur all over again except this time it will be the Indian taxpayer's money that will be invested in these plants rendered inoperable owing to lack of enriched uranium fuel supply. France and Russia will not be any more lenient in insisting that India keep to the non-proliferation straight and narrow, any departure from which, like the resumption of testing, will immediately bring down sanctions. Would it not be better, under the circumstances, for India to put its money and diplomatic and, commercial effort into constructing more of the Trombay-designed and developed INDU heavy water moderated natural uranium reactors here in India and to sell these reactors to energy-deficient countries abroad, thereby cultivating an external market for indigenous reactor technology and generating both funds to amortise the investments made in this sector over the last 50-odd years and revenues for the Indian civilian nuclear industry?

Dr Anil Kakodkar, Chairman of the Atomic Energy Commission, could have informed the PM about natural uranium sufficiency and the dangers of buying sensitive technologies abroad. Not only did he fail to do that, he has shown himself to be too weak to protect the integrity of the nuclear energy programme he heads by agreeing to a "separation plan." The Indian nuclear scientists are uniformly against any separation of civilian and military use facilities, materials and manpower because, unlike in other weapon states, in India, owing to the weapons capability being an offshoot of the broad-based civilian nuclear energy programme, these two functions and missions are wholly integrated and inseparable.

The point to make is that rather than looking to foreign sources for uranium supply or for nuclear power plants as last resort, the Congress government is reaching for foreign uranium supply and foreign reactors as the preferred policy at the expense of national security, strategic independence, and autonomy of the country's nuclear programme. In the event, this course of action makes no sense and is inherently unjustifiable. Particularly when, as a Planning Commission study has concluded, the projected production of electricity from the country's hugely augmented civilian power sector is expected to account for only 6% of all electricity produced in 2020.

The growing unease in official circles is also because of the unexpectedly strong resistance to this deal here as also in the US. With the US Congressional approval difficult at best, the Manmohan Singh regime is clearing an own escape route for itself. It has over the last few weeks changed its stance from initially accepting the American premise that all civilian nuclear power plants would go into the civilian net and under international safeguards—to wit foreign secretary Shyam Saran's speech to IDSA—to now when, a number of these dual-use power plants able to output weapon-use plutonium and tritium for boosted fission and thermonuclear armaments along with all of the breeder programmes are sought to be kept within the military ambit.

Then again, given the generally weak-kneed posture of the Indian government, this may only be the initial position that will be negotiated away once the American team piles on the pressure and warns of Washington's having to rethink its policy of helping India become "a major power," etc. But according to a stalwart nuclear engineer brought into the loop after criticism that no technically competent person was involved in the negotiations, any Insistence by the US that all nuclear power plants be sequestered only for civilian use, would be a "deal breaker." But whether the phrase "deal breaker" merely denotes a hollow threat will soon become evident. With the non-proliferation lobby in Washington too drawing its own red-lines—witness the visiting US Senator John Kerry's statement that it is better to have three-quarters of the Indian nuclear programme in the safeguards net than not to have any of it subject to international monitoring and inspection—the Prime Minister may soon be facing a serious dilemma. Whether President Bush will be able to get the US Congress to okay the deal or not, Dr Manmohan Singh will find getting Parliament to accept it a politically Herculean task. Among his coalition partners, with the election campaign soon getting underway in West Bengal, the Left parties' ideological opposition to having truck with "imperialist" America will grow more vociferous. The Samajwadi Patty is stirring things up for a fight and, thanks to an apparently dim-witted law minister, the Bofors bribes controversy is revived, providing the Bharatiya Janata Party combine with the heavy artillery to keep the ruling coalition distracted and on the defensive.

(*The Asian Age*, January 17, 2006)

14. The Nuclear Poison Pill

BHARAT KARNAD

The advocates of the proposed nuclear deal with the United States are getting shrill as they see its prospects dimming, a denouement not anticipated by its promoters within the Indian government and the media. To try and sell a patently bad agreement with the capacity seriously to injure national security and India's strategic interests on the basis that it will enhance relations with America, procure needed civilian nuclear technology from abroad, and gain Indian entry into the big power ranks as "international balancer," is at best to misread the fundamentals of international power politics and, at worst, cynically to engage in trepidation-mongering—fall in line or miss out on the main chance.

But history suggests only the strong become decisive players in the international arena. And genuine strategic military power—in the present age, this means high-yield thermonuclear forces with reach provided by intercontinental ballistic missiles and nuclear-powered submarines—is the key. It requires visioning based on historical constants, rather than on nonsensical notions of Indian "exceptionalism" that translate into riding piggyback on the US, and on expediting policies to acquire the necessary strategic wherewithal. The complementary attribute of a hig economic growth rate on the other hand, would benefit from plugging into the competitive global trade and commercial environment and, at home, from dismantling Socialism-inspired public sector and facilitating private sector efficiency.

One of the main reasons why the nuclear deal is hitting road-blocks is because its champions here are incoherent on the technical aspects. How else to explain the charge that rejecting this deal will result in "technology thralldom"? Come again! If ignorance of laws is no excuse for violating them, unfamiliarity with the science and technology involved cannot reasonably be the vehicle for nuclear policy propagation. Importing nuclear technology or nuclear fuel, rather than self-reliant development, surely, will result in dependence, slavery, and "thralldom" (to use a string of synonyms to emphasise the point). This is so obvious a fact, one would have thought it needed no iteration.

Further, how many of the indigenously developed power plants and what other nuclear facilities to put under international safeguards is not, as per the July 18 Joint Statement, a matter of negotiation but, as Prime Minister Manmohan Singh declared in Parliament July 29, solely for India to decide and, like in the matter of the four other NPT-recognized nuclear weapon states, for the US to accept. That New Delhi has to produce a "credible, defensible" separation plan which will pass muster with the US Congress is a later construction of American officialdom. Unless Dr Singh was not being candid in Parliament, it is not the Indian government's responsibility to inflict hurtful measures on the country just so it enables their American counterpart to push this deal on the Capitol Hill. The more the Manmohan Singh regime bends backwards to accommodate the George W. Bush administration, the more dubious the deal becomes in the eyes of the Indian people.

India has to do what other major powers have done—surrender no options, give as little ground as possible where its nuclear programme is concerned and restrict international monitoring to the barest minimum. If this is not possible, then to junk the deal and get on with life.

The larger issue involved is adherence to a principle of conduct established long ago by Dr Homi J. Bhabha, the great visionary and architect of the country's nuclear programme, and Jawaharlal Nehru, the most strategic-minded of India's Prime Ministers. They decided early that international safeguards were acceptable *only* for installations built with foreign help and material assistance. The reason they adduced was simple: international safe-guards hampered and hindered technological innovation and the development of indigenous technology. And they stuck by it at a time when India was vulnerable. Brazil, for example, which had no such, far-sighted leaders, is now discovering that for advances to be made in locally produced technologies, like the centrifuge cascades, mindlessly put under safeguards, require prior approval by the International Atomic Energy Agency in Vienna. It is the frustration with its loss of freedom and with international red-tape which has led Brazil to not permit IAEA inspection of its newest centrifuge units. Its plea is that technological innovations are protected by Intellectual Property Rights and cannot be disclosed. The irony is that even as India is getting out from under the economic jackboot of a "licence and permit raj," New Delhi is seeking to subject its most valuable technology enclave—the Indian nuclear programme—to an international "licence and permit raj" run by IAEA.

There is also plain ignorance about the breeder programme in the pro-deal camp. Few countries other than Indian are pursuing the fast-breeder route primarily because they have alternatives. President Jimmy Carter closed down the American breeder project in the late Seventies and France shut down its Super Phoenix reactor because, in both instances, this technology was deemed redundant to their needs. The French breeder is run on spent uranium fuel from power plants of which there is a plenty. This is unlike the

Indian breeder reactor designed directly to utilise thorium in which India is super-rich, having in excess of 70 per cent of the estimated world reserves. So it is hard to see just how and where foreign technology can help this programme.

Moreover, the Indian breeder reactor has definite military uses. A breeder reactor being essentially a "refinery" for bomb-grade fissile material, one 500 MW breeder—like the prototype coming up in Chennai—will produce more weapons-useable plutonium than as many as five power plants operating at low burn-up rates. This is the main reason why the United States desperately wants the Indian breeder programme under safeguards and included as part of the IAEA-monitored, permanently civilianised, nuclear sector in the separation plan, and why New Delhi should zealously protect it.

It is significant that other than Dr Anil Kakodkar, the current chairman of the Atomic Energy Commission, who, perhaps, feels compelled to toe the government line, no eminent nuclear scientist or engineer has expressed support for it. Indeed, stalwart nuclear scientists and engineers, including Dr A.N. Prasad, retired director of the Bhabha Atomic Research Centre, and Dr A. Gopalakrishnan, former chairman of the Atomic Energy Regulatory Board, have publicly slammed the separation plan as detrimental to sovereignty, national security, and the integrity of the nuclear programme, and have advised a minimalist principle for separation, which paraphrased reads: "When in doubt, keep it out (of the safeguards net)." This conforms better with the Nehru-Bhabha principle than buying into the expansive American non-proliferation line swallowed whole in official quarters who, to invert the adage, are missing the trees for the forest. Strategy conceptualised with an eye to the sky is in danger of stumbling on the shrubs.

When you scrape away the questionable premises, what remains in the case made by the *pro*-deal *wallahs* is their fear that better relations with the US hinge on this agreement, when actually they do not. Some 12 years back in a book—*Future Imperilled: India's Security in the 1990s and Beyond*—this writer had fleshed out a security architecture ("an Indian Monroe Doctrine"—an India-centric concept derived from Nehru's impracticable "Asian Monroe Doctrine" of the late Forties) and a mutually beneficial strategic tie-up with the US based on the limits of America's interventionary capability and India's emerging clout, under its own steam, as a credible military and economic counterweight to China in Asia. This analysis was published at a time when most of the analysts now incessantly cawing about an India-US partnership, had quite different views.

The bedrock of strong strategic ties is the "defence cooperation framework agreement" worked out between defence minister Pranab Mukherjee and US defence secretary Donald Rumsfeld last summer. The nuclear deal owing to its skewed nature is, as I have detailed in these columns, a "poison pill" that is likely to embitter relations in the future and stop the promise of full-scope defence cooperation from being realised. This argument, incidentally, is echoing in Washington where people like Leonard Spector—one of the principal authors of the Non-Proliferation Treaty, and Michael Krepon of the Stimson Center are pleading that there are too many positive factors animating the India-US relationship for it to run aground because of a failed nuclear deal.

Spector, in fact, mentions that India and Israel are in like situation *vis-a-vis* the US. Tel Aviv has emphatically resisted the imposition by the US of IAEA safeguards on any part of its nuclear programme and has otherwise rejected truncating its nuclear options in any manner for any reason and under any guise. This has not impacted adversely on Israel's bilateral relations with the US because Washington needs a strong Israel in West Asia. A strategically-oriented India standing up for its nuclear interests will only draw US respect and consideration, because a comprehensively powerful India is more beneficial to long-term American national interests than the meagre non-proliferation returns from a punitive-minded nuclear deal at the present time.

(*The Asian Age*, January 28, 2006)

15. Do as the U.S. would

BHARAT KARNAD

It is a supreme irony that safeguarding Iran's nuclear weapons potential is agitating the partners of the ruling Congress Party-led coalition—the Left parties and the Samajwadi Party—more than the proposed nuclear deal with the United States, which poses imminent danger to national security and India's strategic independence. The Communist Party Politburo and Mulayam Singh Yadav may be better advised to draw red lines where the N-deal is concerned.

In, perhaps, the most detailed exposition of the American negotiating position to-date US ambassador David C. Mulford in an interview to the PTI (*The Asian Age,* January 30, 2006) stated that the "separation plan" the Indian team had offered the visiting under-secretary of state Nicholas Burns, January 10-20, simply did not pass "the test" and "did not meet the minimum standard ... required for Congress to act favourably" in a way "that would also be acceptable to the Nuclear Suppliers' Group." This means, Mulford clarified, that the bulk of the 22 reactors operating or being built should be in the safeguards net and as fair as the- other parts of the Indian nuclear programme are concerned, for the separation plan to show that India's "basic (nuclear) industry is moving strongly into the civilian side."

Alighting, on an acceptable separation plan may not be "rocket science," as G. Balachandran, a technically savvy analyst, opined in an op-ed piece (*The Indian Express,* January 27, 2006). But it is curious he has not argued that India ought strictly to follow the separation principles the US applied to its own N-programme. As far as is known, the Indian team, perhaps because it was not aware of these principles, has not formally insisted on demarcating its N-programme in the manner the US had done. Such an Indian tack would be the safest, precedent-based, most prudent thing to do and, by way of a negotiating tactic, put the onus on the Americans to be reasonable. Adhering to these American principles, besides providing the necessary latitude for separation purposes, will reflect the Indian government's long-held desire to be treated on par with the five Non-Proliferation Treaty-recognised weapon states, "nothing more and nothing less" in foreign secretary Shyam Saran's words. After all, the sauce deemed right for one gander will surely do for another gander.

According to a Congressional document, a deputy under-secretary of state testifying before the US Senate Foreign Relations Committee in 1979 laid down the following four principles for bifurcating the American nuclear energy programme. No nuclear-research and development facility, nuclear installation production unit or, laboratory or any other nuclear usable entity (and attached man-power) will go-under safety-guards if (1) it is currently used for military purposes; (2) is co-located with military-use units, (3) is occasionally used for military purposes, and, (4) its inclusion in the safeguarded list poses "an incremental risk" to national security.

All the constituent parts of the Bhabha research establishment in Trombay; the Beryllium plant in Vashi, the entire Chennai nuclear complex, inclusive of the entire breeder programme, which once its gets off the ground, will become critical for military purposes, the nuclear powered submarine power plant test bed, the Rattehalli centrifuge facility, the Raja Ramanna Centre in Indore, the Nuclear Fuel Complex at Hyderabad, all mining facilities, the variable energy cyclotron in Kolkala (useable for tritium production), and almost any other aspect of the nuclear programme of remotely strategic import must be kept outside the safeguards regime. The co-location principle, for instance, allows the two power reactors (MAPS I & II) in Chennai to be part of the military sphere, along with CIRUS and Dhruva in Trombay. But the weapon grade material the two dedicated Trombay reactors and the two power plants annually produce barely allows the country to keep pace with a lowly Pakistan, whose weapons-usable fissile material production capacity is augmented by the Chinese built reactor in Chashma. Indeed, the "incremental risk" principle caution dictates, should be utilised expansively to delineate India's military nuclear sector and to keep safeguards at bay.

Given India's big power attributes—not all of them as yet realised, "national-parity" with China is the minimum standard the Indian thermonuclear strategic programme ought to hew to, as I have elaborated over the years. In which case, the question becomes how many of the remaining nine unsafeguarded power plants to keep aside for possible military use, keeping in mind the fact that while designated military-use reactors can be used for civilian purposes to produce electricity, the safeguarded units cannot, under any circumstances; revert to militaryaise. Here a simple rule of thumb makes sense. Once the Prototype Fast Breeder Reactor under construction begins functioning, say, 15 years from how after the normal start-up glitches are resolved, it will begin producing as much plutonium. as five regular power plants. So five-six power reactors are definitely needed to produce fissile material in the next 15 years in the volume the PFBR will be able to do thereafter. That will leave only two-three of the 11 currently unsafeguarded, power plants, but little else, headed for the IAEA net. Safeguards may be negotiated for power plants under construction once they become operational, depending on the military need at the time, without any prior commitment.

This is about the extent to which India can realistically and pragmatically accommodate the George W. Bush administration.

The scheme (minus/plus a power reactor) sketched here—inadvertently in line with the first three US separation principles—reportedly constitutes the Indian plan presented to Burns, which did not meet with Washington's approval. Under the circumstances, the issue boils down to whether the Indian government will summon the nerve to stand its ground or will it buckle under 'pressure?' or, put another way, how despirate is the Manmohan Singh government to obtain this deal considering that even with optimal utilisation, imported and indigenous nuclear reactors will be able to source no more than 6 per cent of the total energy produced in the country well into the future? Is risking the country's strategic options worth this exchange?

Leading advocates of the deal argue that India has to toe the American line on safeguards or face technological oblivion. This is rubbish as the record shows. Despite decades of US-led sanctions the Indian nuclear programme has flourished; among other things, it has developed a new heavy water-moderated reactor type—INDU, certified by IAEA, is a leader in breeder reactor research, engineered its own uranium enrichment centrifuge technology, and is conducting cutting edge work in a host of areas, like laser enrichment etc. It has in addition exhibited innovative verve in configuring new nuclear and thermonuclear weapon or warhead designs, which need validation by testing (and, therefore, the sequestration of a quantity of fissile material for this purpose).

If the Indian nuclear programme were the backwaters as these apparently motivated advocates make it out to be, logically, there would be little interest in bridling India's nuclear capability, under non-proliferation or any other guise. After all, a technologically inconsequential India that has chosen to remain outside the NP slip-stream and posed no danger to any of the five so-called Non-Proliferation Treaty-recognised states (P-5) or to the existing nuclear order, could be safely ignored. It is precisely because India by the dint of its own effort has proved itself an indefatigable technology producer and innovator and overcome obstacles deliberately placed in its path by the P-5, and NSG, combined with the country's galloping economic growth rate, that has made these great powers apprehensive. It is the prospective loss of relative advantage and their unwillingness genuinely to share great power space with India, which impel them to try and curb India's independent technological progress and strategic security wherewithal. A collaborationist media and an economics-wise canny but strategically short-sighted and too ready-to-compromise Congress Party regime may just be playing in their hands.

There is, moreover, a cautionary tale in the unfolding Iran case that New Delhi should take note of. The case for stopping Tehran short of the weapons capability by any means is promised on Iran's NPT signatory status and the legal obligations. It undertook. The proposed deal with the US will, for the first time, entangle the Indian nuclear weapons programme in a legal web that will likewise strategically constrain this country and immeasurably raise the cost of disregarding undertakings. In view of the uncertainty attending on the emerging international order it may be wise not to get into a position from which this country may need to backtrack.

Jawaharlal Nehru had stated that India had missed out on the gunpowder revolution leading eventually to its enslavement but, he asserted, the country would not miss out on the nuclear revolution. On the cusp of reaching Nehru's threshold of true strategic power and independence, one hopes the Manmohan Singh government does not fritter away the hard-won advantage and choke the country's strategic, nuclear programme in the mistaken belief that this is the way to go and the price to pay to ensure India's future and America's goodwill.

(The Asian Age, February 4, 2006)

16. Nuclear deal is Insidious, Unfair

Having done their worst (by way of economic sanctions and technology denial regimes), but failing to slow down India's acquisition of critical nuclear technologies and growingly respectful of this country's slow and steady—rather than snazzy—technological progress in this field and realising, moreover, that India cannot be intimidated or stopped by hard measures, the international nuclear oligopoly of the five so-called non-proliferation treaty-recognised nuclear weapon states and the Nuclear Suppliers' Group have, chosen a softer, ostensibly more convival and cooperative strategy. It is a strategy to deprive India of wins hard-earned energy and strategic options that plays to Indian rulers' and elite's weakness for flattery and blandishments.

The United States is demanding that India separate its fully integrated nuclear energy programme into military-use and civilian-use sectors and, in-Senator John Kerry's words, put "three quarters" of its nuclear programme inclusive of manpower and especially the entire plutonium breeder reactor project and the follow-on thorium cycle—which last will provide the country with unlimited electricity some 30 years from now when the thorium reactor using the mineral of which this country owns three-quarters of the world's reserves, comes on·stream—under International Atomic Energy Agency safeguards.

In return, the US has promised to:

- Pull down the offending and oppressive international instruments and mechanisms (NPT strictures, NSG guidelines) that India has managed by its technological accomplishments to reduce to irrelevance.
- Pull India into the "uranium economy" by lifting the bar on the sale of enriched uranium-run reactors, which will make India a prisoner of foreign uranium fuel supply, and prey to threats of cut-off as happened with the two US supplied and financed Tarapur reactors, except it will be tens of billions of dollars of Indian capital that will now be uselessly locked up.
- Absorb the Indian fast breeder reactor and the successor thorium-reactor technology development programmes—research in which India

is the leading country—into something recently dreamt up by Washington: the "Global Nuclear Energy Partnership."

- Involve India in the high-cost International Thermonuclear Experimental Reactor project the US has lessened its financial stake in because the technology is expected to take too long to mature for it to be good investment. It is an enterprise that will cost India dear, requiring a contribution of some Rs. 2,500 crores over the next decade.

If each of these sub-offers is further deconstructed, the insidious intent becomes starker still. Take GNEP, for instance. This hastily concocted programme to tempt the Indian government to sign the nuclear deal is aimed to minimise the military utility of the proposed Indian breeder reactor by pushing this country into accepting a collective design, which is proliferation resistant, meaning one that maximises the production of the higher isotopes of plutonium and trans-Uranic elements which, owing to their unstable nature, are unsuitable for weapons use.

The American insistence on the separation of capabilities in the allied space sector, moreover, shows what to expect in the nuclear sphere. Senior Defence Research and Development Organisation (DRDO) officials are prevented from accessing Indian Space Research Organisation (Isro) facilities and, in fact, have to sign in when entering Isro premises. This entry-exit register is periodically scanned by US agencies. For another, as R. Ramchandran writing in the *Hindu* (February 11, 2006) has revealed, the transaction processes and costs of dealing with the US are unbearable. It is difficult, he writes, for Isro, despite making every attempt at satisfying the US government, to do business because its rules and regulations are just too onerous. He is sceptical about the supposed pay-offs from cooperating with the US and wonders whether using Indian rockets to launch 2-3 ton American payloads into orbit will ever materialise and whether such contracts are at all worth the trouble Isro is going through to court US custom.

A similar denouement awaits the nuclear deal. Consider this: Should any Indian private sector company, like Larsen & Toubro and Godrej, which have developed sophisticated manufacturing expertise in the nuclear field, decide to commercialise their skill-sets and seek to work with any NSG firm, they too will be required to separate their military and civilian portions and adhere to American norms and domestic laws. In time, the fear of losing foreign business or the mere possibility of facing harassment on account of not meeting some US legal standard, may force them to terminate their long-standing relationship with the Indian nuclear military programme with devastating consequences for the Indian deterrent. This is bound to happen and as a US policy to undermine the burgeoning Indian private sector's role in the nuclear security of the country, it cannot be over-emphasised.

All this is staring the country in the face if only the Prime Minister's Office and ministry of external affairs—the two lead agencies involved in cutting this deal with the US, had the wit to think and strategise beyond the context of extremely short-term goals and benefits. If the strategising is being left to the newly founded Commission on Strategic Perspectives, then its chairman's writings in the last couple of years, inspire little confidence that the strategies have been got right. It may be a post-Cold War and newly globalising world, but the US as the strongest nation persists in shaping its security policies on at once the meanest and the most expansive definitions of national interest in order to ensure American primacy at all costs and whatever it takes. The Indian policy mindset is exactly the opposite but needs to reform in light of the relative strength of India increasing by leaps. It makes no sense to cut deals egregiously hurtful of Indian interests now, rather than wait for the country to acquire the necessary heft to bargain from a far more advantageous position for far bigger prizes some years from now.

Notwithstanding the fact of this nuclear deal resulting in a smaller, less autonomous, more dependent India, if the Manmohan Singh government is nevertheless inclined voluntarily to cap and contain the country's nuclear military prowess and potential and its civilian nuclear energy independence, which are in a symbiotic relationship, and try and achieve the result the US-led nuclear oligopoly failed to do despite their most strenuous non-proliferation efforts, it is apparently because the Prime Minister believes it serves some idea of "enlightened" national interest that he holds privately or collectively along with his advisers, Cabinet colleagues, and senior ruling Congress Party members.

But history suggests that any time a head of government begins qualifying large concepts like peace or national interest, he is setting the country up for a fatal compromise. Recall the British PM Neville Chamberlain's declaration on his return to London from his parleys with Hitler in Munich that peace "in our time" was at hand. Prime Minister Manmohan Singh bears the historic burden and responsibility of ensuring India does not for any reason whatsoever kowtow to the paramount power of the day and sacrifice the wherewithal and the means of this country's nuclear military security and energy independence.

In case he justifies the manifestly unfair nuclear deal on the cards on the basis of sufficiency of stockpiled fissile material for a "minimum credible deterrent," it will be because some physicists are touting the fact that India already has 80 nuclear warheads which are adequate as "minimum deterrent" and because they point to the ten tons of stockpiled spent fuel from the unsafeguarded pressurised heavy-water reactors over the years, enough they claim for "1,000 weapons." What they do not say is that this large mass of spent fuel is not weapon-grade plutonium and should these be used for military purposes will produce very inefficient nuclear weapons that will pose enormous problems in storage as well as in contingent use. But should this same spent fuel be put in a breeder reactor, it will fetch high quality weapons usable plutonium, which is what the country needs. This is one of the critical reasons why the breeder programme needs, to be kept out of the international safeguards net. The Congress Party coalition government has to make sure that India ends up with a consequential nuclear force, quality- and quantity-wise, which will meet the criteria of sufficiency enunciated by US President Richard Nixon in 1971 of being able to not only militarily dissuade, the most powerful adversary but also deter "coercion" from any quarter.

February 20 and his statement in Parliament will show whether Dr Singh has discarded his economistic blinkers and has the stuff in him of a hard realpolitik statesman the country desperately needs and the world can respect.

(The Asian Age, February 15, 2006)

17. Down to the Last Atom

When the July 18, 2005, joint statement between India and the United States covering the nuclear deal was signed, there was considerable euphoria over the implicit formal recognition of India's nuclear weapons status and a possible opening up of opportunities for it to become a global player in nuclear energy. The wordings in the statement were straight and clear: India with its strong commitment to preventing WMD proliferation, and as a responsible state with advanced nuclear technology, should acquire the same benefits and advantages, reciprocally assuming the same responsibilities and practices as other leading nations with advanced nuclear technology such as the US. Prime Minister Manmohan Singh reiterated this to the Parliament in his statement on July 29, 2005. Seeing the trend of negotiations, however, this seems to be only on paper.

While the joint statement elaborates on what these responsibilities and practices should be and the actions to be taken by both sides, the ongoing bilateral discussions seem to have run into rough weather over identifying civil and military facilities, with the US now stipulating that the separation should be credible, transparent and defensible; and that the civil list should be long. In particular, the Indian proposal to exclude fast breeder reactors (FBRs) from the civil list has become a sticking point.

Obviously, these stipulations, like the big discount sales ads whose innocuous asterisks lead to the fine print "conditions apply", are missing in the joint statement! It is true that in diplomacy, it is prudent for both sides to remain engaged but the decision should not be hasty and to the detriment of long-term national interests. There are some analysts in India who are vehemently arguing that we should accede to the demand for inclusion of FBRs in the civil list and get on with the deal. Since this is a serious issue, it deserves some discussion in perspective.

At the outset of our nuclear programme, fully realising the limited uranium resources and very large reserves of thorium in the country, Dr Homi Bhabha took a conscious decision that the nuclear power programme should develop in three phases to ensure long-term energy independence. Prior to induction of power reactors, R&D was given top priority which resulted in acquiring capability to set-up industrial-scale plants, right from mining and milling of uranium to fuel fabrication, spent fuel reprocessing and nuclear waste management as well as heavy water production to complete the fuel cycle.

In the first phase of power generation, PHWRs (pressurised heavy water reactors) were chosen, as they are good plutonium producers using natural uranium available as initial fuel. A bilateral cooperation agreement was entered into with Canada to build PHWRs at Kota, Rajasthan. Simultaneously, a bilateral agreement was entered into with the US for light water reactors. The US undertook to supply low enriched uranium (LEU) as raw material, that was to be indigenously converted to ready-to-use fuel for the lifetime of the reactors, assessed at 25 years. These reactors were chosen to get hands-on experience in the operation of nuclear power reactors and generate experienced manpower.

After our 1974 peaceful nuclear experiment (PNE), both the US and Canada unilaterally abrogated the bilateral agreements midway, leaving us high and dry in spite of us not violating any of our international obligations as a non-NPT country. Till 1974, PNEs were considered as peaceful for a variety of applications. This was propagated at international meetings in which India used to participate. With the abrogation of bilateral agreements by the US and Canada, our scientists accepted the challenge and made phenomenal progress in developing indigenously the technology for design, construction and operation of PHWRs. It is heartening to note that the Indian industry rose to the occasion and successfully produced various complex equipments and components. Regarding the fuel for the Tarapur reactors, a mixed oxide fuel fabrication facility was hurriedly set-up to stretch the availability of fuel. Part of the reactor core was loaded with this fuel to partially offset the denial of LEU by the US.

It is thus clear that while India was never averse to international cooperations, its subsequent experience showed that these are highly undependable and subject to humiliating restrictions, embargoes and denials of supplies and technology on flimsiest pretexts. Thanks to the foresight of Homi Bhabha and the inherent strength of our world-class R&D built over the years, our nuclear scientists have been able to overcome the pitfalls of dependence on imports. Success always comes by facing challenges; it is foolish to belittle this strength that not even some of the advanced countries possess. It is this aspect that has made our country proud in the nuclear field and helped us in commanding respect the world over.

In this context, it is highly demoralising that one of the leading daily newspapers in this country has been publishing articles casting aspersions on the DAE (Department of Atomic Energy) for expressing caution in taking decisions while pursuing the present Indo-US deal. Scientists do not derive fun by struggling under heavy odds to develop complex technologies if they are freely available. The ground reality is that if one gets used to easy imports, gets tripped and is forced to fend for oneself, it is a lot more difficult, experience shows, to pick up the threads again.

Coming back to the FBRs, it is the most important intermediate step in the second phase of our nuclear programme which uses plutonium from the first phase and converts thorium partly into Uranium 233, a fissile material like plutonium (separated from spent fuel), and Uranium 235 (enriched from natural uranium), in addition to producing more plutonium. While the first breeder power reactor as a prototype capable of producing 500 MV of electricity is under construction at Kalpakkam in Tamil Nadu, considerable R&D has also gone on the fast breeder test reactor at a number of world-class laboratories built at the Indira Gandhi Center for Atomic Research. Many of these R&D studies are being carried out for the first time by stretching the expertise to the maximum, out of dire necessity forced by circumstances, not by choice, as some analysts tend to believe. Thanks to dedicated scientists, young and old, the results so far have been highly encouraging. This needs to be kept up.

Yes, such endeavours do involve time and patience and there is no short-cut. Technologies, even if available, can at best be "black boxes" and do not in the long-run give us either confidence or make us self-reliant. It is therefore advisable at this stage to keep the FBR out of safeguards, as past experience shows that exposing R&D to international inspections is detrimental and stunts the growth of R&D itself. Freedom is the keyword in R&D. An honest, highly competent research scientist cannot tolerate at work even his own boss breathing down his neck, forget an international inspector!

It is not only the question of inclusion of FBRs. Apart from R&D facilities, the whole lot of facilities upstream and downstream will be up for safeguards that have not been focused on so far. Safeguards are like cancer. Once they get into the system, they spread throughout under the "pursuit and contamination provisions" of safeguards agreements, which can't be avoided and are also not amenable for negotiations. Only those who know the intricacies involved can appreciate the complex issues, not armchair analysts! These should be left to the professional scientist to decide, as he is the one who has to face the music and deliver the goods!

Given the peculiar situation we are in, in the ultimate analysis, thorium has to play the key central role in our long-term energy security. In the third phase the reactors are operated with Uranium 233 from the second phase as core fuel along with thorium in the blanket to produce more Uranium 233 and make it almost self-sustaining. When once we succeed in reaching the third phase of our nuclear power programme, we will be virtually world leaders in this technology. As per current estimates, a staggering 530,000 MW of electricity can be generated for 300 years out of the assessed thorium reserves in the country. This could make fossil fuels irrelevant. The road ahead is full of challenges and excitement and what is required is to provide flexibility and encouragement to the scientists. To achieve such a tremendous goal, time and money spent should be considered worthwhile investments as the ultimate stakes are very high. Already considerable R&D work has gone on regarding the entire thorium fuel cycle with encouraging results. The scientists are not idling! In fact a small reactor named 'kamini', which has been built and operated, uses Uranium 233 fuel derived from irradiated thorium fuel. It is the first of its kind in the world! To sum up, let me highlight some of the points:

- The July agreement, reiterated by the PM in Parliament, should be taken seriously and the negotiations respect its letter and spirit. The US demands should not be considered trivial and dismissed as part of give and take.
- This is a cooperation agreement and as partners, both sides are bound to benefit. We should not be unduly defensive in putting forth our views and stick to our long-term national interests. Grander vision does not mean signing on the dotted line and surrendering.
- Decisions taken now are irreversible in practice. We should therefore consider all aspects very carefully and leave flexibility for the future if the situation so develops. It is suicidal to tie ourselves up prematurely and suffer in the future. In this connection we should not get unduly pressured to take vital decisions before the visit of US President George Bush. Think and act.
- Scientists as professionals carry tremendous responsibility to implement the ultimate decisions. As far as possible, their views should be respected.

I don't think the DAE is saying the FBRs should never be on the civil list. However, they should not be on the civil list till they reach a level of maturity. This approach should meet the US objective ultimately, though not immediately.

I have been accused in some quarters of being against the agreement. There is no truth in it. I am always of the opinion that for science and technology to flourish and provide benefits to the common man, global interaction will be very helpful. Unfortunately, big power politics has taken precedence on such vital matters. Otherwise the world could have benefited immensely from the high technical skills and manufacturing capabilities.

(*Outlook*, February 27, 2006)

18. George's Nuclear Durbar

BHARAT KARNAD

But for Dr Anil Kakodkar's coming out publicly, albeil a bit late in the day, against the proposed nuclear deal with the United States and the lining up of nuclear establishment stalwarts, like Dr P.K. Iyengar, Dr A. Gopalakrishnan, Dr A.M. Prasad and even Dr M.R. Srinivasan who was consulted by the Prime Minister's Office, behind the current chairman of the Atomic Energy Commission, this transaction would have gone through on largely American terms as Washington had hoped it would. This nearly occurred because the media uncritically bought the line that India should not miss out on this "strategic opportunity" to ride the US coat-tails to great power.

It apparently matters little that most of the advocates of the deal are unfamiliar with the nuclear technologies involved and the implications for the country of voluntarily restraining their continued indigenous development. Indeed, the most vociferous among them have tried to make such ignorance out to be a virtue by arguing that technical details should not obscure the larger political aims that are ostensibly served by falling in with the Americans! In an effort, moreover, to browbeat a Congress Prime Minister with a questionable grasp of foreign and security policy, the case of Indira Gandhi's accepting US violation of a binding international legal contract to supply enriched uranium fuel for the lifetime of the two Tarapur Light Water reactors, has been exhumed. The exact opposite lesson needs to be learned from the Tarapur episode, namely that unless a supplier country is dragged into court for not meeting contractual obligations and made to pay stiff damages, the same country can turn around, as the US has done, and offer still more audacious deals in the belief that these can be forced down the apparently willing throat of the Indian government and that there will be no costs for violating with impunity any understanding. Had the Tarapur case been taken to international arbitration, Washington would have been wary of promising this country the (energy) moon-*qua*-imported reactors. On this last issue, moreover, is it enough for New Delhi to link the safeguards to uninterrupted foreign fuel supply? How is India going to be compensated for the Rs. 250,000 crores (Dr A. Gopalakrishnan's figures) it will have to ante up for the reactors imported from the US, France, or Russia producing 35,000 MW of electricity? And should the Indian government not insist contractually on supplier countries guaranteeing the return of this vast sum (after depreciation) in case they cease supply of fuel for any reason?

It is the historical and geopolitical *raisons d'etre* provided by K. Subrahmanyam and embroidered by his associate, which are legitimating this deal among the unthinking political class, and the Foreign Office and other bureaucracies, and need to be contested. Subrahmanyam has referred repeatedly to two historical examples of great powers helping lesser states with potential to become major powers. The first case pertains to a supposedly weak Imperial Japan in the early years of the 20th century which, according to Subrahmanyam, was assisted by Britain, the then predominant power, to "balance" an expansive Czarist Russia in the Far East. But historical facts, alas, suggest something quite different. With the restoration of Emperor Meiji, after the Tokugawa period, and the impetus given to "westernisation" and military modernisation by him, Japan had, by the 1890s built up a huge economic, political and industrial presence in China and the Korean peninsula. Britain, as one of the main beneficiaries of the "Open Doors" Policy, had likewise acquired a significant stake in China. Almost on par militarily, Japan and Britain, desirous of protecting their investments in China and Korea, decided on jointly checkmating Russia's ambitions to carve out territories at their expense. They agreed in January 1902 on a naval treaty, which prevented Britain—"perfidious Albion"—from expediently joining Moscow to neutralise Tokyo's naval war plans which ended in the decisive Japanese naval victory over the Russian fleet in the Tsushima straits in 1905. To construe this as in any way an analogue of the US helping India become a counterweight to China in the 21st century is to reduce history to a joke.

The other example Subrahmanyam is prone to cite, concerns China accepting US "help" in the Seventies leading to Deng Xiaoping's economic reforms, opening up of the American market to Chinese exports etc. Mis-analogy is even more marked here. China, was by the late Sixties in a position militarily to deter the US with its small number of thermonuclear megaton war-headed-intercontinental ballistic missiles targeted at the US west coast, and in 1969 proved its conventional military prowess against the Soviet Union in the clashes on the Ussuri river. China's all round military heft made it a preferred candidate for Washington to court in order to tilt the balance against Moscow in the Cold War.

Now how exactly do these historical cases fit the purported American intention to build India up into a consequential-power? If anything, these cases prove the thesis this analyst has been pegging away at for some 20 years now, which is that first acquiring strategic military wherewithal—especially megaton thermonuclear-ICBM forces—is a prerequisite for India to be perceived as a substantive system "balancer" and to attract powerful friends to achieve this goal. Strategic military weakness in a state only invites derisory deals of the nuclear kind mooted by the US.

This brings us to the state of the nuclear negotiations on the eve of President George W. Bush's visit. The near hysteria in official circles resembles the tizzy the colonial government was in, as described by James Morris, the most engaging chronicler of the British Empire, before the 1911 Durbar featuring another George—the "King Emperor" George V. It manifests the Indian habit of genuflection, now as then, at its most cringe-inducing. It has led naturally to the US National Security Adviser Stephen Hadley conceiving of the Bush visit in terms of its "function" to "force" or even sweet-talk Dr Singh into, presumably, making concessions on the separation plan.

His February 27 statement in Parliament notwithstanding, the Prime Minister cannot afford to concede any ground whatsoever on four issues, no matter what bait, lure or temptation is dangled by President Bush. For reasons of national security and long-term energy independence, India cannot afford to:

1. bring (or ever think of doing so) the fast breeder reactor programme and the follow-on thorium cycle under safeguards now or in the future,

2. agree to a safeguards regime on any reactor or nuclear facility in "perpetuity"—something the US has rejected for its own nuclear installations,

3. allow any even remotely weapons programme-usable nuclear facilities anywhere in the country, and

4. commit the five indigenous power plants under construction (other than the two Russian reactors at Koodankulum, which are safeguards-bound) to international inspection *a priori,* considering that seven of the currently 11 un-safeguarded dual-use power plants—Manmohan Singh's "65%" of all active power reactors—are to be brought under international supervision; the most that may be promised is a case-by-case examination depending on the military requirements at the time.

These measures alone will preserve a modicum of manoeuvring room, continuing leverage, and strategic autonomy for the country in the years to come. Bush has also to be reminded that India's sovereign nuclear interests and policies cannot be fashioned to please either the US Legislature or the Nuclear Suppliers' Group and that he better begin expending his political capital to push this deal, rather than rely on India to do all the heavy lifting.

(*The Asian Age,* March 1, 2006)

19. Don't Compromise India's Dignity

A. GOPALAKRISHNAN

The Indo-US Nuclear Deal is nearing its first milestone. Whether or not the deal will indeed move to its logical next step will depend greatly on the success of finding mutual agreement at this initial stage, during the forthcoming Presidential visit. In a timely manner, the Prime Minister's statements in both houses of parliament on Feb. 27, 2006 have re-asserted the government's stand that the deal, if taken forward, must strictly be in accordance with the letter and spirit of the July 18 th. agreement he signed with President Bush. The PM has listened to all shades of opinions on this deal, and has finally come to his own conclusion that the arguments presented by the Department of Atomic Energy and many of us in the scientific community have great validity.

The subject on which a great deal of controversy has already surfaced is the separation of India's nuclear facilities and programs into civilian and military ones. Though it appears that the Indo-US Working Group discussions also included the type of IAEA safeguards and the Additional Protocol which will be acceptable to India, no speculations are available in the open on these aspects.

The main differences between the Indian and US positions on the separation question are on the minimum number of pressurized heavy water reactors (PHWRs) the Department of Atomic Energy (DAE) would like to retain in the military list and the DAE's view that the fast breeder reactor (FBR) program will have to stay out of the civilian list for the foreseeable future.

The number of PHWRs to be retained in the military list, in my view, is closely linked to the inventory of tritium we need to produce and maintain for the weapons program, as well as the additional stock of reactor-grade plutonium (Pu) required for the un-safeguarded FBR program.

The link between the FBR program and the strategic weapons program in the initial years depends on the true current inventory of weapon-usable Pu in Indian hands. No country makes an open declaration of this inventory, and all the available western data on this are based on simplistic calculations and incorrect assumptions of primary operational data of our reactors. I have reasonable basis to assert that currently India requires a part of the accumulated reactor-grade Pu, in addition to the stock of weapon-grade Pu from CIRUS and Dhruva reactors, to meet the needs of the 'minimum credible deterrent', as envisaged in the country's nuclear doctrine.

Those who have an understanding of fast reactor development know that it is a complex process of linked activities, wherein there are at least four major zones where reactor-grade plutonium could be present at the same time. These are in the overall storage or 'inventory bank' of reactor-grade Pu, the Pu loading into the operating FBR(s), the out-of-reactor experimental (future) core-making which involves Pu fuel, and the spent-fuel reprocessing plant where separated reactor-grade Pu will become available. Even if we assume that India today has enough reactor-grade Pu in our inventory to meet the supplementary needs of the weapons program, this inventory will seriously diminish in the initial years, because of the large withdrawals of Pu to fuel the FBR(s) and for simultaneously fabricating advanced fuel assemblies for subsequent loading, and we could therefore be passing through some long periods of lower-than-required amounts of overall weapons-usable Pu stock. The opportunity to replenish the inventory of reactor-grade Pu back towards the required level arises only when the spent-fuel from the FBR cores are reprocessed and the Pu so obtained is put back into the inventory bank. If, however, the FBR program is put under safeguards as desired by the US, the associated spent-fuel and reprocessed Pu will also become part of a safeguarded civilian program, and then this Pu cannot go from the civilian side back to an un-safeguarded Pu inventory which will be shared also by the weapons program. Thus, if the FBRs are put in the civilian list, the inventory of rector-grade Pu we have today will continue to be drained off for use in the FBRs, with no opportunity to replenish it back. This, in my opinion, is the crucial linkage between the FBR program and our weapons program which Dr. Kakodkar may have been alluding to in his recent interview.

As we proceed, the inventory of total Pu in the 'bank' will therefore fluctuate with time. In the initial years, it could mostly fall to quite low levels, but it will start building up slowly in spite of the ongoing FBR projects, once the Pu obtained from reprocessing the FBR cores is available to replenish it. The breeding process also will contribute some net build-up of reactor-grade Pu and, in addition, there will be the steady but slow addition of weapon-grade Pu from the continued operation of CIRUS and Dhruva reactors. Thus, we will reach a future date beyond which the weapons-grade Pu inventory alone will be sufficient for our strategic purposes and we may not have to rely on reactor-grade Pu at all. By then, the FBR development process may also be nearly completed and the entire question of safeguards for the FBRs can be re-examined, if it is of mutual benefit.

Though nothing much is heard about the government's views on the subject of IAEA safeguards and the Additional Protocol, I am sure it is realized that both these are as crucial as the matter of separation of facilities. In my view, we cannot agree to a blanket imposition of INFIRC-66 type perpetual safeguards on all civilian facilities, without associated qualifying conditions. As a minimum, India must insist on the right to withdraw any civilian facility from safeguards, if essential materials, equipment and spare parts which need to be imported for its continued operation are denied through unrestricted international commerce. In general, the clauses in the safeguards agreement and its Additional Protocol will have to be suitably modified to ensure that the inspection activity is not misused to extract intellectual property information from our R&D programs or to satisfy the bursting curiosity of certain nations to snoop into the details of our indigenous nuclear developments over the past 30 years. India must also retain control over the 'pursuit' clauses in the protocol to prevent companies like the BHEL, L&T, Godrej Manufacturing, etc., who have been carrying out manufacture of nuclear components, from being subjected to intrusive inspections. In this case, many of their same shop floors are also involved in fabricating the components for our indigenous nuclear submarine project and hence such locations should be made 'out-of-bounds' for IAEA inspectors. These and many more fine-print details in the standard safeguard and protocol agreements need to be very carefully studied and modified to suit the Indian requirements.

What then is the bottom line? India will have to retain a few PHWR power reactors and the entire FBR program out of safeguards for the indefinite future. The BARC, IGCAR and CAT research facilities, the uranium enrichment plant in Mysore, the ATV project facilities, etc. shall certainly remain outside safeguards. This would still leave six power reactors already under safeguards and perhaps around nine additional PHWRs which India can offer to place under safeguards, making it a reasonable total of fifteen out of the twenty-three power reactors for inclusion in the civilian list. In addition, if and when the support facilities exclusively used only by these fifteen reactors are separable from the rest, these can also be put under safeguards in a phased manner. In addition, India must carefully negotiate a special safeguard agreement and an Additional Protocol which guarantee adequate limitations on the inspection access of sites and data, as well as the protection of our intellectual property, so that the IAEA inspection process is not reduced to an overt exercise of intrusive evaluation of our indigenous nuclear development program.

We must also recognize that it is demeaning for India to accept the US offer to join their Global Nuclear Energy Partnership (GNEP) as a 'client state'. According to the statement of President Bush on February 22, 2006, "Under the GNEP, America will work with nations that have advanced civilian nuclear energy programs—such as Great Britain, France, Japan, and Russia— to share nuclear fuel with ('client') nations like India that are developing civilian nuclear energy programs". This is in direct contradiction to the

President's July 18, 2005 statement in our joint agreement that India is "a responsible state *with advanced nuclear technology,*—which should acquire the same benefits and advantages like other such states". In seven months, the President has decided to remove India from the exalted status of a country with advanced nuclear technology to one among some 180 nations who have no such capability ! How are we to trust this country and its Head of State who reverses his position to suit his day's policy?

(*The Asian Age,* March 1, 2006)

20. Questions for PM on CIRUS Reactor

A. GOPALAKRISHNAN

The India-US nuclear deal seems to have crossed its first milestone with the agreement reached on its crucial elements during last week's visit of President Bush. While waiting to hear from the PM on the details, a story of some concern has emerged in the last two days, alluding that India has agreed to close down the CIRUS reactor within the next five years, as part of the Indo-US nuclear agreement.

This reactor of Canadian design is of late-1950 vintage, and since then research reactor technology has advanced considerably. In recent years, CIRUS has undergone a cost-effective refurbishment, just to eliminate all the safety concerns pointed out by the Atomic Energy Regulatory Board (AERB), but not really to expand or modernize its research capabilities. But, no doubt it has been serving partly as a key plutonium (Pu) producer for our strategic weapon program. India's official position has been that we need the weapon-grade Pu from *both* the CIRUS and Dhruva reactors to meet the requirements of our minimum nuclear deterrent. If so, how can we afford to close down CIRUS as a result of the India-US deal, unless the government intends to replace this reactor in time with a more modern research reactor of similar kind?

We know that there has been strong pressure from the non-proliferation lobbies in both the US and Canada to place CIRUS in the safeguarded civil list, because of their contention that in using the Pu from this reactor in the Pokhran-1 nuclear test, India has broken the agreement that we will use it only for peaceful purposes. India, on the other hand, has steadfastly held on to the not so tenable position that we have never used CIRUS for anything other than peaceful purposes.

In the case of CIRUS, since it is located amidst the BARC military facilities, we cannot let IAEA inspectors or foreigners walk through there in the name of safeguards inspection. Therefore, I am sure the Prime Minister should unequivocally reject any US demand to place the CIRUS reactor under IAEA safeguards. But, I hope the PM will kindly recall an already announced plan of the DAE and the government to build a modern, natural uranium fuelled— heavy water moderated research reactor, perhaps now in the 60-80 MWth power range, for carrying out advanced experiments in neutron physics, materials development, etc. and for isotope production. Such a reactor will also, incidentally, produce more weapon-grade Pu than what CIRUS provides today. I would urge the government to give immediate financial approval for such a reactor to be designed and built within the BARC military facility domain, to be commissioned by the DAE positively within the next five years. Once this latest research facility goes into operation, we could consider shutting down the CIRUS reactor and transferring the useful Indian-built equipment and components from it to other projects within the DAE military list. Thus, a good portion of the expenditure we recently incurred in refurbishing CIRUS can be recovered, and there will also be no questions raised about any interruption or decrease in our weapon-grade Pu production rate due to this change-over.

Of course, all the spent-fuel ever generated by CIRUS during its operation will belong to India, outside safeguards. There can be no US objection to this overall plan, because India, under the current deal, is free to add facilities to its military list as it pleases, and in this case it is only a replacement of a facility and not much of any net addition to our Pu inventory. I request that the PM may please include a comprehensive statement on CIRUS in his address to parliament, to clear the air on this issue.

In the recent negotiations, India has succeeded in finalizing a mutually agreed separation plan for our power reactors. We are also going to retain our fast breeders based on indigenous fuel out of safeguards as long as we wish. As part of the give-and-take in any bargain, India had to agree for IAEA safeguards 'in perpetuity', but these safeguards and the associated Additional Protocol will be made "India-specific," to take care of all our major concerns and to blunt their intrusive clauses.

In this regard, I understand that the United States has already agreed to provide us life-time nuclear fuel supply guarantee for our civilian reactors through three separate and simultaneous modalities: firstly, through a bilateral agreement between the US and India; secondly, by a trilateral agreement between the IAEA, the US and India; and finally, through the creation of a multinational standing-group to monitor fuel supplies to India. The PM in his forthcoming address to the Parliament must, however, spell out all the India-specific changes that will form part of this deal.

(*The Asian Age*, March 6, 2006)

21. N-deal: India must Negotiate Hard

A.N. Prasad

Amid much fanfare, the India-United States nuclear agreement was reached on March 2.

Though the actual details and the fine print are not available as yet, the indications are it is a workable agreement that both sides should strive to move forward.

One important issue made clear is that the fast breeder reactor programme is out of the civilian list, as also are all the research reactors.

This should please our nuclear establishment. One hopes that while finalising the separation list, adequate care is taken in conditionally positioning various nuclear facilities upstream and downstream of the reactors, particularly since most of them are dual-purpose facilities.

This is very important as all of them have been developed and built indigenously through decades of dedicated painstaking research and development efforts.

Let's wait for the details before celebrating.

One also hopes that the deal covers only those reactors in operation and under construction with India retaining the prerogative to classify future reactors built entirely on our own without any external inputs.

It should be ensured that the stockpile of indigenous spent fuel and the separated nuclear material accumulated is kept outside the gamut of safeguards. There is a big question mark as to how the deal will be handled if there is any time limit is fixed—such as 2014, as some sources indicate.

Why is India Rejoicing?

This is an agreement that should benefit both US and India. The US will stand to gain by revitalising its dormant nuclear industry and help in stabilising demand for Middle-East fuel and the cost, as Washington itself has claimed.

It is quite possible that the skilled manpower and manufacturing capabilities of India could also be utilised in the design, construction and operation of American reactors!

In fact, in view of our advanced nuclear capabilities, there is no case for

India to be defensive while negotiating. Except that we are short of uranium, we can deal as equal partners.

N-deal: Coup or Sellout? Tell Us

The 65 to 35 split is itself a generous giveaway. We should ensure we are left with adequate number of reactors under the non-civilian list to meet the demands of fast breeder reactors and strategic requirements.

The deal is still in its beginning and there is plenty of homework to be done by India in negotiating the safeguards agreements—which should not be unduly intrusive.

The weapons States have got away lightly and there is plenty of scope for negotiations with tact and courage. This is a very crucial aspect from now on.

Fortunately, the agreement indicates an India-specific safeguards agreement. Before any firm commitments are made regarding safeguards, it is better to await progress on the US side of the deal.

(Rediff.com, March 6, 2006)

22. N-deal Concerns Remain

A. GOPALAKRISHNAN

During the United States President George W. Bush's India visit last week, the governments of India and the US have reached an agreement on the essential elements of the nuclear cooperation deal.

It is worth looking back at what we have achieved through the past eight months of negotiations, and what the remaining major Indian concerns are.

Officially, there is no word yet from the Indian government on the various provisions they have agreed to.

As usual, much more information can be found at the White House web site, especially in the latest press briefings given by US Under-Secretary of State for Political Affairs, Nicholas Burns.

Finally, India appears to have succeeded in reaching mutual agreement on a separation plan for our power reactors, with around eight out of 22 of these reactors retained in the military list.

All the eight establishments India's Department of Atomic Energy wishes to keep out of safeguards are operating pressurized heavy water reactors. Their use is considered essential for India's strategic weapons programme, aimed at maintaining a minimum credible nuclear deterrent.

The future disposition of the Indian fast breeder reactors had been the subject of prolonged negotiations for some time. The DAE has finally convinced the Americans that our strategic programme and the long-term energy security considerations of the nation will not permit us to place the fast breeder programme under International Atomic Energy Agency safeguards for the foreseeable future.

When and if we wish to change this stance in the future, the decision will be solely India's.

As part of the give and take in this bargain, India had to accept the IAEA safeguards 'in perpetuity' on our civilian facilities.

But these safeguards and the associated Additional Protocol will be made 'India-specific'—to take care of our major concerns and to blunt their intrusive clauses.

In return for this concession, I understand that the US has agreed to provide us life-time nuclear fuel supply guarantee for our civilian reactors through three separate and simultaneous modalities: Firstly, through a bilateral agreement between the US and India; secondly, by a trilateral agreement between the IAEA, the US and India; and finally, through the creation of a multinational standing-group to monitor fuel supplies to India.

The prized concession which the US and Canada wanted from India was to get the 40 MW CIRUS reactor, an India-Canada-US product, within the list of civilian facilities and under IAEA safeguards.

Prime Minister Dr Manmohan Singh is understood to have outright rejected this joint demand. In any case, the Prime Minister has announced that India has decided to permanently shut down the CIRUS reactor in 2010.

The DAE is already in the process of designing a more modern research reactor of about 60 MW to 80 MW capacity, for which notional approval was given some time back.

Soon after New Delhi builds and commissions this new natural uranium-heavy water research reactor at the Bhabha Atomic Research Centre as part of India's un-safeguarded military complex, we should be ready to phase out the CIRUS.

The new reactor will enable India to carry a modern portfolio of research and development tasks to suit our future plans, which we are unable to perform through the 46-year-old CIRUS.

Incidentally, the new research reactor will also produce annually at least the same quantity of weapons-grade plutonium that CIRUS is providing today.

The Americans should have no quarrel with this approach, since it meets their desire to see CIRUS not operating beyond the next six years or so, and our addition of a replacement research reactor in the military side does not violate the terms of the agreement.

In the coming weeks, many of the activities related to the India-US nuclear deal will shift to Washington.

The Bush administration has in its hands the challenging task of convincing the sceptical members of the US Congress and the US non-proliferation lobby that the terms of this deal will, over a period of time, help curb India's nuclear arsenal from getting out of hand, and that it will not encourage some of the current nuclear Non-Proliferation Treaty members to break out from the Treaty and initiate their own nuclear weapons work.

Assuming the deal crosses the hurdle of Congressional scrutiny, it still has to pass the close examination and debate at the Nuclear Suppliers' Group.

Only after both these steps are successfully completed will the question arise of India's negotiations with the IAEA, to put in place a suitable safeguards agreement and an Additional Protocol.

(Rediff.com, March 7, 2006)

23. Why the Nuclear Deal is a Disaster

BHARAT KARNAD

The small print of the nuclear deal which Prime Minister Manmohan Singh struck with US President George W. Bush, is now available and sure enough, it spells trouble for India. It has snared India in a non-proliferation net primarily by getting the Congress coalition government to agree to a fast-tracked Fissile Material Cut-off Treaty and to Comprehensive Test Ban Treaty-like constraints that together will end up freezing the Indian nuclear arsenal on an as is, where is, basis.

The July 18, 2005 Joint Statement ended even the remote possibility of any further testing by India. Ridiculous as Bharatiya Janata Party predecessor Atal Behari Vajpayee's announcement was about a voluntary test moratorium before the test data could be properly analysed a scant ten days after the "Shakti" series of tests in May 1998, what Dr Singh has committed to doing is downright alarming, because a "voluntary" test moratorium can be voluntarily broken, this strictly enforced bilateral agreement may not allow even sub-critical tests.

The reasonable precaution the Congress Party Prime Minister ought to have taken was to insist on making India's non-testing conditional on the five so-called Non-Proliferation Treaty-recognised nuclear weapon states (P-5) not developing and inducting newer, more advanced, warheads/weapons in their inventory, and all states, including the threshold states, refraining from testing. The failure to insist on these conditions has left the Indian N-arsenal frozen at a technologically primitive level even as the P-5 states are free continually to modernise their strategic armaments through other means, like the multi-billion dollar National Ignition Facility in Livermore, California, a facility using which the US, for instance, can test innovative low yield and fusion weapon designs without any of the impedimenta of underground testing.

The Indian nuclear establishment's confidence in indigenous software to simulate fission and fusion explosions to verify and develop new weapon/ warhead designs of varying power-to-yield ratios to fit numerous missile nose-cone geometries, is at once foolish and foolhardy. How the Indian armed forces responsible for triggering these manifestly unproven and unsafe, and definitely unreliable weapons, will deal with this deterrence situation created by the Manmohan Singh regime, remains to be seen. The fact is, no matter how sharp the country's capability in this field, no software can be developed on the basis of explosive physics data from just a single, failed, 1998 test to simulate, say, a thermonuclear explosion.

The amendments to the US Atomic Energy Act of 1954, as amended in 1974, suggested by the Bush White House contain the provision for "Presidential waiver," which presumably, will have to be sought on a periodic (annual?) basis. According to a retired chairman of the Atomic Energy Regulatory Board, Dr A. Gopalakrishnan, some $50 billion worth of reactors will, require to be imported to produce 35,000 MW of installed thermal capacity as contemplated by the Manmohan Singh government. Such large scale investment, in effect, means that the supply of fuel to run these reactors and the electricity in the grid so produced will both become hostage to India's "good behaviour" as certified annually by the US President to enable him to "waive" the non-proliferation laws on the books where India is concerned. While an economically growing India may arguably be able to absorb the loss of $50 billion, the loss of 35,000 MW of power in the national grid would be economically ruinous. Judging India's good behaviour, moreover, may not be restricted by Washington to the nuclear realm but, rather, any marked departure from the US line on other policy issues too could, as a pressuring tactic, precipitate a fuel cut-off. (France and Russia may squawk but will follow the US lead.) Considering the Americans will have India by its short and curlies, the Prime Minister's claim that India can ensure uninterrupted supply of fuel for the lifetime of the imported reactors by threatening withdrawal from the safeguards regime, is non-sensical.

A small, technologically antiquated, and therefore ineffective N-deterrent is also assured because of Dr Singh's commitment to obtain the Fissile Material Cut-off Treaty (FMCT). India will be unable to stretch out the negotiating process to "buy time" in this case to produce a large enough stockpile of fissile material, as it had done in the case of the Comprehensive Test Ban Treaty, to prepare for and test weapon designs on the shelf. New Delhi will be in no position to resist or delay the fast-tracking of an FMCT through the Commission on Disarmament because, unlike the CTBT, the FMCT will have close economic, trade and technological relations riding on its successful completion and ratification by the Indian government. This means the termination of all production of military-use fissile material in India within a couple of years, thereby rendering irrelevant the "separation plan" and the eight power stations, the designated breeder reactors, and the dedicated military reactor (the 100 MW Dhruva) and the rest of the nuclear caboodle consigned to the "military" part of the nuclear energy programme.

The impact would have been manageable if India had been producing weapon grade plutenium in the same quantities and for as long (1945-end 1990s) as the five established nuclear weapon states have done. Even if the

Indian government believes that such large amounts of WgPu are unnecessary for the purposes of the "minimum deterrence" (MD) India has pledged to be satisfied with, surely, prudence necessitates that the inherent elasticity in the MD concept be exploited, and the country stockpile fail-safe levels of Weapon-grade Plutonium (WgPu) just so it is not found deficient in the basic bomb-making material in any conceivable future crisis or contingency. Unless, of course, Dr Manmohan Singh and the strategic analysts he relies on for advice, are satisfied they have seen the future and are convinced India will require, nothing more by way of strategic leverage and protection in the decades to come, which conclusion, given their hubris, they may well arrive at.

A far more pragmatic course may be to task the Strategic Planning Group in the Department of Atomic Energy to estimate the total quantities of weapon-usable fissile material produced by the three leading nuclear weapon states—United States, Russia, and China. A threshold for the Indian WgPu holdings could then be firmed up by pegging the size of India's fissile material stock at, say, 75% of the three-country mean—a not unreasonable figure considering India's power trajectory is now second only to China's. But the question is: is the Congress Party-led government, in its self-imposed position as supplicant, in a mental state to stand up for India? And for a policy of "No FMCT until WgPu stockpile of 75% of the Big Three level is safely reached"?

To add insult to serious injury to India's nuclear independence, Manmohan Singh's desire for "advanced civilian technologies" will result not only in choking off Dr Homi Bhabha's carefully nurtured policy of "growing science" that has fetched the country leadership position in the cutting edge areas of breeder reactor and thorium utilisation cycle technologies—the very stuff of future security and energy independence and self-sufficiency—but in the GNEP member-states acquiring these indigenous technologies with no great benefits to India.

And finally to clear up a mystery: the reason the Americans showed surprising flexibility in the negotiations in the nuclear deal is because, as Under-Secretary of State for Arms Control and, International Security Affairs Robert Joseph confided to Representative Edward Markey, among the most powerful non-proliferationists in the US Legislature, in written replies to questions, "Rather than add additional conditions or seek to renegotiate the Joint Statement, we believe it would be better to lock-in this deal and then seek to achieve further results as our strategic partnership advances."

So, there we have it, the US strategy of "locking" India in a deal as a prelude to soft and hard measures being used to get New Delhi to cede more and more ground under the threat overhang of the "strategic partnership" being ended at any time. The arm-twisting by the Bush administration will begin with or without the imposition of additional conditionalities on India by the US Congress. Despite warnings by the Indian government about new conditions being "deal breakers." Washington is banking on Prime Minister Manmohan Singh ultimately to succumb to American blandishments, and who is to say they are wrong? This economist PM apparently devoid of strategic sense and great power mindset, may well shrug his shoulders and say: *Kee pharak painda ha* (What difference does it make)?

(*The Asian Age*, March 18, 2006)

24. Turning India into a Nuclear Cripple

BHARAT KARNAD

A Pakistani columnist, Ejaz Haider, of the *Friday Times,* has observed the strange phenomenon of the preponderant view in the United States being against the nuclear deal, while in India it is the supporters of this transaction who rule the roost. This is verily the truth, but it gets a twist when set alongside the findings of the Pew Global Attitudes Project, which reveal that two-thirds of the people in Britain, its closest ally, view the US and its foreign policy with trepidation, even as India. China and Indonesia—previously countries known for their anti-Americanism—perceive the US as benign. The difference may be attributable to the long exposure of the British to Americans and US policy motivations compared to the complete unfamiliarity with them of the Indian, Chinese and Indonesian policymakers, media commentators and the masses alike and whose slant, therefore, owes more to the *Hollywood History of the World* (to use the title of a hilarious book on American films by the novelist George Macdonald Fraser) and to Madison Avenue and slick packaging, than to harsh reality. Further, no country comes close to matching the smoothness of the US diplomatic machinery or the efficiency of its rewards system in moulding the views of opinion-makers and hence public opinion in the developing countries. The results in India are there for all to see.

Be that as it may, the troubles India will be stepping into with the proposed nuclear deal have been foretold by this analyst in a book (*Nuclear Weapons and Indian Security* published in 2002, a second edition out in 2005), in numerous research articles in professional journals (including "Perils of a Tight Embrace: India, US, Kashmir and Non-proliferation Issues" in *Strategic Analysis,* July-September 2002, a journal of the *sarkari* think tank, Institute of Defence Studies and Analyses), in several public forums and panel discussions since the July 18 Joint Statement and in 16-odd op-ed pieces in this newspaper starting in May 2005.

It was pointed out in these writings that with the nuclear deal the Indian government (1) was propelling the country into a "Tarapur trap" and making its strategic posture and foreign policy hostage to a cut-off of enriched fuel for the exorbitantly-priced imported reactors; (2) by agreeing to cease further testing and to fast-track a Fissile Material Cut-off Treaty, it was helping the US achieve its prime non-proliferation goal of "freezing and capping" the

Indian nuclear deterrent at its present small size and technologically primitive quality; (3) was foolhardy in agreeing to a "separation plan" and safeguards in perpetuity conforming to US interests rather than insisting on the same principles of separation adopted by Washington (namely, no nuclear facility currently used for military purposes, co-located with military use installations, occasionally used for military purposes, and whose inclusion in the safeguards list may pose "an incremental risk to national security," will be brought under international supervision) and IAEA safeguards; (4) had not reckoned with the high cost of duplicating some of the nuclear facilities exclusively for the military sphere; (5) initially acted as if unaware of the importance of the breeder reactor to the weapons programme (to convert the stockpile of spent fuel from the civil nuclear power plants into weapon-grade plutonium); and (6) instead of coupling India's ban on testing to the US and the other big powers not inducting new, more advanced nuclear weapons in their arsenals and linking the size of the Indian fissile material stockpile to, say, 75 per cent of the average estimated holdings of the US, Russia, and China, it adopted a rank bad negotiating strategy predicated on giveaways, leading to the US making more demands and asking for more concessions as part of a pressure strategy which the US under-secretary of state Nicholas Burns has dubbed "incremental diplomacy."

In one of my articles, it was also pointed out that Prime Minister Manmohan Singh's habit of being parsimonious with the truth—with his statements in Parliament contradicted by evidence of fatal compromises being agreed upon by the foreign secretary, Shyam Saran, in the negotiations—may eventuate in a Privilege Motion against Dr Singh and, who knows, his ouster from the prime ministerial post.

To retail this is less to thump one's back as to reveal the substantive reasons why the Manmohan Singh regime should have abstained from taking the axe to the country's nuclear and thermonuclear capabilities in the hope that a pleased George W. Bush administration will recast the international non-proliferation order to benefit India. The symbolism of a fake entry into the nuclear club by a hollowed out nuclear India apparently means more to Prime Minister Singh than the enormous strategic-political utility derived from a full-fledged thermonuclear force. Learning nothing from its grievous negotiating blunders, the Manmohan Singh regime is now preparing to surrender what is left of India's sovereign nuclear security imperatives.

The proof of this is available in Saran's recent failed visit to Washington during which his canvassing with American legislators, far from firming up support for the deal, has strengthened the opposition to it. The deal has little chance of approval by the US Congress short of India's accepting additional conditions, like putting all breeder reactors without exception under safeguards and agreeing to immediate termination of all fissile material production. In this context, Burns has welcomed any "conditions" imposed by the Congress "to improve the (nuclear) deal as long as they don't require us to go to back to and break the agreement, reopen negotiations." Speaking to an audience at the right-wing Heritage Foundation, Saran responded by saying that India would "accept revisions" as long as these did not upset, what he termed, the "delicate balance" encompassed in the deal. Between Bums saying new Congressionally-imposed conditions are acceptable and Saran's replying that "revisions" are fine—and both asserting a "no return to the negotiating table" principle—the door has been left wide open for the Indian foreign secretary, under direct instructions from Prime Minister Manmohan Singh in his capacity as minister for external affairs, to expediently accept still more onerous conditions earlier dubbed "deal breakers" and to finish the job they began of crippling nuclear India. Moreover, New Delhi has indicated India will wait indefinitely rather than apply closure to the whole process and trash the deal as India's national interests warrant.

That the Indian government, in fact, intends to accept further limits on the development of the Indian deterrent was revealed by Senator Joe Biden, the senior-most Democratic Party member of the Foreign Relations Committee who, reacted to Secretary of State Condoleezza Rice's testimony on April 5 by referring to the "closed door" meeting the Committee had with Burns on March 31 in which he may have been assured that, as Biden hoped, "India will not have increased their nuclear capacity in sophistication and number in a significant way."

If the energy deficit is indeed the driver of this deal, as the Prime Minister has maintained, the solution surely lies not in gutting the country's strategic nuclear weapons programme, but in accessing the future generation thermal power plant technology via the agreement it signed last week with the US. American legislators opposing the nuclear deal have advised exactly this. "A realistic, safe and practical energy plan for India would be a US-India energy partnership," wrote Representative Edward Markey in the *Boston Globe* of March 27, "to maximise energy efficiency, aggressively pursue renewable energy sources, and support cleaner coal plants."

Clean thermal power constitutes a better option in every respect. The gestation period for the imported reactor projects and advanced thermal power is about the same—20-30 years. Except the thermal stations can be erected faster and electricity from them will flow in greater quantities and at a much cheaper rate. And it will not require India to mortgage its strategic security, hobble its dual-use nuclear programme, undertake one-sided commitments, or to get permanently stuck with a shambolic nuclear deterrent unless, of course, this is what the Congress Party government of Prime Minister Manmohan Singh wants and, in connivance with its US counterpart, is determined to obtain.

(*The Asian Age*, April 7, 2006)

25. India-US Deal will Destroy Nuclear Research

P.K. Iyengar and M. Gupta

The initial impression of the July 18 Joint Statement as an outline of the nuclear deal Prime Minister Manmohan Singh signed with President George W. Bush was that it may herald a new chapter in India-US scientific cooperation. But the PM's *suo moto* statement in Parliament of March 7, 2006 and the recent release of the "Separation Plan," disabused the scientific community of any such hope.

Particularly surprising was the Indian government agreeing to put research facilities like the Tata Institute of Fundamental Research (TIFR); Variable Energy Cyclotron Centre (VECC), Saha Institute of Nuclear Physics (SINP), Institute for Plasma Research, Institute of Mathematical Sciences, Institute of Physics, Tata Memorial Centre, Board of Radiation and Isotope Technology, and Harish Chandra Research Institute, which are legitimately safeguards-irrelevant, under International Atomic Energy Agency (IAEA) safeguards. This is especially disturbing since the Prime Minister owned up to the fact that India had surrendered the right to decide for itself which facilities will come under IAEA safeguards.

Moreover, since the Manmohan Singh government has virtually accepted a non-nuclear weapons state status for the country in the Non-Proliferation Treaty regime, negotiating India-specific safeguards and Additional Protocol with the IAEA, will be worrisome. It is well known that the Additional Protocol has evolved in recent years specifically to deal with "rogue states" attempting to acquire sensitive technology clandestinely. The problem has clearly arisen due to artificially imposed requirements of categorising the various components of the Department of Atomic Energy into "civil" or "military." Thus the Bhabha Atomic Research Centre and the Indira Gandhi Centre for Atomic Research have been rendered strictly "military" to avoid attracting safeguards, when more than 90 per cent of the work carried out in these institutions is "civilian."

It is well known that safeguard inspections by IAEA when applied to non-nuclear states, are extremely intrusive, immensely disruptive, and are often conducted in an atmosphere vitiated by suspicion. Without any substantiated assurances to the contrary, there is little reason to assume that such will not be the case for India. That the "judicious" use of suspicion may serve to irreversibly tilt the balance is best illustrated by the Iranian affair where the right of an NPT signatory to develop technology (in this case, the centrifuge to enrich uranium), is subject to advance approval from the IAEA. The resulting inspection regime, if applied to fundamental research facilities in India, would imply that any or all research may come under scrutiny or have to be first vetted by the large 65 member Board of Governors ruling the intricate IAEA bureaucracy. With India not being a Non-Proliferation Treaty signatory, would the topics "allowed" for scientific investigation not be decided within the framework of rules applicable to non-nuclear weapons countries or, worse, rogue states? What would be the yardstick for deciding what research is "sanctioned"? Would this mean that "civilian" scientists cannot collaborate with their "military" counterparts since separation must be maintained?

To extend the argument, since such constraints would necessarily have to be focused on indigenous research, criteria could be selective (foreign collaborations with "acceptable" countries may not be scrutinised) and/or restrictive (it may become increasingly difficult for India to choose its research collaborators if they happen to belong to the "wrong" country). In such an environment, there will be little scope for pursuing India's tried and proven self-reliance policy in the future since all indigenous work would invite invasive scrutiny. It has been mentioned that in the event of a national crisis, perhaps none of the trained workforce, equipment or any technology fall-out from such research will be available for military work since India has accepted "in perpetuity" safeguards on all civilian facilities and purportedly given up its sovereign right to cite national security reasons for withdrawal—a privilege enjoyed by all technologically advanced nations. Such an artificial "segregation" would create multiple problems of its own. There is adequate proof that the DAE's applied programmes have drawn heavily from human resources developed in these institutions. In the absence of sensible and responsible negotiations, if inspections include "pursuit" in principle, as they may in the case of nuclear fuel, associated universities, grant funding institutions such as the Department of Science and Technology and other organisations like the Council of Scientific and Industrial Research, etc., will be forced to submit to humiliating and intrusive supervision. Gone will be the days of unfettered technology development via collaborative research with, say, a private biotechnology company. An international "licence-permit raj" on Indian scientific creativity will be here to stay and the army of IAEA inspectors will invade all related public and private sector entities, sometimes even without prior intimation. At the very least it would guarantee that scientists and engineers would be endlessly tied up in bureaucratic red-tape so as to satisfy an infinite number of queries so that very little constructive work is actually achieved.

It is far from true that the entities on the list are "merely" academic institutions when one realises that BARC in its entirety was born from TIFR which was the first institute of its kind in the nation devoted to the physical sciences and mathematics. Recall that Homi Bhabha's vision was to build up indigenous capability through promoting manpower generation in the basic sciences. He wrote in 1944 to J.R.D. Tata that the Tata Institute should be created in order to produce the experts for nuclear energy in India when it becomes feasible. With the firm grounding that such training inculcates, professionals can adapt themselves with alacrity to the requirements of creating technology and its spin-offs.

Indeed, this has been the way all technological innovations have happened throughout the world. To enable this in India, the DAE created autonomous institutions like SINP, VECC and others to create and sustain a strong and wide base of specialisations providing an unshakeable foundation for a healthy technological future. Such institutions have also enabled us to initiate new research, such as in the fusion programme. It helped India gain entrance to the International Thermonuclear Experimental Reactor project, and register successes in computing technologies, and space and nanoparticle research and a whole gamut of laser-based scientific research, to name a few areas.

Regardless of the exact nature of the safeguards, the scientific community in India is extremely upset and alarmed that the autonomy of these institutions may now be severely eroded and their research programmes subjected to the worst external interference. Having been put to great inconvenience of the kind related here. NPT signatory Brazil, for example, has finally been forced to object to IAEA inspections on projects funded by the Brazilian atomic energy agency in the university sector. But as a non-NPT state, the Indian government may not have retained an escape route in its haste to please Washington. In advanced nuclear countries such as the United States, premier institutions and universities funded by its atomic energy commission would consider it inconceivable to give up their autonomy, which is jealously preserved to enable new and innovative research in the frontiers of science to take seed, grow and flourish.

There can be no artificial constraints on the dissemination of scientific thought and the world has reaped the benefits of a free system, as has India. To put centres of excellence under safeguards of whatever type, would be to serve a body blow to the future of indigenous Indian science. Since scientific and technological strength has brought us to where we are today, this is obviously too high a price to pay. The negative ramifications of such a drastic step would be hard to envisage in their entirety.

On the whole, it is clear that inserting these facilities into the already complex problem of separating the DAE's civilian and military programmes as required by the nuclear deal is a fatal mistake. If it has happened as a result of bureaucratic oversight, this must be corrected. Scientists must come forward with their concerns and initiate a constructive dialogue with the Prime Minister's Office and the ministry of external affairs to prevent such an outcome. The Government of India needs to be far more transparent and to consult with a range of retired and serving scientists from the science establishment before actively assisting in the demise of basic research in this country.

(*The Asian Age*, April 15, 2006)

26. PM's Nuclear Hara-Kiri

BHARAT KARNAD

During a luncheon session hosted by the Confederation of Indian Industry on April 26, Robert D. Blackwill, a former American ambassador to India and now heading Barbour Griffith and Rogers, a Washington lobbying firm, was asked how, if it is to be a credible counterweight to China, it served the US interests to have an India with a "truncated" thermonuclear deterrent with weapon designs that are not "proof-tested" and, therefore, unreliable—the inescapable consequence of the nuclear deal Blackwill has been hired by the Indian government to push on the Hill? His reply was both candid and revealing. To blunt China's "coercive diplomacy" in the future, India, he stated, must have a "safe and proven" nuclear arsenal—qualities he obviously believes the Indian nuclear and, especially, thermonuclear armaments do not possess. He should know.

A week earlier the Congress Party coalition Prime Minister Manmohan Singh's appointee as deputy chairman of the Planning Commission and, from the role he is playing, also his chief nuclear policy adviser and strategist as well, the versatile Montek Singh Ahluwalia, was equally categorical about the centrality of the nuclear deal with the United States in the ruling coalition's scheme of things. Asked if the regime had a "Plan B" if the deal failed to get past the US Congress, this worthy replied with ironic certitude: "If there is a Plan B, I am not aware of it. If there is a Plan B, it will be a very inferior one to Plan A." When US officials publicly claim that it is India that has all along insisted on nuclear cooperation at any cost and made it the litmus test of the budding relationship between the two countries, we know where the thinking emanated from.

True, it was the preceding Bharatiya Janata Party government, which, seduced by the siren song of "US advanced technology transfers," took the initiative. The then national security adviser Brajesh Mishra's offer of letting "14 of 22 reactors" slip into the International Atomic Energy Agency safeguards net, breached the wall carefully erected around the country's dual-use nuclear energy programme over 50 years in order to render it opaque and immune to international interference and policing. Whether Mishra's pussyfooting initiative would have led to the kind of damaging deal the Manmohan Singh government has "negotiated," is an open question. But, from the disapproving noises being heard in BJP quarters and more directly, from Mishra (though insiders assert he is miffed because he was not "consulted"), the impression is being given that the deal they had in mind was designed to thaw relations with the US, not impede India's natural progress on the weapons front. Whatever the truth, BJP's finally deciding to launch a political campaign against it inside Parliament and outside, may just crystallise the domestic opposition to the nuclear deal.

This opposition has got a fillip with senior Congress Party members voicing concern about it, especially Natwar Singh's waking up to its dangers. Natwar seems convinced by the arguments (made by this analyst over the last 10 months and lately iterated by press commentators) that a legally binding commitment never to test again will end up freezing the yield of Indian weapons in the low kilotons and their quality at a basic technological level, and that agreeing to join in the talks for the Fissile Material Cutoff Treaty will lead to the US fast-tracking an accord which, in turn, will cap the size of the national deterrent. The erstwhile external affairs minister's suddenly seeing the light about the fatal knockout punch to the nuclear programme waiting in the wings, may have more to do with his being dropped from the Cabinet. But this only begs the question as to why he did not see the obvious trap in the reference in the July 18 Joint Statement to India's "voluntary test moratorium" which forms the confused core of the nuclear deal.

Then again, perhaps, there is no confusion at all. Things are panning out exactly as Messrs Ahluwalia, Indian ambassador to the US Ronen Sen, and foreign secretary Shyam Saran and the rest of the not so prescient bunch of prime ministerial advisers, had planned. How else to explain Ahluwalia's cockiness and Saran's uncharacteristically ruffled response on television that India was not going to lie down "and get screwed" (as if, once the deal is done, India will have much of a choice!) or the latter's adding that New Delhi was all along aware of the US non-proliferation laws on the books, but that India sticks by its voluntary moratorium on testing? The only way the twain can meet, under the circumstances, is if the Manmohan Singh regime gives a secret undertaking that the Indian nuclear deterrent will be kept in a state of frozen animation, and that India can be counted on as an American loyalist to enter the international lists, for all intents and purposes, as a non-weapon state under the 1967 Non-Proliferation Treaty. To wit, Ashley Tellis' testimony to the US Senate Foreign Relations Committee April 26: "India has now agreed to obligations that in fact go beyond those ordinarily required of NPT signatories."

The US Congress is thinking of asking New Delhi to commit to "strategic causes" like Iran, etc., and the Bush Jr Administration is talking about imposing new conditions violating the "reciprocity principle" Manmohan Singh has vouched for, like Rice's telling visiting Indian Members of Parliament that India will have to first produce an Additional Protocol and agreement with the International Atomic Energy Agency for safeguards in perpetuity before any changes in US laws can be contemplated—a turn of events anticipated by this writer in these columns at the beginning of the negotiating process. Tellis, who helped under secretary of state Nicholas Burns cement this deal, told the Senate committee that the Manmohan Singh regime and its negotiating team can be delicately pressured and manipulated behind closed doors into taking steps seriously to compromise the integrity of the Indian nuclear weapons programme and the Indian national interest as they have been persuaded to do so far, as long as the fiction is publicly maintained that the deal hews to the "spirit" (as Rice said) of the July 18 Statement. Tellis, originally from Mumbai and familiar with the character flaws of his former countrymen, knows just how to work the Indian system.

Supporters in the Indian media argue that the deal taking shape is in the national interest. Of course, even the daftest, ill thought-out, most criminally intentioned national security and strategic policy will be justified thus by its progenitors. Jaichand's invitation to the Afghan looter Mohammad Ghauri to take the field against Prithviraj Chauhan, for instance, must have made sense to the benighted Raja in terms of Kannauj's "national interest." India has suffered an unending series of Jaichands. Another such regime is historically par for the course. Except the price will be far sleeper.

But surely no rulers of Delhi have proved as connival a lot to do the Jaichand-type of business with than the "high GDP growth rate" blinkers-wearing Manmohan Singh government. Readying to surrender India's nuclear and thermonuclear imperatives and vast areas of the country's strategic policy space and independence, it seems to be neither concerned about the risks it is running nor having second thoughts about pulling the nation in harm's way. Assuming imported reactors and technology are all that they are cracked up to be and make up the energy shortfalls, which they simply cannot, the question is: Does nuclear energy supercede nuclear security? In the ruling Congress Party's and Prime Minister Manmohan Singh's reckoning, it apparently does.

So convinced, the terms of exchange would not seem to matter to the Indian side. Flattery, warm rhetoric, glowing promises, and the sale of mainly Seventies' vintage military hardware by the George W. Bush administration in return for India's disemboweling itself, computing a ritual nuclear hara-kiri, appear to be fine by them. Washington, in its most fevered dreams could not have anticipated that a Non-Proliferation Treaty-chained India would be offered up on a platter by the Manmohan Singh regime, considering how zealously Indian governments in the past had protected the country's nuclear turf.

(*The Asian Age*, May 5, 2006)

27. Parliament must Examine PM's Nuclear Deal

BHARAT KARNAD

Considering India's strong record over 50 years of successfully protecting its nuclear programme and not backing down under the severest pressure, what kind of government in Delhi would lead the country into the sort of non-proliferation treaty trap set by the United States, which the nuclear deal represents? Obviously, one led by a pliant, non-politician who is unaware of India's nuclear history, insensitive to the strategic concerns and interests of the country, and has sold out. The description fits Dr Manmohan Singh with the reported US offer of the UN Secretary-General's job ("PM sounded out for Kofi's job," *The Asian Age,* May 10, 2006) being a deal sweetener.

Hearteningly, the domestic opposition to the nuclear deal is beginning to attain critical mass with political parties and stalwart leaders finally waking up to its dangers. Jaswant Singh, reflecting the Bharatiya Janata Party's apprehensions, has sent a strongly-worded letter to the PM. K.C. Pant, Yashwant Sinha and even Natwar Singh, former minister for external affairs from the ruling Congress Party, have all recently written newspaper articles extremely critical of the deal. Dr Manmohan Singh is in no position anymore to dissemble and defend this "bargain" Post-state elections, only the politically strengthened Communist Party of India (Marxist) can, in fact, compel the Congress coalition regime to back out of this disastrous nuclear deal with the US. But it has to show at least as much concern for saving the Indian nuclear weapons capability as it has done for protecting Iran's nuclear programme. By doing this, the Communists can clean their historically stained record—of working against the Freedom Movement under Stalin's orders, for instance. CPI(M) can rescue India's strategic military nuclear interests imperilled by Manmohan Singh's harebrained scheme involving the party's supposedly greatest ideological adversary, the United States; a scheme which will gut the country's weapons capability in the here and now in return for the promise of small, insignificant, amounts of over-expensive nuclear energy from imported reactors in the indeterminate future.

Should this deal fail as it deserves to, the greatest relief will be felt in the dispirited nuclear establishment fed up with the unwillingness or inability of the current chairman, Atomic Energy Commission, Dr Anil Kakodkar, to ensure that the country's hallowed nuclear policy ground is not handed over piecemeal to IAEA's control, thereby furthering the American design. The US has historically been inclined to denude India of its nuclear weapons capability, failing which to curb it. The foundations of this policy were laid as far back as 1964 when a senior Pentagon staffer, Henry S. Rowen, advocated a policy of containing Indian military nuclear capability because he argued, in a now declassified memorandum, it would (1) enable India to "some day... attack the United States with nuclear weapons," (2) start "'nuclear actions with a fair chance of spreading and involving the United States," (3) reduce "[US] power to influence events in South Asia and to some extent throughout the world," (4) allow "pressures for further proliferation in Asia [to] grow," and (5) make it appear "that the United States ... were unwilling or unable to prevent the [nuclear] spread."

These concerns still animate the American non-proliferation-weighted approach to India at the heart of the nuclear deal. Except now the US policy focus has shifted to inducing an India, which has crossed the weapons barrier, from becoming a consequential nuclear power to complement its natural great power ambition. So confident is Washington that it can secure the deal to bottle up the Indian nuclear weapons programme—incidentally, a goal Pakistan is keen to see achieved—it has been reassuring Islamabad about maintaining, what Pakistan defence secretary Lt. Gen. (Retd.) Tariq Waseem Ghazi visiting Washington in the first week of May has called, "the existing (nuclear) balance" on the subcontinent.

Unfamiliar with such history or, apparently, even his own Department of Atomic Energy's dogged-resistance in the past to American stratagems to encroach on the country's nuclear policy space, Kakodkar has signed up with the Manmohan Singh government on this deal. Shockingly, he has so far neither taken the Atomic Energy Commission and the Bhabha Atomic Research Centre (BARC) Council—the two apex bodies responsible for nuclear activities in the country—into confidence and sought approval for his actions, nor, fearing strong opposition to the ideal and to his role in "negotiating" it, formally discussed the details of the proposed agreement with his scientific colleagues.

But then, in recent times, spineless scientists (or politicised ones) at the helm have established a precedent of deferring to political masters even on technical matters, rather than resigning and bringing things publicly to a boil. The slide began with Dr R. Chidambaram who, after retirement, was made science and technology adviser to the PM. As Dr Kakodkar's immediate predecessor, he succumbed to political pressure from the BJP government and did the indefensible—acquiesced in the "voluntary test moratorium" decision announced in May 1998, which terminated the development of safe and reliable thermonuclear armaments. With the July 18 Joint Statement confirming this moratorium, India, for all intents and purposes, is permanently saddled with a half-baked nuclear deterrent "deployed" in a half-cocked "demated" mode, which will deter and dissuade nobody and, should its nuclear bluff be called in a crisis, would become a liability.

In sync, moreover, with the BJP government's gambit of exploring a nuclear deal with the US, Chidambaram also did what the late Raja Ramanna and P.K. Iyengar previously heading DAE had steadfastly refused to do—extend the International Atomic Energy Agency's control over Indian nuclear facilities through the safeguards route. He agreed, for instance, to change the terms of the contract with Russia for the Kudankulum nuclear power project to permit the reprocessing of the spent enriched uranium fuel from the two safeguarded VVBR 1000 reactors in India (rather than requiring it to be taken back by the supplier as per the original deed). It has thus prospectively brought all upstream and downstream facilities handling this spent fuel under the IAEA safeguards. As going back to the original contract is not feasible, Dr Chidambaram has a lot to answer for. The trouble is, the revised Kudankulum accord is the precursor of agreements relating to reactors the US, France and Russia may sell to India as per the nuclear deal. It will provide Washington with the IAEA safeguards system to more comprehensively reach into the Indian nuclear programme and, in not so slow stages, end India's freedom of action in the nuclear field.

Deficiencies in the Indian variant of the Westminster political system allow any Prime Minister, even an unelected one like Manmohan Singh, legally to commit the country by executive fiat to bilateral and international agreements, however fatally they may damage the country's sovereignty, security and national interests. The Parliament has no role other than as a rubber stamp. It is precisely the absence of a mechanism of active and mandatory legislative oversight that led to India's almost signing the Comprehensive Test Ban Treaty during the BJP regime.

Changes in the Constitution to interpose Parliament between the PM and his foreign policy initiatives so that no international commitments of any kind arc made without the express approval by parliamentary vote, are urgently required. But in lieu of such Constitutional reforms, it has become necessary for a special committee of Parliament representing all parties to scrutinise the India-US nuclear deal. This committee should, in public sessions, solicit views of and question active and veteran Indian nuclear scientists and missile men, serving and retired senior military officers, and strategic policy analysts of repute. The resulting informed consensus should form the core of any final India-US agreement.

An activist Parliamentary committee in the decision loop will (1) prevent mindless and motivated policies concocted by the head of the Indian government of the day from hurting national interests, (2) provide the PM legislative cover to resile from undertakings he may have given (on the plea that he was unable to muster parliamentary support for them) and, in the present case, (3) ease the pressure on Dr Manmohan Singh to stick with a bad nuclear deal. India's strategic future is too important to be left to any Prime Minister alone to ever make or break.

(*The Asian Age*, May 14, 2006)

28. Candy for Gold

India and the United States are presently involved in converting, from the American perspective, the base metal of New Delhi's "voluntary test moratorium" into the gold of permanent ban on explosive nuclear testing by India. The verbal flim-flammery by foreign secretary Shyam Saran and US under-secretary of state Nicholas Burn's meeting in London aside, New Delhi will doubtless end up conceding to the US demands. The problem, a foreign office source was reported as saying, is only with "phrasing" the concession. After all, having swallowed the camel of limits on the quality and the size of the country's nuclear arsenal and the onerous "separation plan" designed to sever the umbilical relationship between scientific research institutions, like the Tata Institute of Fundamental Research, the Saha Institute of Nuclear Physics, etc., which are the brains of the country's nuclear effort and responsible for helping solve tricky nuclear or thermonuclear weapon design problems, from the applications and engineering the weapons, ingesting the straw of test ban cannot be too difficult a trick for the Manmohan Singh government to perform.

Should the current 109th US Congress not legislate changes in the US Atomic Energy Act before it expires, the newly elected 110th Congress in November 2006, perhaps, with the less amenable Democratic Party controlling the lower house, will surely dump this deal. Whence, the whiff of desperation emanating from the George W. Bush administration and its partner in India, the Manmohan Singh regime. With both having invested scarce political capital in the deal, anxiety may propel the Congress Party coalition government in particular into firming up the frightful compromises it has already made where the country's strategic nuclear policy and options are concerned.

The future of this deal hangs on two factors. One is whether the US can wheedle a legally binding commitment not to test out of the Indian government, which may be forthcoming. With India thus locked into a test ban, the second factor is to get New Delhi to acquiesce in the draft Fissile Material Cut-off Treaty (FMCT) which Washington has introduced in the Conference on Disarmament (CD) in Geneva last week with a view, as anticipated many months ago by this analyst, of fast-tracking the FMCT. It is an objective achieved by Article VI (1) of the US draft which conceives of the treaty entering into force once the five NPT-recognised nuclear weapons states (and permanent members of the UN Security Council) resolve their differences and agree on a consensus document. Designed to prevent endless negotiating and to negate the strategy of "buying time" that India, for instance, adopted in the talks on the Comprehensive Test Ban Treaty, countries like India will have no real role in the negotiations other than to make some dissenting noises and sign on. Thus, a universal verification mechanism that India has all along insisted on is anathema to the US administration and, therefore, finds no mention in the American FMCT draft text and will not be part of the eventual treaty.

But any FMCT is hostage to China's desire for linking it to an international accord reserving space for exclusively peaceful uses, because of Beijing's fear of losing out in a space-based arms race. Washington's reason for this draft treaty at this time is that it improves the chances of the US Congress approving the nuclear deal if India is seen by this measure to be brought to heel. Manmohan Singh's support in the July 18 Joint Statement for the FMCT negotiations, is the small hole through which Washington means to drive this big bad, nuclear deal through. The end-state of these clever US diplomatic manoeuvres is what this analyst has been warning since before the Prime Minister's July 2005 Washington trip—a deal packing a one-two punch that will cap the quality and technological level of the Indian nuclear armaments, courtesy the "Voluntary" test moratorium packaged into a binding legal commitment and, owing to the FMCT on the table, to restrict the quantity of available fissile material and hence the number of weapons or warheads in the Indian atomic arsenal.

But the two governments also confront the twin demands by the US Congress that the deal be conditioned on India's first negotiating a safeguards agreement and Additional Protocol with the international Atomic Energy Agency (IAEA). US under-secretary of state for arms control Robert Joseph has categorically stated that the safeguards system for India will be modelled on IAEA's INFIRC (Information Circular) 66 predating the Non-proliferation Treaty rather than on INFIRC/153 dealing with the "voluntary" safeguards system the five NPT-recognised nuclear weapons states (P-5) subscribe which, for instance, permits them to switch facilities from military use to civilian use at will. While the "technical measures" in the two safeguards systems may not differ much, India, Joseph clarified, cannot expect to negotiate safeguards based on INFIRC/153 because, he said, that is unacceptable to members of the Nuclear Suppliers' Group. Since this circle cannot be squared short of New Delhi capitulating, expect the Manmohan Singh regime to do just that in the near future.

The still more alarming prospects facing the Indian nuclear programme is that it is expected to adhere to the 1997 Additional Protocol. Enabled to allow IAEA to collect comprehensive data about any and all nuclear activities and capabilities of a state by means such as short notice inspections, wider area environmental sampling, national independent means, etc., this Protocol generates information about all aspects of "the nuclear fuel cycle" and about the uranium mining operations (including the locations of the mines and quantity mined annually) and, in India's case, thorium concentration plants. Having painted itself into a corner by accepting *de jure* status as a non-nuclear weapons state under NPT, India will have little choice other than to accept the Protocol ensuring that its nuclear military programme becomes an open book, even as the P-5, though subscribing to the same Protocol, will remain free to carry on with their nuclear weapons-activities behind walls of secrecy.

Despite the mounting and unaffordable strategic price that India is being asked to pay in terms of stunting its nuclear weapons programme and rendering it transparent, Manmohan Singh continues to maintain with a straight face that the nuclear deal is crucial to the country's future energy needs. But on what grounds? The reasons for the Prime Minister wanting this deal is not that it will provide access to genuinely "advanced technology" (which no nuclear supplier will part with for love or for money), but because of the deliberate shortages of natural uranium and, of reactors created by the government itself over the years, reactors, the government complains, the Nuclear Power Corporation is incapable of constructing speedily and in the required large numbers needed to meet the energy shortfall.

But this begs the question why, before embarking on a deal that will finish off India's nuclear weapons policy options, did the government not first exhaust the indigenous options? Like, mining the proven uranium reserves in Meghalaya and Nalgonda district of Andhra Pradesh, and the rich veins of uranium ore recently discovered in northern Orissa, at a site not far from Nalgonda, and in Rajasthan, on a war-footing? According to experts, these new uranium finds and proven reserves could make India self-sufficient in uranium. Instead of exploiting this natural resource to the fullest, the government has procrastinated and pandered to the (externally funded?) environmental groups, who have mobilised the local populations. By such ruses New Delhi has created the uranium ore shortage which is used by the Manmohan Singh regime recklessly to push an insidious deal.

And, on the second count, why did the government all these years not finance the construction of the locally designed, manufactured, and cost-efficient Heavy Water moderated CANDU/INDU natural uranium-fuelled power plants, rather than, as they are doing now, preparing to pay out tens of billions of dollars in hard currency for the French Areva 1600 MW reactor, or the uncertified US-Japanese Westinghouse 1000 and the Russian VVER 1000 MW reactors? Could the ruling circles be eyeing commissions in the hundreds of millions of dollars to be raked in on contracts for these prohibitively expensive imported reactors? With the Indian system of government becoming a kleptocracy, this motive credibly explains the Congress Party government's enthusiasm for the dubious deal designed by Washington to blight India's strategic future.

One wishes there was a strong and confident leadership in this country with a sense of national self-worth and matching strategic vision to trash the deal with the US in the manner the Iranian President Mahmoud Ahmadine-jad rejected the European Union's offer of civilian nuclear technology in exchange for Tehran's swearing off nuclear weapons. Iran, he said, was not about to take "candies for gold"! In contrast are the current Indian rulers who, as this analyst concluded in his book *Nuclear Weapons and Indian Security*, "pick-led" in corruption and self-doubt and harbouring mis-placed notions of morality, "responsible" behaviour and "national self-restraint," think nothing of compromising national interests and nuclear security. It is they who constitute the "soft state" which India is rumoured to be, and who actively prevent the country from acquiring the strategic military wherewithal necessary to deal with the extant great powers on our terms.

(The Asian Age, May 27, 2006)

29. India Becomes Easy Nuclear-Game

BHARAT KARNAD

Saying "I told you so" is getting a bit boring for this analyst. Particularly because there is no great skill involved in predicting what Prime Minister Manmohan Singh and his designated diplomatic hitters will do next, by way of compromising national security. Like well-trained seals, they will jump through the newest hoops held up by Washington. Progressively more stringent conditions are being imposed on India, because Delhi is seen as desperate for the nuclear deal which, it believes, confers recognition—however spurious—on this country as a "nuclear weapon state," and to have which it is willing to pay any price.

When many months ago I ventured in this paper that the replacement costs of the proposed "separation plan" added to the price-tag of imported reactors would be in the "thousands of crores of rupees," it was pooh-poohed as an exaggeration by many. The Department of Atomic Energy, having done its math, has reportedly arrived at a still larger figure. This total stands to grow to humungous proportions if, as is likely, the Indian government agrees to the latest American condition carried by a State Department team led by Robert Stratford here to finalise the amended Section 123 of the US Atomic Energy Act, requiring India formally to commit itself to never test again and, in case it does so, to dismantle and return any and all materials imported from the United States and plants and processing or production units set up with American "civilian nuclear technology." This last is a manifestly impractical, even silly, demand made, no doubt, to test how far Delhi will bend to Washington's will. Moreover, permitting India to build up a "strategic reserve" of highly-enriched uranium for the imported reactors—that Dr Manmohan Singh has set his heart on—only makes transacting for them politically less objectionable without making the deal any less onerous for the country, now trapped into a cycle of reactor and fuel dependency and exorbitant payouts.

So far in the give-and-take department, Indian negotiators have been doing all the giving and the Americans the taking, even as after each meeting both sides put up a show of gritty negotiations, as cover for Shyam Saran & Co.'s giving away, another part of the store. If this is the fabled path to great power status, self-respecting Indians are right to wonder if it is any different than reducing the country into an American vassal in the region *a la* Pakistan.

It is a pity that on the verge of genuine great power, India is suffering from loss of nerve and is being transformed into a sovereignty-sapped non-entity doing Washington's bidding by a strategic vision-challenged Congress Party Prime Minister and government. If in Manmohan Singh's skewed intellectual universe, Britain was the locus of modernity, which India benefitted from in the past, it is the United States he now trusts to lead the country kindly into the future. As an influential ideologue in the Communist Party of India (Marxist), who has been tracking Dr Singh's career, put it: "The trouble with Manmohan is that he is always looking for the next master to please." Starting with Sanjay Gandhi at whose behest, as professor in the Delhi School of Economics, he tried to drum up support in the academia for the Emergency and was richly rewarded for his troubles with progressively higher posts in the government. Prime Minister Singh, according to this assessment, has found in the United States someone new to serve. But the good doctor needs to be reminded that playing "follow the leader" in the external realm may personally benefit him (the offer of UN Secretary-General's post, for instance, which reportedly is quite the buzz in Washington and New York). But it will fetch India only contempt in the developing world (likes in the recent non-aligned meeting on "nuclear Iran" in Kuala Lumpur, and permit China to consolidate its advantage by some deft manoeuvring—to wit, China's invitation to Iranian President Mahmoud Ahmadinejad to address the Shanghai Cooperation Organisation), and condescending treatment from the US reflected in the PM's statements in Parliament being routinely contradicted by the developments related to the deal. It seems, however, that these tendencies (or character flaws) of Manmohan Singh's even over-ride reservations that he, as an economist, must have about the nuclear deal as an enormous financial liability.

Restricting further Indian testing and stopping its fissile material production have been central US concerns on which the George W. Bush administration has not budged an iota. US under-secretary of state Nicholas Burns had made it clear from the beginning that the Bush administration would rather do without the deal than have one that retains for India a cost-free testing option or allows it an ample fissile material stock. It was on these fundamental points that the Burns-Saran talks teetered in Washington before the Indian government gave in and the draft for the July 18 statement was cleared by both sides. It conditioned civilian nuclear cooperation on India's not testing again—however this commitment is tagged to India's "voluntary" test moratorium—and on its supporting an FMCT. The arms control bureaucracy in Washington had ensured this. This much can be read in the submissions by Burns and his State Department colleague, Robert Joseph, to Congressional committees and in the tatter's written replies to Senator Richard

G. Lugar, the leading light of the US Senate Foreign Relations Committee and potential facilitator of the deal. It was the proverbial foot-in-the-door that helped Washington methodically to prise open the Indian chest of concessions. Even so, the ease with which the US government was getting its demands met by India—the last great Non-Proliferation Treaty hold-out—must have surprised Washington and emboldened it to make still more ambitious demands, like the ones formally communicated to the external affairs ministry this week.

As an example of Delhi's egregiously craven attitude, consider the case of the 40 MW CIRUS reactor, one of the two reactors producing weapon-grade plutonium (WgPu). Referring to the original CIRUS agreement, US under-secretary of state Joseph testified before the Senate Foreign Relations Committee on November 2, 2005 that the issue of the "illegal" use of this reactor for military purposes by India was "inconclusive owing to uncertainty as to whether US-supplied heavy water contributed to the production of plutonium used for the 1974 device." Notwithstanding this authoritative position, Leonard Spector, among the most vociferous non-proliferationist India-baiters in the US, mounted a public campaign, characterising the use of CIRUS for making weapons as evidence of bad faith and indication that India would again violate agreements. It prompted the Canadian government to formally request Delhi to put the CIRUS reactor under international safeguards, something Delhi agreed to with alacrity. While announcing its "separation plan," the Indian government offered to decommission the CIRUS, without having a ready plutonium reactor to replace it, thereby cutting off the source of 25 kg of WgPu annually. With at most only a two-three-year window available, there is simply no way India can build up adequate fissile material holdings for any and all contingencies in the future.

This decision can be seen as a down payment in terms of the support for the Fissile Material Cut-off Treaty (FMCT) Prime Minister Singh had promised, and which treaty in its US draft form may be expeditiously approved by the five so-called "NPT-recognised" nuclear weapon states (P-5) in the Commission on Disarmament in Geneva. It will, *ipso facto,* cap the size of the Indian fissile material stockpile and hence of the Indian nuclear arsenal. This along with the testing ban, which will freeze the quality of weapons, constitute the US non-proliferation motivation for the nuclear deal with India. Delhi is now being asked to accept these conditions on the basis that this is what the "rights and responsibilities" of an NPT nuclear weapon state, that India is all too keen to accept entail. (The P-5 have ceased testing and production of weapon-grade uranium and WgPu for the nonce, after extensive testing over the years and the build-up of huge fissile material stockpiles.) Talk of being hoisted with one's own petard!

The Manmohan Singh government's soft-headed negotiating strategy has done two things: it has reassured the champions of the NPT in Washington that all is well and that the arm-twisting has worked in obtaining for the US the elusive non-proliferation chalice—the incorporation of India in the Treaty regime as a *de jure* non-weapon state. It is a status that will be formalised with the Additional Protocol preventing India from ever switching the safeguarded civilian facilities to military use as the P-5 can—the real test of a nuclear weapon state under NPT. Curbing India's nuclear capabilities and ambitions by such means is the argument the US is using to sell the deal to the Nuclear Suppliers' Group. And, it has infused new life into a decrepit NPT order, cementing the nuclear status quo of a world divided permanently into nuclear haves and have-nots without the third category of pesky nations to worry about. (Iran and North Korea will be bought off or coerced, and Israel and Pakistan frogmarched, into the regime once India is safely collared.) With the Manmohan Singh government failing to take the basic precaution of insisting from the start on reserving the right to continue testing and accumulating fissile material until such time as certain reasonable levels in these two areas relative to the P-5 states are attained by this country, India finds itself victimised by the negotiating system it helped create.

(The Asian Age, June 14, 2006)

30. Why Indian Scientists are Upset about the Nuclear Deal

A.N. PRASAD

The bill on the India-United States nuclear deal now with the US Congress has left no doubt about the US intention to achieve the twin objective of capping the Indian strategic programme and gaining near total access to its nuclear establishment through International Atomic Energy Agency safeguards inspections.

The sugar-coated language used in the July 18 Indo-US Joint Statement has lifted India to the status of an advanced State to be treated at par with other advanced states like the US. But the ground reality is such that the US calls the shots, leaving India on the defensive in spite of projecting the deal as of vital interest to the US.

There is certainly lot of apprehension among the Indian scientific community in general — apart from top scientists within India's nuclear establishment who are forced to support the deal— as to whether adequate homework has been done in analysing the pros and cons about how the deal serves India's long-term interests.

The views of Indian scientists do not seem to have reached Indian law-makers and a clear direction is lacking. Political and scientific interests have to converge for a deal of this nature, which has long-term national security implications.

This matter is too serious for the government to take a decision without an in-depth debate, and in a hush-hush manner without revealing the various conditions involved. What the knowledgeable public in India is exposed to is bits and pieces of information—that too, trickling from the US!

A major weakness faced by India, in the short and perhaps in the medium term, is the shortage of natural uranium required to push its nuclear power programme from the present two per cent to something respectable.

India seems to be paying a heavy price for this weakness. Having developed full technological competence in the entire nuclear fuel cycle—in spite of sustained embargoes and restrictions—it is not so much the technological know-how that India is looking forward to from abroad, as many seem to think, but a rightful place to play a global role in the nuclear field commercially and technologically.

There is so much that India can offer to the global effort for peaceful application of nuclear energy but it is a pity it is being looked upon with suspicion. Conditions of a different kind are being imposed while grudgingly taking India on as a partner.

Coming back to the bill with the US Congress, there are a few clauses which are detrimental to Indian interests. It calls for India, Pakistan and China declaring a moratorium on the production of fissile material for nuclear explosive purposes. If India were to agree to this it will be at a disadvantage *vis-a-vis* China in terms of stockpile and not serve national strategic interests.

Similarly, the bill talks about implementation of a treaty with the US as a partner banning the production of fissile material for nuclear weapons. This is a big joke. While the US suffers from indigestion with excess fissile material, not knowing what to do with it, it wants India to prematurely shut shop. What a nice way to cap India's nuclear programme before it has even properly taken off! There are also some other conditions in the bill which tend to interfere with our independent national policy.

Perhaps the sticking point in this nuclear deal is the safeguards agreement. At present, the International Atomic Energy Agency has no format or mandate to negotiate an agreement with India which accommodates the country's strategic nuclear applications. The formats in force apply broadly to Nuclear Weapon States and Non-Nuclear Weapon States party to the nuclear Non-Proliferation Treaty with some States accepting intrusive additional protocol.

India, Pakistan and Israel being non-NPT states are following item specific safeguards. As far as India is concerned, the deal will totally change this situation as it will be treated as a non-Nuclear Weapon State with additional protocol leading to a lot of contradictions and difficulties both in the negotiations and later implementation.

It is very unlikely that the IAEA will negotiate a new agreement outside the existing mandate and go to the IAEA board of governors for approval which is a major task by itself. Realising this, the US bill has been cleverly worded to the effect that the American President's determination is required to the effect that an agreement has been concluded between India and the IAEA requiring the application of IAEA safeguards in perpetuity in accordance with IAEA principles, practices and policies to India's nuclear facilities, materials and programmes.

To make matters worse, India's nuclear programmes are also sought to be brought under safeguards under the additional protocol. Where does this lead regarding the India-specific safeguards which India was elated about?

There is no doubt that the safeguards negotiations will be the toughest part of the deal requiring a high level of skill, foresight and care.

To a large extent, the deal will undermine the pride with which Indian nuclear scientists of the past and present developed highly complex nuclear technology under heavy odds. India will be slowly forced to become dependent on imports with practically the entire gamut of activities coming under safeguards inspection with a miniscule of activities left under the strategic category.

(Rediff.com, June 29, 2006)

31. The Indo-US 'Unclear' Deal

P.K. IYENGAR

The Science Behind the Bomb

Nuclear fission, a process in which a nucleus splits releasing 200 million electron volts of energy, was discovered in 1939. This is in contrast to chemical reactions, which typically release only a few volts of energy. In order to cause fission, the nucleus has to be excited, just like you have to heat coal for it to burn. The particle called the neutron can do this effectively, but different nuclei have different thresholds for the neutron energy needed to cause fission. It was discovered that U^{235}, an isotope that occurs in natural uranium to the extent of 0.7%, gets easily fissioned by very low energy neutrons. The process also releases, on the average, 2.5 neutrons per fission. This allows a chain reaction to be established. This is the basis for the production of nuclear energy from a reactor, as well as a nuclear bomb. In 1942 the first chain reaction was established with natural uranium as the fuel. The size of this reactor was very large. However, to make an explosive device, a bomb, of reasonable size, you need to concentrate U^{235}. A minimum of around 15 kg of U^{235} is required for an explosive device. The process of separating and concentrating U is known as enrichment. This process is based on different principles such as electromagnetic separation, different rates of diffusion through a barrier, or through centrifuge action in a cascade of centrifuges. There are other methods, like laser isotope separation, and perhaps many more processes yet to be invented.

In a nuclear reactor the fuel contains some proportion of U^{238}, which cannot be fissioned. This U^{238} gets converted to Pu^{239} by adding one neutron. As a rule of thumb, the efficiency of production of plutonium for every fission that occurs in a reactor, can vary from 0.5 in a light-water reactor, to 0.8 in a heavy-water reactor, to nearly 1.5 in a fast-breeder reactor. One Megawatt-day of energy is produced by burning 1 gm of U^{235} in a reactor. Thus, a 200 MWe power station, which produces 600 MW of thermal power, will burn 600 gm of U^{235} per day, and produce 300-500 gm of plutonium per day. In one year, a 200 MWe power station will produce 90-150 kg of plutonium. Depending upon how long you leave the uranium fuel in the reactor, all this plutonium could be used for making nuclear weapons. Hence the connection between nuclear power and nuclear weapons. It may also be noted that the minimum mass required to make a nuclear weapon out of Plutonium is around only 5 kg, corresponding to a 10 kilotonne bomb.

The science behind nuclear explosives has been with us for such a long time that it is now no longer a secret, and any determined nation can make a bomb with the help of a few bright scientists and the required materials.

A Brief History of the Bomb

The history of attempts to restrain new nations from acquiring the capability to produce nuclear weapons goes back to the late 1940s and the early 1950s, after the use of nuclear weapons on Hiroshima and Nagasaki in 1945. The Americans felt that the science and the technology were so complicated, that other nations would not be able to achieve a breakthrough. However, the Soviet Union, UK, France and China successively detonated nuclear devices. This frightened the Americans. While on the one hand, the US government propounded the Atoms for Peace plan in the mid-50s, they also were worried that the capability would spread. The IAEA, a multi-national UN body, was formed in 1958, in order to propagate the peaceful uses of Atomic Energy, and also in a multi-national way, control the spread of nuclear technology for making explosives. A test ban for atmospheric nuclear explosions was the first attempt at stopping the spread of nuclear weapons. India, under Nehru, was one of the first signatories to this treaty.

However, when the Chinese entered the field with their first explosion, it became obvious that even a developing country, struggling for improving its conditions of living, could think of national security through nuclear weapons. The five nuclear nations therefore formulated the NPT, which recognised these five as Nuclear Weapon States, and all the rest as Non-weapon States— thus introducing discrimination for the first time.

India had produced its own plutonium by 1965, and Homi Bhabha announced that if necessary India could detonate a nuclear device in 18 months time. Unfortunately, Homi Bhabha died in an air crash in 1966, Pandit Nehru, a visionary statesman, had died in 1964, and this nation had severe economic problems. The Government of the time tried to get an umbrella protection from the advanced countries, but failed.

The NPT came into being in 1968, with a blatant, discriminatory motive. It required non-weapon states to abstain from attempting to make nuclear weapons. In return they were promised help in nuclear technology for peaceful purposes. The NPT recognised the right of nuclear weapon states to retain their arsenal, which grew in number due to the Cold War. India decided not to sign the NPT, and upheld its sovereign right to acquire nuclear weapons when the need arose. Even a strong Gandhian like Morarjee Desai, who was

Deputy PM at that time, was against signing the NPT, even though he was not in favour of India acquiring nuclear weapons.

Pokhran-I

The 1960s saw a few wars: one with China and a couple with Pakistan. During this time the US continued to support the unelected military regime in Pakistan. At the end of the decade the political turmoil in Pakistan led to revolt and the formation of Bangladesh, in which India was forced to get involved. During that war, it looked as if America and China would help Pakistan, and the US Navy moved into the Bay of Bengal. This really frightened the Indian government, and Mrs. Gandhi took the decision to ask us to prepare for a nuclear explosion through entirely indigenous efforts. This resulted in the first Pokhran test of 1974. That was the time when the US and the Soviet Union were experimenting with nuclear devices for applications in earth-moving operations on a large scale. Therefore, India named the Pokhran-I test as a Peaceful Nuclear Experiment. It is also true that the device was not engineered to be used as a deliverable weapon, but had to be physically assembled at a depth of 100 m, manually. Pokhran-I resulted in sanctions being applied by all the Western countries, denying to honour obligations made under international agreements, under which the Tarapur reactor was purchased from the US. The Canadians, the French, and the US walked out of the obligations under the bilateral agreements between India and these countries.

The Congress government at that time was willing to accept the challenges that the sanctions threw up. The Indian scientists and engineers struggled to complete and push forward the programmes that had been started with foreign collaborations. The heavy-water reactors in Rajasthan, the fast reactor at Kalpakkam, and the many heavy-water plants at various stages of construction, were all affected. Yet these were successfully completed, and have been operating for a long time now.

The tightening of the NPT regime started when India exploded the nuclear device, and countries like South Africa, Brazil and Argentina had developed their own capabilities for nuclear explosives. It became obvious that no nation could be stopped from pursuing research and development, and innovate technology, for becoming a nuclear power. In order to bring in all nations under the NPT, inducements and punishments were tried. Some of the threshold states were brought into the NPT in this manner. The NSG came into existence, denying technology for peaceful applications, unless nations signed the NPT. Progress in the development of new types of nuclear reactors was curtailed, and this led to the stagnation of nuclear technology for a couple of decades.

Pokhran-II

India resisted all threats and inducements and held to its position to keep the sovereign right of a nuclear option to itself. Meanwhile Pakistan clandestinely acquired the technology for making enriched uranium, and was ready to make the nuclear explosive by the end of the 1980s. The US shied away from putting any restrictions on Pakistan, because of their strategic help in the Afghan war. When it became obvious that Pakistan had indeed assembled a nuclear device and was ready to test, the Government of India decided to carry out a series of test explosions in May 1998, which were soon followed by nuclear tests by Pakistan. India declared itself a Nuclear Weapon country, voluntarily applied a moratorium on further testing, promised a no-first-use philosophy, and enunciated a Minimum Credible Deterrent policy. This resulted in a renewed application of sanctions by the US and other NSG countries, which we took in our stride.

Soon the US recognised the strategic importance of India, for peace and stability in South-East Asia. The NDA Government cooperated by engaging in a series of long negotiations in this strategic partnership. Meanwhile, in the international arena, the CTBT was promulgated and the majority of nations who were party to the NPT accepted and ratified the treaty. It is strange that the US Congress however went against the recommendation of the US Administration and did not ratify the CTBT. The Review Committee of the NPT decided to extend the NPT in perpetuity, which finally left only three nations outside the NPT net—India, Pakistan and Israel.

The Indo-US Deal

It is to the credit of the Bush Administration that the agreement for a strategic partnership, including the agreement on cooperation on civil nuclear power was signed on 18 July 2005. This agreement was well drafted, sugarcoated, and suggested the opening of a new chapter in Indo-US relations. The main points with respect to nuclear policy were the following:

(a) The US recognises that India is a *de facto* nuclear weapon country, and does not object to India having a nuclear doctrine and an arsenal;

(b) The US and its allies in the NSG will cooperate with India in the area of civil nuclear energy, through commercial channels, and participation in international efforts; and

(c) India will, on its part, modify its aversion to the NPT, and will, like other Nuclear Weapon States, join and help the non-proliferation regime by putting its civil nuclear facilities—to be chosen by itself-under IAEA safeguards.

Everybody, including the nuclear scientists thought that this was a break-through, and would help in expanding the nuclear energy programme, which has its effects on restraining green-house gases, energy security, etc. However, a major obstacle for the US was its own Atomic Energy Act of 1954, which prohibits that country from cooperating with any other nation which has not agreed to full-scope safeguards under the IAEA as a non-weapon state. We have all seen the attempts by the Bush Administration to get an exemption for the Indian case, through their Congress.

The progress in this respect is dramatised in the last few months. The details of negotiations between the US and India have come through testimonies in the US Congress, as well as statements on policy by the US Administration. These have been the only source of information for the general public in India. There has been no transparency in what way India will define its obligations and benefits, which was at one time defined as equivalent to that of an advanced nation like the USA. Matters have moved so quickly, especially during and after the visit of President Bush to India. This has resulted in the following:

(1) A separation plan of entities in the Department of Atomic Energy, into civil and military, supposed to come into force over the next few years. India will offer the civil facilities for IAEA safeguards progressively.

(2) The promise that the decision as to which entities will be under the civilian category and which under the military category, will be entirely a decision of the Indian government.

(3) The Indian government will have the option of augmenting its resources for the strategic part, to be decided by itself.

(4) There will be American influence on the NSG to exempt India from the restrictions presently placed on it.

(5) The US will also help to negotiate with the IAEA an India-specific safeguard agreement. This will be different from the agreement applicable to non-weapon states.

Obviously, this is a very involved and complex issue for the Government of India to negotiate simultaneously with the US, the NSG countries, and the IAEA. The US Congress has expressed their desire to see the agreements with the IAEA and the NSG countries, before agreeing to amend their law.

Problems with the Deal

The separation plan as announced earlier, and amended later, has been placed in Parliament. This has raised many questions. The Indian nuclear programme, through the vision of Homi Bhabha, was built with an emphasis on nuclear power production through indigenous technology and resources, with a future expanded programme to be based on thorium, which is very abundantly found in India. The strategic programme was more recent and does not constitute a well-defined set of laboratories, group of scientists, or infrastructure, which could be logically identified and separated.

For the first time, the Chairman, Atomic Energy Commission, made the pronouncement that the US is changing its goal posts, which is a clear indication of the pressure applied in the negotiations between India and the US. The fact that the US was dictating terms as to what facilities must become civilian, and therefore subject to IAEA safeguards, has come from non-proliferation Ayatollahs in the US, like Spector, and Congressional members. Thus, an innocuous reactor like Apsara, which has been in operation for almost 50 years, built entirely indigenously, is being offered to be shifted from BARC in order not to attract safeguards inspection into BARC. It has been declared, in legal terms, that India did not violate any legal agreements with Canada on the utilization of the CIRUS reactor. However, now CIRUS is to be shutdown in the next few years—after it has just recently been rejuvenated.

Around 65% of the nuclear power stations in operation or under construction will be placed under safeguards, irrespective of whether there has been any contribution from abroad or not. All future nuclear power stations, including fast-breeder reactors producing power, will be put under IAEA inspection. The nature of the safeguard agreement with the IAEA is not clear. For example, one is not sure if R&D will be exempt from control and inspection from the IAEA. This will infringe on the sovereign right of the country to be innovative in technology development. In short, even in the civilian power sector, substantial R&D is necessary to establish and consolidate new processes and improve efficiencies, and this cannot be done with the IAEA constantly looking over the shoulders of our scientists and engineers. For example, Brazil has developed a new and more efficient centrifuge process, and is having trouble asserting its intellectual property rights in the face of mandated IAEA inspections.

India has also agreed to negotiate an additional protocol with the IAEA, whose terms and conditions are not defined. This additional protocol, invented in the mid-90s on suspicions of the production of WMD by certain states, is highly intrusive and infringes on the right of a nation to independently pursue R&D in nuclear science and technology. Can and should India subject its scientists to intrusive inspections and questions by an outside body, when vital interests are involved? For example, the choice of the form of fuel for the fast-breeder programme, reprocessing technology involved in the thorium breeding, and the parallel programme of thorium utilization in heavy-water reactors, are all areas of vital interest to this country. There may also be various other methods, simpler and more cost effective, in the area of enrichment and new nuclear systems for energy production.

India has agreed to go along and accept the Fissile Material Cut-off Treaty (FMCT) at a multi-national level, with verification by an external agency. While India has a need for fissile material for its strategic programme, its stock of such material is nowhere near the stocks that are in the possession of the Nuclear Weapon countries. It is thus a dangerous commitment, inconsistent with our declared policy of a minimum credible deterrent for strategic purposes.

The benefits of the Indo-US deal are highlighted as a panacea for the' expansion of nuclear power in our energy sector, offering energy security for the future. This essentially means buying of nuclear power stations, buying of fuel for the reactors, and such other items. Enriched fuel for the power sector may be available under the agreement, but every gram of that should be proven as necessary for utilisation in the power sector. It is not clear whether India will have the option of accelerating its own, well-established, nuclear power programme based on the PHWR. There is no estimate of the economics of imported nuclear power stations, nor a comparison with other sources, such as oil, coal, etc., which will also be augmented by India.

The testimonies before the Congress, the additions to the Bush proposal, which have been recommended by the Congressional committees, have all come as a shock to those who follow the intricacies of the nuclear deal. It is now obvious that in spite of the exemptions to be approved by Congress, the President of the US will have to certify every year, in detail, that he is satisfied with the behaviour and programmes of India in the nuclear field, especially with respect to the augmentation of the nuclear arsenal. He has to certify that no benefit is derived by the Indian strategic programme from the external assistance derived through this deal. This is a very dangerous proposition, for in such a complicated interaction it is very difficult to provide clear evidence to justify such a certification. Therefore, any such certification will be highly subjective and can result in disagreements in the future.

Implications of the Deal

Enough has been written in the media of the political implications of the strategic partnership. India's active cooperation in diverse areas in implementing the non-proliferation regime as seen by the US, may be counter-productive. The mention of Iran is itself extraordinary in an agreement that is only between India and the US. Similarly, there could be objections on the very invasive verifications to be carried out in implementing a stricter non-proliferation regime in the world. This needs very careful analysis, and I am not going to attempt to do this here.

One gets the feeling that these additions to the agreement of 18 July 2005, will, in effect have the following fall-outs: (a) Cap our strategic programme for a credible minimum deterrent; (b) Information on almost all activities on nuclear science and technology, related to basic research or technical development, will be available to the US; (c) India will essentially forgo its sovereign right to develop modern science and cutting-edge technology in areas of nuclear science, strategic devices like nuclear explosives and missiles, and innovations that can have implications on the use of thorium, and in space technology, etc.

As a scientist I feel that the non-proliferation agenda of the US, trying to restrain acquisition of even simple technologies, like that of enrichment, is bound to fail. If one looks at the growth of electronics and the innovations that have been brought about by a deeper understanding of semiconductor physics and innovations in making devices, including computers, imaging devices, etc., it is clear that the sovereign right to be able to develop science and technology is important and necessary for any country. Surrendering these basic rights is dangerous and we will be doing injustice to future generations in India.

It is in this context that one raises the question whether the government should enter into such a complicated and long-term agreement with so little debate and consideration. Debate among informed citizens, called for by our PM, is a pre-condition for any government to enter into such an important deal. From the modifications suggested by the US Congress and Senate committees, it is clear that the intention of the US government is to tighten safeguards, impose intrusive inspections, and to bind this country in perpetuity to the NPT, CTBT and FMCT, to which we have always been opposed. One has to admit that these strategic implications of the 'civilian' nuclear deal cannot be completely discussed in open fora. However, at present there seems to be no mechanism for evolving a consensus on such crucial strategic issues. I trust that the Parliament will enact laws to establish a mechanism by which informed decisions and consensus could be arrived at in a discreet way, without compromising national interests.

I hope articles such as this will trigger further discussion and participation from scientists, policy-makers, and the academic community, who are not under pressure to work out a diplomatic agreement, to come together and analyse threadbare the implications of such a deal, and at the same time trigger a more careful and informed analysis by the government of the strategic aspects. We should recall the 'tryst with destiny' that Pandit Nehru proclaimed at the dawn of our independence. The time has come to revive this call and act accordingly.

(Lecture to the Forum on Integrated National Security,
Mumbai, June 2006)

32. A Deal of Broken Assurances

A. GOPALAKRISHNAN

The Prime Minister and his senior advisers who negotiated the Indo-US nuclear deal, are surprisingly silent after the passage of the recent bills in the US Congress. The reason could only be one of the following two. First, it could be that the PM and his advisers had reached a consensus beforehand with the US side, on the contents of these bills. They are counting on getting the deal through a generally ambivalent Parliament, where the Left opposition may thunder for some days and then meekly go along. The second possibility is that the PM and his advisers are equally taken aback by the total reversal of earlier agreements by the US, based on which the PM had boldly given several binding assurances to the public and Parliament. In any case, the PM, the national security adviser, the foreign secretary, the chairman of the AEC, and the deputy chairman of the Planning Commission and their trusted deputies, who alone were involved in these secret negotiations, have some serious explanations to give in a hurry.

On July 29, 2005, the PM said in Parliament, "Reciprocity is the key to the implementation of all the steps enumerated in the Joint Statement. Indian actions will be contingent at every stage on actions taken by the other side. Should we not be satisfied that our interests are fully secured, we shall not feel pressed to move ahead." On August 4, 2005, the PM said in the Rajya Sabha, "The starting sentence of that (the July 18 Joint Statement) refers to that (sic) all these commitments are to be interpreted in reciprocity. If there is no action taken by the US government—we are completely free, for example, to stay where we are. We are not required to do anything." On February 27, 2006, in his *suo-motu* statement to Parliament, the PM said, "I had stressed that reciprocity was the key and we expected that the steps to be taken by India would be conditional upon and contingent on action taken by the US." Finally, on safeguards, the PM promised in his July 29, 2005 address to Parliament: "Before voluntarily placing our civilian facilities under IAEA safeguards, we will ensure that all restrictions on India have been lifted."

As against these promises, what are the mandatory conditions that the two Congressional bills have now imposed on India? Both require India to first sign a detailed (123) nuclear agreement with the US, to conclude and put into effect an irrevocable agreement with the IAEA to place our civilian facilities (including nine research institutions) under perpetual safeguards, and to obtain a consensus agreement from the Nuclear Suppliers' Group (NSG) to permit supplies to India. In the interim, every month, India is required to provide the details and progress of the India-US and India-IAEA negotiations to the Congress through the US administration. When all these agreements are reached, thereafter India will once again submit these documents to the US Congress, through the US administration. Then, and then only, the matter of waiving and modifying US laws in favour of India will even be debated in detail, let alone agreed to. Hopefully, the Congress will then approve a joint resolution on the Indo-US deal and enact it into law, for the deal to become effective. If not, India ends up having no nuclear cooperation deal with the US, but will still be saddled with irrevocable IAEA safeguards in perpetuity on our civilian nuclear installations.

These bills also contain clauses which totally contradict the earlier assurances of the PM and the US administration on uninterrupted nuclear fuel supply to India. The multiple mechanisms through which this was to be ensured were outlined in the Separation Plan tabled in Parliament on May 11, 2006 and in the earlier assurance given by the PM on March 7, 2006. On that day, he stated: "To further guard against any disruption of fuel supplies for India, the US is prepared to take other additional steps, such as:

(a) Incorporating assurances regarding fuel supply in a bilateral agreement.

(b) The US will join India in seeking to negotiate with the IAEA an India-specific fuel supply agreement.

(c) The US will support an Indian effort to develop a strategic reserve of nuclear fuel.

(d) If, despite these arrangements, a disruption of fuel supplies to India occurs, the US and India would jointly convene a group of friendly supplier countries to include countries such as Russia, France and the United Kingdom to pursue such measures as would restore fuel supply to India."

Compare this against what is now incorporated in the two bills. The Obama amendment to the Senate Bill passed on June 29, 2006, states in Section 102(6): "The US should not seek to facilitate or encourage the continuation of nuclear exports to India by any other party if such exports are terminated under US law." The House Bill goes a step further. In Section 4(d)-3 it states, "If nuclear transfers to India are restricted pursuant to this Act—the President should seek to prevent the transfer to India of equipment, materials or technology from other participating governments in the NSG or from any other source." Thus, it is obvious that these bills shoot down items (b) and (d), contained in the PM's fuel supply assurance to Parliament.

Similarly, if one studies the Schiff amendment to the House Bill and the Chafee amendment to the Senate Bill, which were passed, it is clear that the US will not provide or facilitate a strategic reserve of nuclear fuel beyond a one-year requirement for our plants at any time. This, in effect, negates the PM's assurance given under (c).

We must keep in mind that the waiver of US law under this deal is to be extended on a year-to-year basis, through an annual assessment of India's extent of cooperation in supporting US nuclear and foreign policy objectives. The President has to present this to the Congress every year and get its approval. Therefore, the deal can become null and void at any future date if the Congress determines that India is not cooperative enough in supporting the US endeavours. The Senate Bill makes this amply clear in Section 108 (b)4-B(ii): "...if the President cannot make such a certification (that India is in full compliance) an assessment (should be submitted), of any continued non-compliance, including whether nuclear commerce with India remains in the national security interest of the US."

The danger lies not in these bills alone, but in how the government plans to derive benefits from this deal. A major outcome from this deal is touted to be the enhanced energy security we can get through the import of reactors; if so, the country may invest about Rs 300,000-400,000 crores in foreign exchange over the next decade to purchase about 30,000-40,000 MWe worth nuclear reactors. These reactors will have to depend on imported fuel to be cleared by the NSG for the next 50 years of life. In case India dares to take a foreign policy decision seriously opposed by the US or conduct a nuclear test in the future, the US Congress can terminate the deal, leaving our huge investments in imported reactors idle due to non-availability of fuel. This prospect could tie the hands of any future Indian government and their only option then may be to kow-tow to US policy dictates to avoid this loss.

Therefore, it is most important that the Parliament must decide now whether the Manmohan Singh government should be permitted to go ahead with this deal in its evolving form. Is the PM going to stand by the promises he made to Parliament and either insist on substantial changes to be made to these bills before they are presented to both full Houses of Congress, or else take India squarely out of this deal which will compromise the sovereignty of this country for decades to come?

(*The Asian Age*, July 7, 2006)

33. U.S. Mission is to Cap, Freeze, Control Nuclear India

BHARAT KARNAD

Soon after the 1998 nuclear tests, a US government committee examining the failure of the fabulously-equipped and richly endowed US intelligence agencies to forewarn the White House about the resumption of explosive testing by India, concluded that the Indian nuclear programme and strategic decision-making loops in the government were insufficiently penetrated and the quality of HUMINT (human intelligence) needed upgrading. More recently, Pentagon decided to spend in excess of $300 million annually on "disinformation" campaigns worldwide.

The result of the seamless dovetailing of these two mission areas is reflected, for instance, in the recent unearthing by the Indian counter-intelligence of strategically-placed "moles" assiduously cultivated by CIA, as former senior RAW official, B. Raman, had apprehended early. (Who knows how many more are burrowed in even higher reaches of the Indian policy establishment and where?) And, in the orchestration of public support in India for the nuclear deal via efficient "media management." (Is it a coincidence, honourable exceptions aside, that the bulk of the mainstream English-language Indian print and electronic media supposedly shaping the views of the Indian middle-class have rarely carried articles or presentations critical of the deal?) In attempting to get at the most secret information, highly motivated Indian nuclear scientists and engineers are more difficult to subvert, as the record shows, than politicians, journalists, Indian intelligence agents, civil servants, diplomats, and armed services officers. But this fact may only lead to redoubling of American effort to create a powerful "fifth column."

But then, where's the necessity for the US to go to all this trouble and (albeit, minor) expense when the Congress Party-led coalition Prime Minister Manmohan Singh and his transient government are collaborating with Washington to emasculate the Indian nuclear weapons and missile programmes, surrender sovereignty in the external realm, and generally transform India into a servile security and energy dependency of the United States?

Incidentally, "giving up sovereignty" is how Drs Homi J. Sethna and P.K. Iyengar, illustrious chairmen of the Atomic Energy Commission in the mid-1970s and the late 1980s respectively, described Manmohan Singh's nuclear deal in a July 1 seminar hosted by the Forum for Integrated National Security in Mumbai. Many active members and veterans of the nuclear complex in Trombay were present. They have done their patriotic duty by securing for the country, against all odds, nuclear weapon and thermonuclear weapon capabilities, only to see first Atal Behari Vajpayee prematurely announce a test moratorium the US government has ever since banked on to corner India, and now Manmohan Singh complete the job of frittering away the strategic advantage so gained. It is a measure of the anger and exasperation the nuclear scientific community feels for New Delhi that the scientists present at the seminar unanimously seconded Sethna's startling suggestion. Having experienced the "unscrupulous" ways of the Americans during his time as head of the Department of Atomic Energy, Sethna argued that it would be less calamitous from the point of view of its nuclear military security for India to sign the Non-Proliferation Treaty (NPT) with the sovereignty clause than make bilateral commitments with the US without an escape option.

In the wake of the US House and Senate Bills being voted in committee, it should be clear to everyone that the two principles of "reciprocity" and "parity" Manmohan Singh had promised in Parliament, were not adhered to in the negotiations leading to the final deal. Reciprocity, pertaining to a system of procedural interlinks, was meant to reassure each country about sensitive actions taken by the other in lockstep. But Washington has loaded its legislative measures with conditionalities that have stood the "good faith" element in the Joint Statement on its head, making reciprocity meaningless. Bad enough as this is, not insisting on parity of treatment is going to cost the country very dear. The US government's declared unwillingness to treat India as a nuclear weapon state—refer the Congressional testimonies by senior US state department officials, autumn 2005 onwards—should have led to a breakdown of the deal long ago. But it did not, in the main, because Manmohan Singh and his negotiating team mistakenly believed that the phrase describing India as a country with "advanced nuclear technology" in the July 18, 2005 Joint Statement the PM signed with President George W. Bush, amounted to US acknowledging India as a nuclear weapon state and would eventuate in this country being conferred the same "rights and obligations" as the US, as foreign secretary Shyam Saran had jauntily asserted at the time. And, perhaps because the Prime Minister is personally convinced, in the manner some gung-ho advocates of the American line in the Indian press are, that harping on the "text" rather than on the "context" is "to lose the plot." So, the country is being asked, following the PM's example, not to worry about or to get hung up on the details of the deal, perchance, because the devil resides there.

The final US legislative approval is, in fact, premised on India's accepting a non-weapon-state status under NPT for the purposes of negotiating a safeguards system and Additional Protocol meant to ensure strict and pervasive international scrutiny of its nuclear programme in perpetuity. In the event, the ministry of external affairs team could not have been surprised by the hard line the delegation from the International Atomic Energy Agency adopted in the talks underway since Saturday.

This is because the baseline defined by the enabling US legislation the Dr Manmohan Singh-led group has accepted, makes it imperative for India to (1) stick to a "no testing-regime" on the pain of instant termination of "nuclear cooperation" which (restriction) means imposing Comprehensive Test Ban Treaty strictures by the back door and will qualitatively freeze the Indian nuclear arsenal in its present untested, unreliable, unsafe and technologically primitive form, and (2) accept a Fissile Material Cut-off Treaty, thereby capping this country's stockpile of weapons-usable plutonium and uranium, which will limit the size of the nuclear force India can have. Two of the three longstanding US non-proliferation goals, namely, "capping" and "freezing" the Indian nuclear deterrent will by those means, have been achieved. The unrelenting pace of modernisation of their strategic forces set by the five so-called NPT-recognised "nuclear weapon states" compared to the Indian arsenal at a near "stand still," in any case, renders the third objective of "rollback" of the Indian programme irrelevant.

This deal-making process has highlighted two things. One, the potent role played by the US Congress, in contrast to the complete absence of Indian Parliament from the scene and despite a belated call by the Left parties, for a constitutional amendment requiring treaty obligations the government undertakes to secure express approval of Parliament, the likelihood they will rubber-stamp this transaction. They would rather continue to be in a position to bring concessions from a politically weak government than withdraw support to it and prevent India becoming a subsidiary state in the strategic and energy spheres. And secondly, the appalling degree of gullibility, naivety and ignorance of the Manmohan Singh regime about the nature of the international system and what constitutes foreign policy power and leverage.

The reasons for the US to be enthused about the deal and India to reject it, have been elucidated repeatedly and at length by this analyst in this paper since before and, more frequently, after the July 2005 Washington trip by Dr Manmohan Singh. But let us hear them from Ashley J. Tellis who, on official attachment with the US under-secretary of state Nicholas Burns, helped seal the deal with the Indians. In the late support—"Atoms for War? US-India Civilian Nuclear Cooperation and India's Nuclear Arsenal"—released by the Carnegie Endowment for International Peace on 26 June 2006, a day before the House International Relations Committee "marked-up" the concerned

Bill, Tellis adduced two main reasons why the US Congress should recognise "a great opportunity" and speedily get the negotiated deal underway.

Firstly, dealing with "a relatively geopolitically weak" India, Tellis noted, "bequeaths the United States with greater dividends than would be the case if such cooperation were offered after India had already become a true great power and a repository of sophisticated nuclear technologies—when New Delhi presumably would have lesser need for such cooperation." "Dividends" here refer to the leverage afforded to the US to shape India's foreign and military policies. And secondly, "unfettered access to the global uranium market" (which can always be manipulated by Washington), he asserted, would persuade the Indian government (especially of the economystic, strategically short-sighted kind-headed by Manmohan Singh), to go for "cost- and technology-effective solution to India's clean energy requirements."

What Tellis left unsaid was that weaning New Delhi away from the plutonium economy by making available uranium and uranium-fuelled reactors is a recipe for pre-empting India's dual-use breeder reactor programme and the indigenous development of the follow-on thorium fuel cycle technologies with the potential for virtually limitless energy in the future. And for snuffing out the last best hope of making India strategically strong and genuinely independent, energy-wise.

(*The Asian Age*, July 9, 2006)

34. PM is Outsourcing Policy

A. GOPALAKRISHNAN

The recent Congressional Bills on the Indo-US nuclear deal severely limit our sovereignty in matters of nuclear, foreign, and energy policy, our freedom to conduct nuclear research and development, and the ability to sustain a credible minimum nuclear deterrent. However, the government is busy propagating the misinformation that all adverse clauses in these bills are "non-binding" and these are merely in the "non-operative" parts of the bills. This is a deliberate misrepresentation, put forward to suppress opposition to this deal until these bills are enacted into US law.

The bills contain specific sub-sections on US policies with respect to India, which go beyond the scope of the July 18,2005 nuclear framework agreement. It is true that these clauses in themselves do not dictate that India must fall in line with these policies. That demand is brought in cleverly through a subsequent section of the bill which contains the annual reporting requirements by the President to the Congress. This reporting is to include an assessment as to how rapidly and effectively India is meeting the laid out US objectives, year after year. The bill also indicates the penalty we may pay in case this assessment reveals non-compliance on the part of India.

To paraphrase from the House Bill (HR 5682), Section 3(b), the listed US policies with respect to South Asia are:

(1) To achieve a moratorium on fissile material production for weapons use in India, at the earliest date.

(2) To achieve, at the earliest date, the conclusion of a Fissile Material Cut-off Treaty (FMCT) to which both US and India can become parties.

(3) To secure India's full participation in the Proliferation Security Initiative (PSI) and a formal commitment to its interdiction principles. To secure a *public announcement* by India to join the Australia Group (aimed at controlling the proliferation of chemical and biological weapons) and the Wassennaar Arrangement (related to the control of conventional weapons and dual-use goods).

(4) To secure India's full and active participation with the US to dissuade, isolate, and, if necessary, sanction and contain Iran.

(5) To seek to halt the increase of nuclear arsenals in South Asia, and to promote their reduction and eventual elimination.

That India must make positive and speedy progress on all the above five policy prescriptions, and more, if the Indo-US nuclear deal has to continue to survive year after year is explicit from the mandatory policy objectives given in Section 4(o)-l of the House bill. This Section reads, "The President shall, not later than January 31, 2007, and not later than January 31 of *each year thereafter,* submit to both the Congressional committees a report on:

(A) the extent to which each policy objective in Section 3(b) above has been achieved,

(B) the steps taken by the US and India in the previous year to accomplish those objectives,

(C) the extent of co-operation given by other countries, and

(D) the steps the US will take in the current year to accomplish those objectives.

So, what would happen if India does not make timely and speedy progress in meeting the US policy goals set out in Section 3(b)? The penalty is clearly spelt out in Section 108(b) 4(B) of the Senate bill. It reads to the effect that, "If the President cannot make an annual certification that India is in full compliance with the commitments, he is required to make an assessment of all compliance issues, including—an assessment whether nuclear commerce with India remains in the national security interest of the US." Such an adverse assessment could then directly lead to a suspension or revoking of the Indo-US nuclear deal by the Congress and a consequent stoppage of nuclear co-operation and imports to India.

To cover the above eventuality in the case of nuclear fuel, the PM and the US President had agreed on a multi-path mechanism for fuel supply assurance to India. This was spelt out by US Undersecretary Nicholas Burns on March 2, 2006 in Delhi as follows: "What the US did today was to commit to the Indians that we would work very hard to help ensure a continuous and reliable supply of nuclear fuel to India. First of all, we will embed in the Indo-US bilateral agreement assurances that we will seek to help India secure fuel for its nuclear reactors. Second, we have agreed that India and the US will approach the IAEA for a multilateral regime to supply fuel for India. Third, we have agreed to set up a council of advisors—India and the US and other countries—so that if there is ever a threat of interruption of supply, those countries could meet to figure out how to maintain supply to India". The PM also reiterated the same promise in Parliament on March 7, 2006.

The Congress, in their recent bills, have totally over-ruled this earlier assurance of the US administration. Section 4(d)(3) of the House bill states, "If nuclear transfers to India are restricted pursuant to this Act,—the President should *seek to prevent* the transfer of nuclear equipment, materials or technology to India from other participating governments in the NSG or from any other source".

As for nuclear weapon tests in the future, the PM says he is sticking to his earlier agreement to continue the unilateral moratorium. But, the US Senate couldn't care less about this stand. In Section 110 of their bill, it is made explicit that this nuclear deal shall cease to be effective if the President determines that India has detonated a nuclear explosive device after the date of enactment of this law.

What is touted to be the primary benefit from entering into this deal is the enhanced energy security we are supposed to achieve through the import of 30,000-40,000 MWe of foreign nuclear power reactors over the next 10-15 years. Interestingly, the DAE does not share this enthusiasm of the PM. It is surprising that the PM, despite being an economist, has never bothered to demand a detailed techno-economic analysis of different electricity generation options before the country either from the Planning Commission, the DAE or the Power Ministry. These organizations on their own have also not studied the issue even superficially, and none of them has any firm quantitative projections of (per MWe) and (per KWh) costs for generating electricity from thermal stations using indigenous and imported coal, indigenous PHWR nuclear stations, imported LWR nuclear plants, hydel stations, wind or bio-mass systems. How then are the PM and the Planning Commission suddenly rattling off various MWe numbers for nuclear power requirement? It is a baseless attempt to build up a false case for a rapid increase in nuclear power capacity, knowing fully well that it will mostly have to come through imported reactors. Through this, the government is signalling the US and other Western nations that India is a prospective and eager customer for their nuclear reactors.

From the above discussion, it is clear that incontrovertible evidence exists in these two bills to prove that India is being led into a US trap in perpetuity by this government, knowingly and under false premises, without the consent or knowledge of the Parliament. As years go by after this deal, India would have invested increasingly in foreign nuclear plants, defense equipment, dual-use goods, etc. A disruption of this nuclear deal at that juncture will then be devastatingly costly for India. This prospect will tie the hands of future Indian governments, since their framing of independent policies unpalatable to the US will certainly lead to unbearable losses to the nation.

Thus, once these bills are enacted into US law and the follow-up steps are taken by both sides, India would have effectively, and for decades to come, outsourced our foreign, nuclear and energy policy-making to successive US administrations and Congresses. If this is to be prevented, the Parliament has to act now, and act decisively, to get India out of this binding deal.

(*The Asian Age*, July 13, 2006)

35. We Need More N-Tests for Our Defence

A. GOPALAKRISHNAN

The total silence which the government has maintained on the Indo-US nuclear deal ever since the two recent Bills have been passed by the US Congress, is beginning to be broken, in small steps, through the speech given by the foreign secretary, Shyam Saran, in Delhi on July 14, and the Prime Minister's brief remarks on his return from Russia. Saran has warned that the final legislation in the US Congress "could well include some references that we may find unpalatable—but, we must focus on what is essential. India's obligations will only be those that we undertake in the bilateral 123 cooperation agreement and the safeguards arrangement with IAEA." But these details are known only to the PM and his close advisers and neither Parliament nor the leaders of the major Opposition parties have been taken into confidence.

There is another zone of silence, this time in Washington, which too we need to take note of. The vociferous non-proliferation lobby consisting of arch rivals of the Indian nuclear programme for decades, have been writing strong letters to the US Congress and have given individual and scholarly testimonies to both the Congressional committees ever since July 2005. Their central theme of opposition all along has been that the Congress should intervene in this nuclear deal and ensure that India's ability to sustain and improve its nuclear arsenal is severely limited and curtailed as early as possible. But this opposition has totally disappeared after the two Congressional Bills were passed last month. The obvious reason is that these Bills have fully taken care of all their major concerns, and their silence alone should be a matter of grave concern to our people.

If one studies these Bills carefully, it is easy to understand wherefrom US non-proliferationists are drawing their comfort. To recap, Section 3(b) of the House Bill (HR-5682) along with the annual presidential reporting required in Section 4(o) l(A-D) will make it mandatory that India achieves a moratorium on fissile material production for weapons-use and conclude a Fissile Material Cut-off Treaty (FMCT) to which US and India can become parties, at the earliest possible date. Anticipating that it will take some time to conclude the FMCT, Congressman Schiff has passed an amendment to HR-5682 which requires US to encourage India not to increase its production of weapons usable material at unsafeguarded facilities. If India was hoping to stockpile imported natural uranium in advance, so that our indigenously mined uranium can be used mostly for the weapons programme, this possibility is also blocked by another Schiff amendment which requires that "Indian nuclear weapon programme shall not derive any benefit—from the provision of nuclear fuel (from abroad) in such a manner as to facilitate the increased production of highly-enriched uranium or plutonium..." Add to this India's commitment under this deal to shut down CIRUS, one of the two reactors which produce weapon grade plutonium, by 2010, and we can certainly expect an early capping of the weapon-usable fissile material inventory in India at a sub-optimal level.

After the conclusion of this deal, if the Indian nuclear programme is looking forward to benefit through technology transfer, it is most likely in the areas of spent-fuel reprocessing, uranium enrichment, and perhaps heavy water production. India has certain technologies and plant systems of indigenous design in each of these areas, but they do need substantial improvements before they can reach world standards in performance. A nuclear weapon state (NWS) or a non-nuclear weapon state (NNWS) which is a signatory of the NPT, will have no legal bar to obtain such commercial technologies from developed nations. But because we are insisting on keeping some of our nuclear facilities still outside the IAEA safeguards, Section 106(b)A of the Senate Bill clearly bans "the export to India of any equipment, materials or technology related to the enrichment of uranium, the reprocessing of spent-fuel or the production of heavy water." However, in their own commercial interest, the Bill exempts India from this ban, provided we import such technologies to run a multinational facility in India under safeguards, as part of a multilateral programme to develop proliferation-resistant fuel cycle— thereby also trapping India to be a client state under the Global Nuclear Energy Partnership (GNEP). This would lead us to purchasing foreign reactors for the indefinite future, abandoning the three-stage indigenous nuclear power programme based on Bhabha's vision. In short, the very few technology areas where we were looking forward to gain through this deal, are cleverly banned from inclusion, unless we are willing to be perpetual customers for foreign reactors. This is simply unacceptable.

As expected, the US Congress has ignored India's voluntary moratorium on nuclear weapon testing, and asserts in Section 110 of the Senate Bill that nuclear cooperation will cease if the President determines at any time that India has detonated a "nuclear explosive device." Interestingly, the Senate Bill is explicit in quantitatively defining a nuclear explosive device as any device designed to produce the instantaneous release of an amount of nuclear energy that is greater than the amount of energy that would be released from the detonation of one pound of trinitrotoluene (TNT). (The definition of a nuclear explosive device as given in Section 112[8] of the Senate Bill has a printing error. I am reliably informed that the words "one point" which appear on line six of Section 112[8], have to be replaced by "one pound.") The crucial importance of this definition, coupled with the ban imposed in Section 110 on testing, needs to be understood from the point of view of India's ability to ensure the safety and reliability of its existing nuclear arsenal and the feasibility of making reliable design improvements for higher yield or/and for reducing the size and weight of warheads in the future.

In the absence of full-scale explosive tests, countries will have the alternative of conducting one or both of two classes of lower-yield tests. In the so-called "sub-critical" tests, no critical mass is formed during implosion and no self-sustaining chain reaction occurs. The nuclear energy release will be negligibly low and, according to US interpretation, the Comprehensive Test Ban Treaty (CTBT) will not be violated if such tests are done. In a "hydronuclear" test, however, the implosion causes a supercritical mass to be formed for an extremely small time interval, but not maintained long enough to permit the device to deliver full explosive nuclear yield. During the CTBT discussions, both the US and UK governments had insisted on retaining the flexibility to conduct hydronuclear tests with nuclear yields up to four pounds of TNT equivalent, but under the current deal, the US wants to restrict India to a one-pound TNT limit, just one-quarter of the level which they themselves considered as essential minimum. This would make it extremely difficult, almost impossible, for India to conduct meaningful hydronuclear tests for verifying the safety and reliability of our existing nuclear arsenal or for modifying or compacting the present warheads.

The CTBT was signed by all the five nuclear weapon states on September 24, 1996. France and UK ratified it in April 1998, and the Russian ratification followed in June 2000. The US Senate rejected the CTBT in October 1999, and China and the US are the only two nuclear weapon states which are yet to ratify the treaty. Ever since 2001, however, pressure has been building up in Russia to withdraw from the CTBT in national interest. In April 2002, V. Mikhaylov and Y. Adamov, two former ministers of atomic energy, have expressed the view that "Russia will eventually face the choice of resuming explosive tests or foregoing nuclear weapons altogether." According to them, "although mathematical models, computer simulations, and sub-critical testing may provide some assurances, in the long-run (explosive) tests would be required to confirm both the safety and reliability of nuclear warheads." The US views are not very different.

On January 9, 2002, Ari Fleischer, then White House press secretary, said, "President Bush has said that we will adhere to the no-testing policy, but we would never rule out the possible need to test to make certain that the (nuclear) stockpile, particularly as it is reduced, is reliable and safe. So, he has not ruled out testing in the future, but (currently) there are no plans to do so." On October 7, 1999, Richard Garwin, the renowned US nuclear weapon scientist, testified before the US Senate, "Without nuclear tests of substantial yield, it is difficult to build compact and lightweight fission weapons and essentially impossible to have any confidence in a large-yield two-stage thermonuclear weapon or hydrogen bomb, which can readily be made in the megaton class. This limits greatly the destructive power that can be wielded by newly nuclear states such as India and Pakistan, once they are brought under a test ban." And such a test ban will indeed be achieved indirectly by the US under the provisions of the present Indo-US nuclear deal.

I have never been a participant in the Indian nuclear weapons programme, nor am I hawkish about India becoming a thermonuclear power. But the intention of this article is to point out that many of the contentions of the Indian nuclear establishment about our weapons capabilities are questionable, on the basis of the enormous body of evidence openly available on the weapons development programmes of the five nuclear weapon states. Countries like the US and Russia, who have conducted and gathered data from a total of 1,030 and 715 explosive nuclear tests, respectively, still feel that they cannot ensure the reliability and safety of their arsenal, merely through sub-critical or hydronuclear tests and computer modelling. Nor are they confident that design or configuration changes or size reductions on warheads can be reliably done without explosive tests to validate them.

In contrast, having done just a total of six explosive tests, Indian weapon scientists bragged openly in 1998 that they need not do any more tests and they are capable of making future designs of fission, boosted-fission and thermonuclear weapons on the basis of these meagre data and some computer modelling. It is an open secret that the single thermonuclear warhead we tested in 1998 has failed, as ascertained by a number of weapons specialists who have analysed the data. Our capabilities in computer modelling of weapons performance and in conducting sub-critical and hydronuclear tests are, to say the least, much below that of the US and Russia. Therefore, knowing the competence of the scientists involved, I can only imagine that their open statement was elicited by the BJP government in 1998, just to support its desire to call for a unilateral moratorium on further tests, for political and tactical reasons. But unfortunately, this false over-confidence of the weapon scientists, which has no scientific or technological basis whatsoever, has come to haunt us now, with the Americans taking them on their word and pegging India firmly onto a no-test, no-fissile production path for the foreseeable future through the current deal. The impact of this future path on the minimum nuclear deterrent of India, and whether this deterrent will remain credible years from now, is a matter worth debating before we plunge neck-deep into the Indo-US deal.

(*The Asian Age*, July 21, 2006)

36. Nuclear Deal is without Techno-economic Merit

BHARAT KARNAD

As always, it is the Americans themselves who reveal the nitty-gritty of the bargains they strike, confident that this will in no way harm the US getting its way. Ashley J. Tellis, the Washington security specialist whose services have been extensively utilised by the George W. Bush administration in forging the nuclear deal with India, has confessed that the Congress Party government has given "more" to make it possible in contrast to the Vajpayee government, which "gave nothing in return."

What this "more" is, is no secret—a nuclear de-fanged India. The BJP external affairs minister Jaswant Singh in his memoirs—*Call to Honour: In Service of Emergent India*—discloses this as the end-state his "strategic dialogue" partner, the US deputy secretary Strobe Talbott, was after. The Vajpayee government, however, decided against signing the Comprehensive Test Ban Treaty directly or via the backdoor, as this deal attempts to do, by making the "voluntary" test moratorium a legally binding commitment, which would restrict the Indian arsenal to the only proven and reliable armament in the Indian inventory—the 20 kiloton "firecracker," or getting hustled into joining a Fissile Material Cut-off Treaty that would ensure the Indian deterrent remained forever small-sized. It is on these two counts, contained in the July 18, 2005 Joint Statement, as Tellis has confirmed, that the Manmohan Singh regime compromised. The grievous flaws are then in the basic document itself as much with the conditionalities inserted especially in the Senate version of the amended draft US law, which has yet to be voted on.

Having "negotiated" a rotten fish of a deal, Manmohan Singh seems to have now woken up to the stink. Whence his complaining to the US President at the G-8 meeting about the many provocative new conditions extraneous to the July 18 accord strapped on by the US Congress. Much good this bellyaching will do, considering these impositions had the consent of the Bush administration. Senator Richard G. Lugar, chairman of the Senate Foreign Relations Committee steering the legislative process, has advised the Indian PM not to be "adamant" and warned that non-acceptance of these "constructive changes" would kill the nuclear deal. But foreign secretary Shyam

Saran and the media trumpeters continue to brush aside new Congressional conditions in the House Bill, in particular, as only "preambular" in nature and, by way of rationalisation, refer to China's ignoring similar Congressional terms on the trade-related "most favoured nation" issue. They need to be reminded that China—unlike India—has forced its way into the senior nuclear league, commands respect, and cannot be trifled with by the US. And, that the US Congress is not Indian Parliament, which rubberstamps any deal the government makes however much it may harm the national interest.

The nuclear deal encompassed in the July 18 statement has been ballyhooed as fetching India an energy-cum-technology windfall. This is a lie based on three myths that have been propagated.

No. 1 Myth: India has limited natural uranium resources and will have to rely on the US to ease the Nuclear Suppliers Group guidelines allowing India to buy the ore ("yellow cake") on the world market. But this claim is wrong and does not take into account the proven reserves and the uranium ore-bearing regions of the country that remain unmined. This analyst had pointed out earlier (Desperate for a nuclear deal, The Op-ed Page, January 17, 2006) that the uranium shortage is mostly self-created because of bad futures planning by the Department of Atomic Energy, compounded by a strange reluctance on the part of the Indian government to exploit the ore locally available in considerable quantities. Tellis in his Carnegie report—Atoms for War: The US-Indian Civilian Nuclear Cooperation and India's Nuclear Arsenal—released last month, reached the same conclusion, saying "India has all the natural uranium it needs to produce as many nuclear weapons it may wish without any assistance from the outside, while being able to generate up to 480 GWe (Giga Watt) years of electricity" and that the shortage is entirely short-term and will last only so long as the DAE and Indian government don't get their act together. Tellis' study apparently deflated the arguments of the non-proliferation lobby in the US.

But what Tellis and the Bush White House cannot do is remove the enriched uranium fuel-baited trap set for an India bent on importing reactors, the July 18 Statement conceived and the US Congress has now realised. A condition in one of the enabling Bills in the US Congress requires the US President to dissuade all NSG countries, should India break its vow and test again, from supplying enriched uranium fuel for these power plants, which directly contravenes the undertaking by President Bush in the July 18 Statement to facilitate such supply from other NSG countries if the US is unable to do so for any reason. The Congressional requirement means that India, without assured fuel supply, will be stuck with a host of inactive reactors and hundreds of billions of dollars in dead investment. Further, reactor technology is about the extent of civilian nuclear wherewithal this country will be permitted to obtain from the NSG states, whence a nyet to importing American reprocessing, enrichment and heavy water production technologies by India.

No. 2 Myth: With the fictional uranium shortage as premise, the purchase by India of enriched uranium-fuelled reactors is mooted as a short-cut to meeting at least some of the energy deficit by 2020. But the fact of plentiful uranium in India has led to a recalibrated objective. The proposed deal, Tellis told a luncheon meeting last week, merely offers India "the option," energy economics permitting, to go in for high capacity (1,000 MWe plus) reactors available abroad. But one reason why the 220 MWe capacity level for pressurised heavy water reactors has been persisted with, is because of the poor state of the national grid. A large quantum of power surging through the grid can stabilise electricity supply. Equally, a sudden loss of a vast quantity of power owing to a breakdown of grid infrastructure, can have crippling downstream economic consequences. 220 MW going off-line is bad enough; imagine instantly losing 2,000 MW from a single two 1,000 MWe reactors source!

No. 3 Myth: The case for India's importing enriched uranium-fuelled reactors rests principally on the American conviction, predictably shared by Manmohan Singh's "gang that can't think straight," that the three-stage Bhabha plan of natural uranium reactors in the first stage leading to plutonium-fuelled breeder reactors in the second stage, in turn, providing the feedstock for the third stage thorium-fuelled power plants, is way beyond India's technical grasp. If the last is true then why is the "unsafeguarded breeder" programme again agitating American legislators, which may lead to yet another unacceptable condition being inserted when a final Bill is moved in the US Congress? The Bhabha plan is infeasible, Tellis implied, because of the belief that "breeders don't breed." He pointed to France which after years of effort attained a "breeding ratio" of 1.5. The trouble is Tellis misrepresented France's experience and doubted the success of India's breeder programme. He did so partially on the basis of a recent article by V.S. Arunachalam, former science adviser to the defence minister, who has lately been in the news.

The French Super-Phenix breeder was shut down, not because of any problems with the reactor itself, but because of secondary reasons—a leak of liquid sodium coolant in the adjoining fuel bay. It was not revived because of the plenitude of enriched uranium but, mainly, because President Jimmy Carter's Nuclear Fuel Cycle initiative in the mid-Seventies arm-twisted France, as it did other advanced countries, into abandoning the development of breeder reactors owing to Washington's fear that this reactor type can efficiently convert spent fuel to weapon-grade fissile material. India has experience of the 40 MW fast breeder test reactor generating some 100,000 MW of power per ton of carbide fuel—unmatched by any other state—and, the upscaled 500 MW breeder under construction, is expected to achieve a breeding ratio of 1.5. This means that the reactor can breed a full fuel load of fissile material every five years which, incidentally, is no mean achievement.

With the series of fast breeders as stepping stone, full-fledged thorium reactors are eminently realisable. In fact, a small experimental reactor, Kamini, running on Uranium 233 produced by irradiating thorium, has been functioning for many years now and will help in developing thorium utilisation technologies. Indian scientists, moreover, are strongly against any kind of cooperation with the US under the aegis of the GNEP (Global Nuclear Energy Project) as promised by the nuclear deal, because of their fear the US will milk the Indian breeder programme dry of its technical data and insights and then deliberately "mislead" the Indian scientists into pursuing technically dead-end solutions or try and demoralise them by talking of the technological complexity involved, and persuading Indian leaders to give up on the indigenous effort and grab the "easier" option of importing uranium reactors. In fact, so pronounced has the government's tendency been uncritically to accept external diktat and direction detrimental to national interest and to pressurise the Atomic Energy Commission chairman into doing what it wants him to do, that it is time, as this writer has been advocating for some years, to establish a counterpart of the American "Jason Committee," except that it should be answerable to Parliament. Stalwart Indian nuclear scientists, reputed physicists in the academia, and renowned technologists—all chosen for their probity and eminence, thereby putting them beyond the pale of political pressure—should constitute this committee. It should be tasked with evaluating nuclear R&D schemes, pronouncing on weapons designs, verifying test data, and independently advising Parliament, in camera, on the technical aspects of nuclear and strategic programmes. It will compel the chairman of the Atomic Energy Commission to be more objective in his advice to the Prime Minister.

Be that as it may, considering the upward curve of the indigenous breeder and follow-on thorium technology development, instead of seeking nuclear servitude what the Manmohan Singh government ought to have aggressively demanded as priority is resolution of the Tarapur spent fuel problem. Some 1,800-2,400 tons of spent fuel accumulated over the last 30 years from the two safeguarded light water reactors in Tarapur are proving a serious space and safety risk. The US neither wants to take the spent fuel back to add to its "nuclear waste" nor approves of India reprocessing it for use in the Indian CANDU reactors. The 1963 Tarapur agreement was valid for only 25 years and any strong-minded Indian government after 1988 could have forced Washington's hand, given it an ultimatum to lift the spent fuel, failing which ordered the entire stock of spent fuel rods to be reprocessed and, as per the original contract, without any downstream safeguards obligations on India's part. But successive Indian governments, covering up their timidity with the rhetoric of "responsible behaviour" have, instead, pursued a policy of endless pleading. This was also the course followed when the US violated contractual obligations and stopped fuel supply to Tarapur in 1974 and New Delhi could have approached the International Court for relief, but did not.

Diffidence and absence of self-respect have characterised the Indian government in its dealings with the US and the West. But the country had every right to expect that, in line with its unchained economic prowess, an assertive 21st century India would propel itself to the great power ranks rather than, as the Manmohan Singh regime would have it, get reduced to an American appendage.

(The Asian Age, July 28, 2006)

37. Parliament Must Exercise its Responsibility

A. GOPALAKRISHNAN

The US-India Nuclear Co-operation Promotion Act of 2006 (HR 5682 RH) was passed by the House of Representatives of the US Congress on July 26, 2006. A total of 219 Republican Congressmen out of the total 231, and 140 Democratic Congressmen out of the total 201 voted in favour of this legislation. The US House has taken full cognizance of the cautions and protests they received from the US non-proliferation lobby, and have appropriately modified the earlier version of this bill (HR 4974) to assuage their apprehensions. Thus, the overwhelming support this bill received this week in the full House is only an indication that US requirements have been fully met, while we should also accept it as a strong blow dealt to India's national interests.

In connection with the legislation passed on July 26th, some in the Indian media have gone overboard in their enthusiasm to proclaim that a few "killer amendments," which could otherwise have been "deal-breakers" have been defeated in the process. This spreads the false and comfortable feeling that the legislation as it stands today is benign to India, and all the negative clauses which the Indian critics of the deal have worried about have been eliminated. The truth is far from it! It is only few of the *additional* amendments brought forth in the last few days, to further tighten the noose around India's neck, which have been defeated—All the original restrictions and demands placed on India through HR 5682, as submitted to the House, stay intact. Thus, the linkage to Iran in defining Indian good behaviour, the denial of the multi-path nuclear fuel supply guarantee which the PM had promised to Parliament, the total disregard for reciprocity of actions, the mandatory need for India to co-operate and collaborate with the US on the FMCT, fully participating in the Proliferation Security Initiative, the Australia Group, and the Wassennaar Arrangement, etc. are still very much a part of the passed legislation. Much more stringent restrictions and demands will be forthcoming when the Senate bill is presented later and passed by the full Senate. So, there is a need to be on guard against the misinformation campaign which is going on, especially in these difficult days when the government is facing attacks in the Parliament on all fronts.

Our immediate focus, however, needs to be on how best to protect India's national interests in the near and long-term. Should we entrust this task, in the current context of the Indo-US nuclear deal, solely to the UPA government as we have done so far or should the primacy of the Parliament be enforced to ensure that this government stays within certain mutually agreed boundaries of action? Ironically, the best answer to this question can be gleaned from the views of the US Congress, which also found itself in a similar dilemma over the same deal.

The bill HR 5682 RH was submitted to the House of Representatives along with a detailed report which explains the intention behind each of its clauses. Let me reproduce a few verbatim quotations from this report, which clearly make the case why the US Congress was compelled to proactively participate in shaping the current deal. The report states, "Given the unique and controversial nature of the proposed civil nuclear co-operation agreement and the fact that Congress was not consulted regarding the negotiations between the Administration and the Indian government relating to the original announcement of their intention to negotiate such an agreement, Congressional scrutiny and approval was deemed essential to protect US interests."

The treatment that the Indian Parliament has received from the UPA government is also much the same. The PM sent his advance points-men to the US to lay the foundation for this deal, to discuss the strategic path for converting it into a reality, and perhaps to reach certain unwritten understandings with the US administration, including the potential commercial benefits that the US could accrue through this deal in the areas of selling nuclear power plants to India in the future, arms exports, sales of clean-coal technologies and associated equipment, etc. The government used only a few hand-picked senior officials from then on in handling this deal, persons in whom the PM has trust and who are also well-known sympathizers of the US points of view. The Parliament, members of the Cabinet, and almost all the rest of the bureaucracy and the general public had no inkling of what is being negotiated, ostensibly for the purpose of "enhancing energy security" and for the larger good of the country by leading it into the US camp. Therefore, just as the US Congress did in their interest, it is time that the Indian Parliament also wakes up to the need for this deal to be subjected to parliamentary scrutiny and approval in the Indian national interest.

The US House report further states, "Direct Congressional involvement, especially the requirement for its approval, is also necessary to ensure that the pledges and assurances made by the Administration and the Indian government are actually met and not rendered irrelevant through lack of action or discontinuation of interest. Without enforcement provisions, such statements are obviously little more than promises that may be modified at will, or even abandoned altogether, should circumstances change".

In our Parliament also, the PM has made statements on this deal on four different occasions, giving solemn pledges on specific aspects of the agreement. However, the way matters have turned out, it appears that the negotiators appointed by the PM have totally failed to impress upon the US administration the promises that he had made on these occasions. On the whole, the government has not stood up firmly against the American onslaught on the PM's promises, fearing that the deal may not go through. Inherent in this behaviour is the government's strong conviction that India cannot survive and grow if this nuclear deal with the US collapses, which sadly is a colossal fallacy. In any case, the way events are progressing, it shows a scant regard on the part of this government for the shared responsibility which the Parliament also has in our democratic polity.

I shall close with a third quotation from the US House report which brings out the importance of legislative involvement in such affairs of State. It reads, "Constitution nevertheless vests Congress with considerable powers and responsibilities in the areas of foreign policy and national security, which its Members are obligated to carry out. Fidelity to that trust means that Congress cannot delegate those responsibilities to the executive branch or allow itself to be made irrelevant to government policy in any area."

Our Parliament must also be aware that they hold enormous ultimate powers and solemn responsibilities under the Indian Constitution. They must feel that, at this juncture, they have an unavoidable collective responsibility to steer this government away from the path it is deliberately following, contrary to the promises made in the immediate past. Whether this is achieved through a "Sense of Parliament" resolution or a Prime Ministerial statement to the Parliament is a matter to be collectively decided. All of us do understand that the objective is not to pull down the UPA government, but to make this government understand beyond any shadow of doubt that they have to openly articulate the Indian position to the US administration and to our own nation. While doing this, the government must keep in mind the consensus opinion of the Parliament at all times. We are ready to accept once again a statement from the PM, the fifth of such disappointing exercises on this deal, if that is what the government wants to save its face in the light of the two US Congressional bills, instead of a joint Parliamentary resolution. However, this time we hope the PM will not make promises only to the Parliament alone, but also send a pointed message on specific objections we already see in the two US bills which have come out. There is no wisdom in waiting for the US "to complete their legislative process," because it is high time that the US administration is openly warned that the Parliament and the people of India strongly oppose the specific inserts in these bills which go beyond the July 18, 2005 agreement between the two governments.

(*The Asian Age*, July 31, 2006)

38. Energy Security as Scapegoat

A. GOPALAKRISHNAN

The government and its advisers are promoting the Indo-US nuclear deal on the pretext that it is primarily meant for enhancing the energy security of the nation. As a prelude for making this case, a US-India energy dialogue was launched on May 31, 2005 just few weeks prior to the PM's visit to the US and also an Energy Coordination Committee under the chairmanship of the PM was formed on July 13, 2005. The first meeting of this committee was held only on August 6th after the signing of the nuclear deal. There is no indication that this committee ever had a second meeting. And, the civil nuclear energy working group formed under the bilateral energy dialogue seems to be merely used as a channel to route the US commercial interests and their nuclear non-proliferation requirements into the Indian policy-making process.

Countries interested in enhancing energy security generally follow two cardinal principles in their planning process. First, they rely mainly on primary energy resources which are available in their own territory and on technologies they can develop on their own for the utilization of such resources. Second, they try to make use of all energy resources nationally available, in an appropriate energy-mix dictated by techno-economic considerations. When the Prime Minister over-emphasizes that Indo-US co-operation is crucial for our energy security, and just pays occasional lip-service to indigenous resources and energy technology developments, such a slant towards foreign reliance needs to be tested against the usual norms other countries follow.

India's major primary energy resources are its large coal reserves in the eastern and southern States, the large potential yet to be tapped in the hydroelectric sector, and the vast resources of thorium present in easily mineable areas. If this government is really concerned with energy security, why are we not seeing any concrete actions on their part to utilize the above three forms of energy within the country, with a high priority and emphasis?

For the above three energy resources, are there not indigenous technological capabilities readily available for use or under late stages of development? Unfortunately, Indian coals are of poor quality, with very high ash content and uniquely different chemical and combustion properties compared to most of the foreign coals. Therefore, over the decades, no foreign country has developed effective technologies for using our type of coals. The only notable technological successes achieved in this field are by India, through the joint R&D efforts of BHEL and some of the CSIR laboratories, with some recent contributions from the NTPC.

From mid-1970s, BHEL and CSIR started working on coal-gasification for power generation through the Integrated Gasification Combined Cycle (IGCC) route, which by 1990 had resulted in the successful operation of a small-scale pilot IGCC plant which can gasify a variety of Indian coals. In the meantime, at least four times in the last 25 years, Indo-US technology teams have jointly studied the applicability of the US clean coal technologies for gasifying Indian coals. These studies have confirmed that US does not possess any coal conversion technology which suits our coals. At the last such Indo-US discussion on the subject, organized jointly with the Harvard University in Hyderabad in early 2003, it was strongly recommended that the only option for Indian coals was to up-scale the BHEL technology for clean-coal power generation through the setting up of a 100 MWe IGCC demonstration plant in India, instead of seeking any US technology. But, now we are told that the PM has decided that India would make hard currency payments and join the Future Gen project of the US DOE to "develop" clean coal technologies for us! At the same time, a project report prepared jointly by BHEL and NTPC to up-scale the indigenous IGCC technology, and strongly recommended by the Principal Scientific Advisor to the PM, is languishing somewhere within the government for lack of financial approval. This is yet another example of how this government is blatantly giving the US a back-door commercial and technological entry, in an area where Indian engineers have successfully brought the technology to the threshold of commercial demonstration.

As for indigenous nuclear technologies for the three-stage program, the work is progressing extremely well and we will be commissioning a 500 MWe fast breeder reactor by 2012, at the latest. At this juncture, the PM talks about his vision of adding 30,000-40,000 MWe of nuclear power in the coming 15-20 years, knowing fully well that most of this has to come through imported reactors. And, his promise in the Separation Plan that the US will guarantee lifetime fuel supplies through multiple paths for such reactors has just been summarily shot down by the US Congress. The imported reactors need enriched uranium fuel, but India does not have modern enrichment technology, and importing this is also denied under this deal. The PM understands all this well, and yet he is willing to welcome foreign reactors to "enhance" our energy security. And, this is the back-bone of his argument in pushing the Indo-US nuclear deal!

The DAE insists that the country has total natural uranium ores to support 10,000 MWe PHWRs for their life-time, which will produce enough plutonium to bridge over to the three-stage program leading to thorium utilization. The present uranium shortage is mainly due to the fact that DAE has failed to take advance actions on time and the government in the mid-1990s, when the current PM was the Finance Minister, had denied the DAE the budgetary support required to expand mineral exploration and for opening new mines in Jharkhand and Meghalaya. The government continues to be lukewarm in its support of these activities even today. We must equally blame the DAE for not aggressively pursuing this issue, thus giving the government a chance to push the nuclear deal and the import of foreign reactors on grounds of uranium shortage.

As for the Energy Mix Study, the last time an optimum energy mix for the country was seriously examined was sometime in the mid-1960s. The question which needs to be answered is this: At any given time, what should be the "best" quantitative combination of electricity generation from indigenous coal, imported coal, hydro-power generation from the national river water systems, import of hydro-power from neighbouring countries, indigenous nuclear power based on the three-stage program, wind, solar, and biomass resources, etc. This requires a complex, many-faceted study which should be done collectively, and kept periodically updated, so that India's energy policies and planning can be formulated in keeping with its findings. But, is anyone carrying out such a study? Even with a renowned economist-PM as Chairman, his trusted follower as Deputy Chairman, and an energy economist as Member (Energy), the Planning Commission has totally failed in initiating such studies or basing their policy pronouncements on the basis of such wisdom. The Report of the Expert Committee on Integrated Energy Policy put out by the Planning Commission in December 2005 is full of generalizations and platitudes for the future and does not address the energy mix or the role of indigenous *vs.* imported energy technologies. So, on what basis is the PM expounding on the need for 30,000-40,000 MWe of nuclear power as an essential element for ensuring energy security? Why not a figure like 15,000 MWe or 70,000 MWe instead? The PM's over-enthusiasm for nuclear reactors of the imported kind can only be explained as a deliberate attempt to spread out a welcome mat for foreign nuclear firms to sell their wares in India, and to make the questionable case for promoting the nuclear deal.

India's new-found participation in the ITER thermonuclear experiment, on payment, is heralded as another achievement for energy security. Most scientists admit that ITER, at best, may succeed in producing few kilowatts of electricity in about fifty years from now, and fusion may never become a viable option for power generation. Similarly, the much touted participation of India in the US Global Nuclear Energy Partnership (GNEP) will only be as a client State, and not as a developer of technology. And, the recent Senate discussions make it clear that as long as India refuses to place its fast breeder reactors under IAEA safeguards, we will not be admitted to the GNEP.

It should be clear from the above why the general public, and especially the scientific community, have a diminishing trust in this government's sincerity of approach on energy security and its support to indigenous science and technology. The utter neglect of national energy resources and engineering capabilities in preference to limited and dubious assistance from the US under demeaning conditionalities indeed makes a poor case for this nuclear deal.

(*The Asian Age*, August 14, 2006)

39. How to Blunt US Strategy

BHARAT KARNAD

Certain fundamental aspects of US President George W. Bush's India policy are becoming clearer. Coming to terms with a nuclear-armed India on a fast-paced economic growth curve, Washington settled on a two-pronged approach. The first prong would co-opt the powerful non-proliferation lobby in Washington, once the small print and the Congressionally-mandated conditions in the reformed US laws began to be appreciated as a clever means of bringing India's nuclear military ambitions to heel and its foreign policy in line with US thinking.

The second prong of this strategy, with immediate benefits to American financial institutions in mind, aimed expeditiously to open up the Indian economy, especially the potentially most profitable banking and insurance sectors, and to permit the entry of American "hedge funds"—"hot money" with a proven record of decamping at the first sign of economic downturn or even minor political hiccups unrelated to the economy, precipitating severe crises of the kind experienced some years back by the "little dragons" in Asia.

The two prongs have made unequal progress, the startling success the Bush administration registered with the nuclear deal being as unexpected as its singular failure in getting the Indian government to bend to its will in the economic field. Indeed, it may be instructive to see how and why differently-oriented departments of the Indian government produced markedly different result. The finance ministry and the Reserve Bank of India in the case of economic policy, deflected American pressure and forced the United States to accommodate Indian national interests. Department of Atomic Energy (DAE), in the case of nuclear policy was, however, browbeaten by the Manmohan Singh group working in tandem with the US interlocutors, and acquiesced in the straitjacketing of the Indian nuclear weapons programme.

First consider the success. The Finance ministry was no part of the Bush-Manmohan Singh blueprint for accelerating economic linkages at any cost. The US-India CEOs Forum operating under the aegis of the Planning Commission and directly advised by the deputy chairman, Montek Singh Ahluwalia, was tasked along with the Americas desk at the ministry of external affairs, to further this aim. Predictably, the CEOs Forum hit the ground running post-July 18, 2005, with the Montek—joint secretary (Americas) duo, heedless of the dangers, trying to clear the bureaucratic path for an American plan and timeframe of six to nine months for "opening up" of the country's economy.

This effort, with considerable political head steam propelling it, ran smack into a double wall—the finance ministry and RBI. The finance ministry's unwillingness to consider any radical measures was on the reasonable grounds that it was neither involved in negotiating the original July 18 Joint Statement nor formally participated in the activities of the CEOs Forum-Planning Commission-MEA combine, and therefore needed to evolve new mechanisms. The RBI, on its pail, claimed correctly that a FEMA (Foreign Exchange Management Act) plan for fully opening up the Indian economy but only by 2009, was already under implementation—a dateline its governor, Dr Y.K. Reddy, indicated he would stick by. The period of grace was needed. RBI believed, to prepare the Indian banking and insurance companies to gear up for the coming "open market" and competition. Prime Minister Manmohan Singh could have overruled Reddy, but chose not to do so for the good reason that it would have roused the Communist Party of India (Marxist)-led Left bloc into terminating the Congress Party coalition's rule at the Centre. Now compare this with the spectacular results garnered by the US in the "civilian nuclear cooperation" deal, "spectacular" because of how zealously the Indian government had until the advent of the Manmohan Singh regime protected the country's dual-purpose and versatile nuclear energy programme, which is as capable of producing armaments, heavy water power reactors and plutonium breeders as irradiated shrimp with extended shelf-life. The specialist finance ministry and RBI took their role as guardians of the Indian banking and insurance units seriously and prevented any compromise that could have won them accolades in Washington. DAE chairman, Dr Anil Kakodkar, in contrast, had grave doubts about the deal outlined in the July 18 statement, but caved into the demands of the Manmohan Singh group and cleared the draft document when it was first presented to him in Washington. And this, even though DAE and Kakodkar, like RBI and Reddy with their FEMA scheme, had the official nuclear doctrine advocating a strategic triad, which necessitates a nuclear build-up, and the three-stage Bhabha plan to justify the thwarting of any untoward agreement with the potential for jeopardising DAE's freedom and hard-won competence in the military and civilian nuclear fields.

There were four critical differences. The CEOs Forum with the big Indian guns booming for them nevertheless failed to make headway because the finance ministry and RBI stood firm against the onrushing American tide channelled by the Prime Minister's Office, the Planning Commission and MEA. This stonewalling illustrates the permanent secretariat's sometime virtue of resorting to a bureaucratic run-around to derail a policy with obviously deleterious consequences for the country. The last time this happened in the nuclear policy field was when M.K. Vellodi, secretary in MEA in the late

Seventies, ensured that a consent casually given by the then external affairs minister in the ruling Janata Party government, Atal Behari Vajpayee, to a US-UK initiative that would have hamstrung the country's nuclear weapons programme, was not actualised into policy commitment. Kakodkar, in contrast, fell down at the first hurdle. Had he, for instance, seeing the contents of the final July 18 document in Washington and the shape of things to come, offered to resign there and then, Prime Minister Manmohan Singh would have had to back down. It may have resulted in a failed US visit by the PM but would have preserved India's nuclear sovereigntv and protected its long-term strategic interests. Kakodkar did not display the strength of character or of his convictions which, reportedly, veer towards extreme apprehension about this nuclear deal with the United States. Not having the gumption to frontally oppose the deal, he has tried ever since to get stalwart Indian scientists to influence senior ministers in Manmohan Singh's Cabinet against it. Thus, he gathered a number of his predecessors in office for the celebrations last month to commemorate the 40 MW Fast Breeder Test Reactor in Kalpakkam, in the hope that they would turn the chief guest, defence minister Pranab Mukherjee, against the deal. The planned interaction did not, however, take place.

Secondly, MEA, the lead agency in negotiating international accords, was the main pusher of the deal on the Indian side along with the PMO and Montek Singh Ahluwalia, with the joint secretary (Americas) and the foreign secretary directed by the Prime Minister to cobble together an arrangement, any arrangement, just so long as Manmohan Singh was seen as delivering on promises made to Bush. Thirdly, the finance ministry confidently confronted the Prime Minister and the deputy chairman, Planning Commission, with facts and figures about how allowing an immediate entry of powerful foreign players into the financial sector would grievously hurt the nation's financial security, which case could not be refuted by Dr Manmohan Singh or Ahluwalia. These two would have found impossible to counter Pakodkar's arguments, had he urged a rethink of the deal for technical reasons detailed in papers he could have tasked DAE to produce.

The fourth difference was that economic dangers are easily understood by the political class because a wrong move can lose them votes. Nuclear policy and the secretive nuclear weapons programme, on the other hand, are esoteric issues in which, apart from DAE, no government department has developed expertise or stake. While the undermining of nuclear security can become an emotive issue in the country, the public and the political parties are confused by the technical and legal aspects of the nuclear deal which fact has been exploited by Dr Manmohan Singh tirelessly to repeat his stock declaration that he would not compromise national security nor tolerate any shifting of goalposts by the US. The PM and his team seriously believe, mounting evidence to the contrary notwithstanding, that the principles mentioned in the July 18 document have, by and large, been adhered to and that the onerous conditions imposed by the US Senate and House of Representatives will be excised, when it comes to reconciling the two versions of the draft amended law, by the same legislators who inserted them in the first place. This is to credit George W. Bush with more political clout than a lame duck President can reasonably lay claim to. But, by some off-chance, should Bush prevail over the US Congress, India will get it in the neck. The possibility of being held accountable for this is making many Cabinet members nervous. The trouble is the Manmohan Singh-Ahluwalia team remains rather blase about the steep costs the country will have to pay for its tunnel-vision and single-minded pursuit of a fatally flawed nuclear deal.

(*The Asian Age*, August 16, 2006)

40. Parliament must Assert its Role

A. GOPALAKRISHNAN

The Indian Parliament is likely to see heated debates on the Indo-US nuclear deal and disruptions of the functioning of both Houses in connection with this issue.

In the US Congress, the US-India Nuclear Co-operation Promotion Act of 2006 (HR 5682 RH) was passed by the House of Representatives on July 26, 2006 with substantial bipartisan support.

In doing this, the House has taken full cognizance of the cautions and protests they received from the US non-proliferation lobby, and have appropriately modified the earlier version of this bill (HR 4974) to assuage their apprehensions. Thus, the overwhelming support this bill received recently in the full House is only an indication that the US requirements have been fully met, while India should concurrently understand it as a strong blow dealt to our national interests.

The US House's approval has been misconstrued by much of the Indian media as a great success gained by our negotiators who have been engaging the US Administration for almost a year now.

Unfortunately, this has conveyed to the Indian public the false and comfortable feeling that the legislation as it stands today is benign to India, and all the negative clauses which the national critics of the deal have worried about have been eliminated. The truth is far from it!

It is only few of the additional amendments brought forth in the final few days which have been defeated—All the original restrictions and demands placed on India through HR 5682 still remain intact. Thus, the linkage to Iran in defining Indian good behaviour, the denial of the multi-path nuclear fuel supply guarantee which the prime minister had promised to Parliament, the total disregard for reciprocity of actions, the mandatory need for India to co-operate and collaborate with the US on the FMCT [Fissile Material Cut-off Treaty] on their terms, fully participating in the Proliferation Security Initiative, the Australia Group, and the Wassenaar Arrangement, etc. are still very much part of the passed legislation.

Much more stringent restrictions and demands will be forthcoming when the Senate bill is presented later and passed by the full Senate. So, there is a need to be on guard against the misinformation campaign which is going on, especially in these difficult days when the government is facing attacks in Parliament on all fronts.

Our immediate focus, however, needs to be on how best to protect India's national interests in the near and long-term. Should we entrust this task, in the current context of the Indo-US nuclear deal, solely to the UPA government as we have done so far, or should the primacy of Parliament be enforced to ensure that this government stays within certain mutually agreed boundaries of action?

Ironically, the best answer to this question can be gleaned from the views of the US Congress, which also found itself in a similar dilemma over the same deal

The bill HR 5682 RH was submitted to the House of Representatives along with a detailed report which explains the intention behind each of its clauses. Let me reproduce a few verbatim quotations from this report, which clearly make the case why the US Congress was compelled to proactively participate in shaping the current deal.

The report states, 'Given the unique and controversial nature of the proposed civil nuclear co-operation agreement and the fact that Congress was not consulted regarding the negotiations between the Administration and the Indian government relating to the original announcement of their intention to negotiate such an agreement, Congressional scrutiny and approval was deemed essential to protect US interests'.

The manner in which the Indian Parliament was treated by the UPA government is also much the same. The PM sent his advance points-men to the US to lay the foundation for this deal, to discuss the strategic path for converting it into a reality, and perhaps to reach certain unwritten understandings with the US administration, including the potential commercial benefits that the US could accrue through this deal in the areas of selling nuclear power plants to India in the future, arms exports, sales of clean-coal technologies and associated equipment, etc.

The government used only a few hand-picked senior officials from then on in handling this deal, persons in whom the PM has trust and who are also well-known sympathisers of the US points of view. Parliament, members of the Cabinet, and almost all the rest of the bureaucracy and the general public had no inkling of what is being negotiated, ostensibly for the purpose of "enhancing energy security" and for the larger good of the country by leading it into the US camp.

Therefore, just as the US Congress did in their interest, it is time that the Indian Parliament also wakes up to the need for this deal to be subjected to parliamentary scrutiny and approval in the Indian national interest.

The US House report further states: 'Direct Congressional involvement, especially the requirement for its approval, is also necessary to ensure that the pledges and assurances made by the Administration and the Indian government are actually met and not rendered irrelevant through lack of action or discontinuation of interest. Without enforcement provisions, such statements are obviously little more than promises that may be modified at will, or even abandoned altogether, should circumstances change'.

The PM has also made specific promises regarding the details of the nuclear deal to Indian Parliament on a few different occasions over the last year. However, the way matters have turned out, it appears that the negotiators appointed by the PM have totally failed to impress upon the US Administration these promises that he had made.

On the whole, the government has not stood up firmly against the American onslaught on the PM's promises, fearing that the deal may not go through. Inherent in this behaviour is the government's strong conviction that India cannot survive and grow if this nuclear deal with the US collapses, which sadly is a colossal fallacy.

In any case, the way events are progressing, it shows a scant regard on the part of this government for the shared responsibility which Parliament also has in our democratic polity.

I shall close with a third quotation from the US House report which brings out the importance of legislative involvement in such affairs of State. It reads: 'Constitution nevertheless vests Congress with considerable powers and responsibilities in the areas of foreign policy and national security, which its members are obligated to carry out. Fidelity to that trust means that Congress cannot delegate those responsibilities to the executive branch or allow itself to be made irrelevant to government policy in any area.'

Our Parliament must also be aware that they hold enormous ultimate powers and solemn responsibilities under the Indian Constitution. They must feel that, at this juncture, they have an unavoidable collective responsibility to steer this government away from the path it is deliberately following, contrary to the promises made in the immediate past. Whether this is achieved through a 'Sense of Parliament' resolution or a prime ministerial statement to Parliament is a matter to be collectively decided.

All of us do understand that the objective is not to pull down the UPA government, but to make this government understand beyond any shadow of doubt that they have to openly articulate the Indian position to the US administration and to our own nation. While doing this, the government must keep in mind the consensus opinion of Parliament at all times. We are ready to accept once again a statement from the PM, the fifth of such disappointing exercises on this deal, if that is what the government wants to save its face in the light of the two US Congressional bills, instead of a joint Parliamentary resolution.

However, this time we hope the PM will not only make renewed promises and clarify Indian policy to Parliament, but also thereby send a pointed message to the US Administration and their Congress regarding specific objections we already see in the two US bills which have come out.

There is no wisdom in waiting for the US "to complete their legislative process", because it is high time the US Administration is openly warned that Parliament and the people of India strongly oppose the specific inserts in these bills which go beyond the July 18, 2005 agreement between the two governments.

(Rediff.com, August 16, 2006)

41. The Ball is now Squarely in America's Court

A.N. PRASAD

The direction in which the Indo-US nuclear cooperation deal is being steered by the US appears to focus-more on non-proliferation aspects rather than civil nuclear cooperation. Thus deviating from the July 18, 2005 joint statement, as evident from the contents of the Bill HR 5682 passed by the US House of Representatives in June 2006.

The Bill which comes up for consideration before the Senate next month has created ripples in the minds of various political parties, strategic analysts, media and the top nuclear scientific community in India.

This culminated in a debate in the Upper House of the Indian Parliament on August 17. The prime minister's statement with his detailed response to various points of concern keeping the July 18 Statement and the March 2, 2006 Separation Plan as guiding documents has to a large extent helped clarify the Indian stand.

The ball is now squarely in the US court. It will be interesting to watch whether this will be followed in letter and spirit by both sides and the US reaction. Among the various aspects, the following are particularly worth mentioning.

Inspite of all that has been said by the US president and the Indian Prime Minister, there is still some doubt regarding compliance with the most basic point in the joint statement, namely—India assumes the same responsibilities and practices and acquires the same benefits and advantages as other leading countries with advanced nuclear technology, such as the US.

The most appropriate place where this could be seen to be followed is when the India-specific safeguards agreements are negotiated. This could well become a bone of contention given the complexities involved, particularly in respect of India being implicitly eligible to be treated like a weapons state as per the joint statement without being formally recognised as a weapons state as per NPT parlance.

One has to see how this will evolve. The weapons states hardly practice any rigorous IAEA safeguards regime and there doesn't seem to be any requirement of safeguards in perpetuity. Also, there is no way India could accept an independent safeguards regime from the US as a backup to IAEA [International Atomic Energy Agency] safeguards as is being mooted.

Another point of important concern is in spite of the clear mention of full civil nuclear cooperation there are indications from the US that sensitive technologies such as reprocessing, uranium enrichment and heavy water will be excluded. In the ultimate analysis, nothing short of real, full cooperation is to be accepted by India.

One complex aspect to contend with is that the technologies and facilities involved are invariably common to both civil and military applications as a result of which non-proliferation aspects and safeguards arrangements could get mucked-up. Satisfactory resolution of this requires careful handling.

There are lots of opinions being expressed regarding the binding and non-binding provisions in the Congress Bills. This is highly confusing and though it is more an internal issue of the US, it is interesting to watch how best the President could circumvent objectionable clauses which are not in conformity with the joint statement and satisfy India.

There are other aspects—such as one-time permanent waiver as against annual certification, FMCT [Fissile Material Cut-Off Treaty] to be treated as a multilateral issue, and no conditions to be imposed in the final agreement against India going for nuclear tests in the context of supreme national security interest—that are issues to be tackled.

The bottom line is that it should be understood that India, having developed expertise and capability covering the entire fuel cycle against heavy odds, is really not looking for large-scale technology inputs but would like to play a global role in nuclear commerce, preserving the global norms on non-proliferation as a responsible country.

In fact, India has got a lot to offer to countries like the US by way of expertise and services.

(*Rediff.com*, August 21, 2006)

42. The Civilian Aspects of the Indo-US Nuclear Deal

P.K. IYENGAR

The Indo-US deal has gone through a metamorphosis in the hands of the Committees in the American Senate. The July 18, 2005 agreement recognises that India, though not a signatory to the Non-Proliferation Treaty, has over the years behaved with great responsibility when it comes to non-proliferation. Our record is perhaps better than some of the weapons countries that have signed the NPT. In light of this fact, the statement seeks to give India a status roughly equal to that of the recognised nuclear weapon states, and to bring it into the mainstream of the nuclear community. However, the tone of the Senate discussions, and of the amendments proposed by them, suggests that India still needs to be 'policed' by the US, to the extent that the US President has to give a yearly 'character certificate' to keep the nuclear deal alive. These aspects have been elaborated in these columns. This is clearly contrary to the spirit and words of the July 18 agreement, and absolutely unacceptable to any sovereign nation—a fact that even the Indian government now concedes.

I wish to emphasise here the deleterious impact this 'modified' nuclear deal will have on our nuclear power programme. To understand why the nuclear deal is not something that is essential for Indian nuclear power programme, we must understand the broad contours of the programme.

India has vast resources of thorium, not uranium, and we therefore have a well-thought-out, three-stage nuclear programme, that is based on exploiting this resource. It must be born in mind that this is based on the present understanding of physical laws in nuclear physics. It could change if new discoveries are made. In the first stage, we have chosen to build heavy-water reactors that use natural uranium. It was the Canadian scientists who proved the virtues of heavy-water nuclear reactors for energy·production and the efficient conversion of the unburnt ^{238}U to plutonium. It is these characteristics that have attracted us. South Korea, China and other countries have since, gone for heavy-water reactors, for electricity production. Some countries like US, France, Germany and Russia however have gone for light water reactors which use low enriched uranium as fuel and hence more compact. They would like to sell these types to us. This requires the development of enrichment technology, primarily through centrifuges, which is an unnecessary additional step. If a country develops this technology to be able to produce its own fuel, it has the option to extend this technology to produce weapon usable 90% enriched uranium. Conversely, if the country decides not to develop enrichment technology, then it remains forever dependent on the nuclear powers for fuel for its light-water reactors.

The second stage of our nuclear programme envisages building fast-breeder reactors that generate more fuel than they burn. They use plutonium reprocessed from the heavy-water reactors, and thorium available on the beaches of Kerala, together as fuel. This is a new technology, and we have spent decades mastering it. We have now started building the first 500 MWe Prototype Fast-Breeder Reactor (PFBR) at Kalpakkam, which is expected to be ready in 2010. Since we have the largest resources of thorium, we can ensure energy security for the foreseeable future. The third stage will use uranium 233 converted from thorium and will give us the freedom to use any type of reactors, thermal or fast thus freeing us from any type of restrictions from the resources point of view.

With this background, it can be easily understood that, in terms of relevant nuclear technology, we have little to gain from the nuclear deal. We actually lead the world in fast-breeder technology, and are well on the way to bringing it to commercial fruition. We are not so bothered about technology transfer in fast-breeders, or other areas such as heavy-water production, reprocessing, and enrichment. All we need is to be left alone, so that our scientists and engineers can make further technical advances in these areas. It is especially important to realise that thorium utilization depends on the reprocessing technology applicable to that fuel cycle, which is being researched upon only in India. The successes that we have achieved at Kalpakkam need to be protected and further strengthened, so that in a decade India will have developed all the necessary technology to usher in copious nuclear electricity through fast-breeders, making use of thorium as the basic fuel. This is of course the third stage of our nuclear programme, as envisaged by Homi Bhabha. We should not be side-tracked by non-scientific propaganda that this route is not economically attractive for nobody has so far worked on it consistently.

Until such time as the fast-breeder reactors take over the nuclear landscape, we will depend on the heavy-water reactors. These require natural uranium, which we have not located in large amounts in the country. However, the Department of Atomic Energy estimates that we have sufficient deposits to fuel 10,000 MWe of nuclear power for 30 years. The availability of uranium for our heavy-water reactors can be ensured by our strengthening our exploration and mining operations of uranium deposits within the country. The cost of production may initially be higher than the international cost, but the fact that natural uranium can go into our heavy-water reactors, and its share of the tariff is only a small percentage should be noted. For doing this we have all the technology and experience. These reactors are also more efficient than light-water reactors in producing plutonium, which is essential for expanding the fast-breeder reactor systems. We are also exploring the direct use of thorium in heavy-water reactors—another area of research in which we are ahead in the world.

No scientist opposes a strategic relationship with the US on matters like energy security, development, and stability in the South Asian region. What has to be ensured, however, is that our domestic nuclear power programme, which is based on ground realities at home, and our independence for research and development in nuclear technology, for the benefit of future generations, are not bartered away for a few imported reactors with fuel. Technology is a product of science, and very often new, more efficient technologies are generated by lateral thinking by the scientists and engineers. We see this all around, whether in agriculture, computers, new materials, or engineering practises. But lateral thinking and innovation need a large degree of openness and independence, and are fatally hampered if one is under constant observation and supervision. The recommended provisions of the nuclear deal imply precisely that, and it is clear that this will have a deleterious effect on innovation in nuclear science and technology—and perhaps even in basic sciences, given that institutes of basic research, that are under the DAE, will also come under IAEA safeguards.

If we believe that the development of human resources leading to a knowledge-based society can make a quantum jump in prosperity, we should trust the scientists and take their advise seriously without putting unnecessary breaks on research and development. Their proven competence is recognised internationally. The Congress party, especially the Prime Ministers, from Pt. Jawaharlal Nehru on, have always believed and trusted the ability of scientists. There is no reason why there should be a re-thinking on the issue of future prospects of nuclear energy in this country. Import of technology is not the answer, for we have developed sufficiently in this area and proven that we can, very competitively, enhance our capacity.

(August 22, 2006)

43. Last Chance for the US to Decide

A. GOPALAKRISHNAN

The Prime Minister, in his reply to the Rajya Sabha debate on August 17, has once again reaffirmed the government's position on the Indo-US nuclear deal, more emphatically and lucidly than in the past. It would appear that he has attempted to reasonably address all major issues raised by the opposition parties and the scientific and strategic communities, for the time being. But, in spite of similar statements in the past to the Parliament, the direction in which the US Congress is continuing to frame the associated law is seriously in departure with the stated policies. One therefore hopes that the clear policy stand of the government enunciated in Parliament, in its totality, will indeed be formally conveyed by the PM directly to President Bush immediately, so that the Americans have no excuse later of not having been officially forewarned.

The PM stated that he has "... conveyed to President Bush that the proposed US legislation must conform strictly to the parameters of the July 18, 2005 Statement and the March 2, 2006 Separation Plan. ... I have received an assurance from the President that the parameters of the scope of co-operation would be those contained in (these two documents)". This we will have to take as a basic contention acceptable to all in the country. Incidentally, it appears a little too late in the day to argue that the Separation Plan should be re-examined and changed. Any lacunae or doubts we may have in this Plan can be corrected through suitable clauses in the 123 agreement and the IAEA safeguards and additional protocol agreements we are yet to finalize.

On the possibility of US law restricting the transfer of certain technologies to India, notably those related to reprocessing and enrichment, the PM said, "We seek the removal of restrictions on all aspects of co-operation and technology transfers pertaining to civil nuclear energy—i.e. all aspects of a complete nuclear fuel cycle." The final version of the US law may at best be silent on this issue, while the US government will still retain their policy of not providing the full spectrum of technologies. We need to also realize that in all areas where India wishes to nurture generally the same technologies, plants and activities both in the civilian and military sectors, it will be almost impossible for a donor country or the IAEA to ensure that India may not be using the foreign technology gains obtained for the civilian safeguarded side in their similar applications in the military facilities. Besides, our major confrontation in this regard may not be with the US, but with the entire Nuclear Suppliers' Group (NSG). The 45-nation NSG has already made it clear that they are not contemplating any transfer of reprocessing or enrichment technologies, and in fact are strengthening their controls to ban such transfers. So, India has an uphill task here to get these technologies.

As for reciprocity of actions, the PM has clarified that, "The nuclear facilities listed in the Separation Plan will be offered for safeguards only after all nuclear restrictions have been lifted on India. This would include suitable amendments to the US legislation to allow for such co-operation, the passing of a bilateral agreement with India and the adaption of NSG guidelines". Whether the changes in US laws will precede the bilateral agreement or not is unclear. But, it will be sufficient cover if we state in the bilateral agreement that it will stand null and void if the US laws are not amended to India's satisfaction or if the NSG and India are unable to conclude a satisfactory waiver of NSG rules.

Another important assertion that the PM made is that, "the proposed US legislation on nuclear co-operation will not be allowed to become an instrument to compromise India's sovereignty". In response to the reference to Iran and the Proliferation Security Initiative (PSI) in the proposed US law, he said, "... We reject the linkage of any extraneous issue to the nuclear understanding. India's foreign policy will be decided on the basis of Indian national interest only. ... The PSI is an extraneous issue." The PM did not refer to the US prescription that India is expected to join the Australia Group and the Wassenaar Arrangement, though these two also do not belong in the nuclear domain, and are therefore extraneous issues. But, it is disturbing to note the statement given by Nicholas Burns in Washington on March 16, 2006 that, "India has also agreed to align itself with the other international regimes concerning proliferation. ... The Australia Group and the Wassenaar Arrangement". The government needs to clear up this contradiction. Our negotiators will have to insist that references to Iran, PSI, the Australia Group and the Wassenaar Arrangement should be totally removed from the forthcoming legislation, without taking cover under any excuse that they appear only in the "non-binding" sections.

On the matter of nuclear weapon testing, the PM asserted that, nuclear weapons are an integral part of our national security and will remain so, pending the global elimination of all nuclear weapons and universal non-discriminatory nuclear disarmament. ... The US has been intimated that reference to nuclear detonation in the India-US bilateral agreement as a condition for future co-operation is not acceptable to us. We are not prepared to go beyond a unilateral voluntary moratorium on nuclear testing. The US may agree to omit any mention of testing in the 123 agreement, but the fact remains that as long as the India-specific legislation does not distinctly provide a waiver of Section 129(1)(A) of the US Atomic Energy Act, it will be mandatory on their part to suspend all nuclear co-operation under this agreement, if we ever test a nuclear explosive device in the future. It is also a provision in the US Nuclear Non-Proliferation Act, 1978, and it is therefore highly unlikely that the US Congress will allow such a waiver in the forthcoming legislation.

However, even if India conducts a weapon test in future, Section 129 of the Atomic Energy Act gives the President the option to waive the termination of exports under the nuclear co-operation if he determines that cessation of such exports to India would be seriously prejudicial to the achievement of US non-proliferation objectives or otherwise jeopardize the common defence and security—but the catch is that the US Congress also has to agree with the President's determination in this matter. There is only a very slim chance of a future US President and Congress giving such a waiver, especially since India will continue to insist on pursuing an independent foreign policy in our own national interest.

It should be clear, however, that whether the current nuclear deal becomes a reality or not, the actions which will be taken by the US (and a host of other countries) against India, if we conduct a test, will be just the same. In the case of the US, besides the cancellation of all assistance under this deal, it will include financial sanctions under the Ex-Im Bank Act (Section 2-b-4), the broad sanctions under the Glenn Amendment (Section 102-b) of the Arms Export Control Act, as well as those applicable under the Brownback-II amendment. The difference, with or without this nuclear deal in force, will be very much in the resulting adverse consequences to the Indian economy and to the overall national security. In this regard, if India is well on the road to effectively making use of the nuclear and non-nuclear benefits we can derive from this co-operation deal, the damages consequent to a future nuclear explosive test could be several-fold more intensive as compared to what we may have suffered without this deal in place. So, the question we need to face is whether we can avoid such severe damages in the first place by not undertaking a test or, if we must test at a later date, whether we can withstand these and other severe repercussions and bounce back out of them within reasonable time.

It is clear that there are serious limitations on how far the Indian government has succeeded in impressing on the US administration and, through them, the US Congress about the Indian sensitivities on various issues. The increasing departures between what the government had been repeatedly promising us in Parliament earlier and the contents of the US laws under making show that the US Congress would like to safeguard the US interests in their own unique perception. That being the case, as a proud and sovereign nation, India must also draw a line beyond which we must not proceed with this deal any further. That time will come when the Congress passes the reconciled final legislation on the waiver of US laws. Until then, we must rally behind the PM, but not a day thereafter, if the final product contains clauses we seriously object to.

(The Asian Age, August 22, 2006)

44. PM is Risking National Interest

BHARAT KARNAD

Compelled by political pressure from all sides, Prime Minister Manmohan Singh in Parliament finally defined the limit of concessions beyond which he thinks he cannot go in placating the United States in the proposed nuclear deal without destabilising his government. But this belated spine-straightening act may spur the non-proliferationists in Washington, who want to leave India no wriggle room, into insisting that the Senate version of the amended US Atomic Energy Act containing many of the measures the PM has, in effect, dubbed "deal killers," become law. Short of the US Congress removing the offensive provisions or Manmohan Singh going back on his word, a breakdown of the deal is imminent.

Indeed, it is the politics of US Congress' non-proliferation law-making that all along held out the hope that India would escape strategic strangulation by default, particularly because the Manmohan Singh regime has not shown that it can discern what is in the country's best interests, leaving it vulnerable to the official American line that gives the impression of mutual gain when actually it mostly serves US interests. I said this as a panellist in a discussion held at the India International Centre on August 3, 2005—a prognosis proved right a year later. The Prime Minister keeps justifying what he has done by invoking "enlightened national interest." But according to the evidence thus far, this seems only a rhetorical veil behind which he has felt free to make indefensible concessions.

Understandably, the Prime Minister did not touch upon his main rationale for the nuclear deal. There being simply no strategic sense or logic, as this analyst had noted soon after the July 18 Statement (*A Civilian Nuclear Dependency, The Op-Ed Page,* August 13, 2005) and in many op-ed pieces in this paper since, in curbing the natural augmentation of the Indian nuclear forces or in sacrificing the independence of the country's nuclear weapons programme in return for imported reactors secured at great public expense to produce less than six per cent of the projected total energy production in India in the year 2035. Especially when the indigenous upscaled INDU reactors and the 700 MW advanced pressurised heavy water reactor now in its final design stage, without any downside, will do just as well.

The purchase of foreign reactors fuelled by low-enriched uranium, the supply of which can be cut-off at any time without penalty to the seller country and with no way for India legally to recover the fifty-odd billion dollars shelled out for them is, moreover, a boondoggle waiting to happen. Unless, of course, Manmohan Singh, in his finite wisdom, thinks this vast sum chicken-feed and the nightmarish economic consequences of junking these reactors manageable. Or, worse, he does not foresee the need for India ever to test again. Or, still worse, he concedes the possibility of a military need for testing to arise but does not care that a future Indian government, because of this deal, will be saddled with a gigantic strategico-political-*cum*-economic mess. Any which way one views the deal, the Manmohan Singh regime appears singularly short-sighted for pushing it.

Which brings us to the Prime Minister's "risk taking" prowess he boasted about in Parliament when referring to the economic reforms, he claimed, he initialed. Truth be told, the credit for economic reforms is almost entirely the late Prime Minister P.V. Narasimha Rao's. Here's what happened on the day in 1992 when finance minister Manmohan Singh outlined for Rao the first Congress Party budget after its return to power. According to a senior official present on that occasion, Narasimha Rao, given the parlous economic situation India was in, rejected it outright as a "business as usual-budget" and ordered Dr Manmohan Singh to work up an all new budgetary scheme—which made his reputation—geared to economic liberalisation and reform. But as governor of the Reserve Bank of India he lapsed into his old bureaucratic ways. One of his subordinates recalls how Singh, during his RBI tenure, "abdicated his responsibility" for taking tough decisions, his refrain being "I want no controversies"! It is a refrain reportedly now heard in the PMO. In short, whatever else he is, "risk-taker" Manmohan Singh is not. Furthermore, while he may know a lot about economic risk, he knows little about risk in the nuclear scientific and strategic security spheres.

This makes it hard to explain, the PM's terribly risky policy that has offered the United States an opportunity to capitalise on his unsustainable ideas of "civilian nuclear cooperation" to contain India's nuclear military capabilities. Unless, one factors in Manmohan Singh's personal bias against nuclear weapons. It may be recalled that successively as finance member in the Atomic Energy Commission, economic adviser to the PM, and finance minister in the Eighties and Nineties, he consistently opposed any large expenditure on strategic programmes and also nuclear testing in 1995. It is doubtful he understands the political value of a meaningful thermonuclear arsenal, wrapped up as his approach seems to be, in the simplistic "guns *versus* butter" argument that went out with the Sixties, but which opponents within and outside the Indian government, prompted by Washington utilised to pre-empt nuclear weaponisation by this country for over 30 years. The terrible retardant effects of such thinking on India's foreign and military policy reach and its diplomatic clout is there for all to see—a whale-sized country has had its impact reduced to that of a minnow.

It was originally Bharatiya Janata Party's assessment that access to western "dual use" technologies could be bought by show of "nuclear restraint," which flawed premise the Congress Party coalition government adopted. But Manmohan Singh has gone further by interpreting restraint expansively. And there is nobody in his circle to warn him he is doing wrong. Indeed, his government has no experts in nuclear deterrence and strategic policy heuristic even in its extended nuclear decision loop. This is perhaps how the PM wants it. Of the nine members of the Atomic Energy Commission, for instance, only one is a scientist. Dr. C.N.R. Rao, the other is its chairman, Anil Kakodkar, an engineer; the rest are, like the Prime Minister himself, terminal bureaucrats (principal private secretary to the PM, cabinet secretary, etc.). But Manmohan Singh required a nuclear scientist to advance his policy of nuclear compromise, and he found one in Dr R. Chidambaram, the former chairman, AEC, presently adviser on science and technology to the prime minister.

The breakthrough in the nuclear deal with the US—it is not widely known—was, in fact, made by Dr Chidambaram. Accompanying foreign secretary Shyam Saran to Washington in March 2005, Dr Chidambaram, who had opposed nuclear testing in 1995 and after-the 1998 tests supported the test moratorium—because he imprudently believes that nuclear simulation, rather than actual physical testing, is enough—reportedly assured senior American officials not only about New Delhi's readiness to extend its voluntary test ban into a permanent bilateral commitment but, more crucially, to bring the bulk of India's nuclear programme and the country's extensive scientific research facilities that feed it under international safeguards. These assurances suddenly enthused the George W. Bush administration, eventuating in the July 18 Joint Statement three months later and the controversial "separation plan" announced by New Delhi on March 2, 2006.

This separation plan, by including utmost every nuclear research centre of repute in the country in the civilian list earmarked for IAEA safeguards, may well finish off all independent nuclear research and development—"dual use" and other, in India. Take for example the Institute for Plasma Physics, Gandhinagar, engaged, among other things, in a fusion project using high-energy electromagnets. Designated as a civilian facility, this "Toko-mak" unit can "breed", making it of "proliferation concern" to the US; it can produce Uranium 233 as fuel for reactors by exposing thorium to excess neutrons produced by the plasma at high temperatures. Or, consider the case of the Variable Energy Cyclotron in Kolkata, also in the civilian list. It is likewise jeopardised by safeguards because this accelerator can potentially generate neutrons to produce fissile material for military purposes or to power reactors. An Advanced Accelerator-driven Source for neutrons is, in fact, already operating there. Under the safeguards and Additional Protocol relating to non-weapon states, India will be required to provide a work plan and research agenda for each civilian facility for IAEA to ensure no prohibited (read: remotely weapons-related) work is carried out. New Delhi will soon be disabused by Washington and IAEA of its belief that safeguards will be restricted to imported technology and uranium ore and that research not involving foreign items will be spared attention. In fact, the draft amended US Atomic Energy Act seeks an accounting of even indigenously-mined and processed uranium, what to talk of imported nuclear material.

The key is the safeguards system and Additional Protocol. Originally, the nuclear scientists were at the cutting edge of negotiations on nuclear matters. MEA diplomats, with no technical knowledge and minimal understanding of the nuclear arena involved, have side-lined them. Even without this self-inflicted handicap, it is doubtful India could have avoided harsh safeguards and Additional Protocol considering that Pakistan and Iran on the IAEA governing board will not allow India to be treated as a nuclear weapon state. Manmohan Singh may not lose sleep over this development—it being the result of the many compromises he has made so far. Thanks to this deal, there will be nothing left of the national interest, only enlightenment after the fact.

(*The Asian Age*, August 25, 2006)

45. What PM told us on the N-Deal

A. GOPALAKRISHNAN

On August 26, 2006 Prime Minister Manmohan Singh met with seven senior nuclear scientists for a discussion on the Indo-US nuclear cooperation deal. The group of scientists comprised three former chairmen of the Atomic Energy Commission (AEC), one former chairman of the Atomic Energy Regulatory Board (AERB), one former director of Bhabha Atomic Research Centre (BARC), one former CMD of the Nuclear Power Corporation (NPC) and a former Director of the Indira Gandhi Centre for Atomic Research (IGCAR). Along with the PM, the national security adviser, the principal secretary to the PM, the chairman of the AEC, the principal scientific adviser to the PM, the minister of state in the PMO, and a few other senior officials were also present. The meeting involved a very cordial and useful exchange among all present, and it lasted for about 90 minutes. In the end, the scientists expressed their thanks to the PM for inviting them to meet him and for allowing each of them sufficient time for a very candid expression of views.

The PM, at the outset, assured us that he would not, as Prime Minister, take any action which would weaken the nation's strength or harm its indigenous R&D pursuits. He said he understood our concerns from the letter we had jointly addressed to parliamentarians, and he wanted each one of us in turn to explain to him the specific thoughts each might have on various aspects of this deal. He hoped that each of us, in due course, would also help the government in finding an acceptable path to take full advantage of the opportunities available through this deal, and at the same time identify the potential pitfalls that are to be avoided in doing this, and provide suggestions on how to avert these adverse impacts.

It will not be proper on my part to give a verbatim report on the proceedings of a meeting chaired by the PM, to which we had the privilege of being invited by him. Neither do I wish to take on any self-assigned responsibility of representing the views of the other scientists who participated in this meeting. Instead, the attempt here is to give a summary of my own understanding and analysis of where we stand on this nuclear deal, based partly on the exchange of views at the PM's meeting, but also on several other discussions I have had recently with senior officials.

The government, as I understand, is firmly opposed to any direct or indirect attempt by the United States to limit or slow down the fissile material production in the country. Similarly, India is opposed to the imposition of any curbs on the further expansion of our strategic nuclear programme. It is clear that any clauses in the final US legislation which may directly or indirectly contradict these stands will become "deal breakers."

Another crucial issue is that of India retaining the flexibility to conduct further nuclear weapon tests, in case the future strategic environment necessitates such tests in the interest of our national security. The government appears to concede that such a future need cannot be ruled out, and this is the reason for its repeated emphasis on a "voluntary" moratorium on testing. It is also clear to the government that the final US legislation will most likely dictate the stoppage of the Indo-US nuclear deal in case of an Indian nuclear weapon test. The counter-measures which the government has in mind include a carefully chosen path of development, wherein there will be built-in strategies to withstand the adverse impacts of the US and NSG reactions following a test. These shall also include, but not be limited to, the following precautionary steps which must be part of the modified US law and/or the yet to be signed bilateral 123-Agreement, and the US Congress and its administration must understand that non-inclusion of any of these covering provisions in the final legislation will indeed constitute a "deal breaker."

If the deal is cancelled due to any reason, we need to prevent the stoppage of life-time fuel and spare-parts supplies for reactors and equipment which India might have already imported up to that time. For this purpose, a set of multiple alternative schemes for facilitating the procurement of these items have been worked out and these have been included in the mutually agreed separation plan in March 2006. Stock-piling of such items should be one of the flexibilities made available to India though the government is sensitive to the associated inventory-carrying costs and the burden this will add to nuclear electricity prices. Nevertheless, at this stage, we need to ensure that the US Congress concurs with these parallel supply options and that they agree to retain these in the revised US legislation.

As it stands, the US Atomic Energy Act will require that India will have to return all US equipment and materials supplied to all civilian facilities under this deal, including the spent-fuel and any plutonium extracted from that, in case the nuclear cooperation is terminated. India certainly cannot agree with this requirement. Suitable waiver of this clause in the US Atomic Energy Act will therefore have to be sought in the reconciled version of the legislation.

If the cooperation is terminated by the US while we are in the middle of executing a joint project, the US cannot be allowed to abandon the half-finished project and walk away. The revised legislation must ensure that the

US will have the obligation to provide materials and assistance as originally envisaged, not only to complete the project but also to provide lifetime fuel and spare-parts supplies for such facilities.

As for the disposition of the spent-fuel arising from the use of imported natural or enriched uranium in our civilian reactors, the government's position is that India must retain full rights to reprocess that fuel in India, under safeguards, and use the extracted plutonium in civilian breeders or AHWRs. This provision has to be written into the legislation, since there will be no question of India asking for US permission to do such reprocessing, on a case to case basis.

Both the IAEA safeguards agreement and the Additional Protocol (AP) will be negotiated as India-specific documents. The Government appears to have the full assurance of the IAEA Director General that he will help India frame these as close as possible to the corresponding agreements applicable to the nuclear weapon states under the NPT. How far the IAEA board will go along with this is to be seen in due course. Though not confirmed, it would appear that if the supply of fuel and spare-parts to a set of imported reactors is stopped on the cessation of nuclear cooperation under this legislation, despite the alternative options built into the separation plan, India will insist on the right to withdraw forthwith all such facilities from the IAEA safeguards and the Additional Protocol. In other words, no fuel and spare parts, no further safeguards inspections or return of assets bought and paid for prior to that, while under safeguards! It is necessary that the government incorporates this stipulation in both the 123 Agreement and the agreements which we sign with the IAEA. It is also clear that the separation plan will not involve the bifurcation of personnel into some who can work only in military projects and programmes and others who can be employed only in civilian projects and programmes. Also, the safeguards and the AP will be effective only prospectively, with India not being obliged to discuss past issues regarding any facility we decide to place on the civilian side.

The stated position of the PM on full civil nuclear cooperation is clear from his addresses to Parliament. He has said that, "We will not agree to any dilution that would prevent us from securing the benefits of full civil cooperation." In my view, it would be sufficient if the revised legislation does not specifically bar full civilian cooperation for India, as the current bill does. The NSG is seriously refraining its rules on transfer of enrichment and reprocessing technologies to all countries, and notwithstanding what the US and India may agree on this, eventually the NSG decision will override any bilateral understanding.

At the end of our meeting, the PM made it quite clear that he did not view imports as substituting domestic efforts in any way. He gave the assurance that the domestic R&D programmes and their utilisation, especially in the three-stage nuclear power programme and the scaling-up of clean-coal technologies for power generation, will be pushed forward with no impediment. He closed his remarks by saying that it was his intention that dialogues of this nature (the one he had with the scientists) would become part of the regular process until India eventually reached a decision on the Indo-US nuclear deal. The responsibility to follow-up on this intention of the PM was entrusted to the national security adviser and the secretary, DAE.

(*The Asian Age*, September 22, 2006)

46. What India Needs to do

A. GOPALAKRISHNAN

The United States Senate recessed at the end of September without voting on the India-US nuclear cooperation bill. In January 2007, a fresh US Congress will take office and, if the India legislation is not finalised by December 2006, all procedural formalities completed so far by the US Congress since July 2005 will become invalid and the entire process will have to be initiated afresh.

However, both governments hope that the Senate could still take up this bill around November 13, when its brief 'lame duck' session begins. When passed by the Senate, the amended bill will still have to go to a conference meeting of a group of Senate and House committee members for reconciliation into a unified version, and subsequently approved by a joint session of both Houses of Congress.

All current indications are that the final version of the changes in US law will, most likely, contain a few clauses which violate the major Indian requirements which Prime Minister Dr Manmohan Singh had clearly spelt out in his August 2006 statements to Parliament. In spite of that, if the deal is to be carried forward, certainly there will be concerted opposition from the major political parties outside government and a large section of the scientific community in the country.

On August 26, the Prime Minister and his key advisers met with seven senior retired nuclear scientists, including this author, for a discussion on the India-US nuclear cooperation deal. The Prime Minister, at the outset, assured us that he will not take any action which would weaken the nation's strength or harm its indigenous research and development pursuits. He hoped that each of us, in due course, would also help the government in finding an acceptable path to take full advantage of the opportunities available through this deal, and at the same time identify the potential pitfalls that are to be avoided in doing this, and provide suggestions on how to avert these adverse impacts.

In view of the anticipated actions by the US Congress in the next three months, this article attempts to summarise the Indian position on the subject as on today, based on my analysis as well as the information and views I have gathered from senior officials and others in the know of things. Such a summary should serve us well in the near future, when we will be faced with the final legislation from the US Congress, and the nation has to clearly assess what we stand to gain and lose if that revised law is put into effect.

To start with, as I understand, the government is firmly opposed to any direct or indirect attempt by the United States to limit or slow down the nuclear fissile material production in our country. Similarly, India is opposed to the imposition of 'any curbs on the further expansion of our strategic nuclear programme. There is no doubt that any clause in the final US legislation which may directly or indirectly contradict these stands will become 'deal breakers'.

Another crucial issue is that of India retaining the flexibility to conduct further nuclear weapon tests, in case the future strategic environment necessitates such tests. The government appears to concede that such a need cannot be ruled out, and this is the reason for its repeated emphasis on a 'voluntary' moratorium on testing. It is also clear to the government that the final US legislation will most likely dictate the stoppage of the India-US nuclear deal in case of an Indian nuclear weapon test.

The counter-measures which the government has in mind for this include a carefully chosen path of development, wherein there will be built-in strategies to withstand the adverse impacts of the US and Nuclear Suppliers Group sanctions which would certainly follow such a test. These shall also include, but not be limited to, the following precautionary steps which should form part of the modified US law and/or the yet to be signed bilateral 123-Agreement.

The US Congress and administration must also understand that non-inclusion of any of these protective provisions in the final legislation will indeed constitute a 'deal breaker' as far as India is concerned.

If the deal is cancelled due to any reason, we need to prevent the stoppage of fuel and spare-part supplies for reactors and equipment which India might have already imported up to that time. For this purpose, a set of multiple alternative schemes for facilitating the procurement of these items have been worked out and these have been included in the mutually agreed separation plan in March 2006. Stockpiling of such items should be one of the flexibilities made available to India, though the government is sensitive to the associated inventory-carrying costs and the burden this will add to nuclear electricity prices. Nevertheless, at this stage, we need to ensure that the US Congress concurs with these parallel supply options and that they agree to retain these in the revised US legislation.

As it stands, the US Atomic Energy Act will require that India return all US equipment and materials supplied to civilian facilities under this deal, including the spent-fuel and any plutonium extracted from that, in case the nuclear cooperation is terminated. India certainly cannot agree with this requirement. Suitable waiver of this clause will therefore have to be sought in the reconciled version of the legislation.

If the cooperation is terminated by the US in the middle of a joint reactor project, the US cannot be allowed to abandon the half-finished project and walk away. The revised legislation must include the US obligation to provide materials and assistance as originally envisaged, and the lifetime fuel and spare-part supplies, for such a facility.

As for the disposition of the spent-fuel arising from the use of imported, natural or enriched uranium in our civilian reactors, the government's position is that India must retain full rights to reprocess that fuel in India, under safeguards, and use the extracted plutonium in our civilian reactors. This provision has to be written into the legislation, since there will be no question of India asking for US permission to do such reprocessing, on a case to case basis.

Both the International Atomic Energy Agency agreement and the Additional Protocol will be negotiated as India-specific documents. The government appears to have the full assurance of the IAEA director general that he will help India frame these as close as possible to the corresponding agreements applicable to the nuclear weapon states under the nuclear Non-Proliferation Treaty.

How far the IAEA board will go along with this is to be seen in due course. Though not confirmed, it would appear that if the supply of fuel and spare-parts to a set of imported reactors is stopped on the cessation of nuclear cooperation under this legislation, despite the alternative options built into the separation plan, India will insist on the right to withdraw forthwith all such facilities from IAEA safeguards and the Additional Protocol.

In other words, no fuel and spare-parts, no further safeguards inspections or return of assets bought and paid for prior to that, while under safeguards!

It is necessary that the government incorporate this stipulation in both the 123 Agreement and the agreements which we sign with the IAEA. It is also clear that the separation plan will not involve the bifurcation of personnel into military projects and civilian projects. Also, the safeguards and the Additional Protocol will be effective only prospectively, with India not being obliged to discuss past issues regarding any facility we decide to place on the civilian side.

The stated position of the prime minister on full civil nuclear cooperation is clear from his addresses to Parliament. We will not agree to any dilution that would prevent us from securing the benefits of full civil cooperation, he said. In my view, it would be sufficient if the revised legislation does not specifically bar full civilian cooperation for India, as the current bill does. The Nuclear Suppliers' Group is seriously reframing its rules on transfer of enrichment and reprocessing technologies to all countries, and notwithstanding what the US and India may agree, eventually the Nuclear Suppliers' Group decision will override any bilateral understanding.

At the end of his meeting with the senior scientists, the Prime Minister made it quite clear that he did not view imports as substituting domestic efforts in any way. He gave the assurance that domestic R&D programmes and their utilisation, especially those related to the three-stage nuclear power plan leading to the establishment of thorium breeder reactors, as well as the scaling-up of clean-coal technologies for power generation, will be pushed forward with no impediment.

We need to be absolutely sure that the India-US cooperation in the nuclear and energy fields does not come in the way of fully implementing these assurances of the Prime Minister.

(Rediff.com, October 9, 2006)

47. India's Self-goals

BHARAT KARNAD

Coalition governments have, in recent times, gone through a familiar cycle in foreign and military policy-making. They started with a catholic mindset and listened to diverse views, but eventually settled on policy planks that have consistently ill-served the national interest and the country's legitimate great power ambitions. Thus, the Bharatiya Janata Party-led National Democratic Alliance government first formed the National Security Advisory Board as part of the newly founded National Security Council (NSC) and peopled it with every "known name" in the Indian strategic community. As a result, there were bracing discussions, of a kind perhaps never before witnessed in official circles in the NSAB group, for instance, tasked with drafting the nuclear doctrine. But the sheer vigour of the debates put-off the Atal Behari Vajpayee government and its point man on national security, Brajesh Mishra, who responded by ridding this organisation of those supposedly rocking the boat, even though, all the aggressive bickering eventuated in a doctrine that is extraordinarily imaginative and elastic and protects and preserves very well India's strategic interests and policy options. Subsequent NASBs have been tame affairs never heard from again.

Further, going against the grain of some of the sharpest policy options aired in the first NSAB, the Vajpayee government, having resumed nuclear testing and then undercutting the anticipated strategic gains by imposing a "voluntary moratorium" on tests that froze the Indian weapons technology at the low end of the learning curve, set out to make peace with America, by and large, on US terms. As down payment, it agreed, among other things, to slow down the development of long range Indian missiles systems.

This policy of ceding strategic space to Washington in the hope of accessing, as a junior partner, American advanced technology has been continued by the successor Congress Party-led UPA (United Progressive Alliance) government. Apparently, this is a deliberate policy choice, which followed an initial phase of open-mindedness and desire to hear alternative policy formulations, something reflected in the two-day seminar on "India: The Next Decade" held in Vigyan Bhavan under the aegis of the Indira Gandhi Memorial Trust in November 2004. The proceedings of this seminar, flawlessly edited by Manmohan Malhoutra, among the last of the Oxbridge-trained civil servants, have just been published.

The session or section on "India and the World" at the seminar and now in the book, featured two main presentations along divergent lines. With Sonia Gandhi in the chair and taking notes and Natwar Singh, the then external affairs minister, in attendance, Sunil Khilnani of the Johns Hopkins University's School of Advanced International Studies in Washington DC, while acknowledging the primacy of military power, presented the traditional liberal view of an India hewing to Nehruvian values, but with a twist. He recommended coming to terms with the United States—"the most decisive player in the international held in the manner China has, by cultivating economic leverages."

As the other lead speaker, I emphasised the need for a two-pronged policy dictated by hard realpolitik and the importance of India's obtaining strategic fire power on a priority basis, particularly high yield thermonuclear armaments, and inter-continental ballistic missiles, necessary to realise the country's great power ambitions, protect its expansively defined strategic interests, and to stake out an exclusive "sphere of responsibility" in the Indian Ocean region extending to cast of the Malacca Straits and on the landward side into Central Asia. Such a strategic posture, I suggested, ought to be coupled with a policy of unilateral friendly measures peacefully to co-opt states in widening circles from the subcontinent, starting with the adjoining countries, including Pakistan, in a security architecture and common market beneficial to all. The pivot of this policy scheme was the acquisition of thermonuclear clout as a means, principally, of equalising the currency of exchange where the US is concerned, and to blunt China's political-military edge in Asia. The trouble is, it is precisely the value of a meaningful high yield thermonuclear arsenal with long reach that the Manmohan Singh regime underrates, as did the predecessor government of Vajpayee, and which Dr Singh seems ready to sacrifice in order to get close to the US. Alas, the vehicle he has chosen to partially reach this objective—the deal for civilian nuclear cooperation—has come at a time when the Non-Proliferation Treaty (NPT) order is tottering alone with the other technology denial regimes (like the Missile Technology Control Regime). In the event, India's desire to join the existing non-proliferation order substantively as a non-weapon state, instead of trying to nudge it over the edge, is a military and diplomatic disaster. It is akin to the hapless Abyssinia's expressing faith in the inter-war League of Nations—a touching but ultimately foolish and futile gesture by a weak state—after that world body had failed to reverse Italy's military campaign of occupation against it, a failure that consigned the League to the dust heap of history.

India's 1974 test explosion shook the foundations of the NPT regime, but the status quo quickly firmed up behind a diffident Indira Gandhi's decision to stop further testing and to forsake full-scale nuclear weaponisation. It was the sort of mistake sadly repeated by Prime Minister Vajpayee after the 1998 series of nuclear tests with his announcement of the test moratorium. This national trait of self-abnegation, of the adeptness of the Indian government to score self-goals, is what battles the brightest strategists in the US and seeds doubts about India's mettle as a potential great power in the minds of those shaping long-term American policy.

This sub-surface bafflement with India was evident in exchanges I had with hard-boiled civilian and military thinkers in Washington and elsewhere and on the sidelines of a couple of conferences and seminars I attended in the US during the past one month. The issue is this: powerful elements in the American system refuse to make distinctions between a "good" proliferator (India) and "bad" proliferators (North Korea, Iran), or even between India and Pakistan—the latter a "not so good" proliferator—believing that compromising with India in any way will place the US-led international non-proliferation regime on a slippery slope. If, however, the US establishment were to be convinced by New Delhi's policy hints and indirection that not accommodating India as a nuclear weapon state might cost the extant NPT order dear then, grudgingly, the required changes in the treaty regime will be made, and no nonsense about it. This approach of delicately threatening to upset the apple cart if its demands are not met, has been perfected, for example, by China. For those who are likely to point out that India lacks the heft of a China, look no further than North Korea or Iran. If India is not prepared to play hardball, why pretend to be in the game?

But with the Manmohan Singh government pleading for "civilian nuclear cooperation" with the US and showing its eagerness to play by US non-proliferation rules following Vajpayee's loss of nerve in the wake of the Shaft tests, the Washington strategic policy community understandably believes both that the present NPT regime can be saved and India (and secondarily, Pakistan) brought within its ambit without paying the high political price of changing the treaty. This notwithstanding the fact that the prospect of North Korea's formally going nuclear—which has finally happened—and Iran's preparing to do so, always afforded New Delhi the opportunity to press the US and West to change the global non-proliferation system to acknowledge and treat India as a "weapon state" under NPT. It is an opportunity spurned by the Manmohan Singh government. Prime Minister Manmohan Singh and his foreign policy coterie do not realise that sticking by the demand for NPT status as a weapon power at the cost of any nuclear deal with the United States, will ensure India's inclusion in the group that configures a follow-on non-proliferation regime, which is bound to come, sooner rather than later. This to say that the consequence of India's clambering aboard a sinking non-proliferation ship is that its pretensions to great power as well as its possible role as a notable nuclear player, will sink with it.

Based on the Manmohan Singh government's foreign policy record of readily accepting external nuclear terms of reference and with the limitations of US power post-Iraq growingly obvious, several discerning American strategists, justifiably worry that, considering the political capital being invested by the George W. Bush administration. India may not really have what it takes in terms of mustering the will and "hard power" to lead the strategic opposition to China gradually emerging in Asia. It is a role and mission which, whether anybody in New Delhi likes it or not, India cannot avoid if it means to become a great power in the future.

(*The Asian Age*, October 25, 2006)

48. Bill Paves Way for Covert US Operations

A. GOPALAKRISHNAN

On November 16, 2006, the US Senate discussed and modified its bill No. S-3709 on the Indo-US nuclear deal, which was forwarded to it by the Senate Foreign Relations Committee (SFRC). After debating the SFRC bill, making some amendments and adding a few new clauses, this revised text was inserted as replacement text in the House bill No.HR-5682.PCS, received earlier from the House of Representatives, and gave it a new number, HR-5682.EAS. It is this new version which has now been forwarded by the Senate to the Conference Committee for preparing a unified text, after reconciling it with HR-5682.PCS. The reconciled version in the form of a single bill will then be debated sometime in December 2006 for approval in a joint sitting of the Senate and House. If approved there, this unified bill will go to the US President for his signature for transforming it into law.

During the debate on November 16, amendments were approved in Section 105 and Section 108 of the original bill, and also two new sections (Sec. 114 and Sec. 115) were freshly inserted. What else was introduced and defeated is of little consequence to us, since we need to only concentrate on the acceptability of what is eventually put into HR-5682.EAS, instead of wasting time to rejoice on the false victories over "killer" amendments! Of the changes that were made, what is most appalling is the inclusion of Section 115 which the Senate approved without any vote-counting or voice vote. After reading out the text of this section, Senator Lugar just said one sentence, "I urge adoption of the amendment," and without objection or discussion it was directly "agreed to."

This entirely new section was neither a subject in any of the several open discussions between the US Congressional Committees and the various representatives of the US administration over the last year, nor was it part of any previous versions of the two bills, till it was abruptly introduced and approved quietly by the Senate on November 16. The fact that 100 US Senators belonging to both parties did not even raise a question or murmur about this new section put in front of them is something rare in Senate history. If one reads the rest of the Senate proceedings on that day, strangely, one notices the lengthy debates and differences of opinion which characterised every other amendment which had come to the floor.

It is clear that this subject, therefore, had received sufficient in-camera attention of and provision of explanations to the senators, before it was briefly read on the floor and swept away with a nod from all. Why did the Congress use such secrecy and dubious procedures to rush particularly this specific section through the session? What exactly does Section 115 state? I think the reader must understand this section and, therefore, I have reproduced it completely:

Section 115. United States-India Scientific Cooperative Threat Reduction Program.

(a) Establishment: The Secretary of Energy, acting through the Administrator of the National Nuclear Security Administration, shall establish a cooperative threat reduction program to pursue jointly with scientists from the United States and India a program to further common non-proliferation goals, including scientific research and development efforts related to nuclear nonproliferation, with an emphasis on nuclear safeguards (in this section referred to as the "program").

(b) Consultation: The program shall be carried out in consultation with the Secretary of State and the Secretary of Defense.

(c) National Academies Recommendations:

   (1) In General: The Secretary of Energy shall enter into an agreement with the National Academies to develop recommendations for the implementation of the program.

   (2) Recommendations: The agreement entered into under paragraph (1) shall provide for the preparation by qualified individuals with relevant expertise and knowledge and the communication to the Secretary of Energy each fiscal year of—

      (A) recommendations for research and related programs designed to overcome existing technological barriers to nuclear non-proliferation; and

      (B) an assessment of whether activities and programs funded under this section are achieving the goals of the activities and programs.

   (3) Public Availability: The recommendations and assessments prepared under this sub-section shall be made publicly available.

(d) Consistency with Nuclear Non-Proliferation Treaty: All United States activities related to the program shall be consistent with United States obligations under the Nuclear Non-Proliferation Treaty.

(e) Authorization of Appropriations: There are authorized to be appropriated such sums as may be necessary to carry out this section for each of fiscal years 2007 through 2011.

The Indo-US nuclear deal is supposed to be for civilian nuclear cooperation in the hope that it will enhance energy security of the country. Section 115 of the bill deals totally with matters of nuclear proliferation control. In the guise of conducting joint R&D in nuclear non-proliferation, with emphasis on nuclear safeguards, the US attempt appears to be to use the Indo-US nuclear deal as a vehicle to facilitate a formal entry for the US National Nuclear Security Administration (NNSA) into India.

The NNSA is widely suspected to be involved in a variety of covert nuclear interventions and clandestine operations in many countries around the world on behalf of the US government, and they work in close cooperation with intelligence agencies like the CIA, the US National Security Agency (NSA), and the US Defence Intelligence Agency (DIA). The US state department, US defence department (DoD) and the department of energy (DoE) are also closely involved with the NNSA. Section 115 states that the secretaries of DoD and DOE will be consulted in carrying out the envisaged R&D programme.

While the intention is that the programme will be pursued jointly by scientists from the United States and India, no Indian organisation is mentioned as an Indian partner for this seemingly one-sided effort. However, what should be of grave and urgent concern to the government, the parliamentarians and the general public in India is the fact that our Department of Atomic Energy (DAE) which has the final overall responsibility for all civilian and military nuclear programmes, including R&D, is as much in the dark as anyone else about Section 115! I reliably understand that, as of November 18, 2006, neither Dr Anil Kakodkar, chairman of the Atomic Energy Commission nor the DAE establishment was aware of Section 115 in the bill.

They have also never expressed the need for an R&D programme like the one envisaged in Section 115 of the Senate bill, nor has the DAE ever discussed it with US officials or our senior officials in Delhi in the context of the nuclear deal. During the last four decades, the DAE has steadfastly and strictly refrained from any communication about the weapons programme with even Indian nationals who do not have an absolute need to know. They have all along kept all foreign nationals miles away from the weapon scientists and their facilities. Besides, the DAE is quite competent to develop and use present and future nuclear non-proliferation and safeguards technologies without any external R&D help.

As such, the sudden introduction of Section 115 has come as a bolt of lightning from the sky for the DAE as well, and I only hope that no one in the high-power negotiating team that the Prime Minister had put together in Delhi has been taken into confidence by the US administration on this subject without the DAE's knowledge. I presume it is not the case, and if so, it is most urgent for the Prime Minister to publicly express his resentment over this high-handed, one-sided action by the US Senate. Anything short of a clear and open protest from the PMO and the ministry for external affairs will definitely leave a lingering suspicion that the government in Delhi is deliberately ignoring this blatant US attempt to facilitate NNSA to conduct covert activities on the Indian nuclear programme.

It is worth noting that the NNSA was established by the US Congress in 2000 as a semi-autonomous agency within the US department of energy which has responsibility for all US nuclear weapon programmes. NNSA's missions include maintaining and enhancing the safety, reliability and performance of the US nuclear weapon stockpile, including the ability to design, produce and test, weapon systems in order to meet national security requirements. NNSA's cooperative threat reduction programmes are already active in Russia and the former Soviet states, and their operations are becoming increasingly global and intrusive.

NNSA implements part of its mission through securing nuclear weapons and nuclear and radiological materials at vulnerable sites around the world. Operating with an annual budget of about $9.5 billion, the NNSA has close operational and programmatic links with covert agencies like the CIA, the National Security Agency (NSA), the Defence Intelligence Agency and others in the US. NNSA is also ultimately responsible for the management of all major US nuclear weapons laboratories situated at Los Alamos, Sandia, Livermore. Nevada test site and other locations.

Given these facts, what is the US interest in unilaterally dictating a link between India and an agency like the NNSA, especially when our own weapons programmes and facilities are totally outside the scope of the Indo-US nuclear deal? Agreeing to the NNSA's presence in India and any interaction between them and our weapon scientists will be a most dangerous move, with the potential of leading to much more than the CIA-inspired covert operations in India and the defence leaks which have recently surfaced here, some with the direct involvement of US embassy personnel. We cannot take any such risks with our most strategic nuclear sector. The government of India must, therefore, publicly reject Section 115 of the revised Senate bill immediately, without waiting for the final reconciliation of the two bills.

(*The Asian Age*, November 21, 2006)

49. Was the Government Aware of Section 115?

A. GOPALAKRISHNAN

The recent Senate Bill on the Indo-US nuclear deal (HR-5682.EAS) includes the highly objectionable Section 115 which was introduced for the first time and passed on November 16, 2006 (See Bill paves way for covert US operations, The Op-Ed Page, November 21, 2006). Recently, the DAE Secretary, Dr Anil Kakodkar, has described the new Section as "a matter of additional concern" that "got introduced in the last discussion" (PTI, November 24). He added, "The US is talking about a programme to be piloted by the US National Nuclear Security Administration (NNSA) and they call it a scientific threat-reduction programme, which has come as a surprise. We do not want to get into any activity that will be intrusive for our programme and that is why (we have) these concerns. The deal is for civil applications and it should not intrude into strategic areas." In spite of this, we are yet to get any reaction on this from government sources in Delhi.

The fact that Secretary, DAE was taken by surprise, could mean only one of two things. That Section 115 in the bill comes as a total surprise also to the Prime Minister and his advisers in Delhi. If so, why is there a delay in publicly rejecting this Section as unacceptable to India, without waiting for the reconciliation process? Or, is it that top echelons of the government—except the Department of Atomic Energy (DAE) and its Secretary—were aware of this subject matter, and had deliberately kept the DAE Secretary in the dark? The more the government maintains its silence, the more this latter suspicion will take root in public mind.

Section 115 of the Senate bill relates to the imposition of joint R&D with Indian scientists under a "program to further common non-proliferation goals, including scientific research and developmental efforts related to nuclear non-proliferation, with an emphasis on nuclear safeguards." DAE had never asked for such a joint effort, it is not acceptable to them, and it is entirely outside the scope of the July 18, 2005 inter-governmental agreement.

To understand how this situation has developed, we need to examine three aspects: First, we should be aware of the antecedents and links of the NNSA which has been chosen by the Senate as the interacting partner from the US side. Second, we need to look at the nature of advice which the Senate and the House have been receiving over the last year from US non-proliferation lobbies and think-tanks who are bitterly opposed to this nuclear deal. And, lastly, we need to examine whether there were possible ongoing interactions between the officials of the Indian government (except DAE representatives) and the US administration, where the intent and spirit of Section 115 were indeed discussed, and perhaps mutually concurred.

The NNSA was formed in March 2000 by consolidating the defence, non-proliferation and national security, fissile materials disposition, and naval reactor-related activities of the US Department of Energy (DoE). The FY-2001 budget for NNSA was US $6.2 billion. In presenting the budget, the then Secretary (DoE) said, "A crucial component of our national security budget is our extensive non-proliferation work, which helps to ensure that Americans can enjoy a future that is safe and secure." The first head of NNSA was General John Gordon, who was earlier the deputy director of the Central Intelligence Agency (CIA). Even today the NNSA shares its budget and programmes with other US entities like the CIA, the National Security Agency (NSA), and the Defense Intelligence Agency (DIA), which are all primarily entrusted with national and international covert operations. NNSA, given these links, is certainly not a suitable organisation to be programmatically linked to the Indian nuclear activities or even to our non-nuclear security matters, such as counter-terrorism or border-security, though NNSA participation may well serve the US objectives.

The Senate action in imposing Section 115 on India can be best understood from a revealing article titled, Seizing the Moment: Using the US-Indian Nuclear Deal to Improve Fissile Material Security by Kenneth Luongo and Isabelle Williams (Arms Control Today, May 2006). Mr Luongo is an executive director of the Russian-American Nuclear Security Advisory Council (RANSAC), and was earlier the director of the Office of Arms Control and Non-Proliferation at the US DoE. Previous to that he had served as a staff member in the US Congress in different positions. Over the last year, Mr Luongo and his colleagues have been partly responsible for shaping the views of the US Congress on the Indo-US nuclear deal. I shall, therefore, quote extensively from this article to sharply bring forth the logic used by the US Senate in framing and including Section 115 in the Senate bill.

At the outset, Luongo advises the Congress that "...the ideal trade-off for Congressional approval (of the Indo-US deal) would be a complete cut-off of fissile material production in South Asia. However, there is robust opposition in India and Pakistan to a cut-off at this time. Therefore, a necessary and achievable alternative is to mandate that India engage in a serious dialogue about improving fissile material and facility security... (However,) requiring a discussion of security improvements and successfully implementing them would likely prove to be a touchy issue in New Delhi... Procedurally, such a nuclear security dialogue could be mandated by the attachment of a condition to any legislation approving the agreement... (If this is not done) it would amount to an enormous missed opportunity to improve global security."

On the subject of proliferation, he adds, "Concerns have also been raised about illicit nuclear equipment purchases, sensitive knowledge leakages, and lax export control implementation by India... Officials from each country (India and Pakistan) have stressed in public that necessary steps have been taken to strengthen security standards and that their nuclear programs are adequately secure ... (however) they have provided no concrete evidence to the international community to support claims that their programs are invulnerable... Because of the high international stakes involved if materials and expertise are not secured properly, more substantive cooperation is essential to ensure standards are as stringent as possible."

Regarding a framework for cooperation to be imposed on India, their advice is, "At the top governmental level in India and Pakistan, however, there are likely to be a number of obstacles to engaging in this very delicate dialogue, including political sensitivities, different threat perceptions, and bureaucracy. Future efforts will therefore need to be carefully packaged and executed and will require a higher priority on the political agenda... Both countries are reluctant to allow external access to their nuclear programs and are suspicious about intrusive cooperation... National sovereignty over nuclear programs is a high priority in both countries ... it is very unlikely that either India or Pakistan would allow US officials or laboratory specialists into its nuclear facilities to implement security upgrades (and) the media in each country has already accused their governments of 'selling out' the country's nuclear assets to the United States... (Therefore,) cooperation should focus on opening dialogue on a possible 'menu' of low intrusive tools that could be adopted and implemented unilaterally by either country at facilities across the board, both civilian and military."

The Luongo and Williams statements eloquently summarise the US perspective of the Indian situation and they reflect the collective views of various middle-of-the-road non-proliferationists in the US. No wonder, the US Senate seems to have bought their viewpoint and structured Section 115 of the bill and approved it quietly, with no floor discussion, recognising the "need to carefully package and execute" it.

It should be noted that both the NDA and UPA governments have been conducting periodic bilateral discussions through an Indo-US Joint Working Group on Counter-terrorism, which has been functioning since January 2000. It is not known whether the Indian side headed by the MEA has a DAE representative or not. Other than the contents of the short press releases, nothing much is known about the group's activities. The January 22, 2002 press statement from New Delhi, issued after the fourth meeting of the group, states, "Counter-terrorism officials on the two sides reviewed the anti-terrorism training and capacity building programmes conducted by the United States. The Indian side welcomed the US offer to further expand the programme, covering preventive, protective and consequence management capabilities in both conventional and WMD terrorism. The Indian delegation also welcomed the US pilot project involving equipment and technology to strengthen border management and surveillance." A press release dated April 21, 2006 issued after the seventh meeting says, "The discussions advanced US-India cooperation in areas of common concern such as bio-terrorism ... WMD-terrorism... Both sides agreed to share information on a real time basis, respond to counterterrorism assistance requests expeditiously and collaborate to upgrade preparedness and capability to deal with acts of terrorism."

Given these ongoing interactions, there is concern whether the intent, details and spirit of the new Section 115 of the Senate bill were indeed discussed over some of these group meetings and mutually agreed on between the two governments, totally unknown to the Parliament and the public. Even so, the Secretary, DAE should have been party to that decision. If he was not, and our government has taken a decision on matters like WMD terrorism without his knowledge, then there is something seriously wrong with the way this government is arriving at critical decisions. To say the least, all this calls for an urgent clarification to Parliament from the highest level of government to clear up the confusion.

Finally, we must keep in mind that India is also entitled to get assistance from the IAEA on nuclear facility and material security, under the International Physical Protection Advisory Service (IPPAS), even without signing the Indo-US deal or the NPT. Though the DAE has not so far sought any such help, if ever the country needs it, opting for such international assistance is any day safer than involving the US in a bilateral mode.

(*The Asian Age*, November 28, 2006)

50. Strategic Reduction of India

BHARAT KARNAD

The current Indian foreign policy is propelled mainly by Prime Minister Manmohan Singh's conviction that becoming part of the "unipolar" international order presided over by the United States will benefit the country. Cooperation in the high-value nuclear technology field is seen as the cherry atop the new policy cake. The PM has failed to see that Washington, for its part, is intent on using the nuclear deal to draw India into the 1967 Non-Proliferation Treaty net and to zero out the chances of India's ever acquiring a consequential nuclear deterrent—a recipe for the strategic reduction of India.

Given the insularity of our rulers, the wonder is that, other than getting the economists-playing-deterrence strategists in Manmohan Singh's inner circle into a huff and rousing the Opposition parties in Parliament into a state of wakefulness, such warnings compelled Manmohan Singh to define in Parliament the red lines the US should not cross. But, this is precisely what the US Congress has done with the reconciled bill likely to retain at least some of the offensive clauses, confident that the Congress Party-led government will compromise to protect its considerable Investment of political capital in this deal. The reason for this American confidence may be the approach of the PM's special envoy, Shyam Saran which, according to Washington insiders, was to seek enough room for "interpretation" to steer a manifestly unacceptable "123" agreement past a confused and confusable Opposition at home. Apparently the Manmohan Singh regime's tactics are to get the deal past Parliament by presenting it as a *fait accompli*. Acting as if the nuclear deal was already a done thing, the minister of state in PMO Prithviraj Chavan claimed in Parliament that a new core was being fitted in the Apsara reactor in Trombay as part of what he culled reciprocal actions required by the deal with the US. He also revealed that talks were underway with France, South Africa, etc. for civilian nuclear collaboration. Washington has also been promised that at least two reactors of the initial purchase of eight-light water reactors will be from American companies, leading to US nuclear industry representatives camping in the country, talking procedures and modalities with the Nuclear Power Corporation.

The truth is, Saran was informed by the US under-secretary of state Nicholas Burns of the offending Sections 105, 106, 107, 108, and 115 in the

US Senate draft version of the bill before it was voted on, but other than pleading for a tempering of the language to provide Manmohan Singh the cover for accepting it, he raised no particular objection. This notwithstanding the fact that the aforementioned Sections, in breach of the understanding in the Joint Statement, have codified both India's status and treatment as a non-nuclear/weapon state under the NPT and, more significantly, India's formal acceptance of such status and treatment by the US, the Nuclear Suppliers' Group (NSG), and the International Atomic Energy Agency, signalling acceptance by India of the NPT and the Comprehensive Test Ban Treaty norms and restrictions without its being a signatory to either! These Sections, among other things, mandate IAEA safeguards in perpetuity for the designated "civilian" nuclear reactors and facilities, intrusive policing and inspection by IAEA and, when that's not possible, by American personnel, monitoring of the activities relating to India's mining its indigenous uranium ore, and verifiable evidence on an ongoing basis of India's not encouraging proliferation by countries like Iran. Further, the stockpiling of uranium fuel for imported reactors will not be allowed—closing the option of stockpiling foreign low-enriched uranium or processed natural uranium far in excess of immediate needs in order to avoid the ill-effects of unexpected termination of fuel supply, and India will be unable to access the latest uranium enrichment, plutonium reprocessing and heavy water production technologies.

Worse, the government's original *raison d'etre* for the deal that imported reactors will make up the energy deficit in 20-25 years is patently false. Even with an additional 20 imported reactors, electricity from nuclear sources will still account for no more than 5-6% of the total energy produced in the country in 2035—not sufficient incentive, surely, to "freeze and cap" the Indian weapons programme. And should India test again which it will have to do, the hundreds of billions of dollars spent on imported reactors will have to be written-off, the "nuclear cooperation" will, willy-nilly, end, and all the imported materials and plants and assemblies will have to be repatriated to the original supplier at India's cost. Considering that mostly adverse effects will follow from this deal, why is Manmohan Singh sticking to it, limpet-like, risking political rejection in Parliament and personal infamy for himself? Perhaps, because the PM is simply not clued into power politics. How else to explain his acceptance, in the first place, of the Joint Statement predicating all civilian nuclear cooperation on India's never testing again—a prohibition guaranteed to prevent this country from acquiring a credible deterrent, leave alone newer, more sophisticated, nuclear armaments in the future?

The PM and his benighted advisers may, therefore, gain from a simple six point-primer in international relations and nuclear security:

1. International relations is jungle-raj and, like in the badlands of Uttar Pradesh, might is right.

2. In this tussle, hard (thermonuclear military) power with reach matters the most, offering the country absolute security and immunity against pressure. It is decisive in the rank-ordering of countries; soft power only embroiders and augments this hard power of the state.

3. Powerful countries may humour weaker states but do not help them become strong, thereby adding to the competition.

4. States generating cutting-edge technology do not sell or transfer it to any other country for any reason. Ask America's closest ally, the United Kingdom about being denied the atom bomb in the Forties and, more recently, the set of critical Joint Strike Fighter technologies, both of which it helped finance and co-develop!

5. India's economic card has historically been trumped by the foreigner's military card, meaning the decisive military technology and capability of the day. India lacked a meaningful navy in the 17th century. It did not help that the country was an economic superpower at the time. The military card that cannot be beaten today is the trial of frightening megaton thermonuclear weapons, intercontinental ballistic missiles and nuclear-powered submarines, which has to be secured on a war footing. It will provide the security overhang beneath which the Indian economy can grow rapidly, unmolested.

6. Resumption of open-ended testing is a technical imperative, necessary to obtain boosted-fission and fusion weapons that are safe, proven and reliable—qualities, incidentally, missing in the existing Indian deterrent. Ties with the West disrupted by the Indian tests will quickly return to normal, because the advanced economics are hooked profitably into the comparatively advantaged techno-economic sphere in India, because of the lure of huge profits that make the Indian market irresistible to NSG states and render long-term embargoes unsustainable and, because, pushed to the wall, India could turn into a mean trouble-maker—the sort of entity former US President Lyndon Johnson advised it was better to have inside the tent pissing out rather than having it outside pissing in.

So, Mr Prime Minister, straighten up, inject some steel into your spine, behave as the leader of a great power on the rise, one willing to deal with fellow big powers only on equal terms. Continue speaking softly, Manmohan Singhji, but see how much more traction you get by carrying a megaton thermonuclear weapon-spiked stick in your hand. You have so far acted the leader of a feeble country—an India of the past. Retooling your mind is of the essence. Obtaining political leverage and the military wherewithal to service India's great power ambitions requires burying the nuclear deal.

(*The Asian Age*, December 6, 2006)

51. Nuclear Jewel is up for Sale

A. GOPALAKRISHNAN

The US Congress has enacted the Hyde Bill of 2006, which is the culmination of the Congressional efforts on the Indo-US nuclear deal initiated between the two governments in July 2005. The final bill in this regard has been forwarded to US President George W. Bush, and once he signs it, this would be the overarching legal framework which will limit and shape all ensuing actions by both countries, including the bilateral 123 agreement as well as the US interactions with the Nuclear Suppliers' Group (NSG) and the IAEA. However, upon closer examination, it is clear that the Hyde Act has retained the worst of all clauses in the former House and Senate bills from the Indian standpoint, and violated almost all the assurances given by the Prime Minister to Parliament and senior nuclear scientists in August 2006. This makes this final US law totally unacceptable to India.

Under the above circumstances, the overwhelming opinion of the scientific community, the opposition political parties and a large segment of the public is that the government must not proceed further with the Indo-US deal under the stipulations contained in the Hyde Act, which is not only the US law, but also binding on all future Indian nuclear arrangements with that country. Indian Parliament must, therefore, outright reject the Hyde Act and direct our government not to proceed any further with the Indo-US 123 agreement, discussions with the IAEA on the associated safeguards and Additional Protocol, or any planned meetings with the NSG on the basis of this Act.

During the last week, a number of articles appearing in a small section of the print media have brought out the views of a few of the experienced strategic analysts who have clearly delineated the serious drawbacks of this Act, on a clause by clause basis. These authors include some well-respected scholars who were till now strong supporters of the deal, but who have now expressed serious reservations. But surprisingly, almost all of the visual media and the bulk of the print media have been projecting a rosy picture of success, and almost deliberately suppressing the negative implications of this Act to make it appear extremely favourable to India. One cannot but suspect that there are strong forces behind this motivated euphoria and distortions of fact. It is, therefore, necessary that some of the key pieces of misinformation which are being spread around for public consumption are countered in simple language for the awareness of the general public.

One statement often repeated in the last week has been that the Hyde Act is purely a US domestic law, and what really will matter to India are the contents of the 123 agreement which the two countries are yet to finalise. This is a total misrepresentation of facts. The overarching terms of Indo-US cooperation have been finalised in the Hyde Act by the US Congress and no 123 agreement to follow can circumvent or negate the stipulations of this Act. For example, the Act in more than one way bars any possibility of long-term nuclear fuel supply assurance for any period more than a couple of years at a time and that too as long as the annual "good behaviour" certificate for India given by the President is approved every year by the US Congress. The government and the media would like us to believe that we could now incorporate into the 123 agreement all the earlier fuel supply assurance clauses from the separation plan of March 2006 (which this Act has already specifically negated), and that these clauses will thereafter over-ride the Act and be operative in India's favour. The Americans are not foolish enough to work hard and produce an Act to protect their views of the non-proliferation regime, only for these to be thwarted by the bureaucrats in India who plan to write a clever 123 agreement!

Mr Pranab Mukherjee told the Lok Sabha on December 12, "We fully expect the July 18 Statement and the March 2 Separation Plan to be reflected in the text of the 123 agreement." But I am sure Mr Mukherjee is perfectly aware that many of the stipulations in the July 18 Agreement and the Separation Plan have been totally negated and summarily rejected in the Hyde Act cleared on December 9 by the Congress, and anything we may now include in the 123 agreement has to be strictly within the provisions of the new law based on the Hyde Act.

Same is the case regarding the references to Iran in the Act. Even if the 123 agreement we formulate is totally silent on Iran, every year the US President will be required to keep the Congress informed on whether or not India is adequately assisting the US in containing and dissuading Iran from its nuclear enrichment efforts. Any lack of such assistance to the US could become a potential reason for the Congress to slow down or stop Indo-US nuclear cooperation, since the Act could impose such punitive action. In any case, let us also not forget that eventually the 123 agreement has to be approved by both Houses of Congress, and irrespective of what we may incorporate in it, the Congress will approve only what is consistent with the letter and spirit of the Hyde Act. Similarly, there are many other adverse stipulations in this Act, but it is certain that none of these can now be reversed through any further bilateral agreements in the making. Therefore, the government of India and its staunch supporters in the bureaucracy, business federations, and the media are fooling the general public and Parliament that somehow we will rectify all the current shortcomings in the next step.

This being the situation, what then has the Indo-US deal—lauded today as one of the greatest achievements of the Manmohan Singh government—brought for India? For one, this deal will indirectly close all options for any future nuclear weapon tests by India, while Pakistan, China, the US and a host of other countries will be free to further improve and expand their nuclear arsenal through future weapon tests. India will remain frozen in time with 1998 weapons technology, with not even the freedom to do low-power hydro-nuclear tests for ensuring the safety and reliability of our limited arsenal. With North Korea having gone nuclear and Iran clearly on the same path, it will be suicidal for India to close out the option to test, if we are interested in sustaining a healthy and current nuclear deterrent. I suspect this is happening mainly because the key top leaders of the current government were never supportive of India's nuclear weaponisation in the past and they now seem to be willing to remain ambivalent onlookers and silent collaborators, while the US is achieving its long-cherished objective of weakening our strategic nuclear capability with the aim of eventually eliminating it.

Equally damaging will be the large scale import of nuclear power reactors, at a heavy additional cost compared to the indigenous PHWRs, and at a large loss of production activity and sales to be incurred by the Indian nuclear equipment manufacturers like BHEL, L&T, Godrej and a host of medium-scale high-tech companies. In his address to the Lok Sabha, Mr Pranab Mukherjee makes the case that, "The nuclear understanding with the US is significant from the larger perspective of our energy security."

The Indo-US deal mainly provides an opening for US firms to sell their nuclear reactors in India at exorbitant prices, while the US holds Indian foreign policy and sovereignty at ransom on a yearly basis, and with constant imposition of demeaning and intrusive inspections of our indigenous nuclear facilities by US inspectors. It is also deplorable that neither the PMO nor the DAE has produced a thorough document on the techno-economic comparison of indigenous nuclear plants *versus* imported ones.

Mr Mukherjee went on to add that, "India is today seriously pursuing several energy options, including clean coal technologies." The factual position is that there is no government attention at all to clean coal projects. A BHEL-NTPC proposal to set up a 125 MWe clean-coal IGCC demonstration plant, approved by the PM's principal scientific adviser, is collecting dust because of certain blocking tactics by the top management in NTPC and the laxity on the part of the power ministry to do any follow-up. I had specifically brought to the Prime Minister's attention the importance of this project during our meeting in August 2006, but unfortunately, nothing seems to have changed since then. So much for the PM's great concern for energy security!

Let us face it, the PM and his top echelon are weaving a baseless case to justify the Indo-US nuclear deal on the basis of energy security, while in reality the deal is certainly not for enhancing the nation's energy security, but rather for ensuring the financial security of certain Indian and US energy companies and their powerful middlemen in India and the US. Big money is most likely behind the push for the Indo-US deal, and this is evident from the enormous amounts of funds that business associations and lobbyists have spent over the last few years to get the deal cleared.

It is sad that in 2006, we have ended up with a government which mostly disregards the views of its Department of Atomic Energy and its nuclear scientists. I had the privilege of starting my career as a very junior scientist in the days of Homi Bhabha, and I have watched the DAE grow from strength to strength under national leaders like Jawaharlal Nehru and Indira Gandhi who truly supported and motivated indigenous science and technology efforts. Mrs Gandhi and her early successors took the international technology sanctions, mostly imposed by the US after Pokhran-I, as a challenge for pushing ahead with indigenous development and did not succumb to bartering our nuclear sovereignty and national dignity for few crumbs they could also have picked up in return. Today, we have deteriorated to the state where the DAE establishment, which is an indigenous jewel created by past leaders, scientific and political, is put out for sale by the present government to the same Americans who tried their best but failed to demoralise this establishment for the last three decades. The science and technology community in this country must fight this attempt of this government at all cost, because their very survival and dignity depend on doing just that.

(*The Asian Age*, December 14, 2006)

52. Nuclear Testing is the Crux

BHARAT KARNAD

The real problem with the eventual 123 agreement is that it will meet the standard laid down in the July 18 Joint Statement, which predicates any civil nuclear cooperation on India's continuing with its "unilateral test moratorium"—a side-door entry for this country into the defunct Comprehensive Test Ban Treaty regime. (Incidentally, the Norwegian foreign minister Jonas Gahr Store at a Delhi seminar last Friday implied that the only reason Norway might join the consensus to ease the Nuclear Suppliers Group guidelines is because the nuclear deal will have CTBT-type consequences for India.) In fact, the Henry J. Hyde United States-India Atomic Energy Promotion Act of 2006 goes beyond CTBT and prevents India from conducting sub-critical tests, assuming the country can, at some time in the future, afford the necessary extraordinarily expensive facilities.

When even an M.R. Srinivasan, a former chairman of the Atomic Energy Commission who provided the Manmohan Singh government with some comfort by giving it the benefit of doubt, excoriates the Hyde Act as something that will result in the "total loss of control" by India "over its future nuclear policies" *(Hindu,* 14 December 2006), a stand buttressed by the senior scientists' group meeting in Mumbai on December 15, then the nuclear deal, as far as this country is concerned, has no scientific leg to stand on.

Preventing India from ever testing again, as this analyst has been stressing in his articles in this paper and other writings since Manmohan Singh's July 2005 Washington visit, is the chief American motivation for the deal, because it achieves two of the three longstanding US non-proliferation goals of "capping and freezing" the quality of India's nuclear weapons technology at the 20-kiloton fission level. The third objective of "eliminating" Indian weapons will occur naturally with the technologically primitive Indian weapons becoming progressively irrelevant with the continuous upgrading of nuclear arms in the neighbourhood (by China and Pakistan) and by the great powers. Thus, India will not be able to transform its existing inventory of "boosted fission" and fusion weapons of doubtful quality into a safe, proven and reliable arsenal.

Facing the predicament he has contrived to get India into, Manmohan Singh can walk away from the deal and protect the national interest. Or, as is more likely to happen, he will dissemble in Parliament, sign a 123 agreement forever hobbling the country strategically, and then justify this, as semi-official supporters of this deal are doing, by saying that testing is not an option because, deal or no deal, the US will clamp down technology, trade and capital-flow embargoes bringing the Indian economy speeding at 8% growth rate to a grinding halt, which this country cannot afford. But the US imposed embargoes after the 1998 tests and had to withdraw them because other countries, more intent on profiting from the Big Emerging Market, benefited vastly from America's absence from the scene. India today is in a far stronger position to frustrate US-engineered bans and other punitive measures. As far as advanced technologies are concerned, in the nuclear realm there is nothing intrinsically advantageous about 1,000 MW reactors procured from France, Russia or the US, considering that these will be perennially hostage to instant fuel cut-off, the International Thermonuclear Experimental Reactor is a test-bed for a distant technological dream, and the Generation Next Energy Programme will not involve participation by India other than as a paying customer. And, in the military sphere, India will be allowed to access Sixties' vintage hardware of the F-16/18 type when more modern systems are already available from other suppliers. In any case, no cutting-edge dual-use technologies will be accessible under any dispensation because the US, according to the Hyde Act, will be establishing the standard.

If the nuclear deal is being sought to meet immediate shortages of natural uranium, then there is even less reason to forsake the testing option. Especially because indigenous ore-bearing areas, like in Domiesat (Meghalaya) and Nalgonda, identified long ago, can be brought on stream within 12-18 months from the word go. This will necessitate working the existing reactors at lower capacities for a short period of lime. But that's definitely preferable to a legal obligation never to test which will be tantamount to gutting the nuclear weapons programme. It is one thing for the government of the day to decide not to test during its watch so as to not hurt the flourishing trade and economic links with western states. It is quite another thing for Prime Minister Manmohan Singh to decide that because he deems testing inadvisable at the present time, that the option will never be required to be exercised any time in the future and, therefore, can be done away with altogether. This is criminal folly of the highest order. Great powers or would-be great powers leave open not even the smallest window of vulnerability. But the PM is taking the roof-off of our nuclear weapons programme.

But, what is behind the set of complacent beliefs that has spawned the Manmohan Singh government's readiness legally to acquiesce in a non-testing regime? It is the concept of "minimum deterrence" articulated, in the main, by K. Subrahmanyam, the influential ex-civil servant regarded by those advising the PM, including national security adviser M.K. Narayanan as their "guru" on nuclear matters. Subrahmanyam is essentially a votary of "existential deterrence," believing that because of the physical enormity of the scale of nuclear destruction disparity in armament quality and numbers does not matter, that a few, simple, atomic weapons in one's armoury, however deployed (including in a "de-alerted, de-mated" mode), can deter another country equipped with more numerous and more powerful nuclear armaments. This simplistic argument does not reckon, for instance, with the reality of masses of megaton-yield thermonuclear weaponry with an adversary, like China. If readied in a crisis for possible use, these can be expected to psychologically disable an Indian government (which as the record shows, can be unnerved by very little) with only kilo-ton-yield weapons in its employ. Originally, when McGeorge Bundy, US President John F. Kennedy's national security assistant, conceptualised "existential deterrence"—the Bomb exists (in whatever form) and, therefore, it deters—it was at a time when surveillance and mobile target-seeking and tracking technologies slaved to precision-guided conventional munitions were not as developed as is the case now. These technologies (that China is set to acquire by 2007) can pre-emptively wipe out small nuclear forces without offering nuclear provocation.

In the event, genuine city busting megaton-yield thermonuclear armaments, which occasion unparalleled dread and hence can deter even the most powerful countries, are the urgent need. The best India can theoretically muster is a 200-kiloton weapon. It can, moreover, be certain of its reliability only after many more tests, because the sole fusion weapon design tested in 1998 was not up to mark. And simulation, based on single test data, cannot help obtain reliable weaponry. But Subrahmanyam, rooted in his existential deterrence ideas circa the Sixties, does not mind India not being able to test again under any circumstances nor unilaterally agreeing to a test ban. He strongly opposed any testing in the period before the 1998 tests, believing that the one-off test carried out in 1974—compared to the 1,000 plus conducted by the US, the 750-odd by Russia and the 74 tests by China—was entirely adequate for the purposes of configuring a credible Indian deterrent! And he advocated India's signing CTBT in 1996 which advice, Prime Minister Deve Gowda, fortunately, rejected.

Further, if deterrence is a mind-game then, in the context of the nuclear deal with the US, India will not be able to compete at the strategic-global level or even the regional level with the five so-called "NPT-recognised" nuclear weapon states or even Pakistan—all of which, unconstrained by any legal undertakings, will remain free to test, design new weapons, and improve effectiveness of the existing ones in their inventories. But Subrahmanyam is pitching for this deal on the basis that it will help the US install India as a counterpoise to China in Asia. How credible will such an attempt at balancing China be if it simultaneously ensures that India cannot emerge as a consequential thermonuclear counterweight, he did not explain. But neither did Ashley Tellis, one-time adviser to US ambassador Robert Blackwill, when asked this question at a Confederation of Indian Industry do several months back. There is, after all, only so much political punch a nuclear-wise fly-weight India can pack in a world dominated by nuclear heavy-weights and a muscular middle-weight, like China, bulking up to enter the higher weight class. Cobbling "strategic partnerships" with various countries, which Subrahmanyam recommends, will not be able to compensate for India's lack of strategic wherewithal and heft.

Subrahmanyam, hailed as the Bhishma Pitamaha by the strategic community (and his *chelas* in government), might care to remember that the *Mahabharata* grandee, for all his sagacity and wisdom, ended up supporting the wrong cause and on the wrong side of history.

(The Asian Age, December 18, 2006)

53. The Nuclear Ice Age is here to Stay

A.N. PRASAD

Ever since we conducted a nuclear test in 1974 there have been concerted efforts, particularly in the West, led by the US, to isolate India from becoming a global player in the nuclear field. Over the last three decades, the international community has formed a cartel of forty-five countries, called the Nuclear Suppliers' Group (NSG) which has been carrying out research on how to deny countries like India who are not party to the Non-Proliferation Treaty (NPT), nuclear cooperation through various technology control regimes, embargoes, restrictions, etc. In fact, the NSG has formulated detailed guidelines and a long list of items of equipment and items including those which are of dual use type to be denied to India unless it joins the NPT or Full Scope Safeguards which it has been consistently resisting, to preserve its independent nuclear policy.

In spite of all the technology denials over the years, India has made steady progress by facing up to the challenge posed by the nuclear supplier countries. The 1998 serial nuclear tests at Pokhran in Rajasthan and the commencement of construction of an indigenously designed 500 MW Prototype Fast Breeder Reactor (PFBR) at Kalpakkam in Tamil Nadu, are demonstrations of levels of advanced technology that India is capable of achieving. It is a clear indication, that India is heading towards realisation of its ultimate goal of utilising vast thorium resources to gain long-term energy security and independence. These developments might have compelled the US to take serious note and start engagement with India through the currently discussed civil nuclear cooperation agreement. This welcome shift in the US attitude towards India after all these years of nuclear squeeze resulting in the July 18, 2005 Joint Statement between US President Bush and Indian Prime Minister Manmohan Singh is laudable. For the first time, there was formal recognition of India's nuclear capability and its impeccable non-proliferation record. The Joint statement clearly expressed the US intention to take India as a strategic partner allowing the same advantages and benefits and to be treated at par with other advanced countries including the nuclear weapon states. Pious words indeed! But the subsequent events culminating in the final Bill of the US Congress awaiting US President's signature to become an Act has turned out to be a damp squib belittling expectations on all the crucial aspects of the July 18 Joint Statement which is highly disturbing.

Systematically shifted

During the course of the evolution of the final US Congress Bill there were opinions expressed in India by the scientific community, strategic analysts and the media highlighting the direction in which the US legislation is steering the Bill and the way the goal posts as identified in the Joint Statement of July 18 and March 2006 Separation Plan have been deliberately and systematically shifted unilaterally.

Our Prime Minister aptly pointed out the areas of concern and assured the Parliament in August 2006 that there would not be any compromise on the basic issues and the same was reportedly conveyed to the US. Yet, the US Congress chose to ignore all our concerns and the US President kept beating round the bush saying that the 123 Agreement, yet to be negotiated will address them and the Indian government kept on saying that our strategic national interest will be protected. It is not comprehensible how Bush can keep his commitment when he himself will be signing the final Bill, which is so blatantly deviating from the Joint Statement, into an Act.

. Let us look at some of the serious issues involved.

Firstly, the final Bill is more about non-proliferation aspects, stipulating for India do's and don'ts to keep in line with US interests, objectives and policies. It talks about congruence with US policy on Iran, permanent moratorium on nuclear tests, stop production of fissile materials for nuclear weapons, cap production of weapons and eventually eliminate them without using the term roll back! They even expect India to join R&D with the US on non-proliferation issues along with various agencies and departments of the US government totally extraneous to the civil nuclear cooperation deal. If this is the intention with which the deal will be steered, if not immediately, in course of time India will lose control of its nuclear future.

Secondly, the deal was supposed to include full civil nuclear cooperation, but now the US Bill seeks to give a new definition to the very meaning of the nuclear fuel cycle to exclude fuel reprocessing, enrichment and heavy water technologies which is highly preposterous. Some may argue that since we have already developed these technologies we should not care. This is a bizarre argument. By agreeing to this, we not only violate the very principle of full nuclear cooperation but also live with all the embargoes on nuclear trade with the NSG on various items of commerce. What have we achieved? No access to international market on any items leave alone technologies!

The Tarapur Experience

Thirdly, in view of extremely stringent conditions of the US Act and vagaries of future administrations and based on our own experience with Tarapur, we have to safeguard our interests in assured fuel supply to our future reactors. Though in the March 2006 Joint Statement this was agreed to by the US the

Final Bill goes back on this. No strategic reserve of uranium will be permitted. This is a crippling issue we cannot live with and has to be opposed.

Fourthly, fuel reprocessing is a central issue for the success of our three stage nuclear programme leading to thorium utilisation through fast breeder reactors. So, putting restrictions on our reprocessing programme and denying us right to reprocess in our national facilities even under safeguards cannot be accepted. The Bill seeks to place restrictions, by making co-operation contingent on, reprocessing spent fuel arising from imported uranium in a multinational facility which is too restrictive.

There are many other issues pertaining to Proliferation Security Initiative (PSI), Wassenaar Arrangement, and the Australia Group which are totally outside the scope of the Joint Statement.

In view of the highly depressing final Bill we are faced with and the high improbability of any bilateral agreement sustaining for long without the backing of the US Act, it is time for the Government of India to seriously ponder over the issues in detail and any future negotiation for the 123 Agreement should reflect our areas of concern effectively and adequately.

While the US is making use of think-tanks for inputs on specific issues to help in the formulation of the Bill systematically extending its tentacles to all facets of our nuclear activity, civil and strategic, our government has not thought it fit to commission such think-tanks of strategic analysts, scientists and other interest groups and intellectuals.

(*The Deccan Herald*, December 18, 2006)

54. Is N-testing a Purely Political Decision?

BHARAT KARNAD

Speaking on "India-United States Understanding on Civil Nuclear Cooperation: The Way Ahead" at the Habitat Centre in New Delhi on January 10, 2007, Shyam Saran, the Prime Minister's special envoy, identified this country's right to reprocess spent fuel from imported nuclear power reactors, and to not accept a legal obligation beyond its "unilateral test moratorium" as the issues on which a "123" agreement could get stuck.

As regards the "unilateral test moratorium" mentioned in the July 18, 2005 Joint Statement, Saran opined that this concept was synonymous with the "voluntary test moratorium" announced by the previous Bharatiya Janata Party government. But sharp legal eagles will point out that a commitment to refrain from testing even if other countries tested is a connotation the qualifier "unilateral" carries that the adjective "voluntary" does not.

Saran further declared that there would be "no limitations on India's strategic programme" and, in the next breath, referred to "globalisation" increasing "interdependencies" along with "vulnerabilities," indicating, in the first case, that he has not a clue about nuclear weapon matters, and implying, in the other instance, that the compromises required to forge the nuclear deal will, in fact leave the country more vulnerable. Saran thus provided evidence of muddled thinking, of course, but also of the rank bad scientific advice the government is getting. The fact that the PM, Saran, *et al* are ignorant of even the rudiments of nuclear weapon technology and development and about what is needed at a minimum to obtain a safe, proven, and reliable nuclear arsenal, can, however, be laid at the door of the current chairman, Atomic Energy Commission, Dr Anil Kakodkar, who seems adept at running with the hares and hunting with the hounds.

I mean, is it conceivable that Manmohan Singh, heading a coalition government, would have so readily agreed to compromise the nuclear deterrent and national security if Kakodkar had officially expressed grave doubts about the deal as he has informally done to former colleagues, resisted it tooth and nail from the start, and threatened to resign if his professional advice was disregarded? On issues relating to the country's strategic "crown jewels," the chairmen of AEC, Indian Space Research Organisation, and head of Defence Research and Development Organisation, have in recent times, acquired a veto on policies impinging on their respective turf, so much so that their actual resignation can trigger unpredictable effects. Constituent parties in a coalition government can decide to pull out rather than get tarred by policies harming the country's security. But it needs chairmen with a sense of self, the desire to protect the integrity of the strategic programmes in their care, and the guts to take on the political establishment when it obviously errs. These are attributes that Kakodkar has shown he lacks. He has thereby put himself in the position of having to push the same laughable rationale his immediate predecessor Dr R. Chidambaram first retailed, to wit, that the indigenous computing and simulation prowess is such as to render any and all future testing by India unnecessary. It has damaged his personal reputation and professional credibility, as it did Chidambaram's, because his views contradict those of his illustrious former colleagues, who have gone public with their apprehensions about the conditionality (to not test again), as also the empirical record and loads of practical experience stalwarts of the more advanced nuclear weapons programmes elsewhere have brought to bear on the subject of testing.

Richard Garwin, one of the main creators of the American hydrogen bomb and member of the secret JASON Committee of experts the US government depends on for objective advice on science projects of strategic import, appearing before the US Senate Foreign Relations Committee in October 1999, for example, pleaded thus for the ratification of the Comprehensive Test Ban Treaty (which, fortunately for India, did not materialise) by the US Senate. "Without nuclear tests of substantial yield," Garwin testified, "it is difficult to build compact and light fusion weapons and essentially impossible to have any confidence in a large yield two-stage thermonuclear weapon or hydrogen bomb, which can be readily made into the megaton class." "Further-more," he added, "even in the yield range accessible to fission weapons, thermonuclear weapons are attractive because of their economy of fissile material, their compact size, and their improved safety." Coming to the main point of his advocacy, he then referred to hydrogen weapons requiring repeated testing, which "would be readily detected and would therefore be prevented by the CTBT." This, Garwin averred, "limits greatly the destructive power that can be wielded by newly nuclear states such as India and Pakistan." Its newfound desire to help India become a "major power" notwithstanding, Washington, it is clear, will do all it possibly can to prevent India from becoming a genuine great power with proven strategic capabilities, namely, a megaton thermonuclear punch and intercontinental ballistic missile reach. If a pliable Indian government can be persuaded to shackle the country's nuclear weapons programme, so much the better!

In the context of America seeking to "constrain" (to use Garwins word from the Congressional testimony given here) India by whatever means, let us evaluate the most disturbing of Saran's pronouncements during his Habitat Centre talk. Brushing aside the issue I had raised in the interaction period about the curious phenomenon of serving scientists, like Kakodkar, ostensibly supporting the government's initiative while retired Indian nuclear scientists and engineers of greater renown publicly questioning the no-testing predicate of the deal, Saran, with his forefinger jabbing the air for emphasis, delivered himself of this gem: 'Testing," he intoned, "is a political decision," meaning, presumably, an exclusively political decision. Really?

A decision by an established nuclear weapon state to test is a "political" decision because it might involve a new nuanced armament whose non-induction will not weaken the strategic forces nor affect nuclear security, but physical testing of which may prompt resumption of tests by the other so-called "recognised" nuclear weapon powers and rile the international milieu. In the case of the Indian nuclear weapons programme still in its infancy, it is easy to see that testing is a military imperative and essential for the elementary purpose of vetting, verifying and calibrating the explosive characteristics of the basic "boosted" fission and fusion weapons in its inventory, which has not so far been done. And that the decision to delay testing, leave alone to never test again, has to be made on the basis of the proven and physically certified performance of nuclear weapons rather than on Kakodkars say-so. Either this or the political leaders formally assume the responsibility for the manifestly flawed nuclear and thermonuclear weapons, whose effectiveness is contested by veterans of the weapons project. At the very least, weapons of doubtful provenance and questionable yield undermine the official claims of an in-place "credible minimum deterrent."

If despite the patented need for more testing, the present government is willing to go ahead with the deal, then its concern about not linking it with the test moratorium appears dubious because it, in effect, means hankering for a thin legal pretence rather than wanting genuinely to keep the testing option open. But if testing is deferred for political tactical reasons, when India does test, all nuclear cooperation will be instantly ended with the US and, as mandated by the Hyde Act, also with the other member-states of the Nuclear Suppliers' Group, and imported reactors and materials will be turned into dead investment worth tens of billions of dollars. So, if testing is inescapable, does it make any economic or strategic sense to sign this deal knowing fully well it will break down? An affirmative answer leads to a sinister interpretation; that India is sought to be locked into a system of constraints, which can be over-turned by a future Indian government deciding to test but at an economic cost so high as to deter such decision.

Without many more test explosions involving the basic devices and new weapon designs to fit warheads on proposed land-fired and submarine-launched ballistic missiles of various ranges, India, moreover, will be permanently saddled with a security liability no major nuclear weapon state in history has ever risked, namely, fielding largely untested, unproven, unsafe, and unreliable "boosted fission" and thermonuclear weapons.

(*The Asian Age*, January 9, 2007)

55. The N-Deal is Dead

BHARAT KARNAD

A canny Mumbai-based senior financial analyst with one of the biggest international consultancy firms has an interesting take on the controversial nuclear deal on the anvil. It is this: The current high economic growth rate in the country owes more to the innate dynamism of the Indian private sector than to any substantive economic reforms—like slashing the huge government spending-linked fiscal deficit—promised but not delivered by the Congress party-led coalition government. But it is the political cover provided by the economy that the present government had no real hand in making buoyant, and which Prime Minister Manmohan Singh is using to push forward the prospective accord with the United States for "civilian nuclear cooperation" that fatally weakens India's nuclear sovereignty and security. Who is to say this Mumbai analyst is wrong?

Recent developments in New Delhi and in Washington, however, have slopped this misbegotten nuclear deal in its tracks. The basic problem is the Henry J. Hyde United States-India Promotion of Nuclear Cooperation Act of 2006 promulgated by the US Congress. Not so ironically—considering its hard non-proliferation intent—this Act is an insurmountable barrier to realising a mutually acceptable "123 Agreement" necessary for nuclear cooperation legally to get underway. At the Indian end, the Hyde Act generated a lot of uninformed euphoria in the press and in official circles about India being recognised as a nuclear weapon state, etc. Access to the so-called "advanced technology," it was stated, was just a matter of finalising a 123 Agreement.

Indeed, Prime Minister Manmohan Singh's special envoy to these nuclear talks, Shyam Saran, has, in fact, spent less time parleying with his American counterpart, US under-secretary of stale Nicholas Burns, than in flying around the world dying to convince the 43 other Nuclear Suppliers' Group states to be on the same page as India and the US. For all his persuasive skills, Saran found most of them non-committal or sceptical. Apparently, they were better clued into the problems inherent in the politics of negotiating this agreement than he was.

The points on which a prospective 123 Agreement has run aground relate in the legally binding non-testing clause the Americans have insisted on, as also the provisions preventing reprocessing by India of the imported spent fuel and, in case of a deal breakdown, requiring materials, technologies, and whole reactors bought from NSG to be returned to the supplier. One hopes other equally worrisome aspects of the Hyde Act are taken up with Burns. Like the requirement that the US government ensure other NSG states adhere to similar punitive-minded terms and conditions in their transactions with India, which makes nonsense of Delhi's confidence that it will be able to do business with NSG states not open to American pressure. Even Russia toes the US line on non-proliferation matters, to wit its threat of nuclear supply cut-off to Iran.

Taking the soft line, Burns and Company are trying to sucker India into this deal by suggesting, disingenuously, that on issues pertaining to testing and reprocessing, for instance, the differences could be papered over by the deft use of diplomatese, thereby hinting at an escape route embedded in a potential 123 Agreement India could avail of in case the deal ever sours. Hence, the US state department team headed by Richard Stratford in Delhi to resume negotiations today with MEA, will be preoccupied mostly with creative diplomatic language writing. The beguiling possibilities therein notwithstanding, the Americans will be seeking to minimise opacity and the Indians to maximise the latitude for interpretation.

The trouble in the Manmohan Singh regime has all along stuck pigheadedly to its belief that India is not bound by anything in the Hyde Act—a US domestic law, but only by such commitments as the Prime Minister made in the July 18, 2005 Joint Statement. It is a position ignorant of the stipulation in the Hyde Act that any 123 Agreement negotiated with India would have to secure prior approval of the US Congress before it can become part of the Act itself, and facilitate nuclear commerce. As a means of softening up the Indian side, the Americans have hinted artfully at how some of the provisions in the Hyde Act can be circumvented. But will this ruse succeed?

Benighted Indian policy circles are of the view that once an agreement containing the ambiguous language-*cum*-escape route filled negotiated 123 Agreement is ready, the onus will be on George W. Bush to get it past the US Congress. Assuming he was ever really willing to scuttle the traditional US non-proliferation approach and policies, which he never was, the popular President Bush, circa 2002 or 2003, had the political credibility and muscle to do so, what with his Republican Party running both the Houses of the US Congress. A long since lame duck chief executive, the Bush of 2007 with his political capital spent and his presidency shredded by the misadventure in Iraq is, alas, in no position whatsoever to push India's case, leave alone shove aside the resistance of the non-proliferation and anti-Iran hardliners now strategically-placed in the Democratic party-controlled US House of Representatives and the Senate to make any further "concessions" to India.

Burns may have reassured Saran that even an ostensibly hostile US Congress can be brought around on the 123 Agreement. This is wishful thinking. The Hyde Act, it must be understood, is a systemic constraint on the Bush administration and there is no point in having delusions about escaping its hold short of this Act itself being amended—of which there is not even the remotest chance. In the event, the only way a 123 Agreement acceptable to the American legislators can be obtained is if the PM lets the US have its way, a solution implicit in Burns' statement that the differences between the two countries are such only "political intervention at the highest level" can resolve them.

Despite the loud clanging of alarm bells, a strategically short-sighted Manmohan Singh, with his record of insensitivity to nuclear security, would have chosen this course of action for two reasons. Firstly, because he is fiercely anti-nuclear bomb by conviction, and in his various capacities as Deputy Chairman, Planning Commission, Finance Minister, and now Prime Minister has acted as if determined to, if not kill the Indian nuclear weapons programme, then severely to limit its reach and clout. And secondly, because of his warm relations with President Bush, he is personally committed to making this deal work. It has resulted in the Indian government accepting the American policy; premises and predicates of the deal *in toto,* something reflected in the fact that Delhi did not evolve its own alternative plan. Consequently, the negotiations so far have proceeded on the basis of official US drafts of the Joint Statement, the "separation plan" (to divide the dual-use nuclear energy programme into its military and civilian components), a possible safeguards scheme to be negotiated with the International Atomic Energy Agency, and of the 123 Agreement. Washington, therefore, funds itself in the happy position of leading India by the nose.

The spoiler, from Manmohan Singh's perspective, is his fast shrinking space for political manoeuvre. The unfolding events—ruling Congress party's electoral defeats in Punjab and Uttaranchal, its dim prospects in the upcoming polls in Uttar Pradesh, and restive coalition partners inclined to form a "third front" to fight the next general elections, have changed the political context. Simultaneously, the Left-Right of Centre combine of the Communist parties (which post-Nandigram will want to appear stridently nationalistic) and the Bharatiya Janata Party-led National Democratic Alliance, are now both better informed about the non-proliferation traps in the deal and ready to battle it out in Parliament, even as important elements within the ruling Congress party are developing cold feet. To top it all, the chairman of the Atomic Energy Commission, Dr Anil Kakodkar responding no doubt to the new political environment, has publicly slammed any giveaways in the 123 Accord.

Survival instincts have prompted Manmohan Singh belatedly to erect a firewall as protection by having foreign secretary Shiv Shankar Menon, not

Saran burdened with the baggage of the past, forward an Indian version of the 123 Agreement to Burns during his recent visit to the US—a paper mindful of the country's nuclear security concerns and strategic interests.

But no amount of fancy diplomatic footwork is likely to rescue the nuclear deal. If bureaucratic behaviour is any kind of indication, it is, in fact, as good as dead. Serving Foreign Service officers, for instance, are reportedly distancing themselves from this nuclear initiative. So much so, MEA has faced difficulty filling the supposedly prized post of "Joint Secretary, Americas" at the cutting edge of the deal.

(The Asian Age, March 26, 2007)

56. Amend US Law, or Reject Nuclear Deal

A. GOPALAKRISHNAN

Now that the Henry J. Hyde United States-India Peaceful Atomic Energy Cooperation Act, 2006 has been signed into law, the 123 Agreement currently being negotiated must conform in letter and spirit with the provisions of that Act.

Any modification of the requirements under this Act cannot be brought about through merely word-engineering a cleverly drafted agreement to be settled between the two executive branches of government.

Let us not forget that this agreement will have to be presented to both Houses of US Congress and approved by each before it becomes part of the overall deal.

Therefore, while the recent discussions between the two governments have helped to clarify the Indian stand, the US administration must now present a revised case based on our stand to US Congress and seek appropriate amendments to the Hyde Act.

As long as the Act remains what it is today, no 123 Agreement can be used to override its legal provisions.

Knowing this, the US efforts are to push India to agree to positions in conformity with the Act's current provisions, rather than take the legal route of getting the Act amended to accommodate the Indian prime minister's assurances to Parliament.

In the eagerness to see the deal through, India should not succumb to the US ploy and help their approach by over-dramatizing the importance of the 123 Agreement to the Indian public.

If the US administration is not willing to approach its Congress to amend the Act suitably, the only recourse India must take is to outright reject the nuclear deal.

In the rapidly changing global strategic environment, the maintenance of a reliable and adequate nuclear deterrent may necessitate future Indian nuclear weapon tests.

In the interest of our national security, future Indian governments should not have to face severe economic hardships in case of testing—and therefore be inhibited from conducting such tests—because of the type of nuclear agreements we may enter into with the US, the International Atomic Energy Agency and the Nuclear Suppliers' Group.

This translates into the absolute requirement that India must be assured lifetime fuel and spare-part supplies and stockpiling of unlimited fuel reserves for all nuclear reactors included in the civilian list and put under the IAEA's India-specific safeguards. Simultaneously, amendments to the Act permitting India to retain possession of all assets gained under the deal will also have to be insisted.

We must agree to keep these reactors under perpetual safeguards, with the condition that suitable amendments to the Hyde Act are put in place and the law modified beforehand as required.

India 'retaining the right to take corrective measures in the event fuel supplies are interrupted,' as the PM stated in the Rajya Sabha on August 17, 2006, is not a solution to the problem.

If this means that India will withdraw its civilian reactors from IAEA safeguards, that still would leave us with no fuel to feed the reactors already set up at a huge cost running into thousands of crores of rupees.

And such a blatant unilateral violation of a safeguards agreement will lower India to the level of countries like North Korea and could result in Chapter-7 United Nations resolutions against us in the Security Council.

As it stands, Section 103(a)(6) of the Hyde Act stipulates that if US exports were to be suspended or terminated pursuant to US law, it will be US policy to seek to prevent transfer of nuclear equipment, material or technology from other sources.

Furthermore, according to the Congressional Report, US officials have testified to Congress that America does not intend to help India build a stockpile of nuclear fuel for the purpose of riding out any sanctions that might be imposed in response to Indian actions such as conducting another nuclear test.

To cover this aspect, Section 103(b)(10) of the Act is structured to limit nuclear power reactor fuel reserves to an amount commensurate with reasonable reactor operating requirements.

These two provisions in the Act directly negate the earlier bilaterally agreed and multi-layered lifetime fuel supply assurances contained in the Separation Plan of March 2, 2006.

No clause to be incorporated in the 123 Agreement can override these basic provisions in law, and these sections of the Hyde Act will therefore necessarily have to be amended for India to ensure uninterrupted fuel supplies.

Section 123(a)(4) of the US Atomic Energy Act gives the US government the right to require the return of any nuclear material and equipment transferred under this deal and any special materials (like plutonium) produced through the use thereof, if India conducts a nuclear test or terminates or abrogates the IAEA safeguards agreement.

Presently, the Hyde Act does not authorize the American President to exempt India from this clause, and if we are to avoid the 'right of return,' Section 104 of the Hyde Act needs to be amended to include this waiver authorization.

Another contentious issue is the denial of technology transfer for uranium enrichment, spent-fuel reprocessing and heavy water production.

As stated by Prime Minister Manmohan Singh in Parliament, "the objective of full civil nuclear cooperation is enshrined in the July 2005 Joint Statement. This objective can be realised when current restrictions on nuclear trade with India are fully lifted. We will not agree to any dilution that would prevent us from securing the benefits of full civil nuclear co-operation."

But, the US in recent times has decided that 'full' nuclear cooperation, in its definition, will not include technologies for enrichment, reprocessing and heavy water production.

The July 2005 Joint Statement, in effect, accepts India as a *de facto* nuclear weapon power and yet we are specifically denied these technologies under Sections 103(a)(5) and 104(d)(4) of the Hyde Act, while neither the US Atomic Energy Act nor Article-IV of the Nuclear Non-Proliferation Treaty denies the right for these technologies even to non-nuclear weapon States.

In future, if we may need any import of nuclear technology know-how, it could be in one or more of these three areas. Therefore, it is important that we insist on a suitable amendment of Sections 103(a)(5) and 104(d)(4) to lift the current restrictions in law.

Section 123(a)(7) of the US Atomic Energy Act requires that India should provide a guarantee that no material transferred to us under this deal or produced through the use of any material, production facility or utilisation facility transferred pursuant to this deal will be reprocessed, enriched or otherwise altered in form without the prior approval of the US government.

In simpler terms, this means India cannot reprocess any spent fuel to be discharged from imported reactors or arising from natural uranium bought from abroad, without prior permission of the US.

This restriction on reprocessing will hold even if the nuclear deal is terminated or abrogated, though the fuel would have been fully paid for by India and irradiated in an Indian facility.

Without such reprocessing, the major objective of using the separated plutonium from the spent fuel, in a subsequent civilian breeder reactor or AHWR, cannot be met.

We, therefore, need to insist on a permanent prior consent for reprocessing built into the 123 Agreement and a waiver from Section 123(a)(7) of the US

Atomic Energy Act, to avoid our having to seek case-to-case permission in future.

There are many more important deviations from the PM's assurances to Parliament and what appears as law in the Hyde Act. None of these deviations can be compensated for through the 123 Agreement, contrary to what the Prime Minister's Office and the Ministry for External Affairs would have the Indian public believe.

The Department of Atomic Energy is aware of this only too well. And they are resisting the attempts from Delhi for them to compromise.

Indication of a shift in the Indian stand can be noted in the recent remarks of the external affairs minister that 'India and the US are committed to implementing the understanding expeditiously in a way that it adheres *as closely as possible* to the framework of the July 2005 Joint Statement and the March 2006 Separation Plan.'

Compare this with the PM's assurance in Parliament on August 17, 2006: "... concerns have been expressed regarding possible deviations from assurances given by me in this august House on the July 18, 2005 Joint Statement and the March 2, 2006 Separation Plan. I would like to state categorically that there have neither been nor will there be any compromises on this score and the government will not allow such compromises to occur in the future."

The external affairs minister is a seasoned politician and a staunch nationalist. No one needs to teach him where the national interest lies.

But, he must also be aware that any leeway to unilaterally deviate from the Prime Minister's assurances to Parliament does not any longer lie with him or the MEA, or for that matter with the PM himself.

It can only come about, if at all, from a conscious decision of Parliament as a whole, after a detailed debate of the pros and cons.

(Rediff.com, May 14, 2007)

57. Nuclear Deal Will Gut India's Security

BHARAT KARNAD

US under-secretary of state Nicholas Burns is confident that the nuclear deal will be done soon, fresh from his Washington trip, foreign secretary Shivshankar Menon too sounded optimistic. This is a bit baffling, as none of India's concerns have been addressed, leave alone resolved.

The mystery can be explained by the government's game plan outlined by external affairs minister Pranab Mukherjee. Speaking at an India-US business forum in Delhi on May 4, he voiced the desire to obtain the nuclear deal "expeditiously in a way that it adheres as closely as possible to the framework of the July 2005 joint statement and the March 2006 separation plan."

"As closely as possible" is another way of saying that, under American pressure, Delhi has chosen to de-link the mention in the Joint Statement about India's accepting the same "responsibilities and practices" as the United States from the requirement that the same "benefits and advantages" enjoyed by America, accrue to India. The reciprocity principle of "no equal treatment as a nuclear weapon state, hence no deal" has been ditched; Manmohan Singh's solemn promises in his *suo moto* statements in Parliament in March 2006 and again in August last year notwithstanding.

The new Indian thinking is the outcome of the American strategy combining a full-court press by the US (inclusive of the orchestrated hoo-ha over an alleged DRDO role in passing an obsolete missile-useable microchip to Iran) with targeting the weakest link in the decision chain—the strategically blinkered Manmohan Singh!

Personal calls by the US President to be followed up by George W. Bush squeezing the Indian Prime Minister in the proposed one-on-one meetings, are expected to deliver Washington the goods.

To minimise the risk of failure, US officials reportedly convinced Sonia Gandhi to encourage Dr Manmohan Singh to accept the 123 agreement. Happily for the Americans, Sonia Gandhi understands no more about nuclear matters, about what is involved in the deal and how it will irreparably damage India's sovereignty and nuclear security, than do the Prime Minister, the Prime Minister's Office, and the MEA negotiating team.

Attempts by the nuclear establishment to involve scientists in the negotiations have been rebuffed. Indeed, the government seems not to care whether the Department of Atomic Energy supports this initiative or not. In a meeting the foreign secretary sought before he left for Washington, DAE chairman Dr Anil Kakodkar reportedly hinted to Menon that he would resign if the MEA failed to protect and preserve the country's nuclear estate and interests.

Earlier, Manmohan Singh had ignored the plea by retired senior nuclear scientists and supported by Kakodkar to involve scientists in the negotiations so that the technically proficient American negotiators don't make monkeys out of their Indian counterparts.

Keeping the scientists out, resulted, for instance, in the March 2006 separation plan that bears the stamp of generalist novices on the Indian side. Hence, the criteria for safeguardability found mention in the preamble of the separation plan—something Washington is bound to use to hinder the development by India of dual-purpose nuclear facilities and technologies in the future.

With the advice from the Trombay Complex going unheeded, the predictable has happened. The US has consistently bamboozled first Shyam Saran, the PM's special envoy, and now Menon, by using empty phrases the Indians have mistaken for substantive concessions. Remember Saran's crowing in the wake of the Joint Statement that the US had accepted India as "a state with advanced technology" and therefore as a nuclear weapon state?

Condoleezza Rice had responded quickly and sought to disabuse gullible Indian policymakers by asserting that the deal in no way conferred nuclear weapon status on India. But Delhi continues to be guided by Saran's original confused take.

Had scientists been involved in the talks leading to the Joint Statement they would, for example, have quickly pinned the Americans down technically and specifically on just what they meant by this phrase, and how it would affect India.

What transpired in the run-up to the Hyde Act and in the negotiations on the 123 agreement since then have confirmed Washington's priority of pushing India into the Comprehensive Test Ban Treaty regime and the Non-Proliferation Treaty net. Little else has mattered to the Americans than thus "capping and freezing" this country's nuclear weapons programme.

Ironically, it is an unelected (and unelectable) Prime Minister who is seeking permanently to strategically hobble this great democracy.

Consider this the offer of uninterrupted fuel supply for imported reactors (that Menon carried back with him) tries to get around the clause preventing the stockpiling of fuel by offering no reliable alternative other than restating what is in the explanatory note attached to the Hyde Act.

The continuity of fuel supply, this note says, is limited to contingencies when there is "disruption due to market failures or similar reasons" whereupon "friendly supplier countries" can be expected to redress the situation. Permission to reprocess spent imported fuel, and the mooting of a joint mechanism to consider how best to mitigate the effects of the inevitable economic and technology sanctions should India ever test again—that Menon supposedly wrangled—are executive measures that the Bush administration may, in fact, concede in order to seal the deal, but these mean nothing.

The permission to reprocess fuel will be ended as abruptly as the fuel supply when, not if, owing to the politico-technological necessity, India tests again. Here the government's willingness to make the resumption of nuclear tests by India palatable to Washington by linking it to renewed testing by the US and China presumes that the unproved, unsafe, unreliable and hence non-credible Indian thermonuclear designs, whose performance need desperately to be validated by rigorous physical testing, are on par with the thoroughly tested, verified and versatile thermonuclear American and Chinese arsenals, which can do without further tests.

This is taking delusional strategic thinking to a new high, and India will pay dearly for it.

Testing aside, the truth is, in case India violates any of the Non-Proliferation Treaty constraints in any manner or form or falls short in any of a myriad ways detailed in the Hyde Act and in the umbrella US Atomic Energy Act like, for instance, in observing the stringent reporting requirements and the non-nuclear weapon state-related IAEA safeguards and norms, and in adhering to the restricted technology trade strictures of the Non-Proliferation Treaty and the Missile Technology Control Regime—how has the mention of the unconnected missile technology sneaked into the Hyde Act?—neither of which technology denial regimes India subscribes to, its Section 129 kicks in and the nuclear deal is instantly terminated in whole and in its parts.

Agreeing to these provisions, moreover, signals the Manmohan Singh government's formal acceptance of non-nuclear weapon state status for India under the nearly defunct NPT.

The likelihood of other Nuclear Suppliers' Group members helping out is voided by the Hyde Act enjoining the US government to ensure NSG solidarity.

As far, as the joint mechanism is concerned, what can it reasonably be expected to do once India tests, as it must for its nuclear weapons to pack even minimal credibility, considering a presidential waiver can be countermanded by a Congressional vote at any time?

Short of radical overhaul of the Hyde Act and the overarching US Atomic Energy Act, which is ruled out, there is little to prevent the economic and technology sanctions from coming down automatically, the underway nuclear transactions from ending mid-stream, and India being left high and dry.

And note, if the US applies closure to the deal at any time and for any flimsy reason, the Indian civilian nuclear facilities will continue to be under the non-nuclear weapon state-related International Atomic Energy Agency safeguards and Additional Protocol.

Further, there has been no movement whatsoever in resolving major differences regarding a host of other negative provisions in the Hyde Act. For instance, the US Congress, under the guise of end-use monitoring has, vide Section 104, conceived of "fallback safeguards" and under Section 115 accorded the US National Nuclear Security Administration a parallel role with the International Atomic Energy Agency in policing Indian nuclear activities, gathering sensitive information, and as per Section 109, in even suborning Indian scientists! Besides GNEP (Global Nuclear Experimental Project), that India can access but only as a customer, will be used, as Secretary Rice indicated in an April 2006 US Senate hearing, to tap Indian nuclear and other high technology talent.

Worse, even as the Hyde Act requires India to respect the NSG and MTCR prohibitions, it clarifies that India cannot benefit from open commerce with the member states. And the impracticable clause in the Hyde Act requiring India to return all materials and technologies in case of the deal breaking down remains untouched.

As does the part of the Hyde Act predicating "civil nuclear cooperation" on India's harmonising its Iran policy with US objectives—a linkage confirmed by leading US legislators in their recent provocative letter to the PM.

And finally, there is absolutely nothing in the Hyde Act or the proposed 123 agreement offering financial relief to India in terms of reimbursing the costs of importing reactors and building up the related infrastructure and compensating for the economic losses incurred by an abrupt cut-off of fuel supply and hence of electricity in the grid.

This deal will not only gut India's nuclear security, compromise foreign policy options, and hold energy security, economic progress and the testing option hostage to the threat of fuel supply cut-off, but cost the exchequer; hundreds of billions of dollars.

The innumerable provisions in the Hyde Act contextualising the 123 agreement, which are detrimental to India's sovereignty and strategic independence and contravene the Joint Statement and the Prime Minister's promises in Parliament, remain intact. Prudence, abundant caution, and some sense of national self-respect ought, therefore, to persuade Manmohan Singh to reject a 123 agreement and the nuclear deal. Or, is that expecting too much of a PM who seems bent on proving himself a sap and India a sucker?

(The Asian Age, May 18, 2007)

58. Hyde is Reality Behind Bush Smokescreen

A. GOPALAKRISHNAN

When a US President signs a bill into an Act, he may issue a written statement implying that he differs with certain provisions of law in that Act, due to reasons he indicates in the statement. Such documents, called "Presidential Signing Statements," were used by several past Presidents mainly to clarify Constitutional positions, but the more recent ones have increasingly contained one or more challenges or objections to the laws being signed. The objections are usually on the grounds that they infringe on the authority granted to the executive branch by the Constitution.

On December 18, 2006 President Bush signed the Henry J. Hyde United States-India Peaceful Atomic Energy Cooperation Act of 2006 into law, based on the bill approved by both Houses of the US Congress. Just hours later, he also signed a "Presidential Signing Statement" for this bill, which was then promptly published in the US Federal Register. In this, he stated, "Section 103 of the (Hyde) Act purports to establish US policy with respect to various international affairs matters. My approval of the Act does not constitute my adoption of the statements of policy as US foreign policy... The executive branch shall construe such policy statements as advisory. Also the executive branch shall construe Section 104(d)(2) of the Act as advisory ... (and) shall construe provisions of the Act such as Sections 104 and 109 in a manner consistent with the President's Constitutional authority to protect and control information that could impair foreign relations."

Interestingly, this presidential signing statement was used promptly by Mr Pranab Mukherjee, India's external affairs minister, who, just hours after its release in Washington, read it out verbatim to the Upper House of Parliament (Rajya Sabha), where the government was facing severe criticism during a debate on the deal. After reading the statement, Mr Mukherjee said, "That is the interpretation of the person who is instructed by law to implement the Act. That is the rationality in which the PM assured the House yesterday, despite knowing the extraneous and prescriptive provisions, not all but some, of the Hyde (Act)." Thus, Mr Mukherjee successfully used the US signing statement as a means to temporarily shield the government from the sharp criticism of the Opposition parties and the scientific community.

The Indian public may be left with the impression that Bush has overruled the unacceptable sections of the Hyde Act as merely "advisory," and will not abide by them while implementing the Indo-US deal. Thus, around the corner, we may get placatory arguments from both governments that the signing statement is binding on the US Congress and that India need not worry about the various adverse provisions in the Hyde Act. But, unlike vetoes, presidential signing statements are not part of the legislative process as set forth in the US Constitution, and have no legal effect. A signed law, like the Hyde Act, is still a law, regardless of what one President says in an accompanying signing statement.

In that case, can we trust that the statement will be enforceable over a long period, during which time several US Presidents and Congresses will come and go? The answer is a resounding "No"!

The rest of this article briefly examines various aspects of the presidential signing statement, and especially its validity and enforceability. Since I am basically a nuclear engineer, in doing this, I have relied not only on the exhaustive literature search I have carried out, but more importantly, on direct consultation I had with senior Constitutional lawyers in both the US and India to verify the accuracy of my statements.

Perhaps the most learned US expert in presidential signing statements today is Prof. Christopher S. Kelley of the Department of Political Science at the Miami University in Oxford, Ohio. His doctoral thesis earlier and the past 12 years of his research interest have been on studying presidential signing statements. Regarding the signing statement of Bush in the case of the Hyde Act, Prof. Kelley says, "Further, it is also quickly becoming clear that the challenges in the signing statement may not have much to do with separation of powers concerns, or concerns over presidential prerogatives, but rather domestic and foreign politics. But from the President's point of view, he was catching a great deal of heat from India over what they perceived to be overly hostile language from the Congress, and language that does not treat their country as a sovereign nation. The signing statement was a way for President Bush to placate the Indian elites. So it gives us a nice insight into some of the pressures that drive a signing statement, and that it isn't always just the protection of prerogatives despite what the language may say."

Prof. Charles J. Ogletree, Jr, Jesse Climenko, Professor of Law at the Harvard Law School, in his testimony before the US Congress on January 31, 2007 has said, "One example of the potential dangers in the use of presidential signing statements is the recent passage of the Hyde Act, 2006. The Indian government considers the signing statement that accompanied the law as an indication of how the US plans to interpret those sections. Thus, even if signing statements are not enforceable, this raises the concern that foreign countries might have expectations that we will interpret laws as signing statements announce. Additionally, there is a real concern that a country like India would worry that a future President could choose to interpret the law differently."

It is clear from these two comments that the US signing statement was more of a ploy to help cool down the tempers of Indian Opposition parties and senior scientists, and to help the Manmohan Singh government in face of the severe criticism it was facing, rather than any serious attempt to take on the US Congress!

When Bush says he considers a section in the Hyde Act as "advisory," he is reserving a broad leeway for himself for a full spectrum of actions anywhere from "full compliance" to "no compliance" with that section. Furthermore, an incoming future President need not be bound by Bush's signing statement, and if he wants he can decide to fully enforce the Hyde Act provisions.

Prof. Kelley concurs with me on the above interpretation, and he has given me an example where President Clinton ignored the statements of earlier Presidents Reagan and George H.W. Bush, when he came to power. Thus, even with the Bush signing statement on the books, India can never be sure which provisions of the Act may be enforced on India at what time in the future.

As Prof. Kelley reminds us, "The signing statement is only as powerful as Congress is willing to allow it. In the past, Congress has forced the President to back off on signing statements by vigorous oversight, by refusing to confirm appointees until the administration backs-off, or by cutting-off financial appropriations. These and many more are tools Congress has at its disposal." Therefore, assertive Congressional action against India, in future, cannot be overruled.

Very few really think that the Congress can successfully sue the President before the Supreme Court about a signing statement. However, on May 9, 2007, House Speaker Nancy Pelosi is reported to have said, "We can take the President to court... The President has made excessive use of signing statements and Congress is considering ways to respond to the executive branch's over-reaching." The American Bar Association (ABA) appointed a task force on presidential signing statements in June 2006, and its report has been unanimously accepted now as ABA policy. Specifically, the ABA has termed the misuse of presidential power through signing statements as contrary to the rule of law and the US Constitutional system. In July 2006, Senator Arlene Specter introduced the "Presidential Signing Statements Act, 2006" (S. 3731) in the House Judiciary Committee.

This bill is likely to be re-introduced in the current 110th Congress, and it aims at curbing presidential misuse of such statements. Another bill,

Congressional Law-making Authority Protection Act, 2007 (H.R. 264), was introduced in January 2007, with the same objective. With the Democrats in control of Congress and Bush's power and authority waning, such Congressional actions are bound to gain momentum.

From the above, one can see that the decks are heavily loaded against the enforceability of presidential signing statements. The MEA and PMO must study these aspects more fully before plunging headlong into the nuclear deal. The Hyde Act is the specific US law which governs the Indo-US nuclear deal and no presidential signing statement or Indian 123 agreement can permanently or effectively dilute or over-ride any section of it.

(The Asian Age, May 23, 2007)

59. Our Rush to Disaster

BHARAT KARNAD

Disturbing news from the nuclear establishment suggest that, notwithstanding every good and sensible reason to reject the nuclear deal with the United States, an increasingly antsy Manmohan Singh has issued a *finman* to the Indian negotiators that he wants a 123 agreement both he and US President George W. Bush can support when they meet during the upcoming G-8 summit, and he does not care what compromises are made to get it ready.

The method being worked out is to ensure that none of the offending clauses and provisions in the parent Hyde Act finds mention in the 123 agreement. This, the Manmohan Singh government hopes, will help it to claim that the document meets all the commitments the Prime Minister made in Parliament. Uniquely for an Indian Prime Minister, who by convention is also concurrently minister for atomic energy. Manmohan Singh apparently trusts the US government. which expressly seeks to limit India's nuclear capabilities and ambitions, rather than heed the country's nuclear scientists pleading with him to not imperil the integrity and operational freedom the Indian nuclear programme has always enjoyed, and Indian governments of whatever party-hue have up until now fought strongly and successfully to protect.

The Congress party-led coalition government is seemingly so determined to cut a deal with the Americans, come what may, that even remote contingencies are being factored into the calculus and appropriate action take. Thus, the Parliament was *adjourned sine die* the day before the public interest litigation concerning the deal came up for hearing in the Supreme Court. A stay order from the highest court would have put a crimp in the negotiations and prevented the government from reaching an understanding with the US on the 123 agreement that large sections of the society, persuaded by the legitimate concerns of the country's nuclear scientists, believe will injure vital national interests.

Having asserted its light as the executive to make and sign any treaty the Manmohan Singh regime is relying on the esoteric nature of the nuclear issues involved to brazen it out in the belief that much of what is transpiring escapes the understanding of the common man. It is moreover, convinced the deal cannot emerge as an issue to mar the party's prospects in the next general election. It is a conviction fuelled by the failure of the Opposition parties to convert the nuclear deal into an emotive, high octane public campaign of the "The Indian Bomb is sacrificed" variety.

The other day at a panel discussion in Delhi on the nuclear deal, the highly respected retired diplomat, ambassador Chinmaya Gharekhan, with vast experience of engaging with the US in the United Nations and elsewhere, posed a singularly apt question that needs to be pondered and which those around the table advocating the deal were unable to respond to. "If the deal is, from India's point of view, so good, why," he asked pointedly, "are the Americans pushing it?"

The answer, of course, is that if India gets something as a consequence of the deal, the US stands to gain a whole lot more, which means that it will finally realise its non-proliferation goal that has so far eluded it, namely, locking India into a position at the low end of the weapons technology learning curve (by pre-empting its testing option) and pushing it into the Non-Proliferation Treaty regime and Comprehensive Test Ban Treaty net.

Even with a favourable deal, many US non-proliferation and South Asia experts expect this deal to trigger endless bickering between the two countries, with India trying to secure the maximum possible payoff from the deal, and the US side trying hard to minimise India's offtake and the uncertain ramifications on the existing global non-proliferation and security order of this tug-of-war.

The outcome of the US ultimately prevailing is not in doubt, except that India's nuclear facilities will have passed permanently into the International Atomic Energy Agency safeguards bag. Much as Delhi may wish, the IAEA, backed by Washington, will simply not allow "India-specific" safeguards and Additional Protocol to be conditioned on the deal panning out as Delhi expects it to.

Worse, there is every possibility of lack of consensus in the Nuclear Suppliers' Group remaining unresolved. Already the Australian mines minister has declared that India will get uranium from his country only if India signs the Non-Proliferation Treaty!

Both countries may soon wish they were rid of this bothersome policy monkey on their backs, leaving them free fruitfully to explore areas of occasional and episodic military, political and scientific and technological cooperation to complement the natural growth in trade and economic relations. India is a rising power seeking to change its rank order in the international community and hence the *status quo*, and the US is the main beneficiary and prop of the current international order. The ambitions and objectives don't meet—a fact the Manmohan Singh regime studiously refuses to acknowledge.

As this analyst predicted long ago, this deal is a "poison pill" that both countries should beware of, because it has seeds in it of serious rift, making the breakdown of the "civil nuclear cooperation" deal inevitable. Bitterness on the Indian side will be fuelled when a future Indian government finds itself having to make the difficult choice between testing and seeing the deal end with quite considerable economic and energy supply dislocation, and not testing and seeing the strategic imbalance with China and the international system generally steadily grow. It will also be severely tested by the exploitative nature of the nuclear transactions with the US and other members of the Nuclear Suppliers' Group and the limited access to advanced technology that will be on offer to India.

Expecting big commercial pay-offs in terms or huge contracts for reactors and big military sales the US, on the other hand, will be disappointed by reactor contracts going mainly to its competitors, France and Russia, with the better, more modern, reactors and the military hardware contracts being monopolised by these two states, Israel and the United Kingdom—the outcome of "the US as unreliable supplier"—worries the Indian armed forces are seized by, topped by a progressively more wary Delhi, which will be unwilling to allow the US to have its way, as it did on the nuclear deal.

But the most subversive and far-reaching aspect of the nuclear deal is that it will forcibly render the Indian nuclear energy programme transparent—a process begun by the guileless cobbling together of the "separation plan" by the Manmohan Singh regime. This plan and the deal will be the means to impose increasingly greater pressure on India to reduce the military-related research and development activity.

In 322 BC, Chanakya declared that "The biggest *guru-mantra* is to never share your secrets with anybody! It will destroy you." In 2007 AD, a strategically naive Manmohan Singh with his telescope fixed on the economic "pie in the sky" promised by the supposed free market interaction with the US, is about to neuter India's prized nuclear weapons programme. By ignoring the concerns of the scientists, who are at least vocal in their opposition, and of the armed forces who, as tradition demands, are silent on the issue but, as the end-user, immensely anxious that the under-rested thermonuclear weapons they will be asked to fire will not work as advertised, he has ensured that a question mark will always hang over the country's strategic deterrent.

(*The Asian Age*, May 29, 2007)

60. Controversy over the Nuclear Deal

P.K. IYENGAR

At the time it was struck, the July 2005 India-U.S. nuclear agreement appeared historic. The compromises by both sides looked acceptable then. The U.S. seemed to agree to recognise India as a nuclear weapons country, and to not interfere with its nuclear doctrine, strategic programme, or further development of its nuclear arsenal, which includes design, development, and testing of new nuclear weapons. Secondly, the U.S. recognised the need for more nuclear power in India, and was willing to do commerce in civil nuclear power, and encourage the Nuclear Suppliers' Group to do the same, subject only to the condition that such reactors and their fuel would be under IAEA safeguards specific to India. In March 2006, the U.S. gave assurances that in order to avoid situations like Tarapur, where fuel was denied to us after the 1974 Pokhran test, they would guarantee fuel supplies to these imported reactors for their lifetime, and, if necessary, help us build fuel stockpiles.

The U.S. also agreed that our efforts for nuclear energy based on a three-stage programme could continue unrestricted, with fast breeders and thorium reactors, and that we would have the opportunity to collaborate with the U.S. on their R&D efforts for a new generation of nuclear reactors. The Prime Minister repeated these promises in the Parliament many times, and it was said that the only thing we were committing was the continuation of our voluntary moratorium on nuclear testing and a separation plan such that our strategic programme and R&D would not be subject to IAEA inspection. It was claimed that this separation plan would be entirely voluntary.

However, when subsequent changes in the U.S. position made the deal unpalatable for India, the Indian negotiators failed to hold to the Prime Minister's stand. Delivery of fuel was linked to non-testing and fuel supply was no longer guaranteed. Reprocessing, which is essential for our three-stage programme, was specifically disallowed. Instead of participating as an equal in R&D programmes, India would now only be a bystander. All these changes were codified in the Hyde Act—an appropriate name, given the Jekyll and Hyde Act that the U.S. government is pulling!

These serious changes alarmed the community of nuclear scientists. A number of us who have led the civilian and strategic nuclear programmes in the past found it necessary to express our grave reservations in writing. This had its effect, with the Prime Minister giving a detailed reply and categorical assurances in Parliament that India would not play a game with "shifting goalposts." However, our statement also received criticism from some quarters, which alleged that this was tantamount to interference in the government's executive rights and responsibilities. This criticism is obviously unjustified because it was not just our right but also our responsibility, as people with the relevant technical expertise, to provide appropriate advice to the people, the Parliament, and the government of this country.

In this context, it is interesting to recall a letter written by Hans Bethe to President Clinton in April 1997, advising him to cease all research, even computer simulations, into a new generation of nuclear weapons:

"As the Director of the Theoretical Division at Los Alamos, I participated at the most senior level in the World War II Manhattan Project that produced the first atomic weapons. Now, at age 90, I am one of the few remaining senior project participants. And I have followed closely, and participated in the major issues of the nuclear arms race and disarmament during the last half century. I ask to be permitted to express a related opinion. It seems the time has come for our Nation to declare that it is not working, in any way, to develop further weapons of mass destruction of any kind. In particular, this means not financing work looking toward the possibility of new designs for nuclear weapons. And it certainly means not working on new types of nuclear weapons, such as pure-fusion weapons...

"The underlying purpose of a complete cessation of nuclear testing mandated by the Comprehensive Test Ban Treaty is to prevent new nuclear weapons from emerging and this certainly suggests doing everything we can to prevent new categories of nuclear weapons from being discovered. It is in our national and global interest to stand true to this underlying purpose."

In his reply, President Clinton wrote:

"Thank you for sharing your thoughts on nuclear weapons with me... I am fully committed to securing the ratification, entry into force and effective implementation of the CTBT. By banning all nuclear explosions, the CTBT will constrain the development and qualitative improvement of nuclear weapons and end the development of advanced new types of nuclear weapons. In this way, the Treaty will contribute to the process of nuclear disarmament and the prevention of nuclear proliferation, and it will strengthen international peace and security... I have also directed that the United States maintain the basic capability to resume nuclear test activities prohibited by the CTBT in the unlikely event that the United States should need to withdraw from this treaty..."

Look at the tone of Prof. Bethe's letter. Now imagine the consternation if an Indian scientist were to use such a tone in a letter to the Prime Minister!

The reply from President Clinton is also interesting. He openly states America's willingness to resume nuclear testing should such a situation arise in the future. He also indicated that the national laboratories will maintain an alert group to redesign new weapons of mass destruction, for which new facilities are being approved. We now know that even this exit clause was not considered sufficient, and the U.S. Congress refused to ratify the CTBT. In June 1996, India withdrew from the CTBT Conference because of its discriminatory nature, and because the way to nuclear disarmament is not through imposing such limited agreements on some, while others are carrying out research towards discovering new weapons.

Such research is probably not restricted to the Americans. In June 2006, the Russian Foreign Minister told the Duma that the Americans were already experimenting with deep penetrating mini-nukes called 'bunker-busters.' This suggests that perhaps even Russia is trying such innovations. In spite of agreeing not to develop anti-missile defence systems in the 1970s, the U.S. unilaterally withdrew from that treaty. The Chinese have even demonstrated recently that they could bring down satellites in orbit.

The supporters of the nuclear deal argue that it is essential to augment nuclear power to support our rapid growth, and that this requires the nuclear deal. The first part of the argument is correct. Where they err is in not understanding that the nuclear deal will not achieve this goal, that we will lose more than we gain through the deal. For one, we are getting neither nuclear fuel nor reactors for free or at a low cost but at the prevailing market price, and this is definitely more than the cost of indigenous nuclear power. Secondly, the promise of nuclear technology rings hollow—it comes too late and offers too little. Today we are quite self-sufficient in the technology of heavy-water reactors, and are world leaders in the technology of fast-breeder reactors. These are the technologies we have chosen for our three-stage nuclear programme, with good reason.

The light-water reactors (LWRs) we may buy use only 0.5 per cent of the uranium mined, leaving the rest to be stored if the fuel is not reprocessed and reused, as in the once-through cycle. It is more profitable to reprocess and extract the plutonium from heavy-water reactors and use it as fuel for the fast-breeder reactors, which is the essence of our three-stage programme. They have also been shown to be more economical in terms of capital cost and tariff. Imagine the benefits that would accrue if we succeed in burning up to 10 per cent of the uranium mined as well as the thorium that we use, in a once-through cycle. Efforts are on to achieve this through our own research and development.

Yes, we would be happy to have more reactors if they are economically viable, such as the LWRs we are buying from Russia—without having to sign any nuclear deal from them. But the price we are being asked to pay by the U.S. is too high: no testing, no reprocessing, no guarantees of future fuel supplies. Once we sign the deal we will be at the mercy of the U.S. and the NSG for our energy security.. This is hardly a situation a country that sees itself as a future superpower should place itself in. There is another solution to the problem of generating more nuclear power: rapid expansion of the indigenous programme with more capital for more reactors, greater exploitation of our uranium resources, greater urgency to our fast-breeder programme and thorium utilisation.

Scientists Ignored

Unfortunately, in India, scientists no longer have influence on the nuclear policy of the government. Technical realities and long-term programmes based on scientific expertise and the collective wisdom of half a century are dismissed with neither thought nor debate. The vision of a self-reliant nuclear India that Jawaharlal Nehru and Homi Bhabha envisioned, and which Indira Gandhi and Rajiv Gandhi nurtured and sustained, seems now ready to be consigned to the dustbin of history. It is true that there are new pressures and new imperatives in a changing India. But equally, there are no quick fixes. FDI will not turn nuclear power economical, and outsourcing nuclear power will not ensure our energy security. It is the creativity of Indian scientists and their work in Indian laboratories alone that can prove beneficial to the future of this country. It seems to me that already great damage has been done to our strategic planning. Nine years after the Pokhran II tests, we haven't evaluated the detailed requirements for a minimum credible deterrent, including delivery systems. Our R&D limps on, while elsewhere a new generation of efficient nuclear weapons and their delivery systems is being actively worked on. Decisions need to be taken, and urgently, for the civilian and strategic nuclear programme, but not without thought, consideration, consultation, and an appreciation of scientific realities. This is a time not for politics but for statesmanship.

(*The Hindu*, May 31, 2007)

61. PM must be Careful about Nuclear Pitfalls

A. GOPALAKRISHNAN

Over the past two years, much has been written on the Indo-US nuclear deal. Many assurances have been given by the government and the Prime Minister to assuage the deep concerns of the Indian public. Yet, the majority of Indians are concerned that the UPA government, in its hurry to secure the deal, will compromise national interests in the process. There remains a serious deficit of trust in the government's reasons for entering into this deal, the doubtful objectivity with which it has evaluated it, the biased choice of the Indian negotiating teams, and the general lack of transparency.

Within the next two weeks, the PM will be meeting first with Nicholas Burns, US under-secretary of state (political) in Delhi, and later with President George W. Bush on the sidelines of the G-8 conference in Germany. The Indo-US deal will be the major topic to be discussed, and the objective, we understand, will be the finalisation of the deal. To help the PM in these discussions, we hope the PMO prepares for him a focused aide-memoire outlining all the concerns and pitfalls which many of us have repeatedly pointed out in the past.

Both Burns and President Bush are likely to point out the existence of a beneficial "Presidential Signing Statement," which Bush created on the same day he signed the Hyde Act into law. Both are certain to tell the PM that India need not worry about many of the unacceptable provisions in Sections 103, 104 and 109 of the Hyde Act, because Bush has set them aside as "advisory," and they will not therefore be applicable as far as the US administration is concerned.

But the PM must know that the Bush signing statement cannot be relied on, and that it has no legal standing under US Constitutional law to override the Hyde Act. In this regard, it would be helpful if the Prime Minister's attention is drawn to the article on this subject titled 'Hyde is reality behind Bush smokescreen' which was published in this paper on May 23, 2007.

The hullabaloo that the PMO and the MEA are making about the 123 agreement is really a charade, since the US law, which the Americans have to adhere to, is that which is clearly spelt out in the Hyde Act, and not the 123 agreement. To imply that our negotiators are sweating it out to incorporate the right clauses in the agreement to get around the decisive stipulations of this Act merely amounts to a blatant attempt at duping the Indian public. According to Constitutional legal experts, no cleverly-drafted 123 agreement or presidential signing statement will enable the PM to meet his commitments to Parliament.

The Hyde Act threateningly points towards several eventualities of policy differences which, when compounded through the annual Congressional review process, could lead to the termination of the nuclear cooperation envisaged under this deal. India's testing of a nuclear explosive device is only one of such situations. Another could be India's refusal to stop assistance or interaction with Iran, and the US Congress' insistence that we do so. The US could also rake up some false accusation of nuclear export violations by India which it may claim are serious threats to its security. Has the PM thought through the severe economic and technological hardships we will face if such abrupt termination of the deal occurs?

It is to cover for such eventualities that India must absolutely insist on getting life-long nuclear fuel assurances under this deal for our safeguarded reactors, uninterrupted supply of spare parts to keep them running, and the waiver from having to return any prior supplies we might have received. None of these is assured today, even after several rounds of 123 negotiations. Indian concerns in this regard can be removed only if the US Congress suitably amends the definitive sections of the Hyde Act which deal with these aspects.

Besides the purchase of reactors, the purpose of this deal is also to enable us to acquire updated civilian nuclear technology which we could use in future in areas such as reprocessing, enrichment and heavy-water production. Since we already have indigenous technologies in all these fields, there should be no bar in providing improved technologies, under safeguards, if we need them. But the Hyde Act specifically denies such transfers, which goes against the letter and spirit of the July 18, 2005 joint statement.

On another front, the Hyde Act does not waive the need for India to seek and obtain US permission every time we wish to reprocess the irradiated imported fuel from our reactors. These US denials are not acceptable and the PM must clearly seek related corrective amendments to the Hyde Act, since the 123 agreement cannot remove these restrictions in law.

If the Prime Minister believes that coming "as close as possible" to his categorical earlier assurances to Parliament on this deal is sufficient achievement in these final rounds of high level negotiations, he is seriously misreading the mood of the country.

For the UPA in power, the finalisation of this deal has now become an urgent political necessity. The UPA government is also emboldened by the fact that the Left parties have given a clear signal that they will not unseat the

Manmohan Singh government, irrespective of what the final decision on this deal is. The Left must realise that if the nuclear deal is allowed to go through as it is, a vast majority of the public and almost the entire science and technology community in India will put the primary blame for that on the Left parties, for merely providing the rhetoric all along, without contributing any substantive corrective action at the end.

Lastly, the PM must insist that we will not allow this nuclear deal to be utilised by the US to dictate foreign policy prescriptions to India. Ever since the UPA government has come to power, its heavy leaning towards US policies has been quite evident, and it has now culminated in this deal which both governments are in a hurry to finalise.

Taking advantage of the Indian government's over-eagerness to conclude the deal, the US has coerced India to vote against Iran at the IAEA twice in recent times. Now through Sections 103(b)(4) and 104(g)(2)(E)(i) of the Hyde Act, the US is attempting to permanently put a stranglehold on our Iran policies. The Prime Minister must insist that these clauses in the Hyde Act be removed during its amendment.

(The Asian Age, June 1, 2007)

62. N-deal Compromises National Security

National security adviser M.K. Narayanan will formally offer further compromises to Nicholas Burns when he visits Washington. These will reportedly go beyond the offer to construct at our expense a plant to reprocess imported fuel under safeguards and to accept the concept of a multilateral fuel-bank to get around the Hyde Act prohibition of US guaranteed fuel supply. It is supposed to get the stalled nuclear deal moving.

But sidestepping the other, equally damaging, provisions in the Hyde Act won't be as easy. Among these are the issues related to safeguards in perpetuity, end-use verification under Section 115 allowing the US National Nuclear Security Agency to snoop on Indian nuclear military activities, reconfiguring Indian policies on Iran and the Fissile Material Cut-off Treaty in line with the US thinking, return of US-sourced material and technology in case the deal breaks down, and the American option to terminate nuclear cooperation for any reason, other than resumption of Indian testing, that Washington at any time deems as being in its "supreme national interest."

Manmohan Singh's historically false belief that economic growth supersedes national security concerns, is the Indian-supplied propellant for this deal. Finding his government bare of the requisite talent, the Prime Minister has relied on K. Subrahmanyam to make the popular case, until now when he has invested the latter's efforts with an official seal. Subrahmanyam, as head of a committee with two MEA stalwarts—Shyam Saran, the PM's special envoy, and Arundhati Ghose, former ambassador to the UN Commission on Disarmament in Geneva—is tasked with moulding India's long-held positions on the Comprehensive Test Ban Treaty and the Fissile Material Cut-off Treaty to fit the requirements of the Hyde Act.

As part of its deliberations, this committee has met with senior members of the strategic community but generally avoided those who have opposed the nuclear deal. Many who have interacted with this committee have come away with the impression that Subrahmanyam in the guise of seeking a consensus, is preparing the ground, for instance, for India's accepting Washington's point of view that the FMCT should not be verifiable other than by "National Technical Means." This is a signal departure from India's traditional insistence that, to prevent the possibility of cheating, compliance of the FMCT has to be physically verified by international inspectors, something the US objects to because it fears its secret weapon-related research and development activity will be exposed.

Why is this issue important? Because "National Technical Means" (NTM) refers to satellite sensors and other such advanced technologies able remotely to sniff out fissile material production. It is technology available only with the United States, its European intimates and, perhaps, Russia.

Do Messrs Subrahmanyam, Saran and Ghose envisage that, lacking any such technical wherewithal itself, India will plug into the American NTM system in the hope of detecting treaty violations by countries of concern? If so, what is the assurance that all the intelligence obtained by the US NTM will be communicated to Delhi directly in its raw form and not in bits and pieces of processed, sanitised, and pre-digested information?

In any case, is India in a position to know the difference? And, what guarantee is there that the NTM will not be turned against India, as former Prime Minister Atal Behari Vajpayee, correctly apprehends? (Refer his statement released on July 6, 2007.)

Further, is it wise for India to bank on America in this respect, considering that Washington has, for reasons of state, winked at sustained proliferation by China? Who is to say, US' signature on the FMCT notwithstanding, it will not turn a blind eye to similar developments in the extended region detrimental to India's security? Or, does this committee believe that India is already on par with the US, Russia and even China on the NTM technology front and, therefore has nothing to fear?

The fact is that as a result of India's signing the US-drafted FMCT already tabled in Geneva—something not anticipated by the masterminds in the Manmohan Singh government responsible for the deal, this country's fissile material production will be rendered transparent to America and the other big powers, but Delhi will have no like insight into the fissile material production activities of the five so-called Non-Proliferation Treaty-recognised nuclear weapon states (the United States, Russia, China, the United Kingdom, and France), and Pakistan and a host of nuclear weapon threshold states.

This verification aspect incidentally, is actually of secondary concern. The primary worry of the nuclear establishment and the military is, as it should be, that if the FMCT comes into force anytime soon—and Washington will ensure precisely this—it will result in corking India's still quite meagre fissile material stockpile. Unless one buys the line retailed by the nuclear minimalists that warheads in double digits are enough by way of a deterrent, even as they pooh-pooh the strategic and political consequences for India of a galloping Chinese strategic weapons programme, the continuing impact of the huge and modernising US and Russian weapon inventories, and of the retention of lethal nuclear arsenals by Britain and France.

The fact is India will simply not be able to do in the FMCT negotiations what it managed in the talks on the CTBT—stretch these out over years in order to buy time for a new series of tests, the continued augmentation of its fissile material holdings, and for development of advanced weapons-related technologies.

But thanks to Manmohan Singh's seemingly stubborn simpletonism (reflected, for example, in his repeated insistence that the deal is an energy panacea despite every evidence to the contrary), acquiescing in the "no testing" condition will result in India's entering the CTBT by the backdoor. And signing a flawed FMCT will severely limit the country's fissile material stock. US' long-held non-proliferation goals of stunting India's nuclear weapon technology and capping the size of the Indian deterrent, will thus be achieved, as some of us Cassandras have been incessantly warning. It is the realisation of these non-proliferation aims that will be the proverbial foreign policy feather in the cap of the outgoing US President, not the deal itself.

And finally, in a setting where abject surrender has followed indefensible compromise, for the Prime Minister to label those opposing the nuclear deal, and that includes almost the entire political Opposition (Bharatiya Janata Party, the newly minted "Third Front," and the Left parties propping up the ruling coalition), and the community of alarmed nuclear scientists and just as anxious senior serving and retired military-men, and a few strategic analysts as "unpatriotic," is an extraordinary display of cheek and Orwellian double-speak.

Manmohan Singh is personally committed to delivering the deal to his good friend George W. Bush even if it undermines India's vital national security interests. Now, what's that old saw again about "patriotism being the last refuge of scoundrels"?

(The Asian Age, July 14, 2007)

63. Does N-deal Really Solve Issues?

A.N. PRASAD

Instead of coming out clean on the text of the 123 agreement by making it public, both India and the United States in collusion have chosen to keep it under wraps and are selectively issuing rosy statements that all is well and all our concerns have been fully addressed.

While one wishes it is really satisfactory, it is unfortunate that the Cabinet committees, the political parties and the public are deprived of constructive analyses and unbiased expert opinions. What we are fed up with is one-sided interpretation of the text by the official side though there is promise that the text will be made public soon in consultation with the US. The article which said that India has same rights as nuclear weapons states based on off the record briefings, which appeared on rediff.com makes one wonder how far the government is attempting to sugarcoat.

Some of the points made in this article do not need the full text to comment.

If the July 18, 2005 joint statement where India was lifted to the moral high ground is kept by the side of the Hyde Act, a legally binding document based on which the 123 Agreement will largely actually be implemented, it is not difficult to see to what extent India has been given the same rights and privileges of a Nuclear Weapons State.

As just one example, while a Nuclear Weapons State can voluntarily place under civilian list any of their nuclear facilities and exclude any facility as military facility and make changes at will, India was made to fight for every facility during the preparation of the separation plan.

Also, the safeguards' implementation as far as Nuclear Weapons States are concerned is hardly intensive and India can never hope to get that sort of parity judging by many of the stipulations in the Hyde Act.

It is to be expected that while negotiating a bilateral agreement there will always be constraints on both sides. However, in this case it is the US, by passing the Hyde Act disregarding the concerns expressed by Prime Minister Manmohan Singh [Images] and his commitments to Parliament has left India to compromise.

More than the substance, the negotiators seem to have concentrated more on fixing the language to make the text look palatable on paper. So far, we have only the negotiators' interpretation of the deal without the access to how the various issues are actually worded. The government seems to be working on garnering support from various quarters to gain psychological advantage before releasing the text.

The reprocessing issue is still confusing.

Contrary to what is being told in the briefings there seems to be conditional clearance with actual bottlenecks still not being fully removed. This is where the text is important to really ascertain whether our interests are fully protected.

It is reported that the Japanese model is followed. If it is so, I can say with my experience it is not too pleasant in practice. They have in the past suffered under the US restrictions.

On the issue of the fate of the cooperation agreement in case of testing, there is no ambiguity as far as Hyde Act is concerned. What seems to have been achieved is language couching, vague complex wordings to circumvent and give an impression of having adequately addressed the issue. This is nothing but absolute fooling! When implemented in the present form, there is no doubt that in future, any government in power will be constrained to decide in favour of testing, having dug deep into foreign investments in nuclear power plants and pressures on the political and economic fronts among others.

The government during the negotiations may be under advice from certain influential quarters that actual testing could be replaced by computer simulation. This is a dangerous prospect indeed! On this issue, there seems to be no escaping the Hyde Act and supreme national security concerns.

On the issue of full civilian nuclear cooperation, it is amazing to see the new definition given by the spin-masters on both sides. What is simple and straight forward, at least in definition, is being made to look oversimplified. Part cannot be full as US wants to define. If recognising our strategic programme, allowing us to import reactors and fuel and have the right to reprocess and enrich uranium and also export heavy water through our own efforts could constitute full civilian cooperation, what is the big deal?

It is being argued that we have the technology in the entire fuel cycle and why do we bother? If it is so, we have the technology for designing, building and operating reactors. Why are we going in for this technology import? Are we getting over the embargoes on import of equipment and components and any other materials on all parts of the fuel cycle, specifically including enrichment, reprocessing and heavy water, flagged by the Hyde Act or restricted to only those parts of the fuel cycle like reactors which are of commercial interest to suppliers? There seems to be a calculated move to denigrate critics who really care for long-term interests in energy and national security of having defeatist mentality and paranoid about the deal. They should bear in mind that some critics among former nuclear scientists have spent their professional careers in the nuclear establishment and helped build a strong foundation showing achievements as a consequence of which India has been able to stand up with its head high. India could not have been discussing this deal without their contribution in the first place. They do not have any vested interests, nor need for protecting the chair they once occupied. Their only interest is to see that the inherent strength of the country in the nuclear field is suitably harnessed to grow even stronger.

Weakness of Uranium shortage is a known factor and it has been factored into the Indian nuclear programme for more than five decades now. Long-term energy independence cannot be driven by externally controlled imports. Thinking ahead and cautioning against hasty actions detrimental to national interests cannot be termed inferiority complex.

A deal, which can truly takes us out of the shell and allow us to interact as a global player on honourable terms, is always welcome. We should not be treated as receivers of technology but we are capable of offering a lot in the nuclear field.

Let us not consider ourselves as weak partners in this game and compromise. We should stand up fight for our rightful place.

(Rediff.com, July 27, 2007)

64. Indo-US Nuke Deal: Is it a done Deal?

A.N. PRASAD

The text is expected to be released any time, but the July 27, 2007 press briefing on the status of 123 text gives it away. Even before the text of the 123 agreement is made public, with the approval of the Cabinet Committees, the deal seems to be as good as through as far as India·is concerned. It will go through the motions of Parliament deliberations perhaps with no scope for making any changes to the text as it has already been put in a straight jacket. It appears to be a clever move by the government not to release the text until they had an opportunity to soften possible adverse reaction by releasing in bits and pieces to the political parties, press briefings and media interactions painting a rosy picture thereby giving a spin on the favourable aspects of the deal selectively. There are some reports that suggest the US cooperated to hold back the text until India is ready! While the text is expected to be released any time now, the July 27 press briefing by the US Under-Secretary Nicholas Burns on the status of the 123 text gives it all. It has been clarified that US has made sure that the text is completely consistent and well within the bounds of the Hyde Act. With the Hyde Act having been debated exhaustively and even our Prime Minister having expressed concerns regarding some of the provisions of the Act and exhorting his countrymen to await the 123 Agreement, perhaps hoping some miracles will happen, we are now left with the inevitable. All along we have been cautioning that the US cannot and will not overstep the Hyde Act which is their legal basis for the whole agreement irrespective of what is explicit or not in the 123 text. Let us consider how some of the most contentious issues have been dealt with.

It has been stated that reprocessing is the major principal issue and things started moving after India offered to build a new state-of-the-art reprocessing facility, fully safeguarded, fully transparent to the IAEA, to the US and to the international community. This is a heavily loaded requirement extremely difficult to live with practically and by committing to these we seem to have put our foot in the mouth so to say. Burns kept on repeatedly stressing that the plant will be state-of-the-art and it could be deliberate. This term, unlike in many other cases, has no real meaning as there is no internationally available yardstick to qualify a reprocessing facility, with no facility built in recent times anywhere in the world except India and the designs of a handful of plants operating in a few countries are kept a secret and considered as sensitive. Will India be able to import some of the special items of equipment and components for the dedicated plant? With the commitment to state-of-the-art design, transparency to the IAEA, the US and other supplier countries, anybody can have a go at this plant and pick holes to put restrictions on reprocessing which has been grudgingly conceded. We have to take permission to reprocess from those countries supplying uranium! What appears to be on offer is only consent for reprocessing in principle with a set of arrangements and procedures under which reprocessing will take place, as called for in Section 131 of the US Atomic Energy Act of 1954, to be worked out later when the facility is built which may take many years. This complex provision is worse than the Tarapur agreement in which we are stuck even to this day. This could have far reaching consequences and we could be kept under tenterhooks without getting the reprocessing benefits on some pretext or other!

Safeguardability issue will again crop up. Reprocessing is one of our biggest strengths and it is at the core of our long-term nuclear programme. Instead of negotiating with strength, we seem to have compromised too much and in future we may have to suffer for it. The next issue is testing. It is now abundantly clear that the agreement will not tolerate testing. The text may have done some language fixing to circumvent and make it not so glaring. The fact remains, for all practical purposes, we have to forego testing and this may be a big compromise for national security with our neighbours having no such constraints and with the developing terrorism atmosphere.

There seems to be a consent for our building a strategic reserve of uranium. However, this is nullified by the provision that the US reserves the right of return of equipment and materials in case of withdrawal of cooperation. This eventuality may not arise as we have compromised on our right to test.

There are so many other irksome provisions in the Hyde Act which are not even being debated. On the whole, it appears that while the US is always concerned with its laws, conforming to Hyde Act and so on, the same is missing on the Indian side. Even the Prime Minister's assurances are not complied with in many respects.

(*The Deccan Herald*, August 2, 2007)

65. 123 Agreement: US can Remotely Drive India's Nuke Programmes

A.N. PRASAD

The agreement to operationalise the Indo-US civil nuclear deal has compromised India's case to a large extent and the United States could "remotely drive our atomic programmes in the long-run", former Director of Bhabha Atomic Research Centre Dr A.N. Prasad said here tonight. He said the draft text of the 123 agreement, reached in Washington last month, clearly tried to accommodate diverging interests and constraints of both India and US by clever use of the language. "We are now in effect reduced to a mere recipient state mandated by the Henry Hyde Act (passed by the US Congress) to carry out a set of do's and don'ts and strive to earn a good behaviour report card to become eligible to continue receiving what they can offer", he said. "In the process, slowly but surely, they (US) could gain control and remotely drive our nuclear programmes in the long-run," Prasad said. Prasad, who was active in IAEA inspections in Iraq, said "this deal, through the Hyde Act, gives far too many opportunities to penetrate deep into and interfere even in our 3-stage programme to slow down realization of our goal to harness our own vast resources of thorium for long-term energy security." Prasad pointed to two points in support of his view: First revelation by Nicholas Burns, US Under-Secretary of State, during his interview to the Council on Foreign Relations and secondly the duration of the 123 agreement coinciding with the time India intending to take thorium use to a commercial reality. He pointed to Burns' remark that "it had been an easy 'strategic' choice for Washington when faced with the question—should we isolate India for the next 35 years or bring it in partially now (under safeguards inspection) and nearly totally in the future".

Second, Article 16.2 of the 123 text says the agreement shall remain in force for 40 years and at the end of this initial period each party may terminate by giving 6 month's notice. "There is no built-in provision for terminating before forty years even if we were to suffer for any reason in the implementation of the deal. This is expected to cover the period by which we intend to take the thorium utilization to a commercial reality," he said adding "what a coincidence?" Is it not obvious that their intention is to put hurdles on our thorium utilization programme right from the beginning? Prasad said.

Talking about some of the contentious issues like reprocessing of spent fuel issue which has been stated to be the most hotly debated issues, Prasad considered the father of India's reprocessing technology, said, "reprocessing is at the core of our 3-stage nuclear power programme." The irony is that the US, knowing fully well our four decades of experience in reprocessing and aware of its importance in our 3-stage programme, has sought to create impediments and make us cringe for reprocessing consent, that too after accepting us as strategic partner. "Should we call this nuclear cooperation or non-cooperation?" he said. He said it was naive to judge the merits of the civil nuclear deal purely based on the language of the draft of the text of the 123 agreement. "The underlying under-currents and the intentions of the controlling party are important and cannot be wished away as hypothetical or as their internal matter and of no concern to us when they do actually have serious repercussions on our long-term interests", Prasad remarked. He said there has been a careful balancing of US commercial interests with the goal of bringing India into the non-proliferation hold, an obsession they are pursuing for a long time ever since NPT came into existence in 1970. "There have been overt suggestions in the Hyde Act to the US Administration for not only attempting to cap but also try to eventually roll back our strategic programme and report to the Congress", Prasad said. "Try they will but whether we are smart enough to thwart their designs or they manage to succeed given the tremendous access they get through this deal, time will tell", he said.

Prasad said even though there is what is called a fast reactor nuclear fuel cycle, not a word is mentioned in the agreement on fast reactor cooperation while the text calls for all future fast breeder reactors to be put under civil list for applying safeguards in perpetuity just because plutonium extracted from imported uranium spent fuel is fed into these reactors.

(*The Deccan Herald*, August 6, 2007)

66. 123: Thin Edge of the Wedge

A.N. PRASAD

The much awaited 123 text on the Indo-US nuclear deal, ever since it was released on Aug. 2, 2007, has been commented upon and covered in the media profusely. While it is obvious that the text has tried to accommodate diverging interests and constraints of both the parties by clever use of the language and words to give an illusory impression that the concerns are duly reflected. For the sake of public comfort, both parties are loudly saying that they are free to hold on to their respective rights and legal positions though it means hardly anything as far as India is concerned having no leverage to force any of the issues during innumerable consultations suggested in the text, up against the Hyde Act standing like a Rock of Gibraltar!

In fact our case has been compromised to a large extent when once this Act was passed, our Prime Minister's assurances not withstanding. We are now in effect reduced to a mere recipient State mandated by the Hyde Act to carry out a set of do's and don'ts and strive to earn a good behaviour report card to become eligible to continue receiving what they can offer. In the process, slowly but surely, they could gain control and remotely drive our nuclear programmes in the long-run.

This deal, through the Hyde Act, gives far too many opportunities to penetrate deep into and interfere even in our 3-stage programme to slow down realisation of our goal to harness our own vast resources of thorium for long-term energy security. Two points in support of this, which have largely missed notice. One, revelation by Nicholas Burns, US Under-Secretary of State during his interview to the Council on Foreign Relations: "It had been an easy "strategic choice for Washington when faced with the question—should we isolate India for the next 35 years or bring it in partially now (under safeguards inspection) and nearly totally in the future." Two, Under Article 16.2 of the 123 text, it says, the Agreement shall remain in force for a period of 40 years and at the end of this initial period each party may terminate by giving six months' notice. There is no built in provision for terminating before 40 years even if we were to suffer for any reason in the implementation of the deal. This is expected to cover the period by which we intend to take the thorium utilisation to a commercial reality and what a coincidence?

It is naive to judge the merits of the deal purely based on the language of the text. The underlying undercurrents and the intentions of the controlling party are important and cannot be wished away as hypothetical or as their internal matter and of no concern to us when they do actually have serious repercussions on our long-term interests. There has been a careful balancing of US commercial interests with the goal of bringing India into the non-proliferation hold, an obsession they are pursuing for a long time ever since NPT came into existence in 1970.

There have been overt suggestions in the Hyde Act to the US Administration for not only attempting capping but also try to eventually roll back our strategic programme and report to the Congress. Try, they will but whether we are smart enough to thwart their designs or they manage to succeed given the tremendous access they get through this deal, time will tell.

Let me turn to some of the most contentious issues, which are not satisfactorily resolved.

Reprocessing

Reprocessing issue has been stated to be the most hotly debated issue. Let me therefore deal with it in some detail in simple terms to put things in proper perspective.

Reprocessing is at the core of our 3-stage nuclear power programme. It is the interface between the first and the second stage and again between the second and the third stage. In the first step it facilitates extracting plutonium from the spent uranium fuel and feeding to the fast breeder reactors in the second stage as fuel where thorium fuel is also introduced. When thorium is converted into fissile uranium in the fast reactors the same is extracted by reprocessing to be fed into third stage reactors where large-scale thorium utilisation occurs. It was once estimated that with the limited resources of uranium in the country more than 350,000 MW of electricity could be produced through thorium utilisation ensuring long-term energy security. The steady progress India is making with the starting construction of the first 500 MWe prototype fast breeder reactor (PFBR) is an envy of many in the advanced world.

Recognising the key role of reprocessing, development activities were started as early as 1959 much before even the first nuclear power reactor went into operation at Tarapur in 1969. As can be seen, while the first power reactor was imported from US through a 123 agreement, the first reprocessing facility was built entirely through indigenous effort which went into operation in 1965.

The irony is, US knowing full well our four decades of experience in reprocessing and aware of its importance in our 3-stage programme, has sought to create impediments and make us cringe for reprocessing consent, that too after accepting us as strategic partner. Should we call this nuclear cooperation or non-cooperation? What a hypocrisy? Is it not obvious that their intention is to put hurdles on our thorium utilisation programme right from the beginning? In fact, even though there is what is called a fast reactor nuclear fuel cycle, not a word is mentioned in the agreement on fast reactor cooperation while the text calls for all future fast breeder reactors to be put under civil list for applying safeguards in perpetuity just because plutonium extracted from imported uranium spent fuel is fed into these reactors. It is a pity that our negotiators have chosen not to pursue extending the cooperation into the area of fast reactors at least to the extent that we should be able to access international market for equipment and components which otherwise have to be produced by Indian industry with considerable effort.

The way the reprocessing issue has been resolved certainly does not give any comfort. What has been agreed to is consent in principle with the arrangements and procedures to be agreed in the future. Having offered a dedicated facility for reprocessing imported fuel we should have got unconditional upfront consent to be made effective on satisfactory conclusion of safeguards. Intent of the American legislation is to deny reprocessing to those NPT countries who are not already having this technology. We cannot be equated to Japan which is stated to have been used as a model for resolving this issue in one of the briefings of Burns. I can say from personal knowledge that Japan was totally unhappy in dealing with the US while negotiating procedures and arrangements during the late '70s for their reprocessing plant. We should watch out.

Also over the entire fuel cycle, application of safeguards on reprocessing is toughest. Point of concern is, Burns keeps harping that the dedicated facility, though not mentioned in the text, has been offered by India as a state-of-the-art facility. This is a dangerous prospect for conflict during consultations on safeguardability as there is no reference standard on the design of such a facility in the world and information on less than a handful of facilities operating in the world at present is kept secret and not shared. Perhaps the dedicated plant we have offered will be the first plant to be wide open to the outside world and US definitely have a good look at it!

Being a dedicated facility committed to full safeguards it should be our endeavour to obtain special items of equipment and hardware "components from the international market."

Full Civil N-Cooperation

In spite of the Prime Minister's assurances the issue of full civil cooperation has not been resolved in our favour. The text has allowed an unfair definition of this term, with the result embargoes will continue on the most complex part of the fuel cycle facilities such as enrichment, reprocessing and heavy water. Though we may not need to import technology as such, there should have been an opportunity to access world market for specific low quantity dual use items which otherwise have to be produced by Indian industry.

This historic deal not being able to get rid of sanctions in spite of taking on a whole lot of burden on safeguards and other aspects is a big disappointment.

Testing

This is a much talked about topic and any further discussion is like beating a dead horse. Suffice to say, irrespective of what is said or unsaid, we have surrendered our decision, though not the legal right for all practical purposes fearing the consequences. Talk of multi-layered consultations and actions is all an eye wash and public relations exercise.

Fall Back Safeguards

It is surprising that such a hypothetical issue has found specific mention in the text contrary to the Prime Minister's assurance. There is every likelihood that this could be invoked.

Though it is the bounden duty of the IAEA to apply safeguards in Member States in a cost effective manner, there is a large inflow of extra-budgetary grants for this activity. With a huge spurt in safeguards load from India, whose cost substantially has to be met by additional extra-budgetary grants, there could well be a move in future to create a situation that due to paucity of funds IAEA puts its hands up for US to step in. At that point the US inspectors will roam around irrespective of what our Prime Minister has assured.

With the proposed deal we are having in our hands, one statement baffles: "This Agreement is between two States possessing advanced nuclear technology, both Parties having the same benefits and advantages." How I wish this could have been really true! It is hard to find any point on which we have the leverage to dictate with a position of strength in this deal in spite of being rightly labeled as a State possessing advanced nuclear technology.

(*The New Indian Express*, August 6, 2007)

67. India in a Nuclear Trap

BHARAT KARNAD

In the jungle, if a carnivorous animal finds itself in the jaws of an iron trap, it will try and gnaw through the skin and bone of its immobilized leg. The animal gets away, minus a limb, but with its life and freedom intact. A wild elephant in chains on the other hand, lacking a mouthful of sharp teeth to free itself by chewing through its own shin and sinew, can only await a condign fate.

India is a meek-natured elephant all right, which until now had been an elusive non-proliferation target. America, the consummate shikari, has been scouting this animal for over 40 years now. It, finally, "bagged" the big game, herding it into the non-proliferation coral constructed by the Henry J. Hyde United States-India Promotion of Peaceful Nuclear Cooperation Act, 2006.

A fortnight-long effort by the Manmohan Singh government to cover up the fact of a well-laid nuclear trap having sprung shut on India has come to naught. Having portrayed this agreement as something of a diplomatic coup, the Indian negotiators, the text of the agreement suggests, were outmanoeuvred by the professionals at the US State Department. The latter happily traded vacuous language for Indian compliance with the Hyde Act and other US domestic laws on all the critical issues, including testing, reprocessing, assured fuel supply, and the right of return of US nuclear material. In case of the deal breaking down, however, the Americans minorly conceded India the right to "consultations" before the Hyde Act provisions are enforced. Some right!

A rule of thumb in judging the success or failure of any long-drawn-out negotiations is that if there is an inordinate amount of chest-thumping by one side, there is good reason to suspect that that side failed to protect its own interests. This, alas, is what happened with India in the 123 Agreement, the bilateral diplomatic instrument which, once approved by the US Congress, will enable the Hyde Act to be implemented in full.

The text of the 123 Agreement suggests that the Indian negotiators were outmanoeuvred by the US

Each of the 17 Articles in the 123 Agreement reveal a consistent pattern of the US sticking to the letter of the Hyde Act even as the Indians are fobbed off with verbiage. What is troubling is why the Indian government, which for nearly 60 years had deflected non-proliferation pressures and successfully protected and safeguarded the country's dual-purpose nuclear programme, turned against it.

The answers lie in the subaltern thinking fuelling Indian nuclear policy. The self-confidence and an assertive nationalist stance reflective of an emergent, powerful, India is nowhere evident in an agreement that is supposed to redefine India's place in the world. The core problem is the seriously debilitating conviction of the Prime Minister that India can attain great power rank the easy way—by piggybacking on the US. Here President George W. Bush's rhetoric of helping India become a "major power" was the key. Nobody in the government stopped to consider whether this was feasible and what price the country would have to pay for it.

The US was not about to set up a competitor. But absent a strategic vision of his own to anchor policy and with his wilful misreading of the decisive quality of the premier great power attribute in the modern age, namely, a versatile thermonuclear arsenal, Manmohan Singh struck a beggar's bargain— took whatever was offered to him. And what the US offered India was a role as potential regional gendarme. Hardly impressive, considering it is at the expense of India's naturally growing strategic presence and Independent role in the extended region and Asia at large.

Indeed, Delhi was satisfied with only symbolic recognition as a nuclear weapon state. So much so, it unhesitatingly swallowed the line of India's being on par with the United States as a country with "advanced nuclear technology" (the July 18, 2005, Joint Statement)—which it patently is not. Accepting this logic, Delhi found it hard to dispute the US government's contention that, therefore, India had to do what the US and the other four nuclear weapon powers had done, i.e., forswear nuclear testing. But testing is the fulcrum of credible Indian deterrence and the country's great power ambitions. More so because, unlike the US, Russian, Chinese, British and French nuclear weapons and delivery systems, the bulk of the Indian "boosted fission" and hydrogen weapon designs and missiles are inadequately tested, unproven and, hence, unreliable. And, without further testing, India will be saddled permanently with a hollow deterrent—more military liability than political asset.

A nuclear-armed India has deliberately and diplomatically been reduced, courtesy Manmohan Singh the mahout, to the war elephant of yore—all size, finery, and little military substance and with no ability worth the name to break the non-proliferation chains and to strike out on an Independent great power course. What Delhi is left with is a yen for trumpeting that is all noise signifying nothing.

(*Mint*, August 6, 2007)

68. U.S. Hypocrisy Fuels the Deal

A.N. Prasad

Now that the text of the 123 Agreement on the Indo-US nuclear deal has been made public and is being extensively covered in the media, it is time to do some retrospection on how the whole issue started and where we are heading. The preamble in the 123 text is the only portion faithful to the Joint Statement issued by both the parties on July 18, 2005. What follows in the document is an exercise of clever and at times dubious, depending on which side you are looking at it from, use of the language and words to give an illusory impression that the concerns arising from diverging interests and constraints of both sides have been duly reflected.

This is a deal binding India at least for 40 years without an exit clause (Article 16.2). In case India likes to terminate it, if in the opinion of future governments the deal, as it is being steered, is found unbearable, for which the Hyde Act gives ample scope, there is no provision for it. However, the US retains all the rights to terminate cooperation at will on various counts apart from the eventuality of an Indian test. This is a dangerous commitment tying our future national interests.

The text may take solace that such action calls for bilateral multi-layered consultations, but the end result is a foregone conclusion. Either toe their line or face the consequences. While they have a Henry Hyde Act to back their actions, we don't have anything legal even remotely as an equivalent to hang on to. The only documents, the Joint Statements and the Prime Minister's assurances, have been reduced practically to nothing with the passage of the Hyde Act. We cannot afford to ignore the oft repeated statement by Nicholas Burns, the US point man, that they have made sure that 123 is completely consistent and well within the bounds of the Hyde Act with which we have many problems, though for the sake of public comfort, we may keep saying that we are free to hold on to our rights and legal position. It means hardly anything having no leverage to force any of the issues during innumerable consultations suggested in the text. During the "Trimurti" press briefing on July 27 in Delhi, answering a question as to whether under the ambit of the Hyde Act we have mortgaged our right to conduct tests, our national security adviser responded by saying that we have not mortgaged any right but, if anything, we have enhanced our rights. He owes an amplification of this statement. In the same briefing, the foreign secretary said that the finalised text met the concerns and interests of both sides and both sides are free to interpret in terms of their laws. In times of conflicts, I wonder what leverage we have to force the issues our way.

In any bilateral discussion, the two sides negotiate taking into account the limits of their strengths and weaknesses. Having recognised that the cooperation agreement is between two states possessing advanced technology, unfortunately, an important element "both parties having the same benefits and advantages" is conspicuously missing throughout the evolution of this deal. It is therefore imperative to understand that one cannot just go by the wordings of a text, which, as I have pointed out, cannot be respected, but the underlying undercurrents and intentions are important.

As one who has served the nuclear establishment with dedication throughout my professional career, it is hard to see how a state with so much of technological strength built over the years is being reduced to a recipient state fighting for its rights. Let me now turn to some of the most contentious issues, which are not satisfactorily resolved.

Reprocessing

Reprocessing has been stated to be the most hotly debated issue. Let me therefore deal with it in some detail and in simple terms to put things in the proper perspective. Reprocessing is at the core of our three-stage nuclear power programme. It is the interface between the first and the second stages, and again between the second and the third stages. In the first step, it facilitates extracting plutonium from the spent uranium fuel, and feeding to the fast breeder reactors in the second stage as fuel where thorium fuel is also introduced. When thorium is converted into fissile uranium in the fast reactors, the same is extracted by reprocessing to be fed into third stage reactors where large-scale thorium utilisation occurs. It was once estimated that with the limited resources of uranium in the country more than 350,000 MW of electricity could be produced through thorium utilisation ensuring long-term energy security. The steady progress India is making with the starting construction of the first 500 MWe prototype fast breeder reactor (PFBR) is an envy of many in the advanced world. Recognising the key role of reprocessing, development activities were started as early as 1959, much before even the first nuclear power reactor went into operation at Tarapur in 1969. As can be seen, while the first power reactor was imported from US through a 123 Agreement, the first reprocessing facility was built entirely through indigenous effort which went into operation in 1965.

The irony is, the US, knowing fully well our four decades of experience in reprocessing and aware of its importance in our three-stage programme, has sought to create impediments and make us cringe for reprocessing consent, that too after accepting us as a strategic partner. Should we call this nuclear cooperation or non-cooperation? What hypocrisy! Is it not obvious that their intention is to put hurdles on our thorium utilisation programme right from the beginning? In fact, even though there is what is called a fast reactor nuclear fuel cycle, not a word is mentioned in the agreement on fast reactor cooperation, while the text calls for all future fast breeder reactors to be put under civil list for applying safeguards in perpetuity just because plutonium extracted from imported uranium spent fuel is fed into these reactors. It is a pity that our negotiators have chosen not to pursue extending the cooperation into the area of fast reactors at least to the extent that we should be able to access international market for equipment and components, which otherwise have to be produced by Indian industry with considerable effort. The way the reprocessing issue has been resolved certainly does not give any comfort. What has been agreed to is consent in principle, with arrangements and procedures to be agreed in the future. Having offered a dedicated facility for reprocessing imported fuel, we should have got unconditional upfront consent to be made effective on satisfactory conclusion of safeguards. The intent of the American legislation is to deny reprocessing to those NPT countries which do not already have this technology. We cannot be equated to Japan which is stated to have been used as a model for resolving this issue in one of the briefings of Burns. I can say from personal knowledge that Japan was totally unhappy in dealing with the US while negotiating the procedures and arrangements during the late Seventies for its reprocessing plant. We should watch out.

Also, over the entire fuel cycle, application of safeguards on reprocessing is toughest. The point of concern is, Burns keeps harping that the dedicated facility, though not mentioned in the text, has been offered by India as a state-of-the-art facility. This is a dangerous prospect for conflict during the consultations on safeguardability, as there is no reference standard on the design of such a facility in the world, and information on less than a handful of facilities operating in the world at present is kept secret and is not shared. Perhaps the dedicated plant we have offered will be the first plant to be thrown wide open to the outside world and the US will definitely have a good look into it. Being a dedicated facility committed to full safeguards it should be our endeavour to obtain special items of equipment and hardware components from the international market.

Full Civil Nuclear Cooperation

In spite of the Prime Minister's assurances, the issue of full civil cooperation has not been resolved in our favour. The text has allowed an unfair definition of this term, with the result that embargoes will continue on the most complex part of the fuel cycle facilities such as enrichment, reprocessing and heavy water. Though we may not need to import technology as such, there should have been an opportunity to access world market for specific low quantity dual use items which otherwise have to be produced by Indian industry.

This historic deal not being able to get rid of sanctions in spite of taking on a whole lot of burden on safeguards and other aspects is a big disappointment.

Assurance of Uranium Supply

Much has already been written on this. The whole issue is wishy-washy and it is hard to say what conditions will be attached to realise it.

Testing

This is a much talked about topic and any further discussion is like flogging a dead horse. Suffice to say that irrespective of what is said or unsaid, we have surrendered our decision, though not the legal right, for all practical purposes, fearing the consequences. Talk of multi-layered consultations and actions is all an eyewash and public relations exercise.

Fall-back Safeguarded Safeguards

It is surprising that such a hypothetical issue has found specific mention in the text contrary to the Prime Minister's assurance. There is every likelihood that this could be invoked. Though it is the bounden duty of the IAEA to apply safeguards in member states in a cost-effective manner, there is a large inflow of extra-budgetary grants for this activity. With a huge spurt in safeguards load from India, whose cost substantially has to be met by additional extra-budgetary grants, there could well be a move in future to create a situation that due to paucity of funds IAEA puts its hands up for US to step in. At that point, US inspectors will roam around irrespective of what our Prime Minister has assured.

(*The Asian Age*, August 8, 2007)

69. N-deal Relies on God, not Common Sense

M.K. Narayanan, national security adviser to Prime Minister Manmohan Singh, in a press interview, attributed his alleged success in negotiating the 123 Agreement with the United States, to the role "played" by "God." Now that the text of the agreement is available for scrutiny, it is clear the "God" the NSA relied on was in America's pay. How else to explain a deal that will strategically hog-tie India, reduce it to a client state in all but name, and otherwise politically and militarily neuter this country? What Narayanan could have done with is less divine intervention than common sense and old fashioned patriotic resolve to prevent the United States from having its way at India's expense. But then, the Indian government seems happy with only a supposedly cleverly-worded bargain.

The contents of the agreement have come as no great surprise. It was a story foretold in a whole bunch of articles written by this analyst and published periodically in *The Asian Age* over the last three years, starting with the first one in October 2004 when the then recently installed Manmohan Singh regime, keen to revive the deal the Atal Behari Vajpayee government had set aside owing to Washington's intransigence, decided that what was needed was still more give on India's part. It proved the right recipe to get the Americans on board. After all, there is no agreement that cannot be obtained with another country by piling concessions upon concessions on a plate already filled with national security compromises.

The insidious nature of the Indian compromises and concessions evident in the 17 Articles in the 123 Agreement has been adequately analysed in recent reports in this paper, and elsewhere in critical press assessments. What is obvious is that the only thing the US conceded in the negotiations is an intercessionary instrument of "consultations" on a host of issues, like fuel supply and the return of imported nuclear material, should India resume testing. What good Narayanan and Co. think such consultations will do is anybody's guess, considering that the consequences mandated by the Hyde Act cannot be escaped. If India resumes testing—which it desperately needs to do to inject credibility into its unproven and untested thermonuclear deterrent and which, hopefully, a strong future government will order—the US, after a round or two of consultations, will end the nuclear cooperation and terminate the deal in its entirety. The Indian government, for incomprehensible reasons, seems unable or unwilling publicly to admit that the 1954 US Atomic Energy Act (as amended in 1974) and the Hyde Act supersede the 123 Agreement, a fact the Narayanan-led negotiating team acknowledged when it approved the final text.

Three other aspects of the 123 Agreement need to be borne in mind by the Parliament, which will be discussing it. The first is India's acceptance of safeguards in perpetuity on the civilian part of its nuclear programme. This most significantly defines a non-nuclear weapon state under current international non-proliferation law. In the context of the loss, for all intents and purposes, of the testing option and the fast-tracking of the Fissile Material Cut-off Treaty as required by the Hyde Act, the safeguards in perpetuity will lead to the progressive increase in the number of facilities under safeguards and severely limit the prospective growth of the Indian nuclear force to meaningful size. The government, hereafter, will have to be content with what traction the phrase "state with advanced nuclear technology" can muster in international circles, which won't be much.

Secondly, the government believes that the Nuclear Suppliers' Group solidarity is bit of a fiction, that Russia and France, tempted by huge contracts for reactors, will break rank and, in case the US ends nuclear cooperation with India, they will continue to supply fuel and other material on a bilateral, contractual basis. The trouble is, Russia and France have insisted all along that Delhi first meet all the American non-proliferation demands contained in the US laws, before they engage in selling anything to India. Implicit in this is their commitment to hew to the Hyde Act *in toto,* including the provision requiring the other NSG member-states to also cease nuclear cooperation if Washington decides to do so for reasons other than nuclear-related, such as India's continued close relations with Iran. And, in any case, the US is in a position to enforce its diktat in the NSG as elsewhere.

Finally, contrary to Prime Minister Manmohan Singh's pledges in the Parliament and the declaration in the "separation plan," the 123 Agreement requires India to put all breeder reactors under international safeguards, thereby closing that route to weapon-grade plutonium and forcing this country into sharing its technological advances in breeder reactors and thorium utilisation through participation in GNEP (Global Nuclear Experimental Project).

Devastating as the impact of the 123 Agreement will be on India's military atom and the integrity of its civilian nuclear programme, it is important to plumb the sort of thinking and pre-determined negotiating strategy that have produced this accord. What it says about the persons responsible for it and about this government, is another matter. In this regard, consider what Narayanan has said. Asked if he was "100 per cent satisfied with the text of the 123 Agreement," the NSA replied: "I am one of those who believes that if you are negotiating and you get everything you want, then obviously there is something wrong." Meaning, that if by some off-chance he had been presented a 123 draft for approval with "everything" India wanted—free, open and unconditional nuclear trade and commerce and no restraints whatsoever on testing, technology transfer and reprocessing of spent imported fuel. Narayanan would have rejected it, preferring something a lot more onerous. Well, that is what the country is stuck with.

Then Narayanan amplified some more, this time on his boss attitude. "The PM had always taken the view (*vis-a-vis* the Americans)," the NSA revealed, "that if (the Americans have) a legal problem, we will not try to ask (the Americans) to break (their) law." This exceptional kindness on the part of the Indian principals, which the US under-secretary of state Nicholas Burns thanked the Indian negotiators for, leads to the unavoidable conclusion that Manmohan Singh considered the inviolability of US laws, like the Hyde Act, more important than protecting India's nuclear sovereignty and national security and, therefore, that undermining the latter was permissible just so the American side was kept in good humour and a deal, even one damaging to India's vital national interests, could be procured. This is the same Manmohan Singh, it may be recalled, who praised the British for the "benefits'" of the Raj.

No wonder, in his July 27 press conference, a relieved Burns asserted that no other country could expect to get this kind of deal. Then again no other country (with the exception of Pakistan) would be foolish enough to hanker for one and sacrifice so much for it. It brings to mind a battled query by a senior Iranian official to Indian visitors to Tehran recently: "Why does a powerful country like India not act like a big power?" With the 123 Agreement, India has agreed to shore up a tottering global non-proliferation order of which it is the chief victim and to shape its foreign policy as desire by Washington. The reasons for "Rising" India's eagerness to take an axe to its own strategic feet and to crawl back to being a 21st century dependency are a mystery history will unravel. For now, the 123 Agreement provides evidence of quite a spectacular failure of national will, the will to genuine greatness.

(*The Asian Age*, August 10, 2007)

70. 123 Nuclear Deal: National Interest at Stake

A.N. PRASAD

Though the nuclear deal, which is now being debated in the context of the 123 text, is supposed to be on Indo-US nuclear cooperation, it has its overtones on other spheres of our national interest which naturally are best left to be dealt with by foreign policy experts.

The Indian nuclear program is being steered over the years with the specific goal of achieving long-term energy security by tapping the potential of our meagre resources of uranium estimated to support 10,000 MW electricity generation and multiply it to 350,000 MW by harnessing vast resources of thorium abundantly available in the country. For this a three-stage program is drawn-up. The present status of this is that we have mastered all aspects of the first stage, viz. heavy water reactors (HWR), made a beginning on the second stage by starting construction of a prototype fast breeder Reactor (PFBR) and pursuing research and development on thorium-related fuel cycle pertaining to the third stage. In the process, expertise spanning the entire nuclear fuel cycle is accumulated.

In view of stringent restrictions and embargoes by the world community, this program has been indigenous driven effort and the level of technological prowess achieved surpasses even many of the advanced countries. Uranium shortage and embargoes have been factored into the development program. As we have a lot to offer as a global player, we certainly deserve an honourable entry into the world community as a technologically advanced country on our own right denied for so long. Unfortunately, the agreement does not confer that honour adequately as it largely treats India as a recipient State.

The cooperation agreement as it has evolved concentrates broadly on two aspects. Firstly, supply of power reactors, fuel and aspects directly connected with them like safety. That means there is an overtone of commercial interests to the detriment of all other aspects of the nuclear fuel cycle. Secondly, a whole lot of prescriptions to bring India into the global main stream of non-proliferation, an obsession, US has been pursuing ever since the Non-Proliferation Treaty came into effect in 1970.

In operationalising the cooperation agreement, one document that is bound to have over bearing influence is the Henry Hyde Act passed into law by the US ignoring our concerns. It overtly limits the cooperation in the nuclear field to mainly to promoting commercial power reactor trade and practically nothing else. However, it exhaustively deals with non-proliferation and other extraneous issues.

Ever since the full text of the 123 agreement was made public, there has been a spate of clarifications issued by the two parties at the official level. The text has been an exercise of fixing the concerns with clever use of language, being vague at times, or circumventing by suggesting multi-layered bilateral consultations, or subject to amendments to applicable national laws, or avoid specific mention.

The Indian officials who negotiated the text are saying that it meets all our concerns but are evasive on specific issues by brushing aside the as hypothetical. However, on the US side, categorical statements are coming to the effect that the agreement is completely consistent and within bounds of the Hyde Act and the 123 text is left vague to allow interpretations as face-saving measure! In the light of these clarifications, when there are serious problems with the Hyde Act, how can we feel safe with an agreement built on an unacceptable Act?

While the issues like assurances of fuel supply, exercise of right of return triggered by various events are important and covered by the media extensively, at least two issues are still cause for serious concern. Trade restrictions on access to international market for equipment and components are retained as before for most complex parts of the nuclear fuel cycle. No straight relaxation even for dual use items. Some may argue, since we have the technology in these areas, why bother? Then the same should apply to reactors.

We have the technology but still are we not seeking it? The question is, when we are entering into cooperation as "equal partners", so it says in the joint statement, why this limitation? Should we accept selective partial lifting of embargo? We could accept end use verification by International Atomic Energy Agency (IAEA) but trade access we must insist. Also there is no mention of cooperation in the fast reactor fuel cycle even in the future though we are expected to place our fast breeder reactors using foreign origin plutonium under perpetual safeguards.

The second issue is concerning reprocessing. This is at the core of our three-stage power program interfacing between stages. Though the reprocessing right has been conceded in principle after we offered to build a dedicated facility, there could be protracted highly intrusive discussions on procedures and arrangements.

What is agreed cannot be termed as really a consent upstream, but we have to face lot of intrusive consultations which may stall giving effect to this consent. In view of the fact that we had a head start in reprocessing, being the fifth in the world, we should not have compromised but insisted on the consent right without any conditions.

A lot of problems may emerge in this area at various stages as the matter is cleverly kept wide open, not withstanding the artificial time frame agreed in the text. On the whole, this Agreement seems to benefit short-term interest to the detriment of long-term national interest by becoming a dependent country.

(*The Deccan Herald*, August 13, 2007)

71. 123 Agreement is a Gilded Cage

P.K. IYENGAR

For some reason, the text of the 123 Agreement of the India-US "civilian" nuclear deal was kept secret until it was approved by the Union Cabinet. Once the text was made public, the reason became clear. In spite of the best efforts of our negotiators, the United States has succeeded in imposing the Hyde Act on us. The relevant part of the Agreement is Article 2, which states: "The parties shall cooperate in the use of nuclear energy for peaceful purposes, in accordance with the provisions of this agreement.

Each party shall implement this agreement in accordance with the respective applicable treaties, national laws, regulations, and license requirements concerning the use of nuclear energy for peaceful purposes."

The treaties and national laws alluded to above certainly include the NPT and the Hyde Act. Thus, by signing this Agreement we would essentially agree to bind ourselves to the Hyde Act, whose provisions are not acceptable to India as declared by the government of India and the political parties, and not by the scientists alone. This Article can be used by the US government at any time to delay, block, or disapprove collaboration in critical areas dealt with in the 123 Agreement. The consequences are very serious to the future generations of this country, and I therefore have serious objections to this Article. There is a belief in some quarters that the ambiguity in the language of the Agreement will somehow help us circumvent the Hyde Act. Article 2 makes it clear that there will be no ambiguity in the actions of the US if we go against the Hyde Act. Some suggest that our only hope is that the US Congress will refuse to ratify this Agreement, just like they refused to ratify the CTBT in spite of the US administration getting almost the whole world to sign the treaty.

However, since this agreement is a total gain for the US non-proliferation lobby, it may even be agreed to by the US Congress. It is therefore essential that we do not go ahead with this Agreement without further, and explicit, assurances from the US.

We should also be clear about what we can expect to get from the Agreement, if it does go through. The much hyped promise of nuclear technology doesn't translate to much in real terms. Long years of isolation have made us self-sufficient in the technologies needed for our three stage programme, particularly fast breeder technology.

Besides, the American nuclear industry hasn't built nuclear plants in over 20 years. It is more likely that we can help them, rather than that they can help us.

Nor can we be sure that we will get copious and cheap nuclear power. The actual building of nuclear plants will be driven by market forces. It is not clear that such plants will provide cheap nuclear energy, given the high price of uranium in the international market.

Other costs are also likely to be high, and we may well end up with not one but several Dabhols.

The events witnessed in the Parliament on August 14 clearly bring out the fact that there is no national consensus on this issue, with almost all non-UPA parties protesting against the government steamrolling Parliament. The fact that on such a crucial issue of national importance, it is possible for the government to take a unilateral decision against the wishes of the majority of the elected representatives in Parliament shows that there is a lacuna in our political system.

Another weakness comes from the whip system practised by the parties which prevents the elected representatives from airing their opinions openly. But the vigorous debate in the Parliament is also a healthy sign that Indian democracy is showing its teeth for the first time.

It has been sixty years that India has gained freedom from colonialism and asserted its sovereignty.

Through the Dandi March Mahatma Gandhi showed how the most basic rights of the people were being controlled and suppressed by the colonial government, even for a simple matter like producing salt from seawater using radiation from the sun. In the last 50 years, the Department of Atomic Energy and the scientists in particular, thanks to the founders, have maintained our sovereign right to research and develop technologies for practical applications in the nuclear field.

The country has never subjected itself to external restraints thus not agreeing to sign the NPT, which is almost universally accepted. Through the 123 Agreement the US has presented us with a gilded cage. By signing the Agreement we would voluntarily walk into the cage. Then it only remains for the US Congress to lock the door by the simple act of ratifying the 123 Agreement.

(*The Asian Age*, August 17, 2007)

72. 'India First' Alternative to Nuclear Deal

BHARAT KARNAD

The nuclear deal with the United States faces a swift end or a lingering death. The strategic vision-challenged Manmohan Singh government failed to convince the Parliament because it over-sold its benefits just as the allegedly adverse consequences of its termination are now being flogged with large dollops of exaggeration.

The Opposition parties asking the government to treat the 123 Agreement as dead letter, has been interpreted as an irresponsible move that will "isolate" India globally. The facile assumption here being that India is easily isolatable, that its geopolitical standing is the result of American goodwill, not its inherent strengths.

An even worse implication is that the Parliament is less important and less sovereign than the American legislature. Apparently, the US Congress' voting the 2006 Hyde Act that violated the letter and the spirit of the July 2005 Joint Statement signed by Prime Minister Manmohan Singh and president George W. Bush, is fine, but a parliamentary majority seeking to protect India's vital national interests in lieu of the PM's failure to do so, is not.

Opposition to the deal is labelled a throwback to the knee-jerk anti-Americanism of the past Enhancing its role and leverage in the 21st century, it is dubiously argued, requires India to not only side with America on Iran, non-proliferation, and the emerging great power politics in Asia, but also cede Washington its strategic space.

Still more problematically, the US is portrayed as the vehicle for India's great power ambitions. If the cost of the ticket involves compromising national security, undermining the integrity of the dual-purpose Indian nuclear energy programme, and limiting its foreign policy freedom in small and big ways, hey, that is the price to pay if India wants to reach where it wants to go.

Underlying these points are some egregiously flawed premises. For instance, that nuclear arsenals are more hindrance than help in achieving great power, when, actually, the political value and utility of meaningful strategic nuclear and thermonuclear missile forces have never been higher; or that soft power represented by Bollywood and information technology talent transcends the hard, military, capabilities of the state and, by extension, that economic power unrelated to the military clout of a country, is what counts in international affairs, which is rubbish.

Further, India's backing out of a deal when nothing has been signed and no treaty commitments undertaken, it is claimed, will isolate India globally, and reduce its credibility as a strategic interlocutor.

The United States withdrew unilaterally from the 1972 Anti-Ballistic Missile Treaty in order to deploy ballistic missile defences, and Russia is on the verge of disavowing the 1990 Conventional Forces in Europe Treaty to counter NATO's enlarged role with its own beefed up conventional military presence. Great powers routinely abandon treaties perceived as inconvenient and midway chuck those seen as injurious to national interest. The US signed but did not ratify and implement the Comprehensive Test Ban Treaty.

It will, however, be pointed out that India is not the equal of the US or even Russia. Exactly! In which case, how to explain the weak core at the centre of the nuclear deal—Prime Minister Manmohan Singh's factually silly and diplomatically dangerous conviction featured in the July 18, 2005 Joint Statement, which referred to India as a state with "advanced nuclear technology" on par with, and enjoying "the same advantages and benefits" as, the United States in the nuclear sphere?

The Indian government used this supposedly indirect American recognition of India as nuclear weapon state as cover for the serious compromises it knew it had to make, thus setting the country up for the non-proliferation kill. Because, thereafter, Indian negotiators could not resist the American demand that, like the US, India too should forsake nuclear testing, even though such prohibition will leave the country's "credible minimum deterrent" progressively more minimal and less credible. That the phrase "state with advanced nuclear technology" trapped India in the NPT-CTBT web is evident in Washington's insistence on the INFIRC 66 Rev 2 pertaining to non-nuclear weapon states as model for its "safeguards in perpetuity," which Delhi has accepted.

Let us rewind a bit. If the "tactical shortage" of natural uranium ore, is what originally motivated the deal, should the cultivation of the uranium ore-rich non-Nuclear Suppliers Group (NSG) countries not have been priority? An Indian firm has already signed a contract to begin uranium mining in Niger. The government of Uganda has invited India to explore and mine uranium in that country. Investing in uranium mining operations in non-NSG states, would have laid the foundation of a prudent policy.

With India having some 30-40% of the world's thorium reserves, nuclear energy is bound to play a big role in the future. So why has the Indian government since the Nineties when Manmohan Singh, incidentally, was finance minister, not invested massively in bringing the breeder reactor and thorium utilisation technologies on stream as quickly as is possible? Accessing non-NSG natural uranium will help fuel the indigenous power plants in the interim period until the plutonium breeders and thorium reactors become operational, leaving the estimated 70,000 tonnes of uranium ore in the country for exclusively military use. Both the mid-term and long-term nuclear energy needs will thus be met and India's military requirements taken care of as well. The imperative in the short-term to run power reactors at lower capacity would appear to be a small price to pay to keep the country's strategic independence intact.

For reasons unknown, Prime Minister Manmohan Singh continues to ballyhoo the deal as an energy windfall. But nuclear energy available from all power reactors, including 20 imported ones, according to a recent Planning Commission study, will account for only 5-6% of the total energy produced in 2035—a not very significant fraction. His other belief that the deal will be an "Open Sesame" to high technology is equally untenable. Advanced countries develop frontier technologies in autarchic regimes and are loath to sell or share them because technology is what gives them the edge. And, what high-value American technology is made available, in any case, will be on a case-by-case basis, deal or no nuclear deal.

But why did successive governments (Atal Behari Vajpayee's and Manmohan Singh's) alight on a policy template that turned a "Rising India" into a supplicant? Two reasons; one, because *of* the entrenched "have not-ism"—a defensive and diffident habit of mind compelling Indian politicians, officials, and members of the intelligentsia alike to seek hand guts, curry favour and to seek approbation from the West. It follows that these Third World Caliban, inverting the obvious conclusions, would accuse those opposing the deal as lacking "self-respect" and "self-confidence." And secondly, because the country's great power attributes have not been appreciated by the Indian policy establishment, whence no "India First" policies have ensued.

Seriously, do the US and the West have a choice other than to engage India on Indian terms in the regional security, trade, and energy fields?

As a vibrant democracy and economic and military powerhouse wedged in between the two biggest threats espied by the US and the West, namely, an authoritarian and aggrandising China and a zone stretching from the Karakoram to the Maghreb rife with radical Islam and terrorism, only India, with the necessary all round heft, can be system balancer and administrator. Tragically, lacking rulers with the strategic vision and the will to great power, India has thrashed around in the shallows—easy pickings for anyone with the wit to exploit the situation.

(*The Asian Age*, August 25, 2007)

73. Opposition to India-U.S. Nuclear Deal Coherent Left, Incoherent BJP

BHARAT KARNAD

An element of cold calculation, even opportunism, to discomfit the ruling party or coalition and, per chance, to bring down the government on a sensitive and strategically-loaded issue such as the civilian nuclear cooperation deal with the United States, is understandable. But it is necessary for the Opposition parties to justify their belligerent stance in substantive terms. An expedient approach may fetch the desired political results, but bereft of ideological ballast in their views, parties may find both the moral centre for their actions in Parliament and political credibility missing.

Here the Left parties seem to be on firmer ground. Rooted in Karl Marx and Lenin, their world-view of international relations as class warfare writ large, is quaint in its historic irrelevance. But there is a steely certitude to their beliefs, which is refreshing. Whatever the state of the socialist dogma as dialectic, at the popular level, frustrating the designs of an "imperialist" America to turn India into a neo-colonised entity, courtesy a naive Manmohan Singh government, is quickly grasped.

In the general elections, the rationale of the Left parties for ending the Congress coalition rule will be appreciated by the masses. Particularly because such opposition will combine the widespread antipathy of the nuclear establishment to the deal with the patriotic impulse—other than the urban handful habitually polled by the English-language papers and periodicals—of a "rising" India against surrendering strategic options to the US, or seeing energy and technology gains as recompense for the loss of sovereignty and foreign policy freedom, the hostility to the West since Jawaharlal Nehru's days and, considering the government makes light of the economic and political costs involved, with the kindling of suspicion that there is something wrong with a deal peddled as an Aladdin's lamp—promising a lot in return for little.

The coherence of the Left campaign is in stark contrast to the Bharatiya Janata Party's strangely hollow posture. No one on the Treasury or the Opposition benches in either House of Parliament understands the Hyde Act and the clauses in the "frozen text" of the 123 Agreement in all their nuance and detail as do Arun Shourie and Yashwant Sinha. Yet there is a void in their party's stance where an ideological core should be.

The Communists are clear about what they want—an America in retreat, a multi-polar world where western power is balanced by the India-China-Russia triumvirate, an India plugging minimally into the globalised milieu, developing economically at a languid pace in keeping with the continued supremacy of the inefficient and ineffective public sector. Manmohan Singh seems keen to have the nuclear deal facilitate India's transition into a mainly economic power, à la Japan and Germany—the classical client states of the post-World War II era. The nascent "third front" has no firm outlook.

But what is the BJP's strategic vision for India? During the time it was in power and since, there has been no articulation by the BJP leadership of a grand strategy or even a hint of any vision animating it. Hence, it is easy to conclude that the BJP's thinking is generally in sync with the ruling Congress party's, wherein the assumption of America's pre-eminence becomes the plank ·for Delhi's accommodating the US at the expense of India's vital national interests. It is an impression reinforced by the BJP policy that made free trade in nuclear goods and advanced, dual-use, technology the "litmus test" of a *rapprochement* with the US, and thus prepared the ground for Manmohan Singh's nuclear deal. Prime Minister Atal Behari Vajpayee's ultimate good sense in rejecting the American demand to sign the Comprehensive Test Ban Treaty, (permanently preventing India from testing its nuclear weapons designs)—one of the conditions Washington, in turn, had insisted on—retrieved the situation a bit for the BJP.

But this drawing back from the brink only highlighted the fact that the BJP had no alternative vision to offer the country, nothing that would have helped the party to build and consolidate a right-of-centre grouping that provided a clear choice to the people tired of the usual left-of-centre politics.

BJP would have stood out for a brand of uncompromising nationalism able to generate enduring mass support if, for instance, it had enunciated an Indian "Monroe Doctrine" envisaging India as the fulcrum of great power interaction in Asia and the natural guardian of peace, security and stable order in the expanse from the Caspian to Central Asia and in the Indian Ocean littoral from Simonstown, the East African coast, the Gulf to east of the Malacca Straits, with matching military wherewithal—an expeditionary army, an air force with strategic reach and punch, and a genuine blue water navy, all backed by a consequential thermonuclear force featuring intercontinental range and intermediate range ballistic and cruise missiles carrying hydrogen weapon payloads, long range bombers, and a fleet of nuclear missile-armed nuclear-powered submarines. The US, it may be recalled, was militarily incapable of enforcing the doctrine President James Monroe announced in 1823 seeking to insulate North and South America from interventions by European powers, and that only with its acquisition of a globe-girdling navy in the 1880s was it in a position to do so.

But the Monroe Doctrine put down the strategic stakes, precisely what the BJP claiming to be an expansively nationalistic party, ought formally to have done long ago. Such a doctrine would have necessarily required co-opting the adjoining states, especially Pakistan, into the sub-continental security architecture, by affording them substantial roles.

In other spheres, BJP should have honed its social conservatism to preserve and protect the composite socio-cultural fabric of the nation as the best antidote to the virus of violent dissent and terrorism in a manner Edmund Burke might have approved. And, in the economic realm, the nostrums relating to self-help, minimising the state's role, and the free market propagated by Friedrich von Hayek would have helped the BJP shape appropriate measures. Together this body of beliefs, policy guidelines, and attendant value system would have comprised a comprehensive ideology enabling tectonic changes in the state while capitalising on the people's nationalistic spirit, entrepreneurial genius, and the inherently conservative nature of Indian society. Instead, the BJP has opted for the centrist mulch. Absent the grand themes to cotton on to, such nationalism as it is able to muster at the grass-roots level inclines its cadres to Muslim-bashing and external threat-perception fixated on Pakistan—a reason for India's great power pretensions not being taken seriously.

A small indicator of just how difficult it has become to distinguish the BJP mindset from the Congress party's is the fact that those pushing the nuclear deal in print and electronic media since 2005 are, to a man, the same "experts" the BJP government principally relied upon to configure and sell its foreign and military policies at home and abroad. It shows BJP's unwillingness to risk departing from a hoary foreign policy script even though it ill-fits an assertive 21st century India, an India uncomfortable with Delhi rendering it a supplicant for technology or uranium ore or nuclear reactors or anything else, and wishing that the government, mirroring its self-confidence and sense of self-respect, would try and compel the world to deal with this country on our terms.

(*The Asian Age*, September 12, 2007)

74. Congress has a Death Wish

BHARAT KARNAD

Sonia Gandhi was uncharacteristically aggressive at a rally in Haryana in branding those opposed to the nuclear civil cooperation deal with the United States as "enemies of development and enemies of peace." Until a few months back, the Congress party President had wisely stayed in the background, letting a political lightweight and expendable Prime Minister face the music for an ill-thought-out initiative that imperilled India's nuclear security and foreign policy freedom. She thus reserved the option of discarding it along with Dr Manmohan Singh, should the deal sour or the political costs rise radically. That calculus has apparently changed. Mrs Sonia Gandhi now either believes that she and her party can emerge stronger in the wake of this fiasco and win a decisive popular mandate, among other things, on the basis of a deal officially trumpeted as the solution for the persistent energy shortages facing the country, or she thinks that as captain of a ship that has struck an iceberg and is sinking fast, she is honour-bound to go down with it.

This death wish of the Congress party leadership is obviously hard to explain in rational terms. Especially because the nuclear deal is not only marginal to the country's energy needs, it also fatally undermines Homi Bhabha's three-stage plan based on natural uranium reactors, plutonium breeders, and thorium utilisation that will guarantee long-term energy security and independence. Worse, it shuts down the weapons R&D capabilities by diverting the monies from both of these streams of technology development to the purchase of enriched uranium fuelled-reactors from abroad. Owing to the promise of only conditional fuel supply for these imported reactors in the US laws, energy bondage for India comes as bonus! How the Congress party means to paint this deal, clearly an electoral liability, as a would-be policy success, is anybody's guess.

Mounting a massive public relations effort will not work. After all, the deal has floundered despite being strongly pushed by the government and the most powerful private sector companies in the country, incessantly plugged by the giant media houses, including the supposedly influential English language newspapers, periodicals and television channels, exhaustively championed by the bulk of the strategic analysts and think-tanks, and hurrahed on from the sideline by Washington. Notwithstanding this media blitz, the people have grasped the essential kernel of truth amidst all the analytical fluff and rhetorical husk flying around, that this deal, however it is dressed up, augurs ill for the country.

It has burnished the reputation of the Communist parties, who may have ended up doing the right thing for the wrong reasons, and, to an extent, in washing the taint off the Bharatiya Janata Party as originator of this misbegotten deal, but which has since made amends by leading the charge against its new *avatar* in Parliament and outside.

Almost all the lines of argument in support of the nuclear deal have proven to be wrong or unsustainable. There is one last tack the Congress party-led coalition regime has just tried, which also needs to be debunked. A few days back, external affairs minister Pranab Mukherjee pitched the nuclear safeguards agreement with the International Atomic Energy Agency to the Left parties as necessary for the conduct of trade with the Nuclear Suppliers Group countries other than the United States, as if the criteria for nuclear commerce with America were different from that for nuclear transactions with the other NSG members, which is manifestly incorrect. The Hyde Act instructs the US government to ensure that all the NSG states adhere closely to the restrictions on technology sales and transfers imposed by the US domestic laws, a position reiterated in a recent "non-binding resolution" introduced by leading legislators in the US Congress.

As regards the agreement on nuclear safeguards in perpetuity on all "civilian" nuclear reactors and facilities in the country, the fact is the IAEA sent a draft agreement to Delhi. As required by India's status under the 1968 Non-Proliferation Treaty, the draft treats this country as a non-nuclear weapon state and hints at no concession supposedly inhering in the Joint Statement of July 18, 2005 signed by Prime Minister Manmohan Singh and President George W. Bush, which recognised India as a "state with advanced nuclear technology," which phrase the government repeatedly assured the people and Parliament amounted to the US conceding it nuclear weapon state-status.

It was pointed out by this analyst at the time that this self-serving reading of the Statement was so much American-conjured hog-wash. But the concerned members of the department at the Bhabha Atomic Research Centre, led by the chairman, Atomic Energy Commission, Dr Anil Kakodkar and his confidant, V.B. Grover, who were in on the negotiations, are in a dilemma, required as they are to square the circle on the safeguards issue. In the event, the visit by the IAEA chief, Dr ElBaradei, to Mumbai will only highlight the contradictions in India's position, providing further proof, if any were required, that Dr Kakodkar has been the proverbial sap, a pliable tool in the hands of the Manmohan Singh government intent on lashing together a deal to eviscerate the indigenous nuclear programmes and capabilities.

The whole thing is such an embarrassing mess and has created so much bad blood within the nuclear establishment, between the few proponents and the many opponents of the deal, that in a gathering on September 30 to celebrate the 20th anniversary of the Nuclear Power Corporation in Mumbai, Dr R. Chidambaram, Dr Kakodkar's predecessor in office and current science and technology adviser to the PM, was excoriated by BARC stalwarts like Y.S.R. Prasad. According to those present there, he ended weakly by saying that "armchair strategists" have it easier than those making policy. The national security adviser M.K. Narayanan reportedly puts up similar defence of the deal, but uses his characteristic sarcasm, to wit: "Would you like to take my job?" Obviously, neither of these high officials can defend the indefensible, wisely or even well, which is a sorry tale in itself.

It only deepens the mystery about why it is that the ruling Congress party is trying so desperately to shove this deal down the nation's throat, even at the cost of being thrown out of power. It must be some very powerful set of personal and collective motivations indeed, which the US official documents declassified 30 years hence or sooner (courtesy the Freedom of Information Act) will no doubt reveal.

In the meantime, there is no getting around the fact that this deal goes against the grain of the country's nuclear programme. With Jawaharlal Nehru's backing, Bhabha did two things: he implemented the policy of "growing science" at home, in contrast to what all the other ministries in the government were doing—importing technology. And, he put his interlocked three-stage plan into motion, hoping to minimise the country's exposure to the HEU (highly-enriched uranium) economy, which he apprehended the West would push to the detriment of the utilisation of thorium, which India has plenty of. Some 50 years on, Bhabha's worst fears are coming true, and the twin programmatic thrusts are sought to be reversed by the nuclear deal with the United States, ironically, by Nehru's grand-daughter-in-law and her choice as Prime Minister, Manmohan Singh.

(The Asian Age, October 10, 2007)

75. The November Surprise

BHARAT KARNAD

With Prime Minister Manmohan Singh publicly reconciling himself to junking the "civil nuclear cooperation" deal with the United States one day and holding out "hope" for its resurrection the next, what has the Congress coalition government in mind to do? Under pressure from the George W. Bush administration, Manmohan Singh's retinue is exploring options to retrieve a situation that even its most ardent supporters have given up as hopeless. Even so, persistent newspaper reports and commentaries and views of a few observers plugged into the system suggest that there is still a turn or two left for the nuclear deal story to take and involves the Manmohan Singh regime going for broke.

This is how the scenario is supposed to unfold: the Left parties will be lulled by soothing statements and the PM's appropriately subdued mien into enjoying their famous victory, which condition will hold until around mid- to end-November when Manmohan Singh is expected to surprise the Communists and the country by formally signing the 123 Agreement, on the basis that the Left parties, as the Prime Minister has stated, were earlier part of the Cabinet decision to approve this document. The nuclear safeguards agreement, already in its final form, will then be submitted, all signed and sealed, to the International Atomic Energy Agency. The Leftists, realising they have been had, will inform the Congress Party's very own apparatchik as President, Pratibha Patil of their decision withdrawing support to the ruling United Progressive Alliance government. This action, however, will have no immediate repercussions because Parliament will not be in session, and so there will be no vote of confidence to face. With the deal thus paddled back onto Bush's side of the court, the onus will shift to Washington speedily to carry out the final steps—call a meeting of the 44-member Nuclear Suppliers' Group, get a helpful consensus out of it, and then rush an up-or-down vote through the US Congress, latest by end-February or March 2008, to finally put the deal on the rails, ready to run.

Prima facie, this is an implausible scenario for many reasons. For one thing the talk of "vote on account" that will become necessary is being officially pooh-poohed. For another, it presumes the sort of chutzpah—Yiddish for conspicuous brazenness and political risk-taking—this government has not so far shown during its three-and-a-half years in power. In any case, it seems beyond the ken of the "accidental" Prime Minister, Manmohan Singh, or even the Congress Party president, Sonia Gandhi (or, why else would the latter taunt the Communists and, just as quickly, subside?). But brazening-out requires a political gut-feel for what politically will fly and what has no chance of doing so—the sort of thing Prime Minister Atal Behari Vajpayee effortlessly displayed. Had Manmohan Singh possessed such political instincts he would have very early foreseen the problems the Leftists would have with this deal, and insisted on less intrusive, punitive-minded, and stringent Hyde Act. The government could have considered issuing a demarche warning of the political minefield the US law-makers were traipsing into.

Instead, Manmohan Singh went along for the ride, and now finds an absolute majority in Parliament, inclusive of his coalition partners, arrayed against the deal. If the "November surprise" package is still pushed through, it will be tantamount to the Congress Party committing suicide. Unless, Sonia Gandhi and others are convinced it is an issue that will fetch the party votes and facilitate a return to power in a hastily-called general elections. Then, the question to ask is: which line would be easier to sell to a politically-charged electorate—complicated talk about energy deficits minorly made up by imported reactors, which option, moreover, will also drain the treasury, or the more emotive issue of "India's atom bomb being sold out by the Congress Party to America?"

A post-mortem of the nuclear deal will show that the George W. Bush administration while, perhaps, the friendliest so far encountered by Delhi, nevertheless, failed to follow through on its commitments in the July 18, 2005 Joint Statement, in particular, to treat India on par with the United States as a country with "advanced nuclear technology"-qua-nuclear weapons state. The absence of this central pillar in the nuclear deal is evidence either of the Bush White House's deep-down desire to achieve the long-standing US non-proliferation objective to, nuclear-wise, de-fang India or of the need to accommodate the powerful American non-proliferation lobby, resulting in the egregiously flawed and offensive Hyde Act. So, if any one is to blame for the deal going down, it is the Bush administration, which failed to deliver. It is, however, clear that the Manmohan Singh government was complicit in helping Washington prepare the strategic nuclear noose for India.

But the real surprise is elsewhere. Having been presented a full-blown national security election issue on the proverbial platter by the ruling party, why has the BJP leadership turned around and seemingly lobbed the advantage back to Manmohan Singh & Co., by talking about "renegotiating" this deal? Do these leaders believe that they can do better than the present lot in wrenching more favourable terms and conditions for nuclear trade and that too from a less friendly. Democratic Party administration likely to take over in Washington? The two-term Clinton presidency was amongst the worst in terms of its seeking vigorously to rein in the Indian strategic programmes. The non-proliferation ayatollahs—Strobe Talbott Robert J. Einhorn, and their ilk—who made policy then are set to occupy still more exalted posts, reportedly, Talbott as secretary of state, Einhorn as under-secretary of state for non-proliferation, or for policy. India's fat will truly be on fire, if a successor government in Delhi reopens negotiations on the nuclear deal. As it is, Hillary Clinton has indicated that as President ratification by the US Senate of the Comprehensive Test Ban Treaty will be her top priority, and that she will ensure all countries climb on board. India will ipso facto become her prime target. The next Indian government will have to make sure it summons the strength of character and superior will to stand up to the US, come what may, and tell Washington where to get off.

India hereon has single-mindedly to concentrate its human and material resources on the breeder reactor and thorium utilisation technologies as the only prudent path to energy independence, and to get on with the urgent business of obtaining thermonuclear punch and missile reach—required as much for its strategic military value as for its political utility in deterring arm-twisters.

To the media commentators hyperventilating about the ill-effects of the dead nuclear deal, one can only counsel a dunking in ice water! No agreement has been signed, nothing valuable is at stake. If the nuclear deal is buried—the deeper the better, so it is not easily exhumed—the bilateral economic and military relations will continue to grow and flourish. The Nervous Nellies, who seem more aware of India's supposed weaknesses than appreciative of the country's manifold and growing strengths, need to be reminded that India is no banana republic, even though on the nuclear deal it has so far acted like one. It is in the US' vital strategic interest not to antagonise India too much.

(The Asian Age, October 25, 2007)

76. Operation Salvage

Bharat Karnad

The nuclear deal with the United States can go through if, and only if, the Opposition Bharatiya Janata Party joins the treasury benches in approving it, in however attenuated a fashion, in the forthcoming debate in Parliament, because the Left parties will definitely not support it. If, moreover, there is no vote under Article 184, then the "sense of Parliament" could be judged by the Congress Party coalition government to be whatever serves its purpose and, on that basis, to proceed with operationalising the deal and, thereafter, to take its chances with the Communists' winter of discontent.

The last time there was an invasion of Delhi by movers and shakers from the US establishment, it was in March this year, when former ambassador Robert Blackwill and that lot apparently succeeded in changing the Congress Party chief Sonia Gandhi's mind about the deal. These last few weeks, American bigwigs featuring the usual suspects—Henry Kissinger, Frank Wisner, et al—worked on the BJP leadership, succeeding in eliciting contradictory statements.

Having until now skewered the deal as a sell-out, to do an about-turn would have cost the party its nationalist credentials and credibility, whence the BJP's ostensible return to its original line, notwithstanding the tendency of some in the party to perceive dubious policy stakes in the deal.

Atal Behari Vajpayee's decisions to test and bring the Indian Bomb out of the closet and to seek nuclear cooperation on equitable terms with the United States were no more precursors of the present deal that Manmohan Singh has managed to obtain and which is manifestly injurious of the national interest than the last Congress Party PM P.V. Narasimha Rao's gambit in the 1990s for better relations minus economic and technological sanctions.

But the Americans and the Congress Party maintain that the BJP government made transacting in nuclear technology the litmus test of good relations with the US. Whether access to imported uranium reactors would pull India out of "nuclear apartheid" as Jaswant Singh had hoped and straight into a "subservient" relationship that Brajesh Mishra now fears was, as far as one can tell, never seriously debated by the Vajpayee government then or by the BJP since.

Motivated mostly by its right-of-centre ideology and by the promptings of the party's powerful "Non-Resident Indian"-support base in the United States, the BJP, when in power, seemed oblivious to the detrimental consequences of any kind of nuclear dealings with Washington.

The harsh and punitive nature of the US domestic non-proliferation laws was, after all, never a secret. The party's confusion over what position to adopt on Manmohan Singh's deal provided representatives of the US interests the opportunity to try and cajole the BJP leadership into, if not supporting it, then prevaricating on it enough in Parliament for the Prime Minister to claim majority support and send the 123 Agreement to the International Atomic Energy Agency by late January 2008.

The November 4 TV interview by Vajpayee's national security adviser Brajesh Mishra sparked hope for just such a denouement. Mishra said he wanted "credible guarantees" and to be "convinced" that the pace for the nuclear weapons programme that he had established during his time had been persisted with.

As, arguably, the principal author of the testing moratorium announced by Vajpayee on 28 May 1998, he is obviously not as concerned about the no-testing predicate of the deal, which will freeze the Indian thermonuclear technology at the unproven, unreliable and unsafe level of actual armaments.

But—and one can only deduce this—Mishra is worried about the slackening rates of production of nuclear warheads or weapons, and of weapons-grade plutonium, leading him to complain that the Manmohan Singh government is not "enthusiastic" about the strategic programme.

The other equally important aspects of the nation's strategic deterrent, namely, a survivable nuclear command and control complex and the integration of nuclear weapons into the military structure were never prioritised by the BJP government and the successor Congress Party regime and, one can safely assume, do not worry Mishra overmuch.

But he also iterated that a failed deal would have an "adverse impact on the growth of the (India-US) relationship." This last spawned hope in official quarters that the differences with the BJP were bridgeable and the deal could be proceeded with.

It is another matter that apprehensions about bilateral relations nosediving are needlessly alarmist and wrong. According to a recently published report by the rightwing think-tank, The Heritage Foundation, in Washington, DC—one of the strongest supporters of the Bush presidency and of close India-US ties—there will be little lasting negative fallout. Only "for a brief period," it concludes, the two countries "would lessen the intensity of their engagement and approach new initiatives with lower expectations and more circumspection."

This is no bad thing to happen because India is in too tight an embrace with the US and needs to regain some perspective. The US, for its part, needs to be sensitised to India's distinct vital national interests, security imperatives, foreign policy compulsions, and deterrence logic, and quite different domestic political constraints.

Assuming they have not distanced themselves entirely from India's national interest, the question the pro-deal *wallahs* ought to ask themselves is this: Is the liability-heavy deal worth the infringement of the country's strategic and foreign policy freedoms and nuclear security options at a time when India is marching inexorably towards great power status *without* help from anybody? President George W. Bush is supposed to have shaped US national security policies on the basis that even "one per cent" risk to US interests is unacceptable. What level of risk are the Manmohan Singh government and the other hard and soft votaries of the deal willing to run?

Realistically speaking, however, it is not the strategic sense-wise handicapped Prime Minister, the Left parties, or even the BJP who are critical to halting the nuclear deal. It is Sonia Gandhi. If the government has not so far bulled ahead with it as Manmohan Singh has been inclined to do regardless of the consequences, it is only because, as is well known, the Congress Party president has pressed down firmly on the "pause" button.

It is, therefore, reasonable to assume that notwithstanding the canvassing by Manmohan Singh and his associates and by itinerant Americans camping now and again in Delhi, she remains troubled by the possibility—a very real one—of the deal besmirching her reputation and damaging the solidarity of the coalition and her party's electoral prospects.

Sonia Gandhi has so far excelled with her political instincts and done the right thing. One hopes she will prove herself an ardent nationalist and, under the circumstances, do what is politically deft—let the deal slide into a state of "suspended animation." It will save Manmohan Singh's face, outflank the Opposition, keep her coalition government intact, burnish her reputation as a shrewd politician, and leave open the possibility of re-negotiating a less contentious deal with the US in the future, which, if it is not possible, will be no great loss.

(*The Asian Age*, November 13, 2007)

77. Nuclear Power and the Indo-U.S. Nuclear Deal

P.K. Iyengar

Preface

The urge to use neutron-induced fission to produce energy (explosive or continuous) was the main purpose of the Manhattan Project, and they succeeded in both. In addition to the atomic bomb, this resulted in priority for compact-core reactors for propulsion in submarines. That was the beginning of light-water reactors using enriched uranium. This technology was turned over to General Electric and Westinghouse who scaled it up to 220 MW and later to 1,000 MW.

The development of the technology for pressure vessels of this large size depends on industrial infrastructure. India still doesn't have that infrastructure. In parallel, countries like France, England, Canada and Soviet Union developed power stations burning natural uranium which of course produces plutonium as a by-product. The compactness of the light-water reactor eventually took over if the country had enrichment capability due to its defence efforts. Thus, the nuclear weapon countries dominate the scene with light—water reactors.

India chose to follow the Pressurized Heavy Water Reactor (PHWR) route due to the strong collaboration with Canada, who pioneered this reactor. The availability of natural uranium, zirconium, and production facilities for heavy water, in combination with fertilizer plants, gave further advantages to India. From 220 MW reactors it has now built and operated 550 MW reactors. The major advantage of the PHWR is the relative size of the components which could be manufactured locally. Eventually, like in Canada, 1,000 MW PHWRs can also be built.

The development of reactor technology has demonstrated how basic concepts in nuclear science can influence the systems we choose for commercialization. Avoiding enrichment capability, which is expensive, was the main motivation for India to go for this system. Reprocessing is a relatively simpler technique involving chemical engineering. The conversion of 238U to 239Pu is also more efficient in PHWRs. The fast reactor breeds more Pu than it burns. Also, thorium could be used in its blanket to convert it to

233U. Hence, India planned to develop fast-breeder technology and use its vast resources of thorium for deriving fission energy for the future. More modern scientific developments have shown that by an appropriate design of mixed-oxide fuel, one could even burn fertile material *in situ*, in thermal *and fast* reactors.

This paper emphasises the achievements of India in developing a self-reliant fission energy programme for the country. At the same time, the world market for reactors is dominated by the Pressurized Light Water Reactor, essentially arising from the weapon countries. The globalization of nuclear technology was *inhibited* by the Non-Proliferation Treaty promulgated in 1968, and the Nuclear Supplier Group's guidelines much later.

Should nuclear power become a more common source of electrical energy in the world, it can't be monitored by a small organization like the IAEA, unless it has enormous *manpower* strength and financial resources. Just like we cannot safeguard dual-use technology in steel-making or internal combustion engines, one cannot safeguard against the use and mis-use of nuclear technology throughout the world.

Secondly, many practical applications of science are compulsions of local conditions. India, being a vast country, with enormous need for additional electrical power, needs to choose systems which will grow locally without external inputs. While the Indo-U.S. 123 Agreement provides for the import of reactors and the specialized fuel for it, it is *very* expensive in the context of the Indian economy. Moreover, because India is not a Non-Proliferation Treaty country, the 123 Agreement has specified unacceptable political conditions, which makes it sensitive from a political angle. This paper describes the technical alternatives.

Introduction

It is clear that nuclear power is essential to the future of the world. This is based on the high cost of oil, the limited resources of fossil fuels on the planet, and the dangerous effect of emissions from fossil fuels on our climate. For a large, fast-growing country like India, nuclear power is doubly important. The Indo-U.S. nuclear deal is supposed to address our growing need for nuclear power. To decide whether or not this particular deal is truly beneficial for the country, we must naturally perform a detailed cost-benefit analysis. Since these are deeply technical matters, this cannot be done by politicians or diplomats alone—it has to involve the scientists.

It is a matter of regret that based on such an analysis one has to reject the Indo-U.S. nuclear deal in its present form, for the simple reason that its benefits are outweighed by its costs in terms of the conditions imposed on our independence of action.

Need for a Deal

Two major types of benefits are advertised: access to the latest technology to strengthen the indigenous programme, and access to uranium and to reactors to augment our power production. Of these, the former is simply incorrect. Our indigenous programme is based on heavy-water reactors, fast-breeder reactors, and thorium utilization. The U.S. programme is based on light-water reactors—and even these have not been built in the U.S. for almost 25 years. In fast-breeder technology we are well advanced. Unlike us, the U.S. and other Western countries have easy access to uranium and few resources of thorium, so they have no interest in thorium utilization. Finally, around 90% of the components in our reactors are indigenous. So what technology import are we talking about? It would be economically more fruitful for us to instead focus on the export of nuclear technology!

The latter, access to uranium and additional power-producing reactors, is also hyped-up. The deal does not involve selling us uranium at subsidized or fixed prices. It only allows us to buy uranium from the market. Similarly, the deal does not guarantee us a single new reactor. It only makes it possible for us to explore the international market, and negotiate to buy reactors at market prices. The price of uranium is presently $85 per pound, up from $20 per pound three years ago. If the demand from India and China goes up, the price can only go up further. Overall, the cost of electricity from imported reactors will definitely be more than the cost from indigenous reactors. In addition, one can expect a host of legal wrangles, including the issue of government guarantees, in importing such expensive and sensitive items. Further, we have to submit to intrusive safeguards, the character of which have changed in the past and will continue to alter in the future. Being a non-weapon country we will be at the receiving end without any option for withdrawal.

The costs of the deal, on the other hand, are substantial. The most important one is that it will seriously impact national security. Further testing is essential for us to develop and maintain a credible nuclear deterrent. That will become impossible, in spite of the repeated assertions that the agreement does not infringe on our sovereign right to conduct nuclear tests. Imagine that the 123 Agreement is indeed ratified and operationalized, and we have imported some 5,000 MW of reactors. If then changed geopolitical circumstances make it desirable, even imperative, for us to conduct nuclear tests, no reasonable Indian government of the future would dare to do so, given the large dependence on power from the imported reactors. In other words, when we sign the 123 Agreement, we will also be signing away our ability to act independently in the strategic sphere. It is sometimes argued that it is not essential to test. This position is contradicted by the actions of the U.S. itself. Even after sixty years of weapons development and over 2,000 tests, after the end of the Cold War and the emergence of a 'unipolar' world, the U.S. wants to start Reliable Replacement Warhead project, to invent new nuclear weapons and to maintain their stockpiles in operating readiness. Further, the Russians announced the other day a new weapon called the 'father' of non-nuclear weapons. Does this presage a return to the 'Cold War' days, and if so, will we not need to be well prepared?

So, if we need more nuclear power, and if the Indo-U.S. nuclear deal is not acceptable, then what are the alternatives? Let me address these alternatives in some detail.

Our Reactor Options

We have chosen the pressurized heavy-water reactor (PHWR) route to nuclear power. These reactors use natural (i.e. un-enriched) uranium as fuel, and heavy water as moderator. The technology for making the components for such a system, from developing exotic materials like zirconium, to the control electronics, to the turbo-generator, have all been developed in the country. Two 550 MW electrical power stations have been built and are operating at Tarapur, which were recently dedicated to the nation by the Prime Minister. Work is on hand to scale up the design to 700 MW in the new power stations to be built. The economics of nuclear power based on an indigenous industry, has also been proven. The clamour for the import of light-water reactors of 1,000 MW capacity as an additionality, is therefore only like importing high-end cars like the Mercedes. It is not the work-horse for securing nuclear power for the future of the country.

Light-water reactors from the U.S. are not the only option. Recently the head of Atomic Energy Canada Limited has issued a statement (published by the Press Trust of India) which talks of modified Candu reactors which will use MOX fuel involving plutonium and thorium and thus introduce thorium in the fuel cycle earlier than fast breeder reactors—an old concept similar to our Advanced Heavy Water Reactor (AHWR) but utilizing the same hardware of CANDU which will make it most economical. He has also welcomed cooperation in introducing it in India since we have established reprocessing and MOX fuel making facilities long ago some fifteen years. We should grab such opportunities because we have demonstrated successful cooperation with them. It will also free us from the hold of enrichment cartels that can hold us to ransom in the future.

Another direction is to accelerate our fast-breeder programme. Breeder reactors make more fuel than they burn. Theoretical concepts which will allow *in situ* burning of fertile material like depleted uranium and thorium are also coming up, especially from BARC. Because of the high-temperature sodium that is used as the heat removal agent, they have higher efficiency in converting heat to electricity. The Prototype Fast Breeder Reactor (PFBR) project will establish our capability to be on our own in this area. To speed up large scale commercialization we should invest in one more PFBR as well as on reprocessing plants. Dedicated reprocessing plant with IAEA and U.S. approval under additional protocol can be a non-starter if we go by previous experience. The dedicated reprocessing plant as envisaged in the 123 Agreement will at least take ten years to provide plutonium fuel for our fast reactors. Do we wait for another six years or more to reprocess the accumulated fuel from the light water reactors at Tarapur?

Problem of Availability of Uranium

It is true that there has been a mismatch between our mining and processing of natural uranium and our needs, which has produced a bottleneck in our operating PHWR reactors. This is because of several reasons: the high cost of production due to the low grade of the ore, diversion of uranium for enrichment for strategic purposes, lower burnup in the reactors for operational reasons, etc. At one stage one did hope for import of yellow cake from the international market, which was prevented by our dearest friends even though we offered to put them under safeguards. As the Australian PM recently declared, if we sign the 123 Agreement that country will consider supplying uranium to India, for we will then have effectively signed the Non-Proliferation Treaty—something Indian governments have refused to do for years. Should we really panic at this stage? Does this not give us an opportunity to plan better, fuller utilization of the un-burnt fuel in our existing reactors, the Tarapur reactor in particular, and not be content with just burning less than one percent of the uranium that we have mined and utilized? The Canadian approach described earlier is one example of reducing our requirement of fresh natural uranium. The AHWR concept is again a feasible proposition, but has not proceeded fast enough. In any case, for the good of the world, when every uranium atom is fissionable we should try and make it possible rather than wasting most of it as the U.S. has pioneered over the last 35 years. Special scientific committees in the U.S. have advocated reprocessing of commercial fuel and utilization of the fissile material more effectively, but the insistence on the 'black box' non-proliferation regime advocated self-denial in that country. It is only Japan which has very strong interest in reprocessing light-water reactor fuel, to make it a richer energy source for the future.

Uranium ore was not considered a valuable material until the discovery of fission. It had very little practical use as a chemical substance. Therefore, there wasn't much interest in exploration for uranium deposits. It is only now that we find that the uranium is getting to be more important even compared to oil and gas. The resources must be more uniformly spread on the planet than we think it is. Research and development in uranium exploration hasn't received enough attention. Since the discovery of rich ores in Africa, Canada and Australia, and their easy access to the U.S., it prevented commercial interests for exploration. In the Soviet Union, because of its connection with the defence needs, there was no question of costs and therefore exploitation of even low-grade ore has gone on for years. If we prove greater percentage of burn-up of uranium, then the cost consideration may not apply.

What about the availability of uranium in non-Nuclear Suppliers' Group countries? There are several areas in Africa and South America that have uranium ore. They are not members of the Nuclear Suppliers' Group. Unfortunately, the commercial industries in advanced countries quickly grab control over these sources, and prevent free trade. The question may be asked, whether controlling trade in natural uranium is called for to implement the non-proliferation regime. But, it is they who make the rules.

Barter Deals

In our experience, during the early years of our independence, Homi Bhabha complained to Pandit Nehru, that there was an attempt to internationally control even the mines of exotic materials in developing countries. The Atomic Energy Act in India, thanks to his efforts, described in detail the atomic minerals and prescribed that the ownership and control will rest with the government. Once, in Parliament, Panditji even talked of how we cannot agree to international control of mining operations. The export of beach sands was stopped and was taken over by the Department of Atomic Energy. Nobody had a right to export monozyte without approval of the DAE, which bought over that portion of the mineral sands for stockpile. There is a complaint that right now the beach sands are being illegally exported from the southern tip of the country, and there is even a court case in Madurai.

When necessary, Homi Bhabha also resorted to bartering strategic materials in return for equally important equipment. I remember a 6 MeV van de Graff accelerator, a state-of-the-art machine made by High Voltage Corp., then coming into vogue for nuclear research, was imported by bartering mineral sands to the U.S. The beryl ore, which contains beryllium, another strategic material, was bartered with France for sharing the technology of making beryllium oxide, as well as using it as a moderator in a reactor, under joint collaboration with Saclay, France. We have at present capability in nuclear technology, ranging from isotope production, research reactors, use of isotopes in health and industry, heavy water—a very sensitive material for reactors—zirconium and its alloys for components of nuclear reactors, as well as beryllium metal. At a crucial stage like this, when not market forces but international cartels control trade, it is necessary for us to think of bartering this material with non-Nuclear Suppliers' Group countries, who are not bound by Nuclear Suppliers Group rules. Don't forget that there is more uranium dissolved in the ocean waters, and when researchers succeed in extracting that from sea-water, there could be no control over the uranium supply. For that, effective research and development is required.

Separation Plan

In the July 2005 statement India offered to provide a plan for separating its facilities into civilian and military. The option of putting the civilian facilities under IAEA safeguards, and at what time, was supposed to have been left to India. However, it took seven months, until March 2006, in lengthy discussions with the U.S., to arrive at an agreement coinciding with the visit of President Bush. Since the separation plan is applicable only to weapon states, it was presumed that the U.S. had at last accepted India as possessing nuclear weapons and having a strategic programme. However, the non-proliferation lobby in the U.S. had argued that the separation plan violated the Nuclear Suppliers' Group requirement of full-scope safeguards, which means, all facilities should come under IAEA safeguards. The U.S. Congress eventually passed the Hyde Act with the sole aim of restricting the availability of basic material for weaponisation, and putting many restrictions on our reprocessing facilities. This was to make it acceptable to the U.S. Congress, and they in turn brought in the termination clause on the nuclear tests such that India doesn't make further progress in this field. Even though India protested, the U.S. administration could not influence the decision of the Congress. In the 123 Agreement, we see no mention of an agreement with respect to the separation plan, which clearly shows that the U.S. has now left the burden of agreeing to the details of the separation plan to the IAEA, under the India-specific safeguards agreement that is to be negotiated. It was not an easy task for DAE to agree to this separation plan, because the facilities weren't built like that. Now the IAEA can ask for a complete list of nuclear facilities and ask why only certain facilities are put under the civilian list, and question the timing. It can logically put restraints on the use of any of these facilities from one sector to another. When we signed an agreement with Pakistan on not attacking each other's nuclear facilities, we had to declare where and what are the nuclear facilities, which certainly revealed information which was not necessary in the public interest. In the same way the IAEA India-specific agreement may also be injurious to our strategic programme. It is surprising that the separation plan is neither an agreement nor a unilateral declaration by India. The Nuclear Suppliers' Group will again have a chance to pick holes in our separation plan. Therefore, the claim that the 123 Agreement solves all problems satisfactorily is not necessarily true.

Conclusion

The scientists have no fears about importing light-water reactors along with the fuel, to augment nuclear power sources. We have, for example, started off our nuclear power programme with the Tarapur light-water reactors, imported from the U.S. We have the Kudankulam project which has 1,000 MW reactors built in collaboration with Russia, which is an Nuclear Suppliers' Group country and has agreed to supply fuel for its lifetime. Other countries have bought light-water reactors, like Japan, South Korea, China. But what is questionable with the Indo-U.S. deal, is their insistence on conditions extraneous to nuclear power, about which the media have elaborated. Even Supreme Court lawyers and judges have pointed out how amending the national law by the U.S., under the Hyde Act, is not sufficient to give us the freedom to pursue our strategic programme, and continue our three-phase power programme without strings attached. If the US trusts us as a strategic partner, which believes in their non-proliferation regime and will not do anything to support attempts at making WMD in other countries, I don't see why they should not trust that our efforts in enhancing our abilities in reprocessing technology is purely for our fast-reactor programme and thorium utilization. We don't have to fall in line with their thinking on the next generation reactors or what their programme is to enhance nuclear power in their countries. On the other hand, competition in nuclear technology could lead to safer, more economic and cost-effective systems being developed, by India and China, taking into account the much lesser cost for R&D as well as manufacturing of components.

The growth of nuclear power in this country has to be based on expanding our indigenous capability, rather than importing the reactors as well as the fuel for its lifetime. To make a stock for a lifetime of 40 years of a nuclear power station, by investing in the fuel, is certainly not economical, considering the high interest rates obtained in India. It also speaks of a lack of confidence in our own ability to expand the enrichment capability in India, as well as making the MOX fuel, which also can be used in the light-water reactors. We must allow the future generation of scientists and engineers to innovate new systems, so that we demonstrate to the rest of the world that India is capable of leading the world in nuclear technology. The AHWR and the fast-breeders are examples of this type.

Nuclear science will progress, and new options will appear, as long as one is willing to think, experiment and innovate. Cold fusion and low energy nuclear reactions focused in this journal are important. The control on the thinking process is the worst thing that can happen to any country. Well established infrastructure can quickly decay if rational progress is not maintained. Even the US will find it difficult to get manpower if a sudden decision is made to climb back onto the nuclear bandwagon. Political decisions cannot create capability overnight. It has to be nurtured and grown in a systematic manner, without entanglements like in the proposed deal. That is where political decision of a type which goes beyond pure finances and economics, are called for. The debate is about not survival but progress. For example, if we hadn't expanded our agricultural production, wouldn't we be importing food at enormous cost, upsetting our economy? If we hadn't built large-scale steel, cement, etc. industries, would our industrial capacity and growth-rate have the present status? Mere foreign investment in terms of dollars is not enough to sustain a growth-rate, unless it is backed by productivity in agriculture, industry, and in education. We are reaping the benefits of a high level of education in the software industry, but this has to be backed by a sustained growth in technology. The satellite launching capability demonstrated by the Geo-Synchronous Launch Vehicle is an example of how the future can be secured by a consistent policy which is based on self-reliance.

The scientists' opposition to the nuclear deal is not based on capitalism or socialism, but to allow indigenous growth in capability in nuclear technology, which will assure energy security in the long-run. No economist has ever proved that out-sourcing nuclear technology for sustaining power growth in India is feasible or warranted. The sacrifices one has made in the past and that one is willing to make in the future, are testimony to a vision which originated with Nehru and Bhabha, and which was sustained for generations by a political will. One can change perceptions on non-alignment, global trade, etc., but it has to be realistic, taking into account the teeming population, the opportunity for jobs, and building up our capabilities in the industry, defence, and agriculture. A holistic view of progress is what is called for, and perhaps a rededication of what happened in space and atomic energy in the past, is the best way for growth in the future.

(*New Energy Times*, November 2007)

78. A Permanent Nuclear Hobble

BHARAT KARNAD

Whether the nuclear deal with the United States goes through or breaks down along the way, the safeguards agreement the Indian government signs with the International Atomic Energy Agency in Vienna will stay. On being asked repeatedly if this reading was correct, Lalit Mansingh, former ambassador to the United States, and one of the key trumpeters of the deal, recently confirmed and reconfirmed it to this analyst, indicating that the Indian government sees nothing wrong with this development and neither, for that matter, does the country's nuclear estate, represented by Dr Anil Kakodkar, whose tenure as chairman of the Atomic Energy Commission, was extended by two years, in the main, because he has been found by Manmohan Singh and Company to be eminently amenable.

As far as the IAEA is concerned, the accord with India is on a stand-alone basis. If New Delhi and Washington want to make further use of it, well, that is not any of the Agency's business. It is on the basis of the reassurance provided by the safeguards agreement, however, that the US government will convene a meeting of the 44-member Nuclear Suppliers' Group to seek an easing of restrictions on trading with India.

The implications of the safeguards in perpetuity are that the "separation plan" too will be in perpetuity and the fire-walls separating almost all of the leading higher research institutions in nuclear sciences and the nuclear weapons unit at the Bhabha Atomic Research Centre, will be permanent. This is going to hurt Indian weapons designers who have interacted in the past with their peers in the Tata Institute of Fundamental Research and other organisations—listed in the civilian part of the separation plan. Such professional interaction has validated BARC calculations, provided a fresh perspective or pointed to novel solutions for surmounting scientific hurdles in the process of conceptualising and realising new weapons designs and improving older designs.

The IAEA got over its initial apprehensions about even accepting India's "separation plan"—because such separation is only allowed to five Non-Proliferation Treaty-recognised nuclear weapons states (P-5), the United States, Russia, China, the United Kingdom and France—because the bulk of India's nuclear installations and research facilities coming under international safeguards, was a great inducement. For the P-5, this is a good thing to happen because it will decisively hobble the Indian nuclear weapons designing capabilities, and freeze the Indian fission weapons at the existing low yield type, and the half-tested tritium-boosted and thermonuclear armaments technologies at a fault-prone level (evidenced in the one-off series of tests in 1998), with no possibility of arsenal refinement in terms of tailored yield, yield-to-weight ratio, and other performance parameters. And further, that the Indian nuclear weaponeers will be left with only the heavily thinned out resources and nuclear infrastructure to rely on in order to sustain such weapons programme into the future. The constriction of the resource base will begin to tell soon on the already unsafe and unreliable Indian thermonuclear weapons inventory. For this reason, the Indian government should have insisted on the same sort of safeguards as the P-5 enjoy, which permit facilities to be pulled off the civilian list and used for weapons purposes whenever necessary.

But, the unconditional acceptance in advance by Prime Minister Manmohan Singh of the "safeguards in perpetuity"-principle, left no slack for the Indian negotiators, and no incentive whatsoever for the IAEA to agree, for instance, to a minimum prudent "India-specific" safeguards scheme that would become operational if and only if the nuclear deal fructifies, and to last only as long as the 123 Agreement endures, which is 40 years. The safeguards have to have closure or at least to be yoked to the United States commitments, meaning if Washington ends the deal for any reason, the safeguards will end as well. Instead of such a deal, the Manmohan Singh regime seems content with writing into the safeguards agreement, an assurance of the supply of imported enriched uranium fuel for the life-time of the light water reactors India expects to import. This is silly considering the IAEA is in no position to give such an undertaking, as it does not produce the fuel itself and cannot enforce a fuel supply contract India may sign on a bilateral basis with various countries.

But, of course, a "minimum prudent" safeguards agreement won't happen because Prime Minister Manmohan Singh has agreed to unconditional permanent safeguards. This, even though US secretary of state Condoleezza Rice had made it, in her words, "very clear that the permanence of the safeguards is the permanence of safeguards, without condition; China or no China; sophistication of weapons or no sophistication of weapons... In fact, we reserve the right, should India test, as it has agreed not to do, or should India in any way violate the IAEA safeguards agreement ... to which it should be adhering that the deal from our point of view would be at that point off." If Rice was candid, Ashley Tellis—the affable, Mumbai-origin adviser to the US government, who is always at hand to sugar coat the bitter pill, the easier for the largely technically ignorant Indian government officials and audiences he meets up with, to swallow—has been brutally frank. Asked by an online news service about the gains for India from the nuclear deal, feeling, perhaps, a twinge of guilt for his role in obtaining a deal that will eviscerate the nuclear weapons programme of the country of his birth, he replied honestly, "You will save yourself," he said, "a lot of grief over your strategic and foreign policy. But then you won't get energy." But because all the talk of the nuclear megawatts coursing through the electricity grid, is so much hot air, as Parliament and the country now realise, the safeguards-led nuclear deal emerges as the chains India will strategically strap itself down with.

But, we knew where Washington was coming from. The US does not care about India as a counterweight to China, it cares only that its non-proliferation aim is achieved and the potential of the Indian nuclear arsenal restricted. The Left parties fouled up by not recognising the permanent safeguards, for what they are and allowing negotiations with the IAEA. In the event, only Narendra Modi's electoral victory in Gujarat, and not the unanimous opposition in Parliament or Prakash Karat's threat of imminent withdrawal of support, may save the country from a nuclear trap because then the ruling Congress Party will have to choose between the deal and 14 more months in power.

A deadly joke on the country is in the offing, and this is how it will be played out: The nuclear deal breaks down—at the NSG stage—Scandinavian countries like Norway refuse to budge on their stand that all of India's nuclear facilities without exception should come under safeguards. Or, China insists on according Pakistan the same status. Or, at the US Congress' approval stage, the powerful non-proliferation lobby succeeds in asking for a more severe renegotiated deal. But whatever happens to the deal, the safeguards agreement will become functional and most of India's dual-use nuclear energy programme will come permanently under IAEA's and, indirectly, the US' supervision. It is a parting kick Manmohan Singh has reserved for the country before he becomes forgettable history.

(*The Asian Age*, December 14, 2007)

79. Nuclear Negotiators have not Learnt from Tarapur Experience

A.N. PRASAD

With the negotiations in progress regarding the IAEA safeguards agreement, the Indo-US nuclear deal seems to be inching forward to bring it in shape so as to facilitate clinching the same subject to the political hurdles being overcome. To what extent the pros and cons of the deal, hotly debated in the media and elsewhere so far, will have ultimate effect on the final outcome is not clear.

Since the implementation of the deal is "showcased" essentially in the way and the intensity with which the safeguards implementation is carried out, it is important to ensure that all the basic concerns are properly addressed technically as well as legally. Any laxity at this stage could prove disastrous in the long-run as safeguards agreements with the IAEA, once in place, are practically irrevocable, more so when the commitments are in perpetuity. It is in this context it may be appropriate to examine some of the issues of concern in negotiating the safeguards agreement.

The US has made it clear both in the Hyde Act as well as clarifications issued subsequent to the finalisation of the 123 text that the safeguards agreement has to follow the standard IAEA practices, while India has committed to an 'India-specific' agreement. It would have been better if India had insisted right at the beginning and managed to get a safeguards arrangement similar to the one applicable to the weapons states. This would have been in the spirit of the July 18, 2005, joint statement where there was an expression of intent that India will be treated at par with other advanced countries such as the US. Unfortunately this is not to be. In fact throughout the evolution of the deal, since India has not insisted on the parity issue and resigned itself to playing second fiddle as a 'client' State, there are problems galore in having to contend with a deal with conditions heavily loaded against India on technical and economic issues with political overtones.

The IAEA, as per established safeguards practice in dealing with non-weapon States not party to the non-proliferation treaty, will try to stick to the format of its own document INFCIRC 66/Rev2 with the major difference that even those facilities wholly designed and built by India and the R&D

institutions as listed in the separation plan which were hitherto outside the scope of safeguards, as well as all the future civil facilities which will grow substantially in numbers, will be included in the safeguards agreement compulsorily with all the implications, even though in the separation plan document it is stated that the facilities which are to come under civil list will be decided solely by India, obviously only on paper! In contrast, the nuclear weapon States enjoy the privilege of moving facilities from civil to military and *vice-versa*, a flexibility denied to India.

One of the most contentious issues to be resolved while negotiating the safeguards agreement is to address the assurances of fuel supply and building-up strategic reserve to be linked to India agreeing to safeguards in perpetuity. This is a commitment to the nation by the Prime Minister himself.

The so-called 'corrective measures' should address this as well as various other issues such as fate of safeguards agreement when the cooperation agreement gets abrogated or terminated for any reason enumerated in the Hyde Act or any changes, revisions or new Acts passed by the US in future as it happened in the case of the Tarapur agreement when the 1963 Indo-US bilateral agreement was unilaterally dumped by the US when a new nuclear non-proliferation Act (NNPA) was promulgated in 1978 in the aftermath of the 1974 nuclear test by India.

This concern is relevant because in the 123 agreement, India has initialled a blank cheque by agreeing to abide by the US national laws without any qualification by which it gets exposed to any future damaging changes in law. The 123 agreement also has no provision for arbitration in case disagreement persists. In fact, it could be said, 123 agreement provides India with generous opportunities to hold bilateral consultations to resolve disputes with no leverage, leaving the ultimate decision to US to be taken as per their national laws.

Unfortunately, India does not have laws to match the one like the Hyde Act which surely will dominate the operation of the agreement from behind with 123 staying in front for whatever it is worth contrary to what the supporters of the deal are swearing!

The way the sequencing of actions has evolved, it is clear that the Nuclear Suppliers' Group wishes to see India firmly fixed in a system of commitment in perpetuity with IAEA by initialing and then unleash their own conditions for making changes in their guidelines. In all probability NSG will prominently demand no testing by India in future as a precondition. There could be other conditions as well. To forestall these dangers, India while finalising the safeguards agreement with IAEA should proactively avoid getting into a trap by insisting on clear unambiguous language. This is important because in trying to get over stalemates on technical issues, diplomats under advice from politicians could find language fixes and push the issue to be resolved later when the focus is off. This could be really damaging in the long-run. In fact, this is what has happened in the case of the finalisation of the 123 agreement which is a fine piece of artistry in language but quite damaging in content!

One classic example, is the way the core issue of 'reprocessing' is dealt with in the 123 text, which, in all probability, will tie India up in all sorts of knots forcing to wade through uncertainties. It is unfortunate, the negotiators have not learnt from Tarapur experience. It will be interesting to know how this is being dealt with in the safeguards agreement.

One other aspect, which is crucial, is the status of discussion on the protocol additional to the safeguards agreement, which India has agreed to enter into. This is a document which cannot be taken lightly as it will include all the intrusive provisions of safeguards inspections. There is a possibility this could be under wrap or deferred to avoid immediate stalemate. This needs to be gone into in detail before taking any decision to go forward.

The pattern of presentation of the crucial documents to public scrutiny is now set. The 123 agreement was initialled and presented as *fait-accompli* and it appears the same may be done in the case of the safeguards agreement with the IAEA. Instead of discussing the content and extent of damage without any scope for constructive suggestions and changes, one may be left with discussing the status and legality of 'initialing' *vis-a-vis* 'signing' the document!!

(Rediff.com, January 11, 2008)

80. Nuclear Test is a Must

BHARAT KARNAD

Remarkably, in the two and half years since Prime Minister Manmohan Singh signed the misbegotten Joint Statement with US President George W. Bush, neither the government nor the supporters of the India-United States deal for "civilian nuclear cooperation," have been able to counter the substantive arguments about why this deal amounts to death by stagnation for the Indian nuclear weapons programme.

Instead, they have offered polemics—dismissing critics of the deal as "prisoners of the past" or as having "Cold War" mindsets, etc. This may fill newspaper columns and, repeated *ad infinitum*, flesh out the Manmohan Singh regime's approach to sceptics, but it has failed to still the growing doubts about the deal. Periodic statements by US officials, moreover, have only persuaded the undecided that there must, after all, be something dreadfully wrong with this transaction, or why else would the US government want it so bad and push it so hard?

In the sunset period for the deal, with the dispirited Manmohan Singh giving up on it as a lost cause and the professional pushers beginning to pipe down, it may be best to clarify the pivotal issue about why many more tests are needed to turn the boosted fission and thermonuclear designs in India's employ into safe and reliable warheads or weapons and to optimise them for the various vectors—land-based and submarine-launched ballistic and cruise missiles, ship-based missiles, and bomber aircraft.

Indeed, the dubious quality of advanced Indian weapons is such, the question is not whether India will test again, but when. And specifically, which party or coalition government will have the guts to finally act in defence of national interest and order testing so that this country can acquire proven thermonuclear weapons—the prime currency of power in the new millennium. It will require, moreover, that no Indian government again does the damn-fool thing of "'voluntarily" stopping tests after one or a few indecisive underground explosions as Indira Gandhi did in 1974 and Atal Behari Vajpayee repeated in 1998. Manmohan Singh, in a bid to out-do his predecessors, has, with the proposed nuclear deal, reduced testing to only a theoretical possibility. If India wants to be treated as a country of consequence, it better have the thermonuclear wherewithal to match, or it will always get the stick. That is the way it is.

In the main, this means jettisoning the nonsense about computer simulation making physical testing unnecessary. The viability of simulation in designing modern boosted and thermonuclear weapons is determined by three factors. Firstly, the richness of the test data already with the designers. Thus, the American labs at Los Alamos and Livermore can draw upon data gathered from some 1,800 atmospheric and underground tests; even the French weaponeers have 217 tests worth of data to rely on. In comparison, Indian weapons designers have data from a sum total of one boosted fission test and one, and that too only partially successful, thermonuclear test, to work with.

The second factor is the kind of computational speeds available to the design team: the higher the speed, the more detailed and realistic the simulation of nuclear explosions, and the better the eventual design. According to news reports, the Americans have computers capable of 100 trillion operations per second. The most powerful computer with the Bhabha Atomic Research Centre (BARC), the ANUPAM-AJEYA, according to Anil Kakodkar, chairman, Atomic Energy Commission, can muster no more than 3.7 trillion operations per second.

And the third factor has to do with designers having inertial confinement fusion (ICF) facilities, where high energy lasers are used physically to replicate fusion reaction and generate empirical data for designing newer, more lethal and more usable thermonuclear weapons. The US has built an industrial scale ICF unit called the National Ignition Facility in Livermore costing in excess of six billion dollars. The French have erected the Megajoule facility south of Bordeaux to do the same thing. The Livermore ICF, for instance, uses 240-odd lasers. India has a small experimental ICF unit in Ahmedabad, using directed energy from only a relatively few laser beams.

If the United States has test data from 1,800 tests, a computing capability of 100 teraflops and the gigantic ICF facility to obtain miniature thermonuclear explosions, its belief that it can do without testing in the future, is well founded. Even so, the combined team of the US National Weapons Laboratories at Livermore and Sandia in New Mexico, which won the design competition for the new Reliable Replacement Warhead, is not convinced their design is weaponisable without testing.

Here we have R. Chidambaram, science and technology adviser to the Prime Minister, who as Chairman, Atomic Energy Commission, controversially maintained since before the 1998 tests, that the country's laughably minute test data is adequate, its small computing capability sufficient, and its puny inertia confinement fusion facility enough for BARC to design, develop, and deploy a variety of sophisticated boosted and thermonuclear weapons without any of these computer-generated weapons designs having to ever undergo any explosive tests. Welcome to the world of virtual thermonuclear weapons and make-believe strategic reality. Now we know why Chidambaram's reputation is mud in the Indian nuclear establishment. (His successor, Kakodkar, does not count, because he says one thing in public and just the opposite when he is looked in the eye by his colleagues in Trombay.)

Had this nuclear weapons-making standard applied to the Indian Space Research Organisation, for example, ISRO would have been forbidden to launch any large space launch vehicle, been forced to rely on data collected from test-firing only the small Space Launch Vehicle-3 a few times, instructed to design the massive polar orbit and geosynchronous orbit capable space launch vehicles only with the SLV-3 data and entirely on computer, and with this meagre preparation alone, ordered to put some poor Indian into space. If you think this is silly, then consider the danger faced by the country and the less than jocular dilemma confronting the armed forces stuck with untested, unproven, unreliable, and unsafe boosted-fission and thermonuclear weapons.

This is not polemics, but hard facts. India may not be burdened with a legal obligation not to test, but our negotiators have produced a 123 Agreement that has rendered the testing option a notional thing, because the benefits they expect to accrue to India in terms of dual-use technologies and unrestricted nuclear commerce, are predicated on India's not testing again. If India nevertheless tests—and like it or not, it will have to some time in the coming years—the deal collapses, and sanctions are re-imposed. But this is the situation India is in today, Except, and mark this, two-thirds of our nuclear programme is not under safeguards, no light water reactors are imported at exorbitant cost, which money can, more prudently, be invested in the development of thorium reactor technologies at home for real energy security, and fuel supply is not hostage to Nuclear Suppliers' Group diktat. So the issue boils down to Manmohan Singh—a strong anti-nuclearist, being satisfied with a third-rate nuclear arsenal for the country. Because the energy rationale he has offered is a fraud. Umpteen studies in the US and elsewhere have concluded that imported reactors will not increase energy production other than marginally and India's reliance on external oil is not going to be reduced even a bit.

The more the deal is scrutinised, the more it confirms the country's security managers responsible for it and those in the Indian strategic community pushing it, as rank amateurs and Pollyannas hankering for disarmament and a nuclear weapons-free world. This is a bad reputation to have in the serious business of nuclear deterrence and power politics.

(*Tha Asian Age*, February 22, 2008)

81. Nuclear Dilemma: The Road Ahead

A.N. Prasad

With the safeguards agreement with the International Atomic Energy Agency reported to have been concluded at the end of five rounds of formal negotiations, a political showdown seems to be in the offing over the Indo-US nuclear deal. While all those following the progress of the deal are waiting for the outcome of the safeguards negotiations, it may be appropriate to recapitulate the issues involved for fulfilling oft repeated legitimate aspirations.

While the bilateral agreement with the US will broadly spell out the parameters with in which the deal operates, stipulating the rights and obligations on both sides, the safeguards arrangement with the IAEA will showcase the actual implementation of the agreement. It is like a passport which all Nuclear Suppliers' Group members will also look to for satisfying themselves prior to any waiver in the guidelines for nuclear trade with India. It is through the IAEA safeguards agreement that international inspectors gain access to a majority of our nuclear installations which were hitherto forbidden. Hence India needs to carefully incorporate appropriate firewalls to protect strategic interests.

Model safeguards agreements in vogue in the IAEA at present broadly fall into three categories:

(i) Nuclear Weapon States party to the Non-Proliferation Treaty,
(ii) Non-NWS party to the NPT, and
(iii) NNWS not party to the NPT.

As an extension to these there is a fourth category covering states who have signed an Additional Protocol to their safeguards agreements with the IAEA. While there is a Model Additional Protocol (INFCIRC 540) generally applicable to NNWS, each of the five NWS(P5) have adopted Additional Protocols specifically suited to their interests not necessarily complying with the Model AP.

India comes under category (iii) with no Additional Protocol and it is to be seen whether it will be permitted to evolve an India-specific AP somewhat similar to the NWS. This is important as a model AP has provisions for extremely intrusive inspections with no notice or short notice at any time and at locations originally unspecified based on doubts regarding undeclared nuclear activities or unexplained anomalies in nuclear material accounting, physical verification and so on.

India has consistently refused so far to succumb to repeated attempts by the IAEA to sign the AP. The present deal is going to be a different ball game with India agreeing to open up a major portion of our activities to external scrutiny. There is no model available with the IAEA to cover the new category of a NNWS (the tag which India is inevitably accepting) with a nuclear weapons program. This is an issue that should have been dealt with during the negotiations and satisfactorily resolved.

Before moving further it is very essential to see how the main concerns are addressed and how they are legally worded. The following are some of the points relevant in this context:

1. The safeguards agreement with the IAEA is triggered basically by the Indo-US bilateral deal, which also later becomes multilateral with the involvement of the NSG. Though it is not clear what will be the status of the interaction with the NSG in case the US bilateral deal runs into problem for any of the reasons, it is important to know what corrective measures India has insisted on and allowed to incorporate in the safeguards agreement in such an eventuality. Is the safeguards commitment in perpetuity tied up with assurances of fuel supply and currency of the bilateral agreement? Also how is the issue of building up strategic reserve of uranium and right of return of nuclear material and equipment dealt with? These are ticklish issues requiring very careful and detailed scrutiny.

2. Will the final text of the safeguards agreement as and when revealed, be a sanitised version or full text? Is the question of Additional Protocol dealt with now or deferred to a later date? Since this is going to be a highly contentious issue, it is in our interest to finalise it now along with the main safeguards agreement to avoid roadblocks as we go along. It will be a serious lapse if the discussion on Additional Protocol is deferred possibly due to time constraints.

3. The Separation Plan which was agreed to with lot of fanfare during President George W Bush's visit to India in March 2006 has not found specific mention in the 123 text for some reason. It has statements to the effect that India decides which of the nuclear facilities will be included in the civil list and the sequence. It also spells out exclusions of certain facilities and locations as strategic within the prerogative of India. This should be clearly recognised and incorporated in the safeguards text.

4. The question of safeguards on reprocessing is a complex issue requiring tactful handling, since past experience in bilateral with the US on Tarapur was pretty rough. There should not be a repeat of this.

5. Since we have in the 123 text agreed for the implementation of the deal as per national laws, without recourse to any international arbitration, we have to be prepared for possible changes in the US laws in future which could have adverse impact on the implementation of the deal itself and the safeguards arrangement. We did face such a situation in Tarapur where a bilateral entered into in 1963 as per the 1954 US Nuclear Act was superceded by the 1778 Nuclear Non-Proliferation Act (NNPA) and we were denied supply of fuel agreed to earlier. In the present case, if properly interpreted, as per the 123 agreement not only the Hyde Act but also any amendments or new Acts will be applicable to this deal. This is not wishful thinking but based on actual experience. India has hardly any leverage in forcing any interpretation if it does not match that of the US law.

Though the deal has been discussed in detail at various stages of its progress, before taking a final decision, it is advisable for the law-makers to ponder over various issues of concern dispassionately and seriously once again as the stakes are high involving commitments in perpetuity and once entered into is irreversible.

What is being attempted is creating new history and the outcome should stand the test of time for the long-term interests of national security and energy independence. It is dangerous to go with the mindset that our great country cannot survive without this deal! It is an insult to the intellectual strength of our scientists and technologists who have been responsible for making the country proud in this field.

One thing should be borne in mind. If India had not gone ahead with the nuclear tests, US would not be talking to us so seriously and proactively with us about this deal. Let us not underestimate ourselves but act with honour and dignity to play a global role.

(*Rediff.com*, March 14, 2008)

82. There are Weighty Reasons not to Accept the 123 Agreement

P.K. IYENGAR

The US is making strenuous efforts to get India to sign the Indo-US nuclear deal, essentially by threatening that it is 'now or never'. This is in contradiction to the statements made by US Ambassador that a new US administration may be willing to renegotiate the deal within a year of taking over. But this begs the question whether the deal is desirable or not. Obviously, it is desirable from the American perspective because it will, in essence, prevent any further nuclear tests, cap our strategic programme, and bring us into the Non-Proliferation Treaty (NPT) through the back door. But is it in our national interest? The lack of scientific debate in the media has led the Indian people to believe that we need the nuclear deal, and they are in broad support. But the reality is that this deal, in the present form, is just another way of getting India to accept that it is not a nuclear power. To understand this, we must go back to the beginning of the deal.

Joint Statement

After several years of negotiations by the NDA Government and later by the UPA Government, the Prime Minister of India and the President of the United States of America signed an agreement on the strategic relationship between the two countries on July 18, 2005. That agreement devoted three paragraphs to cooperation in civil nuclear energy. Specifically, it said that "as a responsible state with advanced nuclear technology, India should acquire the same benefits and advantages as other such states". President Bush promised that he would "also seek agreement from Congress to adjust US laws and policies, and the United States will work with friends and allies to adjust international regimes to enable full civil nuclear energy cooperation and trade with India ...." In return India agreed to separate its civilian and military nuclear facilities and programmes in a phased manner, to place most of the civilian facilities under IAEA safeguards, to sign an Additional Protocol with the IAEA, to continue its unilateral moratorium on testing, and to work with the US on concluding at a multilateral level the Fissile Material Cut-off Treaty (FMCT).

I, and many like-minded people, welcomed this Joint Statement. Though there was some concern about the statement regarding the FMCT, the statements about 'adjusting' US laws and international regimes suggested that this agreement would bring us to the nuclear table as a *de facto* nuclear power, in recognition of the realities of the day. It would also allow us to augment our indigenous nuclear power programme with imported reactors, such as the Russian VVER reactor already under construction at Kudankulam. Most importantly, it seemed to recognise India's impeccable non-proliferation record since 1974, and to protect our strategic programme. The Prime Minister, in his *suo-motu* statement in Parliament of July 29, 2005 emphasised that "... we have ensured the principle of non-discrimination. I would like to make it very clear that our commitments would be conditional upon, and reciprocal to, the US fulfilling its side of this understanding." He added, "should we not be satisfied that our interests are fully secured, we shall not feel pressed to move ahead in a pre-determined manner." And finally, "our autonomy of decision-making will not be circumscribed in any manner."

The Separation Plan

The problems with the nuclear deal commenced with the very next step—the Separation Plan. This document clearly spells out the guiding principles behind our approach to separation: "Consistent with India's national security and R&D requirements as well as not prejudicial to the three-stage nuclear programme in India"; "must be cost effective in its implementation"; and "must be acceptable to Parliament and public opinion." However, the separation plan was only submitted for information to the Parliament by the UPA Government, not for approval.

The Plan also clearly states that "a facility will be excluded from the civilian list if it is located in a larger hub of strategic significance." However, in spite of the APSARA and CIRUS reactors being located within BARC, which is our largest 'strategic hub', CIRUS is to be closed down, and the fuel core of APSARA will be moved outside BARC and put under safeguards in 2010. Compromises like this weaken the legitimacy of the Separation Plan, and lead naturally to suspicions that on other matters too we may succumb to external pressure. For example, the two ongoing fast-breeder reactors (PFBR and FBTR) have rightly been kept out of safeguards, since the fast breeder programme is in an R&D stage. However, before the fast-breeder technology becomes mature, much more R&D will be required to evolve the reactor design. For this we will need to have more breeder reactors, and related facilities, outside safeguards—and this will be opposed by US. Will the government of the day have the strength to withstand the pressure? Similarly, we are working on a new Advanced Heavy-Water Reactor (AHWR). Since this is for the power programme, it is likely to be designated as civilian, but since considerable R&D remains to be done, it would not be in the national interest to subject that programme to safeguards.

Finally, the separation plan also spells out that "to further guard against any disruption of fuel supplies, the United States is prepared to take the following additional steps." These include: (1) The United States is willing to incorporate assurances regarding fuel supply in the bilateral U.S.-India agreement; (2) The United States will join India in seeking to negotiate with the IAEA an India-specific fuel supply agreement. We now know that the US has reneged on both points. The bilateral 123 Agreement contains only vague reassurances and no concrete assurances, and India is negotiating with the IAEA alone, not jointly with the US. If the US has already, before the deal is done, turned its back on us, it augurs ill for the future of the relationship.

The Hyde Act

After this, the US produced a document and submitted it to their Congress for amendment of their Atomic Energy Act. This was deeply debated in the US with testimonies from several experts in that country. Going through all these statements, the Indian public was worried that the US Congress may prescribe conditions not intended in the July 2005 agreement. By November 2005 the US passed the Hyde Act for Indo-US Cooperation in Civil Nuclear Energy.

The Hyde Act states very clearly that (1) nothing in this title constitutes authority for any action in violation of an obligation of the United States under the NPT; and (2) a determination and any waiver under section 104 shall cease to be effective if the President determines that India has detonated a nuclear explosive device. These statements are not from the 'advisory' part of the Act, but from the prescriptive part. They make it explicit that the NPT will cast its shadow on the 123 Agreement, and therefore that India will not be treated as an equal of the other nuclear powers, in contradiction with the July 18, 2005 Joint Statement. More dangerously, the moment India tests a nuclear device, the entire deal falls through. In essence the Hyde Act, in one stroke, also terminates the development of India's strategic programme. For many of us the Hyde Act made it decisively clear that the US had no intention of treating India as a de facto nuclear power, as the July 18, 2005 Joint Statement seemed to indicate. It became clear that this was only another way of getting us to agree to IAEA safeguards as a non-weapons country, which every Indian government has resisted since Pokhran I in 1974.

Many in and outside the government have argued that the Hyde Act is not binding on India, and therefore we need not worry about its provisions. This reasoning is clearly flawed. That the Hyde Act will constrain the actions of the US government has been made very clear by virtually every major US government official. The Indo-US nuclear deal is between two partners—

India and the US. If the Hyde Act constrains the actions of one of the partners, how can it fail to have an effect on the other? Specifically, if the deal is made operational and we become dependent on imported nuclear plants and fuel, will it be possible for any responsible Indian government of the future to conduct a nuclear test and lose those plants, whatever the geopolitical realities and demands of the day? We should be very clear in our minds that, in the real world, the Indo-US nuclear deal will strike deeply at our strategic programme. All talk of retaining our 'sovereign right to test' is just theoretical rhetoric.

The 123 Agreement

After a series of negotiations the Government of India announced that it has initialed a 123 Agreement, without publishing the details. This created political protests and later, after the Cabinet had approved the draft agreement, it was made public. The text of the agreement confirmed our fears. The 123 Agreement very clearly states that: "each Party shall implement this Agreement in accordance with its respective applicable treaties, national laws, regulations, and license requirements concerning the use of nuclear energy for peaceful purposes." This means that the actions under the 123 Agreement are circumscribed by national laws such as the Hyde Act. By agreeing to the present draft of the 123 Agreement, India has agreed to accept all the provisions of the Hyde Act.

Further, the 123 Agreement also states that "... India will place its civilian nuclear facilities under India-specific safeguards in perpetuity and negotiate an appropriate safeguards agreement to this end with the IAEA." (Emphasis added.) This is a seriously objectionable clause, especially when the 123 Agreement itself is valid only for forty years (after which it can, by mutual consent, be extended for ten years at a time). It is completely unacceptable to place our nuclear facilities under safeguards in perpetuity. This also shows that the 123 Agreement does not treat India as an equal of the US, contrary to the word and spirit of the July 18, 2005 declaration.

The 123 Agreement seems to allow India the right to reprocess irradiated uranium, and carry out several processes towards a closed fuel-cycle, though the details as enumerated are not well thought-out. However, such a reprocessing facility will be under IAEA safeguards. Since India has so far kept the reprocessing technology out of the scrutiny of others, opening it up to the US and an international body like the IAEA will not be in the national interest, and will not help non-proliferation.

Naturally the political upheaval against this agreement was intense. There were debates in public fora, in the committees of the political parties as well as amongst some concerned scientists. However, the offer of foreign investment in billions of dollars for nuclear power stations on a turn-key basis and assurances of supply of nuclear fuel, possible approval by the nuclear suppliers' group to the 123 Agreement which might result in cooperation being extended by other nations, the need for nuclear energy security, have all played a part in swinging the public into favouring the 123 Agreement. Since the stability of the government depends on the support of the left parties in Parliament, which is coordinated by a special committee, the Government had to concede that they would discuss the 123 Agreement with the left parties alone. Those negotiations were continued for months without the leftists conceding their basic objections to the 123 Agreement.

IAEA Negotiations

The 123 Agreement clearly states that the United States will join India in seeking to negotiate with the IAEA an India-specific fuel supply agreement. However, the US did not honour this commitment (which was also contained in the Separation Plan), and India approached the IAEA on its own. The negotiations with IAEA completed six rounds of talks and then it was announced that the text of the agreement was almost final. However, this text has not been made public. There have also been contradicting statements that the agreement is not final. The story goes around that the US has asked India to make IAEA responsible for ensuring fuel supply when for any reason the Agreement is violated by an Indian nuclear test. It isn't clear when, if at all, the agreement will be finalised and made available for scrutiny to Parliament and to the people of India.

End-game

The entire Indo-US nuclear deal started grandly, with the July 18, 2005 Joint Statement announcing that "as a responsible state with advanced nuclear technology, India should acquire the same benefits and advantages as other such states". This had all the connotations of India being admitted to the nuclear club as a card-carrying member, in recognition of both, our achievements and our responsible behaviour. In the three years since then, the arguments in favour of the deal have become weaker. Today the proponents of the deal have two much narrower arguments to make. The first is technical: We are short of uranium and we need the deal to keep our reactors operational. The second is political: This is the best deal we can get, so let us grab it before it disappears. More recently a third has been added: If we don't conclude the deal we will 'lose face'.

Let me take first the uranium problem. For years we have claimed that we have enough uranium ore to support 10,000 MW of nuclear power for 30 years. We have not used up even major part of it, then why this sudden cry? Further, there has been no discussion regarding the economics of importing uranium or the legal issues (related to providing guarantees). The 123

Agreement does not guarantee free or cheap uranium to India. It only formalises the intent of the US government to allow trade in nuclear material and technology, which is presently forbidden. The actual sale of uranium will still be a commercial transaction, governed by market price of uranium, and by commercial terms and conditions, and will be subject to perpetual safeguards. The price of uranium has gone up four-fold in the last three years—from $20 to $85 a pound—and the price will shoot up even more with increasing demand. Therefore, the 123 Agreement is not a panacea for our uranium problems. A cheaper and faster solution would be to spend the money on uranium prospecting, and simultaneously to look towards non-NSG countries for importing uranium.

The second argument is that we should clinch the deal now; otherwise a new US administration may not offer a similar deal. This flies in the face of statements from the US Ambassador that a new administration may be able to negotiate a deal within a year of taking over. In the time-scales of nuclear power, this is not a very long time. In fact, the longer we wait, the stronger the country becomes economically, the better the deal we can negotiate.

Finally, 'losing face' is an argument that may apply to individuals and human emotions. It is scarcely an adequate basis for conducting the foreign policy of a large nation.

Conclusion

It is clear, from the texts of the various acts and agreements, which I have quoted above, that

(1) the 123 Agreement will be circumscribed by the provisions of the Hyde Act;

(2) if India conducts a nuclear test, the 123 Agreement will be abrogated and we will have to return all nuclear material;

(3) consequently the nuclear deal, via the provisions of the Hyde Act, does, for all practical purposes, severely constrain our strategic programme;

(4) the 123 Agreement does not secure our national interests, does not give us a status equal to the US, and is therefore in direct contradiction with the July 18, 2005, Joint Statement and the assurances given by the Prime Minister to Parliament on July 29, 2005;

(5) the US has already, by not joining us in approaching the IAEA, not fulfilled its reciprocal obligations, again contradiction to the assurance given in Parliament; and

(6) given that the purchase of uranium and nuclear technology will be governed by market forces, and safeguarded in perpetuity, it has not been demonstrated that the nuclear deal will be cost-effective in its implementation.

These are weighty reasons why the nuclear deal is not in the national interest. This is perhaps why a majority of Parliamentarians are also opposed to the nuclear deal. Winston Churchill has defined democracy as "the rule of the majority with the willing consent of the minority". Here is a case in which a government in a minority wants to rule without the willing consent of the majority! It would be a matter of regret for the nation if the democratic process is not allowed to play its role in coming to a conclusion on a very important and strategic area of activity. In many countries in the world this could be a subject for a referendum, but we have never experimented with this method.

One is reminded of the call given by Pandit Nehru at the dawn of Independence, on our "Tryst with Destiny". The right to decide our own destiny is what we gained. However, in the last sixty years, we seem to have described destinies on paper but never implemented them effectively. Education for children, emancipation of women, abolition of distinctions have all continued without a firm decision at any time. All the good work done by this government will be obliterated by a single mistake which affects the future generations.

It is also a matter of regret that the government has not considered the advice of senior scientists who appealed to the Parliamentarians in August 2006, to look to the future of nuclear policy in an objective manner and not accept the conditions extraneous to the cooperation in civil nuclear power. It is also regrettable that this country which has grown on its own for the last sixty years still seeks expert advice from outside and does not care for its own accomplished experts. It is not only in the nuclear field such problems exist but also in other fields like in agriculture, health, education and economic policies. Recently, *India Today* quotes former Prime Minister Indira Gandhi as follows: "A nation's strength ultimately consists in what can it do on its own, and not in what it can borrow from others." Let us remember her words, and act by them.

(Organiser, June 8, 2008)

83. A Nuclear King Canute

BHARAT KARNAD

Considering the banner headlines on the US presidential nomination race in Indian newspapers, one would think Barack Obama was in the race for power in India! Relations with the US are, in fact, headed for a downturn should he get elected US president, come November. John McCain is an uninspiring alternative, but at least he talks of "a league of democracies" in which India is bound to feature prominently, and not non-proliferation measures that will end up hurting India that Obama is set to pursue. As far as India is concerned, the main problem with Obama is precisely his non-proliferation stance. He is for preventing states from crossing the weapons threshold and is bent on making an example of India (and Pakistan) for obtaining these armaments; verily a latter day King Canute ordering the nuclear tide to roll back!

But Obama is a mainstream Democratic Party liberal who is easily spooked by nuclear weapons in other than American hands, who swears by the defunct and damaging 1968 Nuclear Non-Proliferation Treaty (NPT), and is intolerant of countries emulating the five (the US, Russia, China, the UK and France) so-called "NPT-recognized" nuclear weapon states. These countries would rather that attention were paid to what they said on disarmament instead of on what they have done in that area, which is nothing. In the India-shackling task, the Indian ruling class high-minded, if appallingly naive, hankering for nuclear disarmament—reflected, for instance, in the international conference on a nuclear weapons-free world hosted by the ministry of external affairs-run Indian Council of World Affairs on 9-10 June—becomes the lever for the NPT-5 to manipulate Indian policy. This is an inversion of Jawaharlal Nehru's realpolitik use of the disarmament issue in the 1950s to put the West on the defensive.

Specifically, a Democratic Party President will mean the return to power of the non-proliferation ideologues such as Strobe Talbott, Robert J. Einhorn and their ilk, who are keen to see India, nuclear-wise, tied hand and foot, than adjust to a world of many nuclear weapon powers. The US senator from Illinois and presidential candidate, prompted by these people, inserted the "Obama Amendment" into the 2006 Hyde Act—the US law enabling civil nuclear cooperation between India and the US. It mandates that, at any given time, any imported nuclear power plant will be allowed to stock up only just enough fuel to meet its "operational requirements", not an ounce more of enriched uranium. The slack the George W. Bush administration tried to build into the legislation permitting India to build up a stockpile of low-enriched uranium to last the lifetime of each imported reactor, thereby addressing Indian fears of arbitrary fuel cutoff (not that this made any material difference to an inherently bad deal), this amendment pointedly took away. Other than the ban on testing imposed by the Hyde Act, which will ensure India forever remains a small, inconsequential, nuclear weapon state, and that its weapon technology wastes away over time, this amendment amounts to guaranteeing this country passes quickly into the ranks of an energy dependency as well, because fuel supply can be severed at the first hint of India not hewing to the American line on some or the other major foreign, economic and military policy line.

Worse, the country will be stuck with a huge dead investment in the form of a host of non-functional reactors to add to our other woes. So, instead of bemoaning energy shortfalls and peddling a nuclear deal manifestly hurtful of the national security interest as a panacea, why has Manmohan Singh not fast-tracked indigenous uranium mining operations and invested in indigenous INDU/CANDU reactors?

If the Congress-led coalition government and large parts of the Indian strategic community are acting as if these very real threats to the country's strategic and energy independence are so much ephemeral then Obama and others in the West can hardly be blamed for exploiting the situation and encouraging Indians to put the shackles on a nuclearized India. Indian history in any case, is replete with instances of foreign powers being helped to realize their nefarious designs by Indian insiders and collaborators. The misbegotten nuclear deal is only the latest example of this sad and debilitating historical reality.

If, despite its inability to muster even a bare majority in Parliament, the present regime pushes this deal through at the eleventh hour, as is being rumoured, we should be aware of what awaits India in an Obama presidency. The US has traditionally been extremely legalistic in interpreting international agreements, especially regarding obligations undertaken by other countries (with little or no sanctity being accorded its own treaty commitments, to wit, the 1963 Tarapur Agreement requiring Washington to uninterruptedly provide the American-supplied reactor with fuel for its lifetime, which was broken with impunity). With Obama, a Harvard-trained lawyer, at the helm, Washington can be expected to realize the Hyde Act in its minutiae. This will leave New Delhi with no room for manoeuvre or for escape from the punitive provisions of this Act—the irrelevant 123 Agreement or no 123 Agreement.

(*Mint*, June 19, 2008)

84. Remote Control in US Hand

A.N. Prasad

The much talked about Indo-US nuclear deal has resulted in deep divisions among political parties on the one hand and utter confusion among the public on the other. In this chaotic situation, the scientists are selectively used as side kicks! The central point of controversy is in the interpretation of the term paramount national interest.

Perceptions, value judgment and priorities could differ but every true citizen is bound to have national interest at heart though in varying degrees. There is no doubt that it is an issue of path-breaking nature. The deal will have long-term consequences with international commitments in perpetuity. The question is, in a democracy, should there not be at least a broad consensus among the stake-holders to carry it through? Should there not be structured, informed debates to educate various sections of society about the pros and cons of the deal? Should such an important issue be decided purely on the basis of constitutional prerogative of the government of the day? The very fact that in view of the complexity of the topic, the public, the law-makers and even scientists are having problems in comprehending the deal even after three years, speaks volumes on the way it is handled.

Alluding to the political drama being enacted to garner support by hotchpotch number crunching in parliament, one commentator went to the extent of joking that India has its own NSG, an acronym for 'Numbers Supplier Group!' The general perception in the eyes of many appears to be, this deal is between George Bush and Manmohan Singh, two obsessed egoistic individuals rather than between US and India. How can a deal born out of bitter acrimony survive the test of time and run smoothly as governments change?

Now that the deal has reached a crucial stage, it may be appropriate to recapitulate the positives and negatives. This deal is being justified at least on two counts: Access to uranium along with imported reactors and to come out of global isolation with advanced technology inflow.

Limitation in uranium resources was known right from the beginning more than 50 years ago and it is not a new discovery. Since India is endowed with plenty of thorium, a three stage programme was specifically formulated to progressively achieve the goal of long-term energy security through thorium utilisation.

Development efforts have gone on steadily, having reached the second stage and it is a question of time before the ultimate goal is realised. For sustaining a growth rate of 9-10 per cent, energy plays an important part and it should be tapped from all options conventional, renewable and nuclear.

However, compromising long-term strategic interests, a quick fix solution of imports is being attempted at costs likely to be high with hardly any control. Perhaps to make the deal attractive, unrealistic projections are being made to the effect that by the year 2020, 40,000 MW of nuclear power could be generated when in reality even the original target of 20,000 MW is a big question mark! It may be recalled that the 2000 MW Enron plant at Dhabol in Maharashtra is lying idle as the cost of power is uneconomic due to high cost of naphtha. What happens if the cost of power through this deal is exorbitantly high? More subsidies?

On the question of isolation and nuclear apartheid, India has been under increasing global embargoes and restrictions since 1974 nuclear test. Undaunted, India has grown stronger to acquire advanced capability in all aspects of the nuclear fuel cycle to the envy of many developed countries. If the embargoes were not in place, with free access to international market, would there have been need and urge to go for advanced research and development? Having reached this level, it is hard to comprehend what advanced technology is going to come through this deal other than a bunch of power reactors of commercial interest?

Among the positives from this deal, there is some short-term gain in getting access to uranium and soften the perennial shortage of power thereby triggering investments in the nuclear energy sector to help increase economic growth with possible avenues for export. Also, nuclear scientists could interact more openly with global peer groups on research and development from a position of strength as equal partners. But all this could come at a cost affecting long-term strategic national interests.

When the Indo-US Joint statement, the Hyde Act, the 123 bilateral agreement and the safeguards document just released are seen together, one can see the writing on the wall. Indian concerns have been progressively diluted and the deal could be driven under US remote control. For example, full civil nuclear cooperation is denied and embargoes on sensitive technologies will continue, assurances of supply requires amendment to US law, spent fuel reprocessing requires separate negotiation and Congress clearance and so on.

Contrary to the claims of the government, the deal will be anchored to the Hyde Act which gives tremendous clout for the US to steer and force things as we go neck-deep and become dependent on external supplies. Also, India has to forget about going in for nuclear tests in view of enormous economic penalties.

(The Deccan Herald, July 13, 2008)

85. Safeguards that Erode Security

BHARAT KARNAD

The civil nuclear cooperation deal with the US is something the country will keep paying dearly for indefinitely into the future. The safeguards document, like the other parts of the deal, has turned out exactly as this Cassandra had warned. The long-standing American aim of roping India into the morally and functionally defunct 1968 Nuclear Non-proliferation Treaty (NPT) regime—an objective serially furthered by the December 2006 Henry J. Hyde US-India Atomic Energy Cooperation Act, the 123 Accord, and now the safeguards agreement—is now fully realized. At each step, progress was made, willy-nilly, at the expense of India's national interests and its nuclear security imperatives.

Unlike what our supposedly hard-nosed negotiators had hinted, there is absolutely no evidence in the safeguards agreement of anything other than relentless concession. "Corrective measures", they hinted, would permit India to procure uranium for imported reactors from anywhere and by any means when faced with a cut-off of fuel supply should India test again, and even withdraw its civilian facilities from the safeguards net.

Alas, there is only a preambular mention of "corrective measures" but no indication of the action India might take should the fuel supply be disrupted. It is claimed sotto voce that India in those circumstances will approach Russia. But why would Russia be interested in bailing it out when Manmohan Singh, during his May state visit, brusquely rejected Moscow's offer to "grandfather" new sales of uranium reactors under the 1982 Koodankulam contract? In international law, not saying clearly what a contracting party will do in case of the deal breaking down actually circumscribes options. And India is expressly barred by the agreement from withdrawing its facilities from the safeguards regime and two-thirds of the dual use Indian nuclear programme is headed into it. Under international law, only the five NPT-recognized nuclear weapon states can put nuclear facilities under IAEA safeguards and remove them at will from international policing. The US has reaffirmed this right in the preamble and in Article 34(b) of the safeguards agreement it signed with IAEA. Similarly, China has trebly protected its interests in the preamble, and in Articles 26 and 34(b)(i) and (ii) of its accord. By accepting this differential standard, India may have become a *de jure* signatory to the NPT, which is what was intended all along.

By the government's own reckoning, preambles in international legal documents are worthless. The Manmohan Singh regime, it may be recalled, took great pains to belittle the preamble of the Hyde Act, which asserts that, among other things, seeking congruence of strategies with India on Iran, the "reduction and eventual elimination" of nuclear arsenals in South Asia, and restricting India's stockpile of fuel for imported reactors to "reasonable reactor operating requirements"—the famous Obama Amendment—"shall be the policies of the US". In the event, how can the Indian government hold the Hyde Act preamble as irrelevant to the deal but hail the preamble of the safeguards agreement as potent?

The Hyde Act preamble is as unlikely to be disregarded by the US Congress as its counterpart in the safeguards agreement is likely to be countenanced as an escape hatch for India.

The fact is, Indian negotiators have acquiesced in an agreement that, in the main, adheres faithfully to the strictures in the IAEA INFCIRC (information circular) 66/Rev 2 of September 1968 outlining the safeguards system and the INFCIRC 153 of June 1972 defining the contents of safeguards agreements the agency can sign with "non-nuclear weapon states" and in the strengthened safeguards schemes (outlined, in INFCIRC 540 and "Strengthened Safeguards: Additional Protocols").

Sovereign countries are free to negotiate any safeguards agreement. What matters is how determined a country is in protecting its interests and preserving its policy freedom. The Congress coalition government negotiated as a supplicant and with the attitude of a have-not country with little leverage and one, moreover, in a hurry to obtain a deal, any deal, and, predictably, ended up with a safeguards agreement entirely harmful to Indian national interests.

Given Manmohan Singh's repeated undertakings in Parliament of the deal being premised on India's winning international recognition as a nuclear weapon state and enjoying the privileges thereof, the enormity of his government's accepting, for all intents and purposes, a nuclear non-weapon state status for India is yet to sink in. The financial resources that could have been invested to accelerate the delivery of indigenous breeder and thorium reactor technologies—something the US, China and others have always feared will endow India with genuine energy independence and too much power and, by this deal, have pre-empted—will now be diverted into importing reactors.

With the growing foreign uranium stake (sales, services, fuel supply and commissions) in the economy and polity, India's testing option will be rendered progressively thin and theoretical. Without further testing, the country's nuclear strategic forces will continue to feature untested and unproven thermonuclear armaments that lack credibility. In time, weapons-making skills and capability will be eroded and the country will be at the mercy of any country willing to call India's nuclear bluff. Why China, it could even be a weak and lowly Pakistan equipped with proven Chinese nuclear weapons.

(*Mint*, July 14, 2008)

86. Is the Nuclear Deal about Big Business?

A.N. PRASAD

Keeping the debate on the merits of the Indo-US nuclear deal aside, there are other aspects not discussed so far which need some attention. At a time when the global nuclear industry is somewhat dormant, India's ambitious plans to increase power generation capacity substantially through the nuclear route has come as a shot in the arm for nuclear suppliers who are looking for big money and to revive their industry. The role of big business firms in the US to lobby actively in getting the legislative changes incorporated in the US law to facilitate trade with India is well known and the Indian industry has not lagged behind in matching these efforts to get their share of the pie.

Weeks before the US Congress passed the Hyde Act, American companies came looking for prospective clients in India's huge energy market. The largest trade mission from the US to any country came to Mumbai in November 2006 and 30 of its 250 members represented 14 American firms in the nuclear sector. The US Business Council is reported to have said at least $100 billion (about Rs. 400,000 crore) worth of investment will be needed to develop nuclear energy in India over the next 20 years. The government which was originally targeting 20,000 MW of nuclear power by 2020, is now talking of doubling it to 40,000 MW. India seems to be under the impression that phenomenal increase in nuclear power generation could at least partially checkmate the rising oil prices.

While all this could prove to be wishful thinking, it is pertinent to consider some of the realities. In India there are some conventional power plants lying idle owing to economic considerations. As an example, the controversial Enron plant at Dabhol in Maharashtra is shut down due to high cost of power resulting from spiralling cost of naphtha.

In the context of the present Indo-US nuclear deal it is difficult to hazard the cost of power with the volatile cost of uranium. This could well be administered with the suppliers forming an OPEC (Oil Producing and Exporting Countries)—like cartel with India having no say like in the case of oil. India cannot afford to be insensitive to the impending high cost of power generation under uncertain conditions which may have a telling effect on inflation, more so when high cost of power could well be subsidised to sectors like agriculture. In a hurry to go for the nuclear deal in a big way we could well be trapped with international commitments in perpetuity without matching benefits. It is not known how far this aspect has gone into the decision-making process.

With the target figures for nuclear power generation being revised upwards perhaps to attract big business interests, it is a matter of concern whether serious feasibility studies have been done in fixing the ambitious targets. In view of the embargoes since 1974, nuclear development in India has progressed at a steady pace, though slow, but on a strong foundation backed by solid research and development carried out in some of the premier R&D institutions like the Bhabha Atomic Research Centre. None of the targets fixed periodically for power generation in the past have been met for one reason or other. The build-up of infrastructure including industry, trained manpower for design, construction, operation and maintenance and so on has gone on in line with the growth.

Expertise in regulatory aspects has also been developed steadily to meet requirements. However, when there is a large influx of reactors pumped in from different countries with different designs through this deal lured by billions of dollars, there is every possibility of slip-ups in safety and regulatory functions.

God forbid, if this results in any mishap the nuclear industry could get a heavy beating not only in India but also globally. One should guard against repetition of history like Three Mile Island and Chernobyl. This is a serious matter because the Atomic Energy Regulatory Body in India still depends heavily on the expertise and experts from the very nuclear establishment they are mandated to regulate! Similarly, selection of sites, environmental safety assessments and public hearings could slow down the process and any short-cuts could prove detrimental in the long-run.

The whole nuclear deal is caught in an ugly debate over the long-term national interest. While there are varied perceptions attached to this and rightly so, most of the problems have arisen because of the issues extraneous to simple nuclear cooperation, as is evident from the Hyde Act.

There is a strong feeling among many of the nuclear scientists and others that once India is brought under the thumb of the international community by heavy dependence on imports, it will constrain it not to take bold independent decisions in the future for fear of adverse economic fallout. The US law provides enough scope for arm-twisting, particularly after heavy investments by India. This and other issues of concern need to be properly addressed.

(Rediff.com, July 15, 2008)

87. Ten Misconceptions about the Nuclear Deal

P.K. IYENGAR

In spite of the fact that the Indo-US nuclear deal is not in the national interest, many in the country, and in the Parliament, support it because of misconceptions about the deal, which need to be clarified.

(1) The nuclear deal is an agreement between India and the US for the US government to supply nuclear fuel and reactors to India.

Contrary to common perception, the nuclear deal or the 123 Agreement is *not* a commitment on the part of the US government to provide us with uranium or nuclear reactors. Presently, American law prohibits nuclear cooperation with India because we have not signed the Non-Proliferation Treaty (NPT). All the nuclear deal does is to grant a 'waiver' from that law, so that American companies can now pursue nuclear trade with India. However, if India conducts a test at any time, the waiver is revoked.

(2) Imported uranium and nuclear reactors will be cheap and cost-effective.

Even if the nuclear deal is made operational, the actual sale of uranium and nuclear reactors will be governed by market forces—there are no guarantees of cheap or competitive nuclear power. To the contrary, there is every reason to believe that it will be expensive. The cost of uranium in the international market has gone up four-fold in the last few years, and will rise further with further demand. The same is true of the cost of steel and other materials used in a reactor. Manpower costs are much higher in the West. The example of the Dhabol power plant has already shown us that importing power plants from the West is not necessarily a viable option. We would do well to learn from that experience.

(3) The nuclear deal will safeguard our energy security.

It is true that nuclear energy is green energy, and therefore essential for our *long-term* energy security. But this does not translate into the nuclear deal ensuring our energy security. Power from the nuclear reactors that we buy will definitely be more expensive than indigenous nuclear power. Further, to keep the reactors running, we will always be dependent on imported uranium, which is controlled by a cartel—the Nuclear Suppliers' Group (NSG). Therefore, the nuclear deal, by making us dependent on the cartel, will only compromise our energy security. Only our indigenous nuclear power programme can truly ensure our energy security. And in any case, for the next few decades, nuclear power will not exceed 6% of our total electricity production.

(4) Importing nuclear plants is a quick-fix solution to the present power crisis.

Nuclear technology is sensitive. Even if the nuclear deal goes through, it will take time to buy and setup new reactors. We have examples of the French reactors in China, and the Russian reactors in Kudankulam, India. It will actually take longer to setup foreign reactors compared to indigenous ones. Just the negotiations and legal formalities could take years. It will be at least eight years before we see the first power. So importing reactors is certainly no quick solution. For the short-term, we will still have to rely on coal and hydroelectricity.

(5) The nuclear deal does not stop India from further nuclear testing, and therefore does not compromise our national security.

It is very clearly stated in the 123 Agreement it will be subject to national laws, and the Hyde Act is a law of the US. Therefore, the 123 Agreement is certainly circumscribed by the Hyde Act, which very clearly states that if India tests a nuclear device, all further nuclear trade is to stop, and the nuclear materials that have already been sold to us have to be returned. No future Indian government would dare to jeopardise such a huge investment in nuclear power, by testing. So, for all practical purposes the nuclear deal caps our strategic programme which is precisely what the Americans intend.

(6) We can pass a national law to counteract the Hyde Act, and this will protect our strategic programme.

Just as the Hyde Act is not binding on us, our laws are not binding on the US. We can certainly amend our Atomic Energy Act to enable participation of the private sector in nuclear power. But if we pass a law saying that we will retain the right to test, it will have no influence on the actions of the US. If and when we test, they can simply quote the 123 Agreement and the Hyde Act, and pull out all their nuclear materials, leaving us devastated. The only option here is to renegotiate the 123 Agreement and have the clause inserted there. However, the Americans are unlikely to agree to this, since it goes against their non-proliferation policy.

(7) The nuclear deal and the safeguards agreement give India the status of a nuclear power.

While the 18 July 2005 Joint Statement did indeed talk about India being treated as an equal by the US, neither the 123 Agreement nor the IAEA Safeguards Agreement, have borne out those optimistic statements. In fact, the IAEA safeguards agreement that has been negotiated is closely based on the model agreement that IAEA has for non-nuclear weapon states. The safeguards agreements that the nuclear weapon countries have signed with the IAEA require them to put very few reactors under safeguards, and allow them to take reactors out of safeguards. India, however, will have to place most of its reactors under safeguards for perpetuity. Therefore, we are certainly not being treated as a nuclear weapons country.

(8) Without the nuclear deal, we cannot get adequate uranium for our domestic nuclear programme.

The Department of Atomic Energy has always maintained that we have enough indigenous uranium for 10,000 MW of nuclear power for 30 years. We are not yet close to that number. The present mismatch in uranium availability for operating reactors is a consequence of poor planning, and inadequate prospecting and mining. There is talk of importing 40,000 MW of nuclear power, which will cost not less than $100 billion or Rs. 4 lakh crores. If even 10% of this money were spent on uranium mining in existing mines in Andhra Pradesh and Meghalaya, on searching for new uranium deposits, and negotiating with non-NSG countries, there will be enough uranium for a robust indigenous nuclear power programme, until such time as thorium reactors takes over.

(9) The safeguards agreement with the IAEA guarantees fuel supplies even if India conducts a nuclear test.

The safeguards agreement only notes, in the preamble, that India's concurrence to the safeguards is linked to getting fuel supplies. However, the IAEA has no role in this matter, and certainly, no such commitment is given in the safeguards agreement. It also notes that India may take 'corrective measures' in the event of a disruption of foreign fuel supplies. It does not specify what these measures will be, it does not provide for any role for the IAEA in this, and it does not bestow legitimacy on any such measures that India may take. It may well be that any such measures that we suggest, such as importing fuel from another country, will be disallowed by the nuclear cartel (the NSG). The only tangible corrective measure is for India to explore and mine more uranium, and to enhance the enrichment capability to provide fuel for those reactors. The latter is subject to uncertainty.

(10) The nuclear deal has no impact on our foreign policy.

The Hyde Act states clearly that it is the policy of the US to secure India's cooperation on a number of issues involving Iran, including its capability to reprocess nuclear fuel (in spite of the fact that Iran, as an NPT signatory, has the right to enrich uranium for use in light-water reactors). This has nothing to do with the nuclear deal, and can only be related to influencing our foreign policy. Recent statements by Gary Ackerman, Chairman of the US House Foreign Affairs Committee, regarding Indo-Iran gas pipeline, only add fuel to such suspicions.

It can therefore, be seen that the Indo-US nuclear deal is not in the national interest. It presents the very serious danger of capping our strategic programme. That alone is reason enough not to go forward with the deal. Additionally, it does not guarantee the energy security that we are seeking, and, in fact, may only end up making us as vulnerable to the nuclear cartel, as we are today to the oil cartel.

It is easy to see why the US wants this deal so badly. At virtually no cost, since there is no commitment towards fuel supplies, they can cap our strategic programme, bring us into the NPT net, through the back door, as a non-nuclear power, keep a close eye on our nuclear activities, including R&D, through intrusive IAEA inspections, and subjugate us to the wishes of the nuclear cartel. If there were no cartel, we could have easily extended the Kudankulam agreement for more reactors, and avoided the present situation. If these are not reasons enough not to go ahead with the nuclear deal, then there are no reasons that reason can find.

(Statement carried by many newspapers and websites, July 22, 2008)

88. How the N-deal will Play Out

BHARAT KARNAD

With the International Atomic Energy Agency (IAEA) giving its tepid approval, the Nuclear Suppliers' Group (NSG) and the US Congress now loom as the big obstacles to the nuclear deal. The dissatisfaction with the so-called "India-specific" safeguards accord voiced in Vienna may take concrete shape at NSG, in which countries such as Norway and Ireland will refuse to play ball. If a "clean, clear, and unconditional" exemption from nuclear trade strictures the Indian government is seeking does not accrue, can a politically hobbled Manmohan Singh regime move forward on the deal?

What is at issue is the ambiguity that made the deal possible in the first place. While New Delhi hints that the "corrective" measures mentioned in the preamble of the safeguards agreement allow it to withdraw its civilian nuclear facilities from the safeguards system if, despite contractual obligations, the supply of nuclear fuel, material, and technology is disrupted for any reason, including resumption of testing by India, Washington takes comfort from provisions in the operative part of the document referring to safeguards in perpetuity that imply rejection of a nuclear weapon state status for India. The US is also categorical that, as required by the 2006 Hyde Act, all cooperation is premised on India's not testing again, notwithstanding anything in the supposedly "superceding" bilateral 123 Agreement. In their eagerness to obtain a deal, the two governments have papered over their differences. This has, however, merely postponed the day of reckoning and shifted the burden of taking hard decisions to successor governments in the two countries.

This is what is fundamentally wrong with the nuclear deal—the incredibly short policy time horizon adopted by the two principals, Prime Minister Manmohan Singh and U.S. President George W. Bush, disregarding in the process the Indian imperatives to test and verify thermonuclear weapons designs in order to make its deterrent credible, and the non-proliferation underpinnings of US strategic interests, respectively. Assuming further Indian tests are held temporarily in abeyance, how will the deal play out?

The most likely scenario is for the Congress coalition to be dumped in the next general elections. It will bring the Bharatiya Janata Party (BJP)-led coalition or the Left-supported "Third Front" to power, whereupon the deal will be dead, as the BJP is committed to "renegotiating" it and the Communist parties to junking it.

In the unlikely event of the Congress-headed United Progressive Alliance returning to power, there will be safeguards on our civilian nuclear programme but no energy windfall owing to the exorbitant cost of electricity from imported reactors, contracts for which will require, at a minimum, a radical dilution of the supplier's risk and liability. With the Bhopal Gas Tragedy as background, this last will be politically infeasible for any government to arrange, even one with a heavy majority in Parliament.

So the costs of risk insurance will end up being subsidized by the Indian taxpayer or folded into the installation and running costs of imported reactors, compounding the already high cost of capital, resulting in high pay-outs all-round. How high? The US government has proposed risk insurance at roughly $500 million for a two-unit power plant. But such insurance costs are nothing compared with the escalating costs of constructing and operating the foreign reactors. The real cost of a new 1,000 MW nuclear power station in Britain, for instance, is believed to exceed $9 billion, twice the original estimate. The cost of a Toshiba-Westinghouse reactor in the US is $10 billion.

Then there are the inevitable time and cost over-runs. The 1,600 MW reactor being put up in Olkiluoto, Finland, by an Areva-Siemens consortium, according to a report in the *Financial Times,* is already 60% over budget and two-and-a-half years behind schedule. Such delays are being experienced by Areva plants under construction in France as well. An insurer covering for the delays in energy delivery would have to ante up some $9 billion—virtually the cost of the plant—for buying alternative energy in the interim. Much has been written in the Indian press of low availability of power from indigenous power plants. But the four newest nuclear power plants in France in their first four years have averaged only 45% in energy availability.

A wisted-up Areva and its American and Russian counterparts will ensure that all the costs for liability and risk Insurance, construction and operating delays, and reactor efficiency and performance penalties will contractually be home by the Indian exchequer. If you thought Dabhol electric power at Rs. 7-8 per unit was scandalous, wait for electricity units priced at Rs. 30 or more.

The PM has talked of imported reactors providing clean energy and energy independence. He is repeating the mistake, which a senior French energy official, Mycle Schneider, says French leaders make, namely, "conveniently confusing" electricity and energy. He explains that while "nuclear energy provides 78% of France's electricity, this corresponds to only 18% of the total energy that consumers use", and imported oil still "meets almost half, and fossil fuels over 70%, of France's total energy needs". If these figures are translated to the Indian scene, the already weak justification for imported nuclear energy—the *raison d'etre* for the nuclear deal—sinks.

(*Mint*, August 6, 2008)

89. Reaction to the Letter Released by House Foreign Affairs Committee

P.K. IYENGAR

The letter released by the Foreign Affairs Committee of the US House of Representatives has clearly shown that

(a) if India conducts a nuclear test, America will immediately abrogate the 123 Agreement, and take back all nuclear materials, including fuel, it has supplied;

(b) there are no guarantees of perpetual fuel supply or provisions to stock for lifetime;

(c) there will be no transfer of sensitive nuclear technology such as reprocessing technology; and

(d) the US does not consider the 123 Agreement as the only document governing civil nuclear cooperation with India—it's actions will also be dictated by the provisions of the Atomic Energy Act and the Hyde Act (see answer 3).

There is nothing new here (though it is disturbing if this letter was not shared with the Indian government). This is what many of us have been saying for a long time. But now, for the first time, these facts are being confirmed by the American government. Should we take note of it or not? The Indian government continues to bury its head in the sand and insists that the 123 Agreement is the only thing it will look at. It is now made explicitly clear that the US government does not share this view, and nor will the NSG. The intention is, clearly, to cap India's strategic programme, and not allow it to grow or modernize. Any non-proliferation law which will enable them to do that, will be applied. Once we sign the agreement we will find that all the implied understandings vanish, and we will be confronted only with the harsh realities of being treated as a non-nuclear power—in direct contradiction with the 18 July 2005 declaration, which the government maintains is the touchstone for the entire nuclear deal.

The government also keeps tiredly reiterating that the 123 Agreement does not prohibit us from conducting a test. But it fails to inform the people that if we conduct a test we will be punished, by the cessation of all nuclear cooperation and the return of fuel. It is very likely that the NSG will also make this a conditionality for their approval. The later this happens, the bigger the financial catastrophe and, even more importantly, the energy catastrophe. Is this punishment acceptable to us? The government does not address this point.

One could ask: Why test? Because, it is impossible to maintain a credible nuclear deterrent, without at least some degree of testing beyond the five tests we conducted ten years ago. Why maintain a nuclear deterrent? Our growing geopolitical presence, and the worsening political situation, in our neighbourhood, in Pakistan, between the West and Russia over Georgia, between Israel and Iran, etc., all point to the need to maintain a strong strategic programme. This is why the nuclear powers are in no hurry to move towards complete nuclear disarmament.

Therefore we find ourselves in the following impossible situation. If we go ahead with the nuclear deal, and, by some miracle, we even manage to import nuclear power at competitive prices (but many years from now), we simultaneously destroy our strategic programme as well as put ourselves at the mercy of the nuclear cartel. In return, we will not even get any sensitive nuclear technologies! How can this deal be in the national interest?

The letter reveals other things that we could learn from. Firstly, the level of technical detail of the questions, which the US government has had to answer. They have not been able to get away with vague generalities, as the government has in India. Secondly, the direct questions asked about PM Manmohan Singh's statements in various fora (questions 42-44), and their implications for the 123 Agreement—there is no pretending that statements made within India are irrelevant to the Agreement. Thirdly, the deep questioning of the meaning of terms, such as 'disruption of fuel supplies' (question 15) and 'corrective measures' (question 25), which again have gone unquestioned in India. All this shows a degree of transparency and responsiveness to the legislative branch of their government, which has been lacking in India.

I hope that our elected representatives take note of the categorical statements made in the letter, as also the depth of technical questioning, and revisit the Indo-US nuclear deal in Parliament. The time to debate these issues need not be constrained by US politics. This is also an appropriate time to ask if the country needs to revisit the 'checks and balances' present in our Parliamentary system, to ensure that governments cannot commit the nation to very serious constraints, without a greater degree of debate and consent.

(Statement released to the Press, September 4, 2008)

90. Realpolitik, not Woolly Policy

BHARAT KARNAD

Now, why is it not surprising—the news of President George W. Bush's declaration to the US Congress that he considers provisions in the 123 Agreement, such as Article 5(6) on reliable fuel supply for reactors sold to India, not "legally binding", constituting merely "political commitments"? Because some of us (alas, too few to make a difference) have been saying exactly this over the last three-odd years, ever since Prime Minister Manmohan Singh returned from Washington in July 2005 wholly pleased with himself for obtaining what he considered a breakthrough accord. Despite the evidence of the primacy of its domestic laws in the shaping of America's foreign policy, the Indian government clings to the belief that the 123 Agreement is decisive and the 2006 Hyde Act is of little account. The irony, of course, is that having invested so much of his personal credibility (for he has no political capital worth speaking of) in this horribly naive and half-cocked venture, Singh finds it impossible to back out of the nuclear deal. Sonia Gandhi, Singh's principal support in the Congress party and the government, can end this dangerous fandango but, instead, has jumped onto the bandwagon.

Let us be very clear that ending the nuclear deal will have no repercussion whatsoever (except on the "commission agents" in the ruling coalition and in Trade and Industry, who will be denied the huge payoffs from the purchase of exorbitantly priced foreign reactors). Close military links and strategic cooperation between the two countries will, in no way, be affected by the ditching of this misbegotten nuclear deal. It may be recalled that the then Defence Minister Pranab Mukherjee's signing the defense cooperation framework agreement on June 28, 2005 preceded the joint statement initiating the nuclear deal. With his misplaced sense of priorities and a singularly fanciful take on imported reactors as the panacea for the energy ills of the country, Singh proceeded, in effect, to try and leverage Pentagon's yearning for the mutual logistics support agreement and the communications interoperability and security memorandum of agreement with India to get the best possible nuclear deal. In this, he was unsuccessful, the Indian negotiating team failing to blunt the non-proliferation thrust of the US policy geared to keeping India below the credible thermonuclear weapons threshold by insisting on the non-testing clause.

New Delhi now hopes to exploit the US' fear of losing reactor sales by hinting at "first-mover advantage" deals with France and Russia. This is, however, to presume that when (not if) New Delhi tests, Paris and Moscow will maintain fuel supply for its reactors in the face of US pressure to cease and desist. But on fuel supply for Tarapur, for instance, France and Russia ultimately toed the US line.

Notwithstanding these negatives, if power plants are imported, then reliable fuel supply will be hostage to India's "good behaviour", which will be ensured by the economic necessity to keep these inordinately expensive reactors from becoming "non-performing" assets, in the event, the best thing that can happen for India is for the US Congress to put off approving the deal. The change of governments in both the capitals in the new year will mean a whole new ball game and a chance for the restoration of the *status quo ante*.

The consequences of even a bad treaty would be manageable if the ministry of external affairs (MEA) treated the international agreements it signs as the US state department and the Chinese zhongnanhai (foreign office) do—as mere pieces of paper, to be violated just so national interest is served. Whence, despite their non-proliferation obligations, the US winked at Pakistan's clandestine nuclear weaponization and Beijing transferred nuclear weapon designs, material and expertise to Islamabad and continues with its military nuclear links.

It is hard realpolitik-driven foreign-military policy that India should emulate.

Alas, MEA's approach is best reflected in the advice to the critics by a stalwart diplomat, Arundhati Ghose, to look at the "spirit", and not the "letter", of the nuclear agreement with the US when, in fact, Washington respects neither the spirit nor the letter of any accord unless it suits its immediate purpose. It reinforces the view of Indian foreign-military policy and diplomacy being of the suckers, by the suckers, for the saps! The larger issue is the urgent need for a constitutional amendment with retroactive effect, requiring the executive to bring any treaty it signs before the Lok Sabha for ratification by a two-thirds vote. The freedom enjoyed by a prime minister in the Westminster system to commit to treaties derives from the "royal prerogative" of an absolute monarch. The Indian Prime Minister is not a sovereign who is free to exercise his whim, push through a deal injurious of the national interest, drum up a simple majority in the Parliament through devious means as was done on 22 July and then, in cahoots with a complicit media, claim popular support for it.

(*Mint*, September 13, 2008)

91. An Ode to Energy Security

A.N. PRASAD

As the Indo-US civil nuclear cooperation agreement inches towards the finishing line, it is worth asking: where are we heading? Normally such a deal should be wholeheartedly welcome to almost all sections in the country, as it provides India an opportunity to play its rightful role as a global player, after having acquired a level of technological competence in the nuclear field. The deal is also seen as addressing near-term constraints, such as uranium shortage and helping increase the pace of development of the nuclear power sector. However, for the US and other supplier countries of the nuclear suppliers' group (NSG) this deal is perceived as a huge business opportunity to gain access to the lucrative Indian market and at the same time an opportunity to fulfil their political agenda. This deal is also an opportunity to help revive the sagging global nuclear industry, more so in the US where it is almost dormant since the 1979 Three Mile Island nuclear reactor accident.

A careful study of the deal in its present form reveals, the terms and conditions fall far short of expectation. At the root are two crucial points in the July 18, 2005 Indo-US Joint Statement, namely,

1. India to be treated at par with other developed countries like the USA in recognition of its advanced technological capability in the nuclear field and excellent non-proliferation record, and
2. The scope to include full civil nuclear cooperation. If only these two basic points had been honoured the outcome would have been different and resulted in much wider acceptance in India. Unfortunately, by yielding ground on these core points we have neither achieved parity with advanced states, nor full civil nuclear cooperation.

In spite of this colossal lapse, the public is being told the goal post has not been shifted. Added to this while the civil nuclear cooperation should have occupied centre-stage, the issue of testing has hijacked the debate. Non-proliferation concerns have all along dominated the deliberations—starting with the separation plan for demarcating civil and military facilities and on to the Hyde Act, the 123 Agreement, the IAEA Safeguards Agreement, the NSG waiver and even in the ongoing debate in the US Congress.

Why this US obsession on non-proliferation? Whatever happened to the pious statement in the Joint Statement? Why did India go on the defensive instead of putting its foot down? In fact none of the weapon states have gone this far in their commitments and are sitting pretty preaching to others after each one of them conducted large number of tests. What sort of parity is this? In the hostile geopolitical region India is situated in, should it not have freedom of national security? The oft-repeated slogan, 'India has protected its legal right to test but the suppliers have the right to react may sound music to some ears. What practical value does this right have, when it could at best be rhetoric? Which government in future will be able to exercise this right, however serious the situation, and face the economic and political consequences after we have made massive investments: deprivation of fuel, equipment, spares and the prospect of return of everything imported and getting stuck with idling infrastructure, perpetual safeguards hazardous nuclear waste which nobody will take back? Let us face the truth. The option to test is as good as dead. No amount of spin can undo this hard reality.

Having failed to contain India through embargoes, denials, restrictions, isolation, an attempt is being made to rope us in as a strategic partner through this deal. It appears the non-proliferation bogey is a ploy for capping India's nuclear deterrence capability prematurely at a qualitatively nascent level by depriving further tests forever.

Testing, which complements computer simulation is a powerful tool for design refinement and sophistication for enhanced quality and credibility of deterrence. Depending entirely on computer simulation and theoretical calculations has its own limitations. If not why have the nuclear weapon states gone in for a series of tests in spite of having powerful supercomputers? The Hyde Act is explicit in its intent to first cap India on testing followed by imposing restrictions on fissile material production for military purposes: two good recipes for complying with the Comprehensive Test Ban Treaty (CTBT) and Fissile Material Cut-off Treaty (FMCT) through the back door.

The Hyde Act will hang like an albatross. It is for the national security experts to assess and conclude whether, in the geopolitical neighbourhood we are situated in, it is safe to close our options as the terms of this deal seem to imply with none of our neighbours having made the voluntary commitments India has made.

Tall claims are being made, like, India's isolation will end, free inflow of high technology will follow, and so on. Yes, much of these could probably have been realised if we had played our cards well. With complex parts of the nuclear fuel cycle excluded, technology and trade still continuing to face embargo, we are now relegated to the position of a recipient state, not a state treated at par with other advanced countries like the USA.

Yet, we continue to dream. The deal is framed in such a way that we are made to fight for our rights at every stage with leverage resting with the supplier states to decide what not to offer. The diplomatic language of the 123 text may be a masterstroke but it is our scientists who have to face the music when it comes to interpretation. We are already seeing a preview of this in the correspondence between the US administration and Congress, with interpretations totally at variance with our understanding on key issues. If this is the predicament even before the deal is inked, we can only imagine how it could unravel with time. Any disagreement in future could escalate into a dispute, with India having no leverage to protect itself against arm-twisting, more so as the 123 Agreement has no provision for independent arbitration. With increasing investments on imports our vulnerability to outside pressures is bound to increase.

While the way the US is interpreting the 123 is a cause for embarrassment, a coverup is being attempted by suggesting we could do business with other countries like France and Russia bypassing the US. With the US having spearheaded the process and being a dominant country, is this a realistic assessment? When the chips are down, all the NSG members are bound to stick together and any attempt to exploit one against the other is bound to prove counter-productive. They are a cartel!

To sum up, this deal is all about lucrative commercial interests limited to trading in power reactors, with conditions attached and not about full civil nuclear cooperation. Embargoes on the crucial parts of the nuclear fuel cycle will continue, a variant of the nuclear apartheid! The net result is our indigenous power programme will be an additionality to the imports.

It is the obituary for the saga of predominantly indigenous development over the last 50 years!

(*The New Indian Express*, September 26, 2008)

92. Indo-US Nuclear Deal: Does it Serve National Interest?

A.N. PRASAD

Indian Strategy for Energy Security

Recognizing the awesome power of the atom, the Indian Nuclear Establishment, following the vision of its founding father Dr. Homi Bhabha, embarked on a systematic programme of comprehensive development for harnessing nuclear energy in all its facets encompassing not only electricity generation but also application of radio-isotopes in industry, agriculture and medicine. In pursuit of this strategy, to achieve indigenous capability in the power sector, development of the entire nuclear fuel cycle was undertaken. The gamut of activities covered mining and milling of uranium, refining of uranium, converting it into fuel bundles with all the special structural components that go with it, building reactors to generate electricity, reprocessing of spent fuel to separate plutonium, radioactive waste management as well as associated activities like heavy water production and uranium enrichment, a womb to tomb approach, so to say. As a result of persistent efforts over the last five decades, it is a matter of pride that India has reached a level of development that it has become the envy of even the advanced countries, many of which have not ventured.

Why India went for Nuclear Test

During the sixties there used to be international meetings discussing peaceful uses of underground nuclear explosions to change the course of rivers, releasing of gas trapped deep underground etc. in which India was also invited to participate. Whether it is a scientific curiosity, political expediency or anything else, it was decided to venture into this domain as it fitted well with the comprehensive development strategy that was being pursued. Accordingly a nuclear test was conducted at Pokhran in Rajasthan on May 18, 1974. This was demonstrative in nature to validate the concept of Peaceful Nuclear Experiment (PNE). Following this test, international meetings on this topic were abruptly stopped and a group of supplier countries having potential for nuclear trade, led by USA, ganged up to isolate India from accessing international nuclear commerce. Thanks to the far sight and firm foundation of technological prowess built with lot of dedication and hard work, India has succeeded in facing the challenge posed by the embargo placed by the Nuclear Suppliers' Group (NSG). The 1998 nuclear tests were more related to national security considerations and to build an effective credible nuclear deterrence. However for the scientists, while it was a proud achievement which raised the country to a different level, it matters even worse with the NSG expanding the list of restricted items, denying even dual use industrial items, fearing indirect use in the nuclear sector.

Three Stage Development of Nuclear Power Programme

Among the naturally occurring atomic minerals, uranium and thorium are basic sources of nuclear energy. A survey conducted more than 50 years ago revealed that India has limited reserves of uranium, mostly concentrated in the northeast region and plentiful thorium, in fact one of the world's largest, in the monazite beach sands of Kerala and Orissa. While natural uranium with a minor fraction of fissile content can be used as fuel after refining, natural thorium having no fissile content needs conversion to a not naturally occurring isotope of uranium in an advanced reactor system before use as fuel. The genesis of India's independent three stage nuclear programme, enunciated by Dr. Bhabha more than 50 years ago, stems from the need to tackle this serious mismatch in the availability of these minerals. The key to achieving long-term energy security was thus recognized pretty early, and it has to be through thorium utilization as the ultimate goal. According to one estimate, the available uranium in the country can support a nuclear power programme of only 10,000 MW meager by any standards. However, with thorium utilization it could go up by a factor to 350,000 MWe. The entire development effort therefore is tuned towards realizing this goal.

Status of the three stages

In the first stage, pressurized heavy water reactor (PHWR), was specially selected as it uses natural uranium as fuel and a good producer of plutonium an essential ingredient for the three-stage programme. Production of heavy water and spent fuel reprocessing were flagged as sensitive technologies specifically targeted for embargo even in the current Indo-US nuclear deal. Reason being, heavy water in the reactor generates tritium used in the nuclear weapons as trigger material and plutonium a main fissile material having use in weapons as well as in the second stage. All the technology involved in the first stage is now fully developed.

Embedded in the first stage is the initial R&D needed for thorium utilization. The activities include separating thorium from the monazite beach sands, purifying to nuclear grade, converting to fuel, irradiating in research and power reactors to convert thorium partially into fissile uranium and reprocessing the irradiated thorium fuel to separate converted fissile uranium.

To take a step further, a mini reactor is specially designed and is operating with uranium produced from thorium. No country in the world has achieved this level of proficiency in the thorium fuel cycle technology.

In the second stage, a different type of reactor, more complex, called fast breeder reactor, takes center stage. Here the plutonium separated by reprocessing the spent fuel from the heavy water reactors of the first stage is mixed with depleted uranium and loaded as fuel into fast reactors. Side by side thorium is also loaded in the peripheral region of the reactor. While initially plutonium is burnt, it is also produced by conversion of depleted uranium, with overall balance showing more plutonium produced than consumed. Hence the term 'breeder' used. The plutonium separated from spent fuel in this stage is used to fuel further reactors of this type for self-sustainable operation and the uranium from thorium is separated and fed into the third stage.

To gain experience in the highly complex fast reactor technology, a 40 MWt fast breeder test reactor (FBTR) was built nearly 20 years ago and is under operation at the Indira Gandhi Center for Atomic Research (IGCAR) dedicated for fast reactor development. As a major logical next step, a 500 MWe prototype fast breeder reactor (PFBR) is now under construction at Kalpakkam heralding the arrival of the second stage. Here again dedicated efforts are on to come to grips with the most complex parts of the associated fast reactor fuel cycle, in particular fuel fabrication, spent fuel reprocessing, high active waste management, involving extensive use of robotics and remote technologies due to intense radioactivity, and development of complex fabrication techniques and equipments in collaboration with Indian industry.

As a prelude to thorium utilization in a big way, a new reactor concept called 'Advanced Heavy Water Reactor' (AHWR) has been developed exclusively, in which plutonium and thorium are used for self-sustaining operation. Work on a 300 MWe version is now on, which should give valuable experience in handling thorium.

Third stage is the culmination of the saga of indigenous development to achieve long-term energy security and independence using the abundant thorium deposits in the country. Here, the uranium derived from thorium in the second stage is recycled as fuel along with fresh thorium to breed uranium in yet another type of reactor and sustain a cycle of its own to produce energy.

This in brief is (but may soon become was with the advent of the Indo-US nuclear deal) the story of the Indian nuclear establishment's grand strategy to overcome the handicap of paucity of uranium by acquiring technological competence to harness vast resources of thorium available in the country. This vision, if allowed to fructify by pursuing to its logical conclusion unhindered, India could well be sitting pretty as world leader in thorium technology. What is most important for achieving ultimate success is patience and perseverance.

Will The Nuclear Deal Help National Interest?

Premise for justification of the Nuclear Deal:

- India to be treated at par with other advanced countries like the USA;
- Full civil nuclear cooperation;
- Come out of isolation and end nuclear apartheid;
- Solution to uranium shortage with assurance of fuel supply and strategic reserve;
- Significant addition to energy production;
- Consent rights for reprocessing;
- Right to take corrective measures if the supplier fails to deliver;
- Access to advance technology;
- Three stage indigenous program not affected;
- Clean and unconditional Nuclear Supplier Group waiver;
- Implementation of the deal solely on the basis of 123 Agreement; and
- Non-interference in the strategic programme and legal right to test protected.

Let us see how the scorecard looks like on the above twelve bullet counts.

Parity of treatment with advanced countries

The Indo-US Joint Statement of July 18, states that recognizing the advanced technological capability in the nuclear field and impeccable non-proliferation record, India deserves to be treated at par with other technologically developed countries like the USA, implying nuclear weapon states. If only this had been followed in letter and spirit, the terms of the deal would have been different. However, there is absolutely no evidence that India is treated anywhere near like a weapon state, leave alone parity. In fact, further deliberations on this deal do not take cognizance of this crucial aspect of *de-facto* recognition as a weapon state. The government owes an explanation on this serious lapse.

Full civil nuclear cooperation

Full civil cooperation is only on paper for public consumption. Complex parts of the nuclear fuel cycle, like uranium enrichment, spent fuel reprocessing and heavy water technology is specifically excluded. How can this be called full when only partial cooperation is on offer? In fact to cover up this abject surrender, 123 text shies away from defining 'full nuclear fuel cycle,' while more obvious terms like 'reactor' are included in the section on definitions. In a bizarre explanation, the government tries to defend this by saying; we have not been singled out as this is in line with the supplier guidelines and US national law. If that is so why did the Joint Statement mention full cooperation? Actually as per the US law, exports of sensitive technologies are denied to those countries that are not having full-scale facilities of this nature and strictly not applicable to India. We not being a party to NPT should not be a condition, in view of the provision in the Joint Statement that has been surreptitiously ignored. Arguments are being put forth that since we are having the technology anyway, why bother. This is untenable, as we should have at least access to international market for equipment and components, which are denied.

Nuclear Isolation and Apartheid

The nuclear isolation we are subjected to since 1974 is a consequence of our nuclear tests. While this has slowed down the pace of development, the hard reality is, we have grown much stronger in our resolve and determination. Systematic progress in our three-stage nuclear power program in addition to advancement in strategic areas of national security bears testimony to the fact that we have been able to convert this isolation or nuclear apartheid into strength. It is worth pondering whether we could have reached this advanced level of technological development in the nuclear field if we were not isolated. It was, in a way a blessing in disguise and a challenge well utilized. In fact, by isolating India the world is a loser as they were deprived of the Indian contributions. Liberation from isolation, therefore, cannot be claimed as an achievement.

Solution to Uranium Shortage

Shortage of uranium was known more than 50 years ago and it is projected as if it is a new discovery. Nature has been kind enough to gift us with abundant thorium to compensate for this deficiency in uranium. It is for us to take up the challenge to exploit it to good use. Accordingly, the three-stage nuclear power program has factored the uranium shortage into solution for our long-term energy needs. However, though the deal is expected to help the near-term needs of uranium, the fact that there is no legally binding assurance of supply is a cause for concern. Both parties in the on-going debate are giving lot of spin on this, which is detrimental to the long-term interests of smooth operation of the reactors. This is particularly so, as uranium is the most crucial ingredient, but for which, perhaps this deal would have been superfluous. Our unsatisfactory experience in the case of Tarapur where the Americans did not keep a fuel assurance commitment is worth remembering. It is unfortunate that the Americans, in-spite of their track record, are allowed to get away making promises on paper even though they are poor, when it comes to delivery.

Significant Addition to Energy Production

By far the most dominant aspect of this deal is attractive Indian market for nuclear power and the urge to exploit the same by the supplier countries for commercial gains. Suppliers are expecting business in the range of 100-150 billion dollars, a whopping sum. No one can afford to risk losing such an opportunity. All the rest in the deal seems incidental and the ongoing debate on the non-proliferation issues, testing, etc. is only for appeasing the non-proliferation lobby in the US. It is unfortunate that India in-spite of its strong position as holder of comprehensive expertise, technological capability and a highly lucrative nuclear commercial market to offer, has not been able to use it as an effective leverage for more honourable terms than what it is at present and meekly surrendered. A glorious opportunity wasted.

India has been projecting a market of additional 40,000 MW of imports over the next 20 years and this could surely be a good recipe for total dependence for fuel, equipment, spares and so on and be subservient! To add to this, to checkmate the opposition to the deal by some members of the US Congress, US is projecting the commercial interests strongly, with the Indian government taking proactive steps to issue letters of intent to promising orders on US firms worth 10,000 MW, which is estimated to be more than the combined expectations from Russia and France. This is akin to match-fixing everyone is familiar with. The irony is, this news is coming from the US senate proceedings and the Indian government has no stomach to take its own public into confidence.

It is questionable, on what basis such commitment is made, that too when the US nuclear industry is dormant with no new nuclear power plant put up since 1979.

On the flip side, here is an opportunity for Indian nuclear engineers and industry to work for the American firms and supply the reactors under their flagship and also help revive their nuclear industry!

Consent Rights for Reprocessing

Spent fuel reprocessing is at the core of the three-stage nuclear programme and India has fully developed indigenous capability for operating industrial scale plants, over the last nearly four decades. In the light of this, it is bizarre for India to seek consent from supplier countries to reprocess sent fuel originated from imported uranium. Though bold statements like 'the question of reprocessing is non-negotiable', were made initially, at the end succumbed to pressure. The result is, we have settled for a convoluted statement in the all-important 123 document where there is consent in principal and subject to procedures and arrangements to be discussed and approved by the US Congress. What a shame it is. Going by the Tarapur experience, one can expect this could well be a contentious issue to be resolved in future. To make things worse, in the 123 an assurance has been taken from India to build a dedicated reprocessing plant for which we are not allowed even to shop for any equipment or components in the international market, leave alone technology. The intent seems to be dubious and we seem to be not bothered. A most crucial issue ineptly handled.

Corrective Measures

The so called 'corrective measures' has remained a mystery throughout. While the Indian public has been told that it refers to 'unspecified sovereign action' to be exercised in future depending on the circumstance, it is rather strange how such a vague interpretation could fly in an International Agreement. Surely this would have been raised in various fora like the IAEA, NSG and the US Congress and the government would have given specific answers keeping its own public in the dark to avoid criticism. It was expected, at least the commitment to perpetuity in IAEA safeguards would be made conditional to failure to assure fuel supply or the cooperation agreement is abrogated for any reason triggering India to retaliate. This has been rejected by the IAEA using a language-fix and the government is giving a spin that it has protected our interests, a standard statement used every time there is surrender.

Access to Advanced technology

Access to advanced technology is an illusion. When the whole deal is about trading in power reactors and practically nothing else worth the name, where is the question of advanced technology coming? Just like in any other contract, certain technological inputs come with the reactors, which is normal. It does not mean the reactor designs can be replicated. Complex parts of the nuclear fuel cycle are excluded anyway. There is no indication or provision in the deal that we could access technology and supplies for the fast reactors as and when they are placed under safeguards. It is presumed that there will not be any embargo on this, possibly to be negotiated.

Three-stage Nuclear Programme

Emphatic statements are being made to the effect that the three-stage nuclear programme will be pursued with all vigour irrespective of the nuclear deal. Good to hear that. But how does it work in practical terms? In the recent past, successive governments have shown scant interest for pushing the nuclear power programme. There have been lapses in timely investment on uranium mining. The Nuclear Power Corporation (NPC) has suffered from resource crunch at crucial stages of the power programme. This has to some extent caused poor showing in the contribution of nuclear power (3%) to the overall energy kitty of the country. NPC is being unduly blamed for this. In contrast, the Nuclear R&D has been getting good financial support; with the result India could build a strong technological base, in spite of isolation. There is thus a payback.

This raises the question, how can the indigenous nuclear power programme, which is not getting adequate support can get a boost when the resources are diverted to imports? The doubt becomes all the more acute when the power programme gets into the domain of fast breeder reactors and thorium reactors of the second and third stages involving complex technologies and higher levels of commitment. Will the onslaught of large number of imported uranium reactors cause diversion of resources, infrastructure and expert manpower from the three-stage programme? Will there be motivation enough to follow a more difficult path with lot of technological challenges yet to be tackled, when an easier path opened by imports is available? Could the future governments be influenced by the uranium reactor lobby to go slow on the risky thorium utilization route citing lack of global experience and uncertainties in this technology? There are many more such questions, which need to be gone into.

Contrary to the claims that imports are additionality to the indigenous power programme, the hard reality could just be the opposite. This is fraught with the prospect of pushing the thorium utilization to further future and keep it on R&D mode much longer. There are already indications at the highest level regarding possibility of deferring thorium utilization to a later date.

Nuclear Supplier Group (NSG) Waiver

Initially there were statements made to the effect that we expect clear, clean and unconditional waiver from the NSG. Down the line word 'clear' was left out, as this has never been a term liked by the diplomats, as clarity is not their forte. When we started mentioning clean and unconditional waiver, Americans resented the use of term 'unconditional' as inconvenient and that left us asking for clean waiver, whatever it means, still undefined. What we are now having is a conditional waiver. After agreeing to a waiver by consensus, though with some arms twisting, the NSG members are now individually coming out with their own interpretations of the conditions in the waiver. Our government has not lagged far behind in this and is busy with its own spin indicating that we could exploit differences in the domestic laws of individual states to our advantage. This is wishful thinking. NSG is a cartel. They sure must be having some basic understanding among themselves and are not likely to function at cross-purposes. When the chips are down, they are expected to stick together. Having done all the work, US cannot be expected to sit watching others walk away with advantage.

On the 123 Agreement

A lot has been said in the media and elsewhere about the 123 text. It is a diplomatically worded document offering plenty of scope for spin and interpretation. It offers unlimited opportunity for India to hold consultations with the US on any issue to resolve differences with final decision resting with them. Though India may not agree openly, US is swearing that it is fully consistent with the Hyde Act and so does the NSG waiver. The only saving grace is many of these are explicit but in the absence of any provision for independent arbitration, the suppliers' interpretation prevails in the case of differences or disputes. Hyde Act is the fall back for them but we don't have a matching law to look to. The way most crucial provisions in 123 are being interpreted in the US even before the Agreement is signed shows the predicament we are in. The very fact we are insensitive to the damaging interpretations indicate the murky, behind the scene understanding that might have reached during the negotiations. The present leaders on both sides may give, off the cuff assurances, but what matters is legally binding documents. 123 lacks clarity and Hyde Act is highly specific and almost like a checklist of do's and don'ts. As the investments on imports grow and become sufficiently dependent, we cannot escape arms twisting and we may well be forced to accept what the supplier decides and prepared to offer rather than making demands.

The way revelations are coming to light in bits and pieces almost on a daily basis, there appears to be clandestine behind the scene understanding on various issues, which could prove detrimental to national interest at a later stage.

Non-interference in Strategic Programme and Right to Test

There are a number of provisions in the Hyde Act mandating the US Administration to keep tab on our strategic programme and report to the Congress. It is naive to think that they will not be engaged in covert action.

The oft-repeated slogan that we have the legal right to test but they have the right to react may sound pleasing to the ears, but the question is can we bear the economic and political consequences of exercising this legal right which is as good as on paper with no practical utility. There is no doubt that there is a firm understanding that the option of testing is given up without saying in so many words.

To Sum Up

Without being intentionally pessimistic but more on a realistic note, the prospects and consequences of the deal could perhaps be expressed briefly as follows:

"India may prosper from this nuclear deal and show higher GDP growth by increasing energy production and collateral benefits in other sectors but the suppliers may control the long-term energy security at least in the nuclear power sector and we may have to reconcile with energy independence through dependence."

Dr. Homi Bhabha was a great visionary. His vision was to see India as a force to reckon with in the nuclear field, achieve long-term energy independence and become world leader by thorium utilization, through predominantly indigenous efforts. This has been the motivation for the nuclear scientists of the past and present who have worked or working with dedication under heavy odds to realize this vision as a goal. The present nuclear deal has all the characteristics of this vision being relegated to becoming a far-fetched dream!

By giving up the fight to maintain the starting goal posts, namely, our right to be treated at par with other technologically advanced nuclear states especially the weapon states and failure to ensure full civil nuclear cooperation, the terms and conditions of the deal have been compromised to the extent that the national interest suffers.

(Paper presented to the Federation of Karnataka Chambers of Commerce and Industry, Bangalore, September 26, 2008)

93. It's Nuclear Slavery

A.N. PRASAD

All seems quiet on the nuclear deal front after a virtual onslaught in media and political circles ever since it was mooted in 2005, with the signing of the Indo-US Joint Statement by President Bush and Prime Minister Manmohan Singh. That it has taken more than three years to conclude the agreement speaks volumes for the way the process has been handled. Now that it has been finalised, it is worth recollecting what we are in for. We have to reconcile to the fact that there is absolutely no correlation between the terms of the Joint Statement and the final shape of the deal. All the talk of India being eligible to treatment at par with other advanced countries like the US, and the offer of full civil nuclear co-operation is eyewash. It was summarily dumped even before the negotiations really got under way. India, by giving up on this, has committed a blunder that has changed the whole complexion of the deal. It has accepted terms and conditions that by no means are honourable.

The US, following a meticulous approach of engaging a number of think-tanks and interest groups with perfect coordination between the administration and Congress, has largely succeeded in achieving its three-pronged objective of roping India into the global non-proliferation mainstream, capping capability to expand its strategic programme and exploit the lucrative commercial market for nuclear power, possibly with an eye on reviving its own moribund nuclear industry.

For its part, India set its priorities on access to global uranium supplies, securing global participation in nuclear power generation to supplement the domestic programme, getting rid of the embargoes through an unconditional waiver from the Nuclear Suppliers' Group, and access to R&D on nuclear power as a technologically advanced global player on respectable terms.

India managed partial success, but the terms and conditions are too harsh to qualify the outcome as being in national interest. At no time did India, unlike the US, show willingness to have broader consultations with other than like-minded parties, and preferred to take unilateral decisions without attempting political consensus. Many retired senior scientists who contributed to the development of nuclear technology were kept out of the loop. A pity that India, in spite of its technological strength and the bait of an attractive nuclear power market, could not use them as leverage in negotiations. In justification, spokesmen for the deal often talk about relief from isolation, access to uranium, accelerated power generation and high technology inflow as strong points.

Let us look at these in perspective.

Isolation began when we carried out the first nuclear test in 1974. We had not built a nuclear reactor on our own then. That did not deter us from facing the challenge of sanctions. The most comprehensive technological development, encompassing the entire nuclear fuel cycle as well as weapons capability, took place mostly during the period of isolation. It was considered the golden era of nuclear development! When we conducted the 1998 nuclear tests we were quite advanced, but the embargoes were made more stringent, denying supply of even dual use items. We took it in our stride. Between 1998 and now we have made more headway, taking major steps towards long-term energy independence through thorium utilisation. The world watched and realised that isolation was not working. So it is strange that we are getting cold feet and switching from independence mode to dependence, giving the impression that we have suffered under isolation. In fact, it is apt to say that world nuclear development suffered by isolating India.

That we lack adequate supplies of uranium and have an abundance of thorium is well known and was factored into the three stage power programme. Suddenly, it is being made out to be a revelation. It will, of course, hurt the power programme in the short-term, but like other challenges can be overcome with will and determination. Only a very small part of the uranium available in the country has so far been mined. Someone should be held answerable for the lapse that created this crisis.

Power is an emotive issue, with the country reeling under shortages. To make the deal appealing, practically unrealisable projections, sounding like political slogans, were made even by those who are supposed to be responsible. For example, it has been repeatedly said that 20,000 MWe will be generated by 2020. If one looks at the breakup given by a senior member of the Department of Atomic Energy in an article published in the IANCAS Bulletin in April 2006, in addition to reactors operating and under construction with a total capacity of about 7,000 MWe, the balance of 13,000 MWe by 2020 has to come from eight pressurised heavy water reactors (700 MWe each), four fast breeder reactors (500 MWe each), six light water reactors (1,000 MWe each) and one advanced heavy water reactor (300 MWe).

All these reactor designs are still on the drawing board, except the LWRs of the Koodankulam type, which are to come from Russia under an arrangement to be worked out. So how realistic is it to expect all this to happen within the next 11 years? Projections are being made that by 2030 installed capacity for nuclear power will be stepped up to 40,000 MWe. These numbers are being rolled out to mislead the country.

Pragmatism seems to have no place

Nuclear power generation is a serious business involving a whole lot of issues such as environmental, sitting, safety, regulatory, economic, legal, technological, human resources, and so on. It is not like putting up conventional plants. One mishap caused by taking shortcuts could lead to a catastrophe with global repercussions. Even for one who has worked on nuclear development it is hard to visualise the nature of the high technology we get access to through this deal.

Such loose talk by responsible persons in government belittles the dedicated efforts of so many stalwarts over the years.

The founder of the Indian nuclear programme, Dr Homi J. Bhabha, thought of nuclear power as a long-term option to be realised through predominantly indigenous efforts. Thorium holds the key. This deal could upset the rhythm and pace of development of the domestic programme, divert it to uranium dependence and make thorium utilisation a dream for the far future. It is hard to imagine how the tempo of the domestic programme could be maintained when the country's resources are used to sustain an import regime.

One should perhaps see the writing on the wall. For the sake of about 40,000 MWe we seem to be mortgaging our future. Bhabha had dreamt of making India a world leader in thorium technology. One can only wonder at his reaction to the demeaning conditions of the present deal. We have let ourselves fall into a trap that will kill our hardearned initiative, keep us constantly looking for uranium supplies and spares, and hand over control to external agencies.

(*The New Indian Express*, November 26, 2008)

94. No More Room for Manoeuvre

BHARAT KARNAD

A new coalition government assuming power after the general election will be shocked to find that its foreign and military policy manoeuvring space has been severely shrunk by the outgoing Congress party-led regime. Recovering Indian independence and initiative will require, in the main, wriggling out of the tight corner the country has been pushed into by the civilian nuclear cooperation deal with the US.

The nuclear deal which, according to Ministry of External Affairs insiders, took up fully 90% of Manmohan Singh's time, proved beyond doubt the Prime Minister's abysmal understanding of international power politics, which consists of sucking up to Washington at every turn. It explains why his government, for instance, refused to order a military response to 26/11. Singh apparently feared that doing so would lead Pakistan to redeploy its forces eastward, undermine the US strategy on Afghanistan-Pakistan and upset the US. But given that the US perceives its interests to be global, not upsetting Washington is a recipe for immobilizing Indian foreign and military policy.

Disregarding a hallowed foreign policy principle from Indira Gandhi's time of abjuring treaties with the potential to hurt the country's nuclear programme and limit its weapon options, Singh signed the nuclear deal. The July 18, 2005 Joint Statement and the subsequent enabling US law, the Henry J. Hyde United States-India Atomic Energy Cooperation Act of 2006, make amply clear the American intention to use the bilateral agreements as legal device to shoehorn the heretofore untrammelled Indian nuclear programme into the non-proliferation treaty net (refer deputy secretary of state James Steinberg's March 24 talk at the Brookings Institution).

Singh's *raison d'etre* for the deal was his claim that it will help the country achieve "energy security". A handful of us critics, including stalwart nuclear scientists P.K. Iyengar and A.N. Prasad, argued at length in our public writings why such and other claims were as fraudulent as Singh's assertions in Parliament—which were belied by the safeguards agreement, that the deal secured for India recognition as a nuclear weapon state. Moreover, by agreeing in effect to forswear testing, he has ensured that the Indian deterrent will lack credibility because its most potent thermonuclear weapons are untested, unproven, and unreliable.

Again, as forewarned, the deal that Singh hatched will be used by the radical non-proliferationists in the top posts in the Obama administration to squeeze this country. Instead of a free flow of civilian nuclear technology that the Prime Minister promised, India will be under the gun to sign the Comprehensive Test Ban Treaty (CTBT) and the Fissile Material Cutoff Treaty (FMCT) and, heedless of the Chinese strategic build-up, to square up on nuclear armaments with a strategically irrelevant Pakistan, a country with a gross domestic product that is less than one quarter of the market cap of the Bombay Stock Exchange.

Consider President Barack Obama's appointees who will be shaping his India policy. At the steering wheel is the special adviser on non-proliferation at the White House, Robert J. Einhorn, a long-time opponent of India's nuclear military programme, whose views are faithfully echoed by under-secretary of state for non-proliferation and international security-designate Ellen O. Tauscher. Until she was picked for the job, Tauscher, a Democrat Congresswoman from California, was distinguished mainly by her toxic rants against nuclear India. Her priority, in line with Einhorn's, is to compel India to sign the CTBT. "Trying to stop Tauscher from getting" her way, writes her friend Joseph Cirincione, who heads the non-proliferation-minded Ploughshares Fund, would be "like trying to stop Sherman from marching to Atlanta". For those not familiar with the US Civil War lore, this reference is to the Union Army Gen. William T. Sherman's "march to the sea" through the rebellious southern states that destroyed the economic heartland of the Confederacy, including its biggest city, Atlanta, which was torched.

Tauscher, the "smash and burn" specialist who makes her predecessor John R. Bolton from the George W. Bush era look positively tame, will be at the diplomatic cutting edge, assisted by arms control expert Rose Gottmoeller, as assistant secretary of state for verification and compliance. Sharing a punitive mindset, these three will insist that India sign the CTBT, quickly agree to an FMCT and comply with every last provision in the Hyde Act, such as the "Obama Amendment". This clause expressly prevents India from reasonably stockpiling uranium fuel for the lifetime of any imported reactors, rendering the reactors a dead investment and India hostage to behaviour that the US deems good. This Act also requires India to be in "congruence" with the US on Iran. If the current US attempts at a rapprochement with Tehran fail, this clause too will kick in. In short, the implementation of this Act in toto will entail a neutering of India.

Do you reckon any new coalition government will have the gall to stand up to the US and its enforcers, Messrs Einhorn, Tauscher and Gotmoeller? Because Singh, should he return as Prime Minister, has shown he doesn't.

(*Mint*, March 31, 2009)

Public Letters and Appeals by Nuclear Scientists Critical of the Nuclear Deal

1. Open Letter to the PM Dr Manmohan Singh

P.K. Iyengar

(Rtd.) Chairman, Atomic Energy Commission

33, Saras Baug, Deonar

Mumbai 400088

23 February 2006

Shri Manmohan Singh

Honourable Prime Minister of India.

Dear Mr. Prime Minister,

I seek your kind indulgence for taking some of your valuable time to present, as elder scientist of this country, a few considerations that you might find useful while giving final shape to the Indo-U.S. Nuclear Agreement.

At the outset, I would like to compliment and congratulate you for adopting an out-of-the-box, and statesman-like approach while responding to the American offer, that could conceivably put an honourable end to the "outcaste" status, unjustly imposed on this country by the big powers, when we sought to pursue an independent nuclear policy in the best interests of this Nation.

In this context, a brief recall of the historical perspective would be useful. The first step down the nuclear road was taken by Komi Bhabha as far back as 1944, when the world was not even aware of nuclear energy. Working closely with Nehru, himself a visionary, Bhabha, in the years following Independence, outlined a clear and systematic strategy for sustaining nuclear power generation by steadily moving forward from our limited reserves of uranium to our vast reserves of thorium, via the intermediary stage of plutonium, produced in our first-generation reactors.

The visionaries that they were, Nehru and Bhabha went even further, using the nuclear programme as a vehicle for propelling this country into high-class science and advanced technology, covering many aspects that ranged from particle physics and innumerable applications of atomic energy for peaceful purposes, to space science and technology. As a scientist who received his education in the West, Bhabha understood the importance of cooperation and did not hesitate to enter into bilateral agreements with other countries, if it benefited the country. Such was his eminence that he, more than anyone else, was asked to chair the historic, First Geneva Conference on the Peaceful Uses of Atomic Energy. That is the great tradition on which our nuclear programme has evolved.

The design and development of nuclear weapons came into the picture only later, when security considerations made that imperative. In the years that followed, many export restrictions were put in place by the Western countries but in spite of it, our scientists and engineers, thousands of them, acquitted themselves most creditably against great odds. As an example, we might mention that the FBTR in Kalpakkam [which has been working since 1985] is the only reactor in the world using an advanced carbide fuel, made using our own plutonium. Similarly, Kalpakkam also boasts of the only reactor in the world fuelled entirely by uranium 233, produced from our own thorium. The technology for the PFBR now under construction, has also been developed entirely in India. It is also pertinent to mention in this context, that very recently, BARC scientists have come out with a conceptual design for a thorium breeder reactor, using a plutonium-thorium feed. Thus, while negotiating the details of the proposed Agreement, perhaps, the following considerations could be kept in mind:

1. In the development of the breeder cycle, much R&D would be required. The construction of our first fast power reactor has just commenced, and the mastery and management of the fuel cycle — the most crucial element of a long-term power reactor programme— should not be allowed to be hampered by considerations of safeguards. This is an area where we simply will not get any help from the international community and in any case, most countries do not possess vast reserves of thorium as we do. Thus, unlike us, thorium utilization may not be of any interest to them.

2. It is perfectly reasonable to put all the new reactors we get from abroad under safeguards. These would be merely power generation units and not vehicles of R&D. The main thrust of our R&D would thus in no way be handicapped.

3. It might also be prudent to emulate what Homi Bhabha often did namely, enter into **bilateral** rather than omnibus multilateral agreements. Thus, one might seriously consider the revolutionary step of placing these new reactors under special **bilateral** safeguards rather than routine international safeguards.

4. In amplification of point 3 above, two clarifying remarks need to be made. Firstly, the IAEA type safeguards with additional protocol, though applied to all, were, historically devised mainly as a means of preventing so-called "irresponsible" and potentially "rogue" States from acquiring nuclear weapons. Secondly, where matters of great importance are concerned, responsible countries have dealt with each other bilaterally rather than under international umbrella safeguards.

When America and USSR/Russia could negotiate on a bilateral basis regarding the reduction of nuclear weapons, it stands to reason that America and India (which is now hailed universally as not only a great democracy but also as a very responsible one and a significant power in its own right), could conceivably enter into a **bilateral** agreement that is to the satisfaction of all.

5. Considering the high regard you personally command in international circles, and the very responsible manner in which our scientists have conducted themselves, both in terms of high transparency of our power reactor and space programmes and in the strict avoidance of either clandestine or proliferation activities, we venture to hope that America could be persuaded to give us the respect and dignity that is our due.

If India's progress could drive the President of America so far as to launch an Advanced Competitiveness Initiative [ACI], (as he declared in his recent State of the Union address), then that says something.

We are confident that under your stewardship, you would, quietly but most emphatically and with dignity, ensure that the morale of our scientific community, the integrity of our R&D programme, and the heritage bequeathed to us by Nehru and Bhabha would be fully protected.

Finally, I trust that the points that I have made, which are born out of our long and direct association with the early days of the Nehru-Bhabha era, would provide you with additional perspective, besides that which those currently in service might have already furnished.

Thanking you for sparing some time for this, and with regards,

Yours sincerely,

P. K. Iyengar

2. Appeal to Parliamentarians on the Indo-US Nuclear Deal

While the nation and Parliament discuss the Indo-US nuclear deal from various angles, we feel it is our responsibility to place before the nation our well-considered views on the impact of this deal on the future of Indian nuclear science and technology, and its effects on the energy security of the nation. We have all worked in the field of atomic energy from the very early years after India's independence. From very small beginnings, we have now reached a stage where we are in possession of all the technologies needed for the production of electricity from indigenous nuclear minerals, and have successfully applied these technologies in diverse sectors from health, agriculture and industry to national and energy security. All this has been possible with the support of the people represented in the government through Parliament, and the outstanding statesmen who have guided and supported our plans. We therefore feel it is our obligation to make public our perceptions for the effective and continued nurturing and utilization of this technology in the country.

Science is universal. Knowledge can be created in any part of the world, and technology comes with experimentation and the willingness to take risks. We have followed all these paths to reach the present stage of development. We are amongst the most advanced countries in the technology of fast-breeder reactors, which is crucial to the future of our energy security. Along the way we have derived benefits from international collaboration. At the same time, we have also shared some of our abilities in this field with the world. Indian scientists have been ambassadors, with knowledge and creativity as their tools. It is of prime importance to uphold these cherished traditions.

It is significant that the most advanced country in nuclear science and technology has come forward to accept us into the international nuclear community, by the historic document signed by our Prime Minister with President Bush on 18th July, 2005. The basic principles for cooperation were well laid out in this bilateral understanding and the Prime Minister has appraised our Parliament of this. No doubt it needs the concurrence of the other nations comprising the Nuclear Suppliers' Group, and of the International Atomic Energy Agency. Based on this agreement, the US lawmakers and the administration are in the process of re-framing their laws, which could change the nature of relations between the two countries. This is a most welcome initiative of the UPA government, and is a continuation of the process essentially begun during the previous NDA government. Thus, there is no question of any political partisanship on this matter.

However, the law-makers of the US Congress have modified, both in letter and spirit, the implementation of such an agreement. At this juncture, among other aspects, it is essential that we insist on the following four central themes:

(a) India should continue to be able to hold on to her nuclear option as a strategic requirement in the real world that we live in, and in the ever-changing complexity of the international political system. This means that we cannot accede to any restraint in perpetuity on our freedom of action. We have not done this for the last forty years after the Non-Proliferation Treaty came into being, and there is no reason why we should succumb to this now. Universal nuclear disarmament must be our ultimate aim, and until we see the light at the end of the tunnel on this important issue, we cannot accept any agreement in perpetuity.

(b) After 1974, when the major powers discontinued cooperation with us, we have built up our capability in many sensitive technological areas, which need not and should not now be subjected to external control. Safeguards are understandable where external assistance for nuclear materials or technologies are involved. We have agreed to this before, and we can continue to agree to this in the future too, but strictly restricted to those facilities and materials imported from external sources.

(c) We find that the Indo-US deal, in the form approved by the US House of Representatives, infringes on our independence for carrying out indigenous research and development (R&D) in nuclear science and technology. Our R&D should not be hampered by external supervision or control, or by the need to satisfy any international body. Research and technology development are the sovereign rights of any nation. This is especially true when they concern strategic national defence and energy self-sufficiency.

(d) While the sequence of actions to implement the cooperation could be left for discussion between the two governments, the basic principles on which such actions will rest is the right of Parliament and the people to decide. The Prime Minister has already taken up with President Bush the issue of the new clauses recommended by the US House of Representatives. If the US Congress, in its wisdom, passes the bill in its present form, the 'product' will become unacceptable to India, and, diplomatically, it will be very difficult to change it later. Hence it is important for our Parliament to work out, and insist on, the ground rules for the nuclear deal, at this stage itself.

We therefore request you, the Parliamentarians, to discuss this deal and arrive at a unanimous decision, recognizing the fundamental facts of India's indigenous nuclear science and technology achievements to date, the efforts made to overcome the unfair restrictions placed on us and the imaginative policies and planning enunciated and followed in the years after Independence. The nation, at this critical juncture, depends on its representatives in Parliament to ensure that decisions taken today do not inhibit our future ability to develop and pursue nuclear technologies for the benefit of the nation.

14 August 2006

Statement issued by:

Dr. H.N. Sethna, Former Chairman, Atomic Energy Commission

Dr. M.R. Srinivasan, Former Chairman, Atomic Energy Commission

Dr. P.K. Iyengar, Former Chairman, Atomic Energy Commission

Dr. A. Gopalakrishnan, Former Chairman, Atomic Energy Regulatory Board

Dr. S.L. Kati, Former Managing Director, Nuclear Power Corporation

Dr. A.N. Prasad, Former Director, Bhabha Atomic Research Centre

Dr. Y.S.R. Prasad, Former Chairman and Managing Director, Nuclear Power Corporation

Dr. Placid Rodriguez, Former Director, Indira Gandhi Centre for Atomic Research

3. Appeal to the Members of Parliament on the India-US Civilian Nuclear Co-operation Agreement

1. We were part of a group of senior nuclear scientists who had in the past expressed our grave concerns and objections to India entering into a nuclear co-operation agreement with the US under the aegis of the Hyde Act, 2006. We had written earlier to the Parliamentarians on this matter, and the Prime Minister had given us an opportunity to meet with him and discuss our views.

2. At this critical juncture, when the Government is about to rush the safeguards agreement through the IAEA, there is a great deal of disquiet among the scientific community at large in this country. Should the country be entering into such a long-term binding arrangement without a detailed and rigorous examination of the IAEA Safeguards? Should a Government, based at best on a wafer thin majority and a divided Parliament, commit the country in this manner? *We, therefore, are strongly of the opinion that the Government should not proceed to seek IAEA Board approval for the current draft safeguards agreement, until its implications are debated more fully within the country, and with a group of experts who were not party to the IAEA negotiations.*

3. The government is enthusiastically pushing the Deal on the basis that it will bring about energy security to India, since it will enable the import of foreign nuclear power reactors. But, analysts have convincingly and quantitatively shown that this additional power will come at a much higher cost per unit of electricity compared to conventional coal or hydro power, which India can generate without any foreign imports.

4. *Once the Deal is in place, it is also clear that India's commercial nuclear interactions with the US, as well as with any other country, will be firmly controlled from Washington via the stipulations of the Hyde Act 2006 enforced through the stranglehold which the US retains on the Nuclear Suppliers' Group.* Any argument to the effect that the Deal will be governed only by the bilateral 123 Agreement is untenable, because this Agreement in turn is anchored in US domestic laws, which include the Hyde Act. And, the Hyde Act contains several stipulations which are extraneous to the issue of bilateral nuclear cooperation, including foreign policy behaviour which India needs to adhere to if the Deal is to be kept

alive. *The real issue facing India, therefore, is whether or not we want this mythical extra 'energy security through this Deal, paying two to three times the unit capital cost of conventional power plants, with the additional burden of subjugating the freedom to pursue a foreign policy and indigenous nuclear R&D program of our own.*

5. The nuclear Deal could also have other serious repercussions, including a potential weakening of India's nuclear deterrent and an inability to protect and promote indigenous R&D efforts in nuclear technology. A combination of the extreme secrecy with which the government has carried forward this deal, the media hype they were able to generate in its favour, the parochial interests of opportunistic individuals and organizations, and the unfortunate ignorance of the issues involved among the general public have put the country on a dangerous path, likely to lead to the detriment of the current and future generations of Indians. Today's urgency to rush to the IAEA Board, in consonance with the American timetable, to get the safeguards agreement approved and thereafter clinch the Deal during the tenures of the current governments in India and the US must, therefore, be replaced with an openness and introspection that is vital for a serious debate which the situation demands.

6. The central issue about the IAEA safeguards agreement has been the doubt as to how "India-specific" these are. *In particular, since it is distinctly clear from the Hyde Act and the 123 Agreement that no uninterrupted fuel supplies have been guaranteed in these documents for reactors which India will place under safeguards,* the Government had assured that this defect will be corrected in the safeguards agreement. Since the IAEA was all along known to be no fuel-supply guarantor, *it is not surprising that Indian negotiators have failed to obtain any assurance in this regard. All that the IAEA Agreement states in its preambular section is that it notes uninterrupted fuel supply and support for a strategic fuel reserve is the basis of placing Indian facilities in safeguards. It places no obligation on the IAEA other than merely noting this. The corrective measures, indicated in the preambular section, have nothing that anchors them to any section in the operative part of the agreement. Against such unspecified and vague mention of corrective measures, India's obligations are clear and binding. In effect, India has agreed to place its facilities that it will list out in the Annex under perpetual safeguards without any link to an uninterrupted fuel supply.*

7. The Government is asserting that the IAEA safeguards have "provisions for *corrective measures* that India may take to ensure uninterrupted operation of its civilian nuclear reactors in the event of disruption of foreign fuel supplies. Taking this into account, India is placing its civilian nuclear facilities under India-specific safeguards in perpetuity". *The nation*

would like to know clearly what these "corrective measures" are, before plunging headlong into this Deal. India being merely allowed to withdraw the Indian-built civilian PHWRs from safeguards, and that too after stripping them of all spent and fresh fuel and components of foreign origin, is no corrective step at all because such action does not ensure uninterrupted operation of these civilian nuclear reactors in the event of disruption of foreign fuel supplies. Even here, Article 32 of the Safeguards Agreement appears to stand in the way of any such withdrawal. *Besides, this relaxation does not apply to the imported power reactors, which will use up the bulk of our investments in nuclear power; these units will perpetually stay under safeguards, even after fuel supplies are denied.* The Hyde Act prohibits the US Administration from directly or indirectly (through the IAEA or other countries) assisting India with life-time fuel supplies after suspension of the Deal. Therefore, the Government owes a clarification to the Parliament and the public about how they intend to avoid the consequential huge economic loss from the non-operation of these extremely costly imported reactors, as a result of fuel denial.

8. The 123 Agreement states that the imports under the Deal "shall be subject to safeguards *in perpetuity* in accordance with the India-specific Safeguards Agreement between India and the IAEA and an *Additional Protocol,* when in force". *While the actual draft of the Additional Protocol (AP) applicable to India may have to be negotiated and agreed to at a later date, it is absolutely necessary that a prior agreement between the IAEA and India on the essential features of such an Additional Protocol must be reached simultaneous with the finalization of the safeguards agreement and certainly before signing it.* The most intrusive actions under the IAEA safeguards are always taken on the basis of this protocol, including the "pursuit clause" which permits interference with our non-civilian programs on the basis of unsubstantiated suspicion. *India needs to make it clear what the limits are beyond which we will not entertain any IAEA action or intrusion, and it should be clear that a standard Model Protocol applicable to non-nuclear weapon States will not be acceptable to India. The leverage to debate and get the kind of restricted Additional Protocol we want will be entirely lost once a safeguards agreement alone is first put in place and the installations put under safeguards.* As we understand, the limitations within which India is willing to enter into the Additional Protocol regime was neither discussed by Indian negotiators at the IAEA nor do they appear in the safeguards draft or its attachments. In this context, the Government needs to clarify their thinking on the Additional Protocol, before entering into the safeguards agreement.

9. Reprocessing the spent-fuel arising from burning fresh imported fuel in our civilian reactors provides us valuable additional plutonium, which in turn can be recycled into future civilian fast breeder reactors (FBRs) or advanced heavy water reactors (AHWRs). Reprocessing, therefore, is at the core of India's plans to build long-term energy security.

    The government had all along pledged to secure an unqualified right to reprocess spent-fuel and even termed India's right to reprocess "non-negotiable". But, in the 123 Agreement, what has finally been obtained is merely an empty theoretical right to reprocess. The actual permission to reprocess will come after years, when a dedicated state-of-the-art reprocessing plant is built anew to treat foreign fuel, along with a host of allied facilities. *There will be a large number of safeguards and Additional Protocol issues related to this, and all these hurdles will have to be crossed to reach the beginning of reprocessing. Much of the fundamental basis on which all this will be done has to be discussed and settled now at the outset, while the overall safeguards agreement is being finalized.* But, the Government has not done this exercise during the recent set of negotiations with the IAEA, and this deficiency will come to haunt India in future unless it is rectified.

10. Similarly, there are many other key safeguards-related issues of crucial importance which have not been addressed in the current draft. *Furthermore, none of the issues included presently has been handled adequately or in an acceptable manner. We therefore appeal to the Members of the Lok Sabha to direct the Government not to proceed further with the current safeguards agreement, and ask the Prime Minister to initiate wide-ranging and structured deliberations on the Indo-US Nuclear Co-operation Agreement, both within Parliament and outside, to develop a broad consensus on this Deal among political parties and the general public, before proceeding any further.*

Signatories:

1. **Dr. P.K. Iyengar,** Former Chairman, Atomic Energy Commission
2. **Dr. A. Gopalakrishnan**, Former Chairman, Atomic Energy Regulatory Board
3. **Dr. A.N. Prasad**, Former Director, Bhabha Atomic Research Center

18 July 2008

Chapters in Books and Articles
in Professional Journals

1. Indo-US Nuclear Cooperation: A Non-starter?

A. GOPALAKRISHNAN

According to media reports, president Bush told foreign minister Natwar Singh during their meeting on April 14, 2005 that India and the US need to work together in the energy area, which would include 'civilian nuclear cooperation'. But, in an interview with the *Wall Street Journal* published on the same day, Condoleezza Rice (US secretary of state) said, when asked about the potential for nuclear reactor technology sales to India, "No, no, we are not there. We have agreed with the Indians that we can talk about a variety of energy sources, but obviously there are NPT implications that are quite serious about civilian nuclear power in India."[1] In spite of this, statements from our ministry of external affairs (MEA) continue to include civilian nuclear technology as one of the subjects under serious discussion between the two countries. As reported in the *South Asia Tribune* dated March 29, 2005[2] the MEA communique issued after the recent visit of Rice to India said, "We have been informed that the US government is considering offering civilian nuclear energy and nuclear safety cooperation to India. These subjects were discussed during the visit of the secretary of state on March 16, 2005. The decision by the US administration to move forward on nuclear energy cooperation is welcome and reflects an understanding of India's growing energy requirements." To say the least, the picture emerging is confused, with neither side willing to clarify where these deliberations stand. With the forthcoming visit of the prime minister to the US in July 2005, the speculation is rife that nuclear cooperation of some kind will be initiated during his visit.

In this regard, the central questions we need to ask are these: What concrete assistance does India urgently need from the US to further our civilian nuclear programme? What is it that the US wants in return from us for providing that help? And, finally, will the US be capable of making good any promise of nuclear assistance to India, given the myriad internal and external pressures on them, including the existing legally-binding commitments of theirs to their national laws and to the nuclear non-proliferation regime and its export control entities? This article is an attempt to look at these issues in perspective and draw some conclusions on the possibility of any breakthrough in nuclear relations.

Irrelevance of US Nuclear Experience

In the absence of any details, the only two items of assistance which the media seems to highlight are the possible import of US nuclear power reactors by India and the cooperation between the two countries in the field of nuclear safety. India today has 15 operating nuclear power reactors and eight more are under various stages of construction or commissioning. Eighteen of these are pressurised heavy water reactors (PHWRs), two are the US-supplied boiling water reactors (BWRs) at Tarapur, two are the pressurised water reactors (PWRs) being built at Kudamkulam with Russian assistance, and the last one is a Prototype Fast Breeder Reactor (PFBR) of our own design, on which civil work has just started.[3] The US has no experience of having designed, built or operated a commercial PHWR. The Tarapur reactors are of the 1960 vintage and no other reactor of this kind has been operating anywhere in the world for the past several years. These reactors were originally supplied by the General Electric Company of US, which can neither provide us any associated spare parts nor expert services today. The PWRs coming up in Kudamkulam are of the Russian WER type, and we have a strong and ongoing technology cooperation with the Russians in this regard. Incidentally, the US has no experience with WERs. As for fast breeder reactors, the US has no fast reactor programme today, and they had shut down all their related facilities almost two decades ago. From all this, it is abundantly clear that the US has no worthwhile current expertise in the design, construction, operation, maintenance or safety of any of the type of reactors existing or envisaged in the Indian nuclear power programme.

Do We Need US Nuclear Safety Assistance?

The US and MEA officials keep hinting that the US is willing to cooperate with India on nuclear safety. To start with, it is clear from the above that they do not possess any safety experience which relates to the type of reactors we have. The idea of safety cooperation is often highlighted by the US state department spokesmen and not by our Department of Atomic Energy (DAE), the Nuclear Power Corporation of India (NPCIL), or the Atomic Energy Regulatory Board (AERB), which are the agencies nationally responsible for nuclear safety. This emphasis on safety is a ploy to indirectly invoke a certain degree of doubt in the minds of the Indian public that perhaps these Indian agencies' understanding and capability to maintain safety in our reactors are inadequate in comparison to the US levels. As a nuclear engineer and a former chairman of the AERB, I am well aware of the Indian and international status in this field. In 1995, when I submitted a comprehensive report to the government on the 'Safety Status in DAE Installations',[4] most of the critical safety deficiencies[5] documented by the AERB had been identified prior to that by the previous DAE managements themselves. The failing was that, having understood the defects, the DAE never took any steps to rectify them over decades. Subsequent to the acceptance of the 1995 AERB report by the government, both the parliament and the government put continued pressure on the DAE to make urgent rectifications. To the credit of the subsequent managements of the DAE, I am reasonably assured now that most of the safety issues pointed out in 1995 have been resolved within the last decade. The Indian nuclear engineers and scientists, along with the national industries, worked in achieving this, without any foreign assistance and often through the development and implementation of indigenous technological solutions. In short, according to several top ranking experts, there is little that India currently needs from the US to sustain adequate safety in our civilian nuclear installations. Any cooperation between the AERB and the US Nuclear Regulatory Commission (USNRC), which may be in the offing, will be solely on the basis of information publicly available in the US and will only be of marginal benefit, at best, to India because of the lack of direct relevance and the paucity of essential details.

Import of US Nuclear Reactors

The glaring indictment against the advisability of importing nuclear reactors from the US is the predicament in which we find ourselves today in the case of Tarapur reactors. These two General Electric units were purchased under a binding commercial guarantee from the US government for fuel supply during their entire lifetime. And yet, this promise was broken soon after the 1974 Pokhran test, and ever since India had been made to go from one country to another seeking enriched uranium fuel to keep this power station running. Now, it looks like we have come to the end of the road, with no country willing to give further fuel, because of the tighter restrictions imposed by the Nuclear Suppliers' Group (NSG). NSG is a grouping of countries formed at US initiative, as a reaction to India's nuclear test in 1974, to impose stricter nuclear export controls on non-nuclear weapon states. The two Tarapur reactors and the two Kudamkulam reactors which are Russian supplies need low enriched uranium fuel, which India is not producing in sufficient quantity, despite our having a uranium enrichment plant near Mysore. All imported reactors will be even today 'guaranteed' life-time fuel supply, but our experience shows clearly that such guarantees, especially from the western nuclear powers, are untrustworthy.

The DAE has made it clear in the past that India's main interest in import of reactors is because of the potential for attracting foreign capital investment into our nuclear sector, and not necessarily for any superior technology inflow. It is, however, clear that no foreign government, international financial institution and company will be willing to give loan assistance for such nuclear projects in India. If the money that we will end up paying to foreign companies for imports can be given to the Nuclear Power Corporation of India (NPCIL), they will be able to instal a larger capacity of PHWRs, for which India possesses all the technologies and materials, except perhaps enough natural uranium to fuel them.

Shortage of Natural Uranium

The impending shortage of natural uranium to fuel even the PHWRs currently under construction draws attention to one of the crucial areas where the Indian civilian nuclear programme could urgently benefit from international cooperation. Interestingly, the DAE and the government remain silent about this need, thus indirectly giving credence to the wrong notion that it is the import of reactors and nuclear safety assistance that we require from the US.

Homi Bhabha had the nation's energy security and self-reliance in mind when he framed the three-stage nuclear power plan for the country, which envisaged the use of our natural uranium and thorium resources to establish a totally indigenous technology base. Today, some 50 years after Bhabha unveiled his plan, his vision rooted in self-reliance still remains the best approach for India in this increasingly unipolar world.

To meet the ambitious nuclear power targets of DAE in accordance with the Bhabha plan, we need to build a sufficient number of PHWRs first, so that adequate plutonium is produced for a rapid enough transition to the second stage breeder programme. However, at present the DAE is beginning to face a serious shortage of natural uranium, even to fuel the 18 PHWRs currently under operation or construction. The NPCIL is deliberately lowering the power production in their operating PHWRs, in order to stretch out the available natural uranium fuel for a longer period. The known uranium resources in Jaduguda mines are depleting fast and the DAE is unable to start fresh mining in Domiasiat in the north-east and Nalagonda in AP due to the local opposition to uranium mining.

The DAE has never discussed the issue of uranium shortage in public, though it has been a major problem for the officials of NPCIL and the Nuclear Fuel Complex (NFC) for some time. All the DAE announcements about building more 540 MWe and 700 MWe PHWRs in the future have no basis unless the uranium supply position is drastically improved. The DAE may argue that depleted uranium available from the spent-fuel reprocessing plants will supplement our limited natural uranium stocks, but in reality this will not lead to any substantial alleviation of the problem. According to reliable sources in NPCIL, there is not much point in rushing to finish the four PHWRs now under construction in Kaiga and Rajasthan, because it is likely that these reactors when finished may have to wait for sometime for fuel to be available. The DAE's latest projection of 10,000 MWe nuclear power by 2010 is very unlikely to be met, and its earlier forecast of 20,000 MWe by 2020 is impossible to achieve, if the firm current indications of uranium shortage cannot be urgently tackled.

Indian natural uranium ores are very low in grade and, mainly because of this, the uranium produced in India is roughly six to seven times as costly compared to its price in the international market. But, currently India is banned from purchasing natural uranium from the international market because of NSG restrictions. Perhaps, the only roadblock in moving aggressively forward with the indigenous nuclear power programme envisioned by Bhabha is this inability to increase uranium supply, it is a result of the DAE's overestimation of the country's uranium mineral reserves, and the consequent strategic error of not stockpiling enough natural uranium in the past from the international market, at a time when there were no bans on India in making such purchases.

Under these circumstances, an area where US cooperation will be very helpful is in their facilitating Indian import of a negotiated total amount of natural uranium from external markets. This amount could be, for example, the life-time requirement of fuel for PHWRs totalling about 10,000 MWe gross capacity. While the US themselves may not be the supplier, removing the NSG objections for such a sale can be influenced and carried out through the NSG only with active US participation.

Future of Tarapur Units-1 and 2

In 1994, when I was the chairman of the AERB, I was asked to explore the possibility of getting the then badly required spare parts and safety services for the two Tarapur reactors, through informal discussions with the then secretary, US department of energy (DoE), Hazel O'Leary. After a quick consultation between the DoE, the state department and the National Security Agency, I was told that these supplies could not be released. The DOE also conveyed its suggestion that it is best to shut down these two US-supplied reactors, in the interest of public safety. However, during the same trip, I found out from senior officials in the General Electric Company of US that they are not in a position to supply the spare parts or services for these very old reactors in any case! Subsequently, DAE engineers went ahead and designed appropriate spare parts, manufactured them in India and installed them in these reactors. The fact that these reactors are still operating well and providing power to the energy-starved industrial belts in Maharashtra speaks volumes for DAE's abilities to beat foreign technology sanctions. At every juncture when a foreign technology or equipment has been denied to the DAE, it has successfully risen to the challenge of developing an appropriate indigenous equivalent. This is the spirit which we need to admire, nurture and protect.

But, the counter-measures we have implemented in the case of technology denial are often not applicable when critical primary materials, like certain ores and minerals, are not available within the country and their import from international market is denied to us. This is the situation in the case of natural uranium needed for fuelling the PHWRs and the low-enriched uranium (LEU) fuel for the Tarapur reactors. As for the continued operation of Tarapur reactors, when the current batch of imported enriched uranium is exhausted, we will again need concessions from the NSG to import additional fuel. With all the nations which produce enriched uranium being members of the NSG, their current rules will not allow any such fuel sales to India. Earlier, China had supplied us fuel with US consent, when it was not a member of the NSG. Russia helped us once in defiance of the NSG rules, but will not dare to do that today, much the same way they have backed off, under US pressure, from selling any more VVER reactors to India. DAE's claim that it has the alternative option of replacing the enriched uranium with plutonium-based fuel in Tarapur reactors is invalid, because reactor physics and safety considerations will preclude the loading of more than 30-35 per cent mixed oxide fuel in these boiling water reactors. Obviously, the small enriched uranium production plant we have near Mysore is not able to meet the requirements of these reactors, either because of operational difficulties or due to alternate demand on that fuel. In the meantime, Maharashtra is facing serious power shortage, and the shutting down of Tarapur reactors will further aggravate this problem. Therefore, US assistance in facilitating fuel supply for Tarapur reactors, for at least another 10 years, is quite crucial.

Prototype Fast Breeder Reactor

The Indian experience in fast breeder technology is mainly from operating a 13 MWe fast breeder test reactor (FBTR) supplied by France in the early 1970s, up to just about one-third its rated power level, for a few years. Based on this limited experience, and some very good research and development work carried out on fast breeder technology over the decades, India has decided to take the bold step of designing and building a 500 MWe commercial scale PFBR. Fast reactors operate at much higher temperatures and with substantially greater plutonium inventories than the PHWRs, making them much higher-risk facilities from a safety and reliability point of view. The widely held view of international experts in the field is that India is taking a very large risk in attempting such a major new technology project with so little specific experience. France and Russia are the two countries which have considerable experience in building and operating commercial size fast breeder reactors, and India could greatly benefit from detailed technical discussions and consultations with these countries on the salient aspects of our PFBR design and its safety philosophy. The DAE and our specialists at the Indira Gandhi Centre for Atomic Research (IGCAR) may not agree with this assessment, but their pride and over-confidence should not be allowed to stand in the way of further strengthening the worker and public safety aspects in this case. But, again, France and Russia can openly interact with India only if the NSG does not raise objections. We will need the US to help remove any NSG objections that may come in the way of India opening bilateral consultations with Russia and France on the design, construction, operation and safety of our PFBR.

In the above regard, we should note that India had signed the International Convention on Nuclear Safety in September 1994 and has ratified it recently on March 31, 2005. One of the objectives of this Convention, as stated in its Article-1, is "the achievement and maintenance of a high level of nuclear safety worldwide through the enhancement of national measures and international cooperation including, where appropriate, safety-related technical cooperation."[6] In case the US or the NSG blocks our attempt to initiate PFBR safety-related interactions with Russia or France, the Government of India could legitimately raise this issue with the International Atomic Energy Agency (IAEA), on the basis of our right, as a Party to the Convention, to benefit from such international technical cooperation.

Indian Priorities in Nuclear Cooperation

In effecting the Indo-US nuclear cooperation, the government's priority concern should be to ensure that the DAE and its sister organisations get the minimum essential elements of assistance they immediately require. In my opinion, these should not include the acquisition of any foreign nuclear power reactors or the acceptance of the mostly irrelevant interactions between the Atomic Energy Regulatory Board (AERB) of India and the USNRC.

As explained in the previous sections, the highest importance should be given to procuring natural uranium fuel for our PHWRs, to consolidate our indigenous three-stage nuclear power programme as envisaged by Homi Bhabha. Secondly, we must seek the continuity of enriched uranium fuel supply for the Tarapur reactors. And, finally, we must seek US assistance in facilitating NSG clearance for formal Indian consultations with France and Russia on the design, safety and operation of our PFBR. Any other items of obvious core interest to the Indian civilian nuclear programme should also be included, provided the DAE and the government are able to make a strong case for each of those needs.

Nuclear Policies of India and the US

A cursory look at some of the long-held policies of the US and India, as they stand today, raises a great deal of doubt on the feasibility of initiating any meaningful nuclear cooperation between the two countries. Most of these difficulties can be traced to India affirming its status as a nuclear weapon state and continuing to be a non-party to the Nuclear Non-Proliferation Treaty (NPT). The US foreign policy formulation is always closely linked to the requirements of the nuclear non-proliferation regime and its associated export control entities, and this linkage further minimises the flexibilities available to policy-makers in Washington.

The Indian parliament has just passed the Weapons of Mass Destruction and their Delivery System (Prohibition of Unlawful Activities) Bill, 2005. The enactment of this law fulfils the mandatory requirements under the Security Council Resolution No. 1540, and takes India a step closer to the demands of the non-proliferation regime. However, the opening paragraph of the WMD Bill states, "India is determined to safeguard its national security as a nuclear weapon state."[7] And, in replying to the discussions in parliament, the Indian external affairs minister assured that "India is fully committed to safeguard its security as a nuclear weapon state... We are committed to building and maintaining a credible minimum deterrent... We continue to observe a voluntary moratorium on nuclear explosive testing."[8] The spokesman for the ministry of external affairs is reported to have said that the WMD Act 2005 is an important piece of legislation in the light of India's emergence as a "nuclear state."[9] These remarks are consistent with the often-repeated elements of the Indian nuclear policy.

In contrast to the above, note the tone and contents of the following excerpt from an official statement given on January 20, 2005, by Andrew K. Semmel, US principal deputy assistant secretary of state for nuclear non-proliferation. He said, "Let me affirm the US position: non-parties (of the NPT) should adhere to the NPT and the associated regime as non-nuclear weapon states and place all their nuclear facilities under international safeguards...In the meantime, however, NPT parties must refrain from any meaningful nuclear cooperation with any non-party. Certain benefits are reserved only to NPT parties, and then only to those that are in compliance with their obligations."[10] Here, the US is openly exhorting all NPT parties (these include the US as well) to refrain from any 'meaningful' nuclear cooperation with countries such as India (a non-NPT party).

On May 23, 2005, at the NPT Review Conference, Semmel went on to further assert the US policy on India as follows: "The United States shares the view that the conference should reinforce the goal of universal NPT adherence. That goal is for Israel, India and Pakistan to eventually join the Treaty as non-nuclear weapon states...We recognise, however, that India and Pakistan may not join the Treaty for the foreseeable future.... As part of our active bilateral dialogues with India and Pakistan, we continue to urge these countries not to conduct nuclear tests, to bring an early end to the production of fissile material for nuclear weapons—and in that context to support the immediate start of negotiations on a fissile material cut-off treaty—to prevent onward proliferation, and to bring their export controls in line with international standards...Our actions with both India and Pakistan continue to be consistent with our NPT obligations and with our commitment to the NSG Guidelines."[11]

The US policy position was clarified even earlier by the US state department as follows: "The RevCon (2005 NPT Review Conference) must continue to uphold NPT universality as our ultimate goal and call upon India, Israel and Pakistan to adhere as non-nuclear weapon states...There can be no significant nuclear supply to NPT non-adherents, and the benefits due compliant NPT parties must be reserved solely for compliant NPT parties. There should be no amending of the Treaty to recognise in any way states outside the Treaty that possess nuclear weapons as nuclear weapon states. The Treaty recognises five states as nuclear weapon states and it should never recognise more."[12]

Nuclear Export Controls Imposed on India

The US government maintains controls on exports of nuclear-related items under the authority of the Nuclear Non-proliferation Act of 1978 (NNPA) in order to advance their non-proliferation policy. Under this act, it is mandatory that the US government shall not have any nuclear cooperation with non-nuclear weapon states that test a nuclear explosive. India is internationally accepted only as a non-nuclear weapon state, which has stayed out of the NPT and detonated nuclear weapons both in 1974 and 1998. Therefore, the US Congress will have to amend the NNPA, if US nuclear cooperation with India is to begin, something which is very unlikely unless India makes substantial changes in its current nuclear policy.

The controls under the NNPA are further augmented by other international nuclear non-proliferation obligations of the US. The US is a member of the multilateral NSG, which it was instrumental in creating in the wake of India's 1974 nuclear test. The NSG, which has 44 nations as members, sets forth export control guidelines applicable to a list of nuclear-related dual-use items. The US also is a member of the Zangger Committee, a multilateral group formed in the early 1970s to establish guidelines for the export control provisions of the NPT. The US regularly consults with non-NSG members as well, to coordinate export controls for nuclear non-proliferation purposes. It is vitally important to the US that they are not seen to be unilaterally violating the clear rules and consensus requirements, which the US has been mostly instrumental in framing, on the basis of which the NSG and the Zangger Committee have been functioning all these years.[13] Thus, even if the NNPA is suitably amended, the US cannot unilaterally initiate any nuclear cooperation with India, since they also have to abide by the rules of these export control entities.

The primary concern of the US is also that they should not be seen as rewarding India through any nuclear cooperation, since most of the non-nuclear states who have voluntarily foregone their right to develop nuclear weapons and joined the NPT will interpret it as a betrayal of a collective trust and an undervaluing of their nuclear self-denial all these years.[14,15] The US will be especially sensitive about recommending any relaxation of export controls for India at the NSG forum, because this group consists also of countries like Brazil and South Africa who once possessed (and later gave up) nuclear weapon technology and/or bombs, and nations like Japan, South Korea and others who are abstaining from starting a weapons programme in spite of having the required nuclear fissile materials and all the technologies for making nuclear weapons. In fact, George Perkovich has this advice for the US government, "The US and others should not adjust the nuclear non-proliferation regime to accommodate India's desire for access to nuclear technology. As a non-party to the NPT, India has the "right" to build and operate nuclear plants. Yet, others have no obligation to assist India in this enterprise. The costs of breaking faith with non-nuclear weapon states such as Japan, South Africa, Brazil, Argentina, Sweden and others who forswore nuclear weapons is too high to warrant accommodating India's nuclear desires. Just as the US and others have not provided nuclear assistance to Israel, they should maintain a similar position regarding India and Pakistan."[15] In pushing India's case, the Americans cannot afford to antagonise a set of important non-nuclear NPT member-states, who may in today's circumstances threaten to leave the NPT and develop nuclear weapons themselves. The result of this cautionary approach of the US will be to compel India to give much more concessions than what we will consider balanced or are willing to concede, so that the US can use that to persuade the NSG to favour India's case for any minor relaxation of their rules. We will have to wait and see what unfolds in this regard.

IAEA Safeguards and the Additional Protocol

As for the IAEA safeguards requirements, currently India has consented only for such safeguards inspection at six of its reactors, viz. RAPS-1 and 2, TAPS-1 and 2, and Kudamkulam-1 and 2, since they are all imported nuclear facilities. Thus, India is presently subjected to limited 'facilitywise' safeguards on these six installations and not to the "comprehensive or full-scope safeguards", which will require similar coverage of all nuclear facilities of the country, including those which we have nationally designated as 'weapons facilities'. The NNPA and the NSG stipulations, however, already call for comprehensive safeguards to be in place before a non-nuclear weapon state is given any nuclear assistance, and most likely this will be the initial condition proposed to India to qualify for any nuclear cooperation.

Having resigned themselves to the fact that India will insist on maintaining its nuclear weapons programme and associated facilities, the US no longer can demand the imposition of comprehensive ('full-scope') safeguards on all Indian nuclear facilities. The advice of US think-tanks to the state department has been to negotiate with India the acceptance of IAEA safeguards similar to those agreed to by the five recognised nuclear weapon states (P. 5), without formally according any nuclear-weapon state status to India. An associated and integral part of this advice is also that, in return, India should not be rewarded with nuclear supplies as long as the country operates any nuclear facility which is not under safeguards.[14,15] This is not a proposal which India can agree to, but there may be room for initiating negotiations here to find a mutually acceptable limited solution.

Furthermore, since 1993, the Additional Protocol to the IAEA safeguards agreement has been introduced, under which a wider range of nuclear and non-nuclear facilities are covered for inspection, the list of information and data to be made available to the IAEA has been expanded, and the demand for short-notice inspections of declared and undeclared sites anywhere in the country has been legitimised. Thus, the additional protocol is much more intrusive and wider in scope than the limited safeguards so far applied to just a few Indian facilities. And yet, in a major policy speech delivered on February 11, 2004 president Bush announced, "I propose that by next year, only states that have signed the additional protocol be allowed to import equipment for their civilian nuclear programmes."[16] So, any future nuclear assistance from the US to India would attract simultaneous imposition of the stringent additional protocol provisions as well.

As a minimum requirement, the US and the NSG will expect India to place all our nuclear reactors and the spent-fuel reprocessing facilities, which will use or handle the supplies of imported natural uranium and enriched fuel, under international safeguards. This would mean the continuation of safeguards at the Tarapur Units-1 and 2 and, in addition, bringing the set of future PHWRs using the newly imported natural uranium also under international inspections.

Is there any Common Ground for Cooperation?

So, in summary, where do the two countries stand insofar as their relevant policies are concerned? India maintains the firm position that it is a nuclear weapon state, considers the NPT and the Comprehensive Test Ban Treaty (CTBT) to be discriminatory treaties and refuses to join them. India has decided to maintain a minimum nuclear deterrent and has, therefore, an active nuclear weapons programme and associated facilities. As such, India cannot agree to the IAEA full scope safeguards applicable to non-nuclear weapon states. India is also unlikely to accept IAEA's right for intrusive, short-notice inspections of declared and undeclared facilities, as required under the additional protocol. India may not join the proliferation security initiative[17] or agree to prematurely suspend the operation of our plutonium producing reactors or the spent-fuel reprocessing facilities.

The US, on the other hand, wants India to join the NPT as a non-nuclear weapon state and would like us to formalise our moratorium on nuclear weapon tests, temporarily halt the production of fissile materials for weapons and join the Fissile Material Cut-off Treaty (FMCT) deliberations.[18] The US has also formally stated that all NPT members must refrain from having any meaningful nuclear cooperation with non-NPT countries like India. The US Nuclear Non-Proliferation Act, 1978 (NNPA) prohibits nuclear cooperation between the US and India, and the US Congress will have to amend the NNPA if it were to happen. The US has the lead role in two multinational nuclear export control groups, the NSG and the Zangger Committee, and both totally preclude any nuclear or dual-use technology cooperation with India, as long as we do not agree to comprehensive safeguards on all our nuclear facilities and materials. Finally, the US wants to make the adherence to the IAEA additional protocol mandatory for nuclear cooperation, a condition not acceptable to India.

Given these sharply opposing stands, the only conclusion one can draw is that any meaningful nuclear cooperation between India and the US is impossible under the strongly held current policies of the two countries. And yet, going by the hype in the news media and the statements emanating from the MEA, the general public is given the impression that such cooperation is feasible in the very near future. The reasons for this anomaly are unclear, and one could only attempt to make a few educated guesses.

Why Then the Indian Interest in Nuclear Cooperation?

It is not possible that the experts in the MEA, DAE and PMO are not fully aware of the policy stances of the two countries, and therefore, are acting gullibly. It is conceivable, however, that the MEA would like to indirectly create an impression in the country that it is indeed succeeding in bringing the US around to an early rapprochement in our nuclear relations. Their task is made easier by the general ignorance of the Indian news media and the public about the intricacies of the complex issues involved, and because of the biases existing in certain segments of the government, media, industry and the think-tank community in this country in favour of that viewpoint.

There is also the possibility that the MEA, under the guidance of the PMO and some of our economic ministries, is offering the nuclear cooperation carrot from the Indian side, as part of a grand strategy of broader optimisation of mutual benefits. The DAE may not have a deciding voice in framing these strategies, though a senior officer of the DAE secretariat was also among the recent Indian delegation which accompanied our external affairs minister to Washington, DC for discussions. Under this approach, the Indian government may be toying with the idea of conceding some ground on our long-held nuclear policies, in return for concrete US assistance involving an agreement to sell high technology non-nuclear components and systems and defence equipment to India, including the transfer of technology and co-production facilities.

The offered assistance could include the removal of all sanctions on high-tech components and sub-systems for India's civilian space programme, assistance from and joint R&D with the US National Aeronautics and Space Administration (NASA) on the Chandrayana-1 unmanned moon-mission project of India slated for 2008, and cooperation in the international marketing of our commercial satellite launching efforts for other countries. On the nuclear technology front, US may offer India an enlarged dialogue on safety with the USNRC *based solely on openly available data,* opportunities for participation in certain multinational futuristic ('Generation-4') reactor design efforts and experimental projects in basic nuclear science, and perhaps some computer code verification work through the 'standard problem' approach. None of these is a crucial necessity for the Indian nuclear programme, and the DAE can function very well without any of these items. As for a broader energy cooperation between the two countries, the US will once again try to dissuade India from going forward with the Iran-Pakistan-India natural gas pipeline project, and instead offer to facilitate our participation in the Turkmenistan-Afghanistan-Pakistan pipeline project, in which there is substantial US interest and involvement.

In the past, two of the major stumbling blocks which stood in the way of Indo-US cooperation were the fear of insufficient protection for US intellectual property related to transferred technologies and the absence of strong export control laws to safeguard against the illegal re-export or leakage of US-supplied technology and equipment. But, with the passing of the Patents Act and very recently the Weapons of Mass Destruction and their Delivery Systems (Prohibition of Unlawful Activities) Act, 2005, Government of India has sufficiently reassured the world that there need not be any concern regarding these two issues any more.

In effecting the optimised cooperation package indicated above, the US will carefully orchestrate their moves in a manner in which they neither violate or disturb their laws, nor go against the major stipulations of the international nuclear non-proliferation regime. But, the losers in this game plan will primarily be the DAE institutions, in not only being denied any meaningful nuclear assistance, but in having to lose some self-respect and sovereignty in nuclear issues which their predecessors have painfully built-up and preserved.

NOTES

1. Statement by Condoleeza Rice, US secretary of state, in the course of an interview with the *Wall Street Journal* in Washington, DC, as reported in the US State Department website (April 14, 2005).
2. Arun Rajnath, 'US Nuclear Offers throw Pipeline Projects with Iran, Pakistan to Disarray', *South Asia Tribune* (March 29, 2005).
3. Information from the web site of the Nuclear Power Corporation of India (NPCIL) on plants under operation and projects under construction.
4. AERB Report on 'Safety Issues in DAE Installations', 1995, Atomic Energy Regulatory Board, Government of India. The AERB issued this report as an open document, but the DAE has subsequently classified it as top secret.

5. A. Gopalakrishnan, 'Issues of Nuclear Safety', *Frontline*, Volume 16, No. 6, March 13-26, 1999.

6. 'Convention on Nuclear Safety', IAEA Document No INFCIR/449 dated July 5, 1994, International Atomic Energy Agency, Vienna.

7. 'WMD Bill passed against transfers', news item from the *Deccan Chronicle*, Hyderabad (May 14, 2005).

8. Statement of Natwar Singh, Indian external affairs minister, in the Rajya Sabha (May 13, 2005).

9. 'Bill will not constrict nuclear programme', news item from the *Hindu* (May 14, 2005).

10. Andrew K. Semmel, US principal deputy assistant secretary of state for nuclear non-proliferation, statement to the international workshop on prospects for the 2005 NPT Review Conference, Bali, Indonesia (January 20, 2005).

11. Andrew K. Semmel, US principal deputy assistant secretary of state for nuclear non-proliferation, 'Regional Issues Relating to the NPT', statement made to the 2005 NPT Review Conference, New York (May 23, 2005).

12. Andrew K. Semmel, US principal deputy assistant secretary of state for nuclear non-proliferation, 'How should the regime be adjusted in a world where nine states possess nuclear weapons?', remarks at the Wilton Park Conference, Sussex, England (December 14, 2004).

13. 'NPT Briefing Book', April 2004 edition, The Mountbatten Centre for International Studies, Southampton, UK (www.mcis.soton.ac.uk).

14. George Perkovich *et al*, 'Universal Compliance: A Strategy for Nuclear Security', Report of the Carnegie Endowment for International Peace, Washington, DC, (March 2005).

15. George Perkovich, 'Israel, India and Pakistan: Regional Security and Politics are the Solution, Not the NPT, paper presented at the Second Moscow International Non-Proliferation Conference (September 18-20, 2003).

16. Remarks by US president George W Bush on WMD Proliferation, Fort Lesley J. McNair National Defence University, Washington, DC, February 11, 2004.

17. John Bolton, US under secretary for arms control and international security, 'Stopping the Spread of Weapons of Mass Destruction in the Asian-Pacific Region: Role of Proliferation Security Initiative (PSI)', address delivered to a multinational task force on PSI, Tokyo, Japan, (October 27, 2004).

18. Stephen G. Rademaker, US assistant secretary for arms control, statement made at the 2005 NPT Review Conference, New York, (May 2, 2005).

Published in: *Economic and Political Weekly*
(Volume XL, No. 27, July 2-8, 2005, pp. 2935-2940)

2. Some Concerns on Indo-US Deal

A. GOPALAKRISHNAN

Given the nuclear policies of the US and Indian governments which existed in the beginning of July 2005, the only conclusion which could be drawn was that no meaningful nuclear cooperation between the two countries was possible in the near-term.[1] But this situation changed substantially by the afternoon of July 18, 2005 after president Bush and prime minister Manmohan Singh signed a joint statement in Washington, which included three detailed paragraphs on a framework for developing civilian nuclear cooperation between India and the US.[2]

The joint statement was greeted with mixed reactions in both India and the US, with both opposition and support coming from important individuals and political parties. Strangely, while the non-proliferation lobby in the US considers that the intended cooperation with India would damage the current nuclear control regime, the Indian opponents claim that the framework will seriously limit the country's nuclear weapon capabilities, harm national security interests and hurt indigenous nuclear development. This article examines the validity of only two of the critical comments raised in India, in some detail.

Indo-US Joint Statement

The joint statement between president Bush and prime minister Manmohan Singh[2] envisages certain steps to be taken by both sides to bring about an Indo-US cooperation in civilian nuclear energy.

It first outlines the steps to be taken by the president, that he would seek agreement from the US Congress to adjust domestic laws and policies to enable full civilian nuclear energy cooperation and trade with India, and that the US will also work with allies to adjust international regimes for that purpose. This is followed by a commitment from the Indian prime minister that India would reciprocally agree that it would be ready to assume the same responsibilities and practices and acquire the same benefits and advantages as other leading countries with advanced nuclear technology such as the US. The document then goes on to outline what these Indian responsibilities and practices consist of:

- Identifying and separating civilian and military nuclear facilities and programmes in a phased manner.
- Filing a declaration regarding India's civilian facilities with the International Atomic Energy Agency (IAEA).
- Taking a decision to place voluntarily the Indian civilian nuclear facilities under IAEA safeguards.
- Signing and adhering to an Additional Protocol with respect to civilian nuclear facilities.
- Continuing India's unilateral moratorium on nuclear testing.
- Working with the US for the conclusion of a multilateral Fissile Material Cut-off Treaty (FMCT).
- Refraining from transfer of enrichment and reprocessing technologies to states that do not have them and supporting international efforts to limit their spread.
- Ensuring that necessary steps have been taken to secure nuclear materials and technology through comprehensive export control legislation and through harmonisation and adherence to Missile Technology Control Regime (MTCR) and Nuclear Suppliers Group (NSG) guidelines.

Criticism within India

Since July 18 several opinions have appeared in the Indian media, both against and in support of the Indo-US nuclear cooperation framework. Various political parties are among those who have expressed their reservations.[3-5] In both houses of parliament, the prime minister has given comprehensive replies to all points of criticism raised in the debate and from outside,[6,7] (A few of the relevant publications in this connection are cited in the list of references.[8-13]). Also included is a recent interview given by Anil Kakodkar, chairman of the Indian Atomic Energy Commission (AEC).[14]

This article discusses the fears expressed about India's ability to maintain a minimum nuclear deterrent after this cooperation, and the alleged inadvisability of separating civilian nuclear facilities and military ones.

Is India Limiting its Nuclear Deterrent?

The fear that the deal will seriously limit India's capability to decide what kind of credible minimum nuclear deterrent it wants, was first expressed by senior weapon scientists who once led the programme, and quickly repeated by senior opposition leaders like Atal Behari Vajpayee and others.[4,5,8,9] The prime minister, however, has assured Parliament that "...there should be no doubt whatsoever that we have done anything which compromises our strategic autonomy in the management of India's strategic nuclear assets."[6]

The problem seems to stem from the differing perceptions of the 'minimum nuclear deterrent' held by various factions in this country. There is a minority which includes some senior weapon scientists, strategic analysts, and political leaders belonging to certain parties (which for decades have urged the full-fledged nuclear weaponisation of India), who believe that the minimum deterrent should be comparable in level and quality with the nuclear arsenals of Britain, France and China. Bharat Karnad, a strategic analyst, has concluded that "A thermonuclear weaponised India, holding all the high cards, will only strengthen its bargaining position by not being seen as too eager for a rapprochement other than on its terms. ... If, however, the government surrenders this country's sovereign rights to test, weaponise and to secure itself against any and all threats for bits of technology, lifting of sanctions, a veto-less UN Security Council seat or whatever, then the odds are that India in the 21st century will subside gently to the position of a minor power."[15] Unfortunately, Manmohan Singh also faces the difficulty of having to deal with an official nuclear weapons establishment within the government, parts of which seem to hold views which tend to be close to what Karnad has expressed.

At the other end of the spectrum, we have a similar small minority which feels India must abolish its nuclear weapons programme and denuclearise completely at the earliest, and strive to promote universal nuclear disarmament. While this group has no definite action plan or suggestions on universal disarmament, they are the first to vehemently oppose all nuclear activities within India. This is the major reason why they are unable to attract many more people to their fold.

This leaves the vast majority of the Indian population, which is more concerned today about economic and development issues and the associated widespread improvement in the quality of life. However, this majority would still want the nation to retain a rational level of minimum nuclear weapon capability in absolute terms, though they are not particular about the comparative strength of our arsenal vis-a-vis those of China, France or UK.

In 2000, P.K. Iyengar, former chairman of the AEC, said, "But now that India has declared its capabilities openly, the time has come for transparency in nuclear policy, in order to inform the Indian people and to evolve a national consensus on the country's short-term and long-term policies on nuclear deterrence and disarmament."[16] Perhaps, it is time that we organise informed debates in this country on such issues. This would also help put the Indian nuclear weapon lobby in consonance with the mainstream thinking in the country, instead of their driving the strategic policy-making in directions they prefer from their powerful positions within the government.

P.K. Iyengar, an authority on nuclear weapons, welcomed the prime minister's recent actions. He is reported to have said, "Nowhere in the Indo-US joint statement is there mention of any interference in our military programme. It's only under the FMCT that the question of restricting the production of fissile materials for weapons comes in. That's a long way off.

The agreement is welcome for the future growth of our nuclear power industry."[12]

To begin with, let us examine the status of materials availability for India's nuclear weapons programme. As for fission-based warheads, India has conducted a total of six tests (in 1974 and 1998), including one two-stage thermonuclear device which used a "boosted-fission" primary. Media reports had indicated in 1998 that at least one of these tests was on a device which used reactor-grade plutonium, with the other five using weapon-grade material. If so, since we could retain the existing large stock of reactor-grade plutonium, the two weapon-grade plutonium-producing reactors, and their plutonium inventory in the civilian list, there should be no shortage of plutonium for making fission devices. In addition, if needed, India can build a third weapon-grade plutonium-producing reactor solely for military purposes. Thus, the proposed Indo-US nuclear deal will not impose any unacceptable restrictions on our plutonium inventory in the future.

Tritium, a radioactive isotope of hydrogen, is needed in addition to plutonium to assemble the boosted-fission and the two-stage thermonuclear weapons. India has detritiation plants which can efficiently extract tritium from the irradiated heavy-water in our power reactors.[17,18] An alternate route for producing tritium is the irradiation of lithium-6 absorber elements in reactors,[18,19] a scheme which India may also have employed in some of its power reactors.

It may be noted that tritium is not a substance coming under IAEA safeguards in any country of the world. But, it is included in the list of dual-use materials by the NSG and our obligation, therefore, under the present Indo-US agreement will be limited only to adding tritium in the list of prohibited trade items under the WMD Act, 2005. In addition, if India's detritiation plants are excluded from the civilian list, tritium produced in these plants will not come under safeguards. In any case, detritiating the irradiated heavy-water in our power plants and research reactors is an operational requirement to keep the radiation dose-rates in the various operating areas and equipment within limits, and this cannot be denied because of the associated matter of personnel safety involved. Added to this, if the current isotope production activities in CIRUS and Dhruva reactors are terminated and the excess reactivity thus made available is used for irradiation of lithium-6, India can produce additional tritium simultaneous with weapon-grade plutonium in these military facilities. Therefore, India does not require the power reactors to sustain an adequate supply of tritium for the thermonuclear weapons.

As far as warhead designs are concerned, India is considered capable of producing boosted-fission weapons of reliable design up to 25-30 kilotonnes (KT) yield, based on the test results and confidence gained from the 1974 and 1998 tests. These will also have yield-to-weight ratios adequate to suit missile-delivered warheads. For more powerful weapons with yields between 30-150 (KT), it will be necessary to use two-stage thermonuclear designs. Though the serious limitation in thermonuclear weapon test data will raise questions about the reliability of yield as the designs move to the higher end of this range, Indian weapon scientists are quite confident that trustworthy designs are possible, with the current database and some additional computer simulation.

The Indian experience with weapon testing is a mixed one. Though India might have completed the minimum number of tests to establish reliable designs of fission and boosted-fission devices up to 30 KT yield, the two-stage thermonuclear designs have to rely on a single low-yield test conducted in 1998. From an evaluation of the data from this test, P.K. Iyengar has said, "This suggests that the fusion core burnt only partially, perhaps less than 10 per cent. However, a thermonuclear device that only burns partially is certainly inefficient. Logically and scientifically, the next step would be to improve the design of the device to achieve greater efficiency. This is particularly important from the point of view of a weaponisation programme."[20] He should know, because most of the work on the thermonuclear device was directed by him during his tenure as director, Bhabha Atomic Research Centre (BARC) and later as chairman, AEC. And yet, based on the affirmation of the scientists, the Vajpayee government rushed to offer a voluntary moratorium on weapon tests in 1998 itself, and maintained that posture through their five years in office. Faced with threats of more serious sanctions, that government felt it wise to stick to the moratorium rather than risk economic trouble by continuing with further thermonuclear tests, though these were needed to establish absolutely reliable fusion weapon designs, according to many scientific evaluations.

Therefore, if the nuclear deterrence level is today limited to weapons of assured high reliability up to 30 KT yield and with reasonably good reliability in the 30-150 KT range, it has mainly resulted from the decisions taken by the Vajpayee government and the weapon scientists in 1998 not to press on with further weapon tests. Even now, the weapons group of the department of atomic energy holds on to the position that no more testing is needed. Under the current Indo-US cooperation agreement, the group can also keep the minimum facilities needed for tritium production (for fusion weapons) and enough plutonium inventories outside the civilian list, so that they also will face no material constraints. Therefore, they too should not have any quarrel if Manmohan Singh has proposed a bilateral agreement with the US which includes a continuation of the Vajpayee government's moratorium on testing.

But, the most crucial point is that even a 15 KT Hiroshima-type fission bomb dropped in a major metropolitan city of Asia could cause catastrophic destruction and death of hundreds of thousands of people within a short period.[21,10] This being the case, do we really need anything more than the capability of making and delivering reliable nuclear weapons, three to 10 times as powerful as the Hiroshima weapon, as a 'minimum credible deterrent'? This is the capability which will definitely be preserved even after the planned Indo-US nuclear cooperation agreement is entered into.

In any case, with or without the Indo-US nuclear cooperation in place, it would be inadvisable now or in future to conduct any further nuclear weapon tests, thanks to the economic growth under five years of the Vajpayee government and under the present regime. As the country begins to move ahead in economic growth, our sustenance of that growth is intricately dependent on cooperation and mutual assistance from the rest of the world. It is true that when the moratorium on weapon tests becomes a part of the Indo-US bilateral agreement, and this in turn becomes the sole basis on which the NSG and other elements of the non-proliferation regime are going to accept the retention of India's nuclear weapons status and provide us the badly needed assistance in material procurement, it will then become a more serious violation if India breaks the bilateral commitment and conducts nuclear tests in future. If we do so, one can be sure it will bring unprecedented international condemnation as well as economic and trade sanctions from most parts of the developed world, and their adverse impact then would be manifold compared to 1998. In this respect, the Vajpayee government's five-year moratorium, coupled with the continuation of this moratorium under the present Indo-US agreement, in effect will be almost equivalent to India signing and ratifying the Comprehensive Test Ban Treaty (CTBT). Though the CTBT is of unlimited duration, Article 9.2 of the Treaty states, "Each State Party shall, in exercising its national sovereignty, have the right to withdraw from this Treaty if it decides that extraordinary events related to the subject matter of this Treaty have jeopardised its supreme interests". We should also insist on the inclusion of a similar clause for withdrawal from the unilateral moratorium, in the current bilateral agreement.

Separating Civilian and Military Nuclear Facilities

A former director of BARC is reported to have pointed out that it is nearly impossible to separate the civilian nuclear facilities from the military ones in India, adding that "We produce what we need for the military programme at any given time and leave the rest for civilian use. Having dedicated facilities will terribly raise the cost of the weapons programme."[8] In a detailed interview given recently, the chairman of the Indian AEC stressed that "what is going to be identified as a civilian nuclear facility is going to be an Indian decision, taken at appropriate points of time. Only that which is clearly of no national security significance, only that part will be civilian."[14] This was a very guarded answer, that can be interpreted in different ways. If both of these views are to be accommodated, there will be very few facilities, if any, to place in the civilian category. And, this will negate the entire purpose of this nuclear cooperation effort. All this also indicates that the DAE has an extremely slow and cautious pace in mind for putting the power reactors in the list of civilian facilities.

As indicated earlier, some or all of the Indian PHWR power stations were perhaps so far used in a few different ways to supplement the material needs of the weapons programme. Both the Canadian and Indian PHWRs are designed for on-power fuel loading and unloading, and they can easily be fed fresh fuel bundles which are then taken out after a low burn-up (short period operation) for reprocessing and recovery of weapon-grade plutonium. But, this will be costly underutilisation of the fuel and will substantially add to the cost of electricity generated. We do have a large quantity of weapon-grade plutonium from earlier operation of our reactors, including the two research reactors. As clarified in the previous section, all other benefits, such as tritium production, etc. for the weapon programme derived from the power reactors till today can still be gained without their use in the future.

The above comments, read together with the earlier section, make it abundantly clear that by no stretch of imagination do we need the power reactors for maintaining a minimum nuclear deterrent. No national security requirement is abandoned by putting all these PHWR power reactors on the civilian list in the first instance itself, while keeping the accumulated spent-fuel from these facilities, and any more spent-fuel that will be generated from natural uranium fuel of Indian origin out of the civilian list. This spent-fuel contains reactor-grade plutonium which is entirely indigenous and it will be needed for the Fast Breeder Reactors (FBRs) which India seems to be initially wanting to keep out of the civilian list,[14] and for possible use in nuclear warheads, if we so decide. In doing this, it will also be crucial what kind of a facility-specific safeguards agreement we negotiate and agree with the IAEA for these reactors.

The prime minister and the prime minister's office (PMO) must, therefore, assert the position that *all power reactors must be included in the list of civilian facilities in the first instance,* under a satisfactory safeguards agreement, except for their spent-fuel of Indian origin. The DAE may raise several counter-issues in this connection, and these should be effectively handled by the PMO. They can do so, only if an expert group is formed within the PMO, which can competently and independently evaluate the positions offered by the DAE and present appropriate alternatives for consideration. This would certainly require the strengthening of the current PMO, including the National Security Adviser's technical secretariat.

Concluding Remarks

There is equally strong criticism and concern about some of the remaining issues which are not covered in this article. Prominent among these are the specific details of the IAEA Safeguards Agreement and Additional Protocol which India has to enter into, the recommended initial list of civilian nuclear facilities and the phased additions to that list, the sequenced processes through which India will ensure the agreed reciprocity in actions from the US side, and the conditions under which India could consider the import of power reactors. Detailed deliberations of these aspects need to be initiated within the government and opinions sought from outside experts to facilitate a better and wider understanding and to develop the required consensus. Transparency to the maximum extent possible in the further processes involved will only help the PMO and the government in carrying these forward to a widely acceptable end-point.

NOTES

1. Gopalakrishnan, A. (2005): 'Indo-US Nuclear Cooperation: A Non-Starter?', *Economic and Political Weekly,* Vol. XL, No. 27, July 2-8, pp. 2935-40.

2. 'Joint Statement between President George W. Bush and Prime Minister Manmohan Singh', released by the Office of the White House Press Secretary, July 18, 2005 (http://www.whitehouse.gov/news/releases/2005/07/20050718-6.html)

3. Press Statement of the Communist Party of India (Marxist) Politburo, July 21, 2005 (http://cpim.org, see under 'Statements').

4. Lok Sabha Debates—Uncorrected (August 03, 2005) (http://loksabha.nic.in/, see under 'Daily Debates').

5. Rajya Sabha Debates—Uncorrected (August 04, 2005) (http://rajyasabha.nic.in/, see under 'Verbatim Proceedings').

6. 'Prime Minister's Reply to the Lok Sabha Debate on His US Visit', PM's Office Website, August 03, 2005 (http://www.pmindia.nic.in/parl.htm)

7. 'Prime Minister's Reply in the Rajya Sabha Debate on His US Visit', PM's Office Website, August 04, 2005 (http://www.pmindia.nic.in/parl.htm)

8. Siddharth Varadarajan, 'Nuclear Bargain May Prove Costly in Long Run', *The Hindu,* July 20, 2005.

9. Bharat Karnad, 'Remember the Tritium', *Deccan Chronicle,* Hyderabad, August 7, 2005.

10. A. Gopalakrishnan, 'Manufacturing the Nuclear Scare', *The Indian Express,* July 29, 2005.

11. A. Gopalakrishnan, 'Baseless Criticism of the Prime Minister', Rediff.com, July 29, 2005 (http://www.rediff.com/news/2005/jul/29guest1.htm)

12. P.K. Iyengar and B. Chellaney, 'Does the N-Deal Weaken US Militarily?' *The Economic Times,* July 27, 2005.

13. M.R. Srinivasan, 'New Opportunities for Nuclear Energy', *The Hindu,* August 2, 2005.

14. Anil Kakodkar, Chairman, Indian Atomic Energy Commission (Interview), 'Identifying a Civilian Nuclear Facility is India's Decision', *The Hindu,* August 12, 2005.

15. Bharat Karnad, 'A Thermonuclear Deterrent', Chapter 4 in Amitabh Mattoo (ed.), *India's Nuclear Deterrent—Pokhran 2 and Beyond,* Har-Anand Publications, New Delhi (1999).

16. P.K. Iyengar, 'Imperatives before India', *Frontline,* Volume 17, Issue 15, July 22-August 04, 2000 (http://www.frontlineonnet.com/fl1715/17151170.htm)

17. T.S. Gopi Rethinaraj, 'Tritium Breakthrough Brings India Closer to an H-bomb Arsenal', *Janes Intelligence Review*, Vol. 10, Issue 01, January 1998.

18. Fact Sheet on Tritium Production, US Nuclear Regulatory Commission, Last Updated on June 10, 2004 (http://www.nrc.gov/reading-rm/doc-collections/fact-sheets/tritium.html)

19. Martin B. Kalinowski and Lars C. Colschen, 'International Control of Tritium to Prevent Horizontal Proliferation and Foster Nuclear Disarmament', *Science and Global Security*, Vol. 5, pp. 131-203, 1995.

20. P.K. Iyengar, 'Nuclear Nuances: Credible Deterrent through Testing', August 2000. (http://www.saveindia.com/iyengar.htm)

21. 'Nuclear War in South Asia', M. McKinzie, Zia Mian, M.V. Ramana, A.H. Nayyar, International Network of Engineers and Scientists against Proliferation, Bulletin No. 20, August 2002 (http://www.inesap.org/bulletin20/bul20art22.htm)

Economic and Political Weekly,
Vol. 40, No. 35 August 27, 2005

3. Nuclear Deal: Partnership or Subordination?

Delivering the 40th Anniversary Foundation Day Lecture of the Institute for Defence Studies and Analyses (IDSA) on 11 November 2005, Prime Minister Manmohan Singh presented some highly debatable and mutually incompatible ideas. He warned about the need to curb defence expenditure, extolled the primacy of *realpolitik* and power politics in international politics, advised abandoning old policy shibboleths, and spoke, among other things, about developing "partnerships in the strategic and technological spheres".

Someone should have pointed out that a policy seeking to accommodate all these notions would amount to trying to piece together a live unicorn from a heap of body parts found at the local abattoir. And that, in the main, *realpolitik* and "power relations" cannot be practised by a strategically weak military power any more than India can become a great power by riding on the back of an extant great power (assuming this great power does not seek to thus create a politico-military dependency). Even less, by putting in hock to the United States the country's security, thereby playing straight into America's strategic plans. But this is precisely what is sought to be done by the Manmohan Singh government with the nuclear deal on the anvil with the United States.

The trouble though is that it perfectly reflects the lack of vision and the confusion existing in policy-making circles about the fundamentals—the ends and the means, the threats, and the nature of international relations and global order. While it was a relief to hear the Prime Minister say at the IDSA function that international politics was "not a morality play", the Indian government and our leading commentators apparently believe much worse, that it is a Fantasy-Boy Scout Land out there where great powers help lesser states become great, advantage is not taken of bone-headed countries (like India) in the neighbourhood by big countries (like China). An India bereft of the necessary strategic vision, self-belief and wherewithal nevertheless will never be accorded great power status and the rights and privileges that go with it, without having earned these the hard way as every other country has done throughout recorded history. In *realpolitik,* there is no such social entitlement even for a big but perennially dim-witted supplicant nation which, for exigent purposes, has to be accommodated. (It reminds one of the reason offered for the appointment of Harold Carswell, President Richard Nixon's ultimately rejected-nominee to the US Supreme Court, that "mediocrity" too needed representation in that august body.)

How else to explain the Indian government's inversely-linked attitude towards the United States and the country's strategic defence encapsulated in the nuclear deal signed by Manmohan Singh and George W. Bush in Washington 18 July 2005, seeking close relations with America at the expense of India's nuclear security? The suspect nature of any deal with the US and the problems India would face were highlighted by this analyst well before and after the Prime Minister's Washington trip and should not have come as a surprise to the policy establishment (See *The Asian Age* of 9 May, 29 June, 14 July, 13 August, 24 September, and 26 October 2005). But it did.

The reference to the nuclear deal in the 18 July Joint Statement issued by the two heads of state was as follows:

President Bush conveyed his appreciation to the Prime Minister over India's strong commitment to preventing WMD proliferation and stated that as a responsible state with advanced nuclear technology, India should acquire the same benefits and advantages as other such states. The President told the Prime Minister that he will work to achieve full civil nuclear energy cooperation with India as it realizes its goals of promoting nuclear power and achieving energy security. The President would also seek agreement from Congress to adjust US laws and policies, and the United States will work with friends and allies to adjust international regimes to enable full civil nuclear energy cooperation and trade with India, including but not limited to expeditious consideration of fuel supplies for safeguarded nuclear reactors at Tarapur. In the meantime, the United States will encourage its partners to also consider this request expeditiously. India has expressed its interest in ITER and a willingness to contribute. The United States will consult with the other participants in the Generation IV International Forum with a view towards India's inclusion.

The Prime Minister conveyed that for his part, India would reciprocally agree that it would be ready to assume the same responsibilities and practices and acquire the same benefits and advantages as other leading countries with advanced nuclear technology, such as the United States. These responsibilities and practices consist of identifying and separating civilian and military nuclear facilities and programmes in a phased manner and filing a declaration regarding its civilians facilities with the International Atomic Energy Agency (IAEA); taking a decision to place voluntarily its civilian nuclear facilities under IAEA safeguards; signing and adhering to an Additional Protocol with respect to civilian nuclear facilities; continuing India's unilateral moratorium on nuclear testing; working with the United States for the conclusion of a multilateral Fissile Material Cut

Off Treaty; refraining from transfer of enrichment and reprocessing technologies to states that do not have them and supporting international efforts to limit their spread; and ensuring that the necessary steps have been taken to secure nuclear materials and technology through comprehensive export control legislation and through harmonization and adherence to Missile Technology Control Regime (MTCR) and Nuclear Suppliers' Group (NSG) guidelines.

The hinge of this agreement is the phrase "reciprocally agree"—the controversial part of the deal relating to procedure. Dr. Singh assured Parliament in his speech of 29 July 2005 that "Reciprocity is key to the implementation of all the steps enumerated in the Joint Statement. We expect", he said, "a close relation between the actions to be taken by the United States and by India. Indian actions will be contingent at every stage on actions taken by the [US]". As predicted by this analyst the deal is likely to fall at the first hurdle because changing US laws, particularly sections 123, 128 and 129 of the US Atomic Energy Act relating to nuclear trade, will not be easy. Predictably, differences have already cropped up concerning who is required to do what first.

If the Indian Prime Minister is definite that the two countries are required to move at the same pace on parallel tracks to fulfil their respective commitments, Washington is convinced New Delhi has undertaken first to not only produce a "credible plan" for the separation of the civilian and military-use nuclear facilities and other parts (including the deployment of skilled man-power) of the dual-use Indian nuclear programme, but one that has to cut ice with the US government. New Delhi has then to go ahead with identifying and separating the vast and intermingled facilities before the US Congress deigns to take the first step.

This last expectation of the US is certainly not in line with what Dr. Manmohan Singh told Parliament about what India is required to do. Because the process of identification and separation involves making some complex calculations of all the technological and manufacturing capabilities that will require to be protected to ensure practical autonomy for the weapons-making portions of the Department of Atomic Energy, including enormous replacement costs of many critical installations. It is clear that the Indian team that negotiated this deal with the US delegation led by Nicholas Burns did not reckon with these factors in their negotiating strategy for the good reason that none of them had the scientific and technical expertise to make an assessment before committing the country to doing things that may end up hurting the national interest. Nor did the Indian government involve DAE experts in the deliberations with the Americans, because Dr. Anil Kakodkar, Secretary of the Department and Chairman, AEC, was flown in from Beijing into Washington the evening before (i.e. on 17 July) the document was finalized. The nuclear engineer was, therefore, not in a position to do more than protest, swallow his disquiet, and reluctantly sign on when told in no uncertain terms that the government was keen on having the accord. However, the agreement was conjured up by the Indian negotiating team, filled with generalist civil servants and diplomats, the fact is they have imperilled Indian strategic interests, of course, but also got the Indian Prime Minister into trouble. There is every chance that a Privilege Motion may be moved against him on the charge of misleading Parliament. In which case, the deal would be as good as dead at the Indian end to match the difficulty it is having at the American end where the US legislature is unconvinced that India should enjoy any privileges of a nuclear weapon state.

Dr. Manmohan Singh may be in a worse predicament on another score as well. In the context of "the defence and security interests of our country [being] our highest priority and will continue to remain so", the Prime Minister emphasized in his speech in Parliament that "there is nothing in the Joint Statement that amounts to limiting or inhibiting our strategic nuclear weapons programme over which we will retain unrestricted, complete and autonomous control". So, how does this square with the US government's understanding of what India undertook to do? The official American position is that there is no question of strict reciprocity or of like parallel actions as Dr. Singh had suggested. And that India needs to do a number of things before the US government will even begin thinking of appropriate measures. This was made plain by the US Under-Secretary of State for Policy, Nicholas Burns and his colleague, Under-Secretary of State for Arms Control and International Security, Robert G. Joseph in Congressional testimonies. Deposing before the US Senate Foreign Relations Committee on 2 November 2005, Joseph, for instance, said that:

> In our view, once India makes demonstrable progress in implementing key Joint Statement commitments—with a credible, transparent, and defensible separation plan foremost on the list -we will be ready to engage with our NSG partners in developing a formal proposal to allow the shipment of Trigger List items and related technology to India.

Just so, there was no confusion about what is acceptable to the US by way of a "defensible" separation plan, Joseph indicated that:

> Obviously, the number of facilities and activities that India places under IAEA safeguards, and the method and speed with which it does so, will directly affect the degree to which we will be able to build support for full civil nuclear cooperation.

And driving the prospective nail into the coffin of the Indian nuclear weapons programme, he asserted that the safeguards regime once imposed on any Indian facility would be "in perpetuity" meaning India cannot expect to negotiate an Additional Protocol with IAEA of the kind the five so-called

Non-Proliferation Treaty-recognized nuclear weapon states have. This would permit them to withdraw any civilian nuclear installation under safeguards at any time—something Indian commentators advocating the deal have misled the public into believing it is otherwise.

As far as the US is concerned, it is not up to India alone to decide how many of the 11 heavy water-moderated nuclear reactors out of the total of 15 operational reactors in the country, for example, presently producing electricity for the national grid and, as and when required also plutonium for weapons purposes, should be safely kept out of the international safeguards net, but rather that this number has to pass muster with Washington. The US government's long-standing intention of curbing India's nuclear weapons capability was never a secret. The question is how did the Ministry of External Affairs and the Indian government miss so obvious a thrust of US policy when cobbling together this deal?

India is an energy-deficient state and can do with a lot more electricity produced by the nuclear energy programme in which the country has invested hugely. The "Janus-faced" programme was conceived by the visionary Dr. Homi J. Bhabha, the first Chairman of the Atomic Energy Commission, with a view to maximizing the returns on investment both in the civilian and military sectors. This meant that manpower, materials and physical facilities were seamlessly integrated enabling the programme to switch from producing a bomb to producing electricity or isotopes for nuclear medicine or irradiation of onions and potatoes, without missing a beat. This extraordinary versatility of a broad-based atomic energy programme obtained for the country tremendous policy flexibility and options and cost-effectiveness in civilian and military streams. It is this capability, reinforced by the ease of progress from the fission to fusion weapons that had always made the Nuclear Haves wary and inclined to impose shackles on it.

And the Manmohan-Bush deal is that tool to limit and control the Indian nuclear weapons capability. As Joseph has revealed, the deal will restrict the buildup of the Indian stockpile of fissile material (by deciding how many civilian-cum-military reactors need to be put under safeguards) which, in turn, will decide how many nuclear weapons India can potentially possess. By succeeding in thus sequestering the bulk of the dual-use reactors, the US can also restrict the supply of tritium, produced as a process by-product from heavy water-moderated reactors, the size and quality of the "boosted" nuclear and thermonuclear weapons and hence the nature of the Indian arsenal. Combined with the mindlessly volunteered test moratorium, which Prime Minister Singh has now bilaterally confirmed in the Joint Statement, India will soon be donning a nuclear straitjacket that will leave it, technology-wise, frozen in the Pakistan-league of nuclear weapon states and end any ambitions India may reasonably entertain of becoming a weighty counterpoise to China, which is not similarly hindered, and of developing into a competing power node on the continent and in maritime Asia.

This would seem *prima facie* to be an unbearably heavy price for India to pay, but in return for what, exactly? If the Prime Minister is to be believed, India desperately needs injections of advanced nuclear technology for its civilian nuclear energy programme for it to begin quickly to produce thousands of megawatts of power (20,000 MW by 2020) to drive an economy set on the path of consistently high rate (7 per cent plus) of annual economic growth. But the US has only enriched uranium-related technologies to offer while the Indian N-programme is based on the plutonium cycle. In other words, there is simply no technological interface, so there is very little India needs from the United States.

If the US is expected to do a Koodankulum and have American companies invest in setting up power stations with, say, imported Westinghouse 1000 enriched uranium reactors in a closed loop arrangement whereby the uranium fuel rods when exhausted are replaced and the spent fuel taken back, in the hope that the power emanating from these plants can be sold profitably to the Indian consumer, then it is one thing. But private US firms, like Westinghouse, are keener on selling its high-value wares to India than investing in and running power stations. In that case, India will be expected to invest tens of billions of dollars of its own monies into these Westinghouse reactor power plants which will then become hostage to enriched uranium fuel supply, the contract for which can at any time be terminated by executive fiat or retroactive legislation passed by the US Congress. Recall Tarapur. Except Tarapur was largely built by American grant-in-aid and was no great loss to the Indian exchequer. This situation is not improved much by France substituting for the US in these deals (as per the loosened norms of reformed Nuclear Supplier Group-guidelines) because Paris is prone to give into American arm-twisting (as evidenced in the Tarapur fuel supply arrangement in the past which France unilaterally terminated).

The real reason why India has cut this awful deal with the United States is because of its grave need for natural uranium to run the thirteen existing heavy water-moderated reactors—the work horse of the nuclear programme—and the eight more in the planning stage, and not because it requires civilian nuclear technology, et cetera from the US—which the Indian government, unfortunately, has misleadingly ballyhooed. The fear is that the country may not even reach the second stage featuring the indigenously developed breeder reactor, leave alone the third stage with the thorium reactor, as per the original Bhabha three-stage interlinked plan because it will be starved of natural uranium to even sustain the prevailing first phase with a host of heavy water-moderated natural uranium reactors. It is the shortfall in natural uranium the Indian government has shied away from admitting, but which is its central motivation for the deal with the US. Easing of the NSG guidelines, it is hoped, will allow India to purchase natural uranium ore or "yellow cake" from British and French-owned companies in Namibia and Niger respectively, if not from Australia and Canada who may be more hesitant to sell it, and thereby permit India's Bhabha plan for civilian nuclear energy to remain on track. In short, it is access to natural uranium ore as a bridge between the first and the second stages that India seeks to solidify as a way of protecting both its civilian energy imperatives and its armament plans and prospects.

The American strategic community is not unaware of the Indian strategy. Robert J. Einhorn, a leading non-proliferation ayatollah in Washington, in his written testimony to the House Committee on International Relations on 26 October 2005 said:

> Under current non-proliferation rules—with India unable to buy natural uranium on the world market—India must use those limited supplies for both civil power generation and nuclear weapons, and the trade-off will become increasingly painful. Under new rules, India could satisfy the needs of the civil programme through imports, freeing domestic uranium supplies for the weapons programme and permitting, if the Indian government so decided; a continuing and even major increase in bomb-making potential.

To prevent India gaining in this manner from the deal, Einhorn and others are urging the US government to wring the maximum concessions from New Delhi, including an immediate and complete cessation by it of fissile material production.

If the basic strategy underlying the Indo-US deal has been correctly deduced by the US strategic community and government then it is best abandoned and the nuclear deal consigned to the dust heap. Because persisting with it will mean playing with a marked deck of cards greatly disadvantaging India. But knowing when a policy has hit dead-end and thinking up a new policy tack requires far more quicksilver agility and fleet-footed policy direction than the Indian establishment has shown itself capable of, so far.

The core problem with this India-US nuclear deal is not its nuclear aspects *per se* which are dubious enough, but the fact that India is getting into a subordinate position *vis-a-vis* the United States. This has eventuated because an uncertain and woolly-headed Indian government has always been hesitant about acquiring the necessary wherewithal of great power, like proven long-range thermonuclear strategic forces. Devoid of such military instruments of *realpolitik* statecraft, New Delhi has found itself boxing well below its weight-class, with the likes of Pakistan. Disappointed with this international downgrading, it has bellyached rather than proceeded to right the situation by securing for itself the unquestioned strategic military heft and to show the willingness to project power and win recognition as a would-be great nation-state.

Post-Jawaharlal Nehru, India has exhibited an abominable lack of strategic vision and game plan—meaning a view of where India ought to be in the international scheme of things and how to get there. Bereft of this, what is visible is only a hankering for great power status, preferably on the cheap and, hopefully, by acclamation, instead of on merit. There is only an attempt then to secure symbols of power, like a Security Council seat without veto, not real political power that comes from owning consequential thermonuclear strategic military forces. Clearly what is missing is self-respect.

With all these infirmities embedded in policy-making, the result is, as Dr. Manmohan Singh admitted in his IDSA lecture, an absence of "long range planning". But all planning starts with visioning. The Indian government is definitely not into it and a proposal, for instance, for New Delhi's articulating "an Indian Monroe Doctrine"—a vital and necessary strategic map for India to seek to impose on regional and international reality, for example, draws sniggers from establishment commentators in the press and the like.

With absence of a great power mindset, outlook and policy approach within the official circles, it is easy, as the Manmohan Singh-George W. Bush deal suggests, for India to be content with falling in with extra-regional great powers' view of what India should be. It is in this context, that the proposed Indo-US nuclear deal apparently seals India's role as an American satrap and stalking horse in the southern Asian region. Surely, India deserves better.

(*Indian Foreign Affairs Journal: A Quarterly of the Association of Indian Diplomats*, Vol. 1, No. 1, Jaunary-March 2006, pp. 7-16)

4. Blighted Strategic Future

BHARAT KARNAD

'Future is like anything that's important. It has to be earned. If we don't earn it, we don't have a future at all. And if we don't earn it, if we don't deserve it, we have to live in the present, more or less forever. Or worse, we have to live in the past.'

Gregory David Roberts, *Shantaram*

The nuclear deal with the United States is about an India without a (strategic) future. It is about this country negotiating away its military-*cum*-political independence and leverage—its nuclear force frozen in its present small size and featuring weapons that are untested, unproven, unsafe and unreliable. Prime Minister Manmohan Singh will be remembered, not for any good he might do to free the Indian economy from the dead hand of government, but for the scale of nuclear politico-military disaster he walked the country into. His team of official advisers will by then have melted into the background, and the cheerleaders for this deal in the media would have done their usual intellectual summersault and slammed the after-effects of the deal. Unlike the Indian apologists who justify this deal in terms of a changed global order that India needs to exploit, the US, as always is pursuing a strategy that serves its narrow national security interests. The difference is in the opposing policy templates.

The American template for this agreement was created by Richard L. Garwin, the legendary experimental physicist who critically inputted into the original US hydrogen bomb project. One of a rare breed of wizards in physics as well as nuclear policy, Garwin in 2002 first laid down the policy parameters that the George W. Bush Administration has scrupulously followed in configuring its approach to non-proliferation generally and to crafting the nuclear deal with India, in particular.

The world, Garwin observed in his presentation on 'Megaterrorism' at the University of New Mexico, had 'survived 60 years of potential annihilation' because of the existing 'nuclear monopoly' and 'deterrence by assured destruction', joint US-Russian interest in non-proliferation, and because of the political, intellectual and material barriers against proliferation. And, in a technical sense, because of the inaccessibility to weapon-usable highly enriched uranium and plutonium.

By way of 'urgent remedies', he suggested 'muscular extension of NPT with universal enforcement' and ensuring a complete ban on testing (with the US, however, having the means to modernize its weapons using the advanced technology National Ignition Facility, the mu-electronic center, etc.). 'The US has no reason to test,' Garwin wrote, 'and every national security interest that Russia and China [and by extension, states with even less developed N-arsenals, like India] not test.' However, in order to meet the Non-Proliferation Treaty Article 1 obligation of helping the signatory states acquire civilian nuclear energy as also to mitigate the consequences of energy shortages, he recommended encouraging the accelerated growth of civilian nuclear power plants from the present 400 plus reactors (15% of the world's electricity) to '3,000 or 9,000' reactors.

Most of these plants, he reasoned, should be light water reactors run on enriched uranium and a yet to be developed 'economical plutonium breeder reactor.' The mining of the ore, fuel fabrication and assured fuel supply for these civilian reactors all over the globe were to be under the aegis of the International Atomic Energy Agency (IAEA). And, he viewed 'The Global Nuclear Energy Partnership (GNEP)', which would have collaborative programmes for developing technologies like the economical breeder reactor, as apparently a stratagem to divert the energies of nuclear capable countries like India..

Now view the India-US nuclear deal in the context of this Garwin policy architecture. His principal concern that resumption of Indian testing not be allowed under any circumstances is met in a two-pronged fashion by the deal. The July 18, 2005 Joint Statement signed by Prime Minister Manmohan Singh and President George W. Bush expressly bars India from resuming explosive testing and, depending on how the text is interpreted, perhaps even from conducting sub-critical tests. These are Comprehensive Test Ban Treaty (CTBT)-like strictures that Manmohan Singh has accepted heedless of the consequences, when an earlier Prime Minister, H.D. Deve Gowda, to his enormous credit, had in 1996 rejected the CTBT as fatally hurting national security. It led to Gowda's instructions to veto the draft treaty at the Commission on Disarmament in Geneva. Atal Bihari Vajpayee began the rot by thoughtlessly announcing a 'voluntary test moratorium', which has given way to a now strictly enforceable bilateral undertaking with the United States. And this when the situation remains pretty perilous where the quality and reliability of Indian nuclear weapons/warheads are concerned.

The 'Shakti' series of tests in 1998 proved only that the miniaturized 20 kiloton (KT) fission bomb design, first tested in 1974, is militarily serviceable. All the other weapon designs—the boosted fission and, especially, the thermonuclear—due to their 'simultaneous triggering' in Pokhran, produced confused multi-test explosion data sufficient to conclude that the fusion design, for instance, did not work because of partial thermonuclear burn—authoritatively established by crater morphology and excessive traces of lithium in the rock and soil samples extracted from the L-shaped tunnel deep underneath the Thar desert where the devices exploded. Moreover, data from just one, and that too failed, test involving the decisive thermonuclear device is simply insufficient to write a software package simulating fusion reaction, leave alone help in developing new and more innovative designs for thermonuclear warheads/weapons of different power-to-yield ratios to fit varying missile nose-cone geometries.

In short, should this nuclear deal be approved by the US Congress, India will be permanently stuck with a primitive nuclear arms inventory which can in no way propel India into the military great power ranks. President Clinton's Under Secretary of State John Holum in his Congressional testimony had declared this as the main aim of US non-proliferation policy, which the successor George W. Bush Administration has now achieved.

The other measure working in tandem to hobble India's nuclear military potential is the Fissile Material Cut-Off Treaty (FMCT) that Dr Singh has promised India will now join in pushing. If there is any intention by New Delhi to stringout the FMCT negotiations and 'buy time' for the Indian nuclear complex to produce weapon-usable fissile material at an accelerated pace and build up its stockpile, the Indian government may be in for a surprise. Unlike the CTBT, India's future relationship with the US is coupled by Washington with an early completion of the FMCT talks and its ratification by the Indian government. Having made pledges on FMCT, New Delhi will be in no position to slow down the negotiating process. Thus, say, in a couple of years at the most—because that is all the window realistically afforded India—New Delhi will have to shut down all fissile material production and the only stockpile of weapon-grade plutonium (WgPu) this country will have is what will be built up in the period between now and when the FMCT comes into force.

But considering the limited production capacity of the two military-dedicated reactors—the 40 MW CIRUS (assuming its close down is not immediately effected by twin Canadian-US pressure) and the 100 MW Dhruva—and the fact that the eight pressurized heavy water reactors (PHWRs) pumping power into the grid have not so far been used in a sustained fashion for weapons purposes which, as per the 'separation plan' accepted by the US, have been set aside to operate at 'low burn-up rates' and output bomb material, India will ultimately have only a relatively small-sized stockpile of WgPu to work with. In that case, the strategic value of the separation plan that earmarked many nuclear facilities earmarked for military use will be zero. Because once the limited store of WgPu in an FMCT regime is used up in weapons/warheads, the 'military use' tag on these military-use installations (including the breeder reactors) will become irrelevant.

In this respect, the Indian government is said to be satisfied with accumulating enough WgPu for an eventual deterrent force of around 100-150 warheads/weapons. This is wilfully to place the country in harm's way because can any of the strategic gurus (such as they are) the Manmohan Singh regime has consulted say with certitude that a strategic force of this strength and one boasting of an array mostly of untested and unproven weapons will suffice in any all conceivable contingencies and crises in the future?

The Indian N-arsenal, according to public sources, of some 80 or so ready 20 KT nuclear weapons, have all used the weapon-grade plutonium (WgPu) obtained mostly from CIRUS and Dhruva. But there are 10 tons of accumulated spent fuel from all the PHWRs operating in the country over the last three-odd decades. This spent fuel, containing heavier isotopes of plutonium (Pu 240, Pu 241, Pu 242), is ill-suited for weapons/warheads, among other drawbacks, because of the uncertainty of the yield of the weapons using this fissile material. In an absolute crisis, there may be no way out other than producing weapons with the spent PHWR fuel. But, surely, this is only a stop-gap, with the real solution lying in converting the spent fuel into WgPu by running it, to begin with, in the prototype fast breeder reactor (PFBR) which may not glitchlessly come on stream until, say, 2012. Moreover, the WgPu so obtained will need several years of cooling-off period before it can be handled to make weapons/warheads. All this requires time, and it is time the nuclear deal does not make available to India. In other words, India's escape hatch will be shut tight.

And that is not all the trouble India faces. The text of the 'Implementation of the July 18, 2005 Joint Statement' is so badly drafted from the Indian point of view (which is not surprising considering that the working draft was of American origin) ~ or, to put it bluntly, acquiesced in by the Indian negotiators led by Foreign Secretary Shyam Saran—that there is every chance that the spent fuel from the indigenous PHWRs sequestered in the civilian sector, could be subjected to international safeguards just because these were products of reactors that will pass under IAEA safeguards. In that case, India's stockpile of spent fuel potentially useable for weapons will shrink alarmingly.

Additionally, Garwin's suggestion that the nuclear civilian energy sector worldwide be enlarged under strict IAEA supervision, is even more directly fulfilled by the India-US deal with the offer of enriched uranium-fueled 1000 MW light water reactors (LWRs) from the US (Westinghouse 1000), France (Areva) and Russia (WER 1000) operating in a closed fuel loop, meaning, exhausted fuel bundles will be replaced periodically from international fuel fabrication centres. Should India import these LWRs with installed thermal capacity of 35,000 MW, it will expend some $50 billion, resulting in handing Washington a powerful lever to get Indian compliance with US demands in the nuclear policy realm as well as outside of it. Assuming the loss of $50 billion is absorbable by a burgeoning Indian economy, India may have to contend with the cut-off of contracted fuel, the shutdown of the imported LWRs, and the loss of 35,000 MW in the grid which could prove economically ruinous for the country. The contract for the supply of fuel for the lifetime of the reactors, it may be recalled, was violated by the US with regard to the Tarapur power station in the wake of India's 1974 nuclear test. Except, that Tarapur was built with US aid monies—so it was no great loss to the Indian exchequer—and the potential loss of electricity was only about 365 MW.

Further, Garwin's design for the GNEP working on proliferation-resistant advanced PHWRs and breeder reactors for universal use under IAEA oversight will seriously benefit from Indian research in it, in the most part because India is, perhaps, the leading country in terms of developing the fast breeder technology. So, the Indian created technologies will go into a finished product which may be sold back to us at a premium—an updated model of classical neo-colonial economics.

At the core of their respective approaches that resulted in the Manmohan Singh-George W. Bush agreement is Garwin's sophisticated all-aspect and comprehensive blueprint for policy that is relentless in reducing any military risk to the United States and acquiring for the US as absolute security as is possible. A friendly India armed with thermonuclear weapons nevertheless complicates the military threat and risk calculus, a complication the United States and the other four so-called NPT-recognized nuclear weapon states would rather do without. It is akin to India's being wary of a nuclearized Iran even though New Delhi is on the friendliest terms with Tehran. And hence the precautions Washington has taken to ensure that the nuclear deal fully defangs India's nuclear stance, even as the latter is allowed symbolically to enjoy the status of a quasi-nuclear weapon state.

Now compare Garwin's hard-edged policy game-plan with the woolly ideas enunciated by K. Subrahmanyam as the intellectual leader of the pro-deal camp, which the Manmohan Singh government has used as scaffolding for its approach; any wonder the ensuing deal has seriously compromised the strategic standing and nuclear security of the country? Subrahmanyam's thesis is that in the emerging international order there will be six great power nodes—the United States, China, Russia, the European Union, Japan, and India, with the dominant country, the United States, being increasingly stretched militarily and hence needing the help of countries, like India, to shoulder the burden of regional security.

So far so unexceptionable (this being a theme many international relations theorists have expounded over the years). But it is Subrahmanyam's follow-on premise that is problematic and which is this: As there is a potential rival, China, for the US to contend with, it is in American interest to help India become a weighty power to counter-balance China in Asia. The fact that there is no instance in history of an extant great power helping a lesser state become a great power, did not deter Subrahmanyam. His arguments on behalf of the nuclear deal was based on a questionable belief that India can play a system 'balancer' but without possessing the necessary strategic military wherewithal of consequential thermonuclear warheaded Inter-Continental Ballistic Missile forces. Great Britain's 'continental strategy' of the 18th and 19th centuries relied on the decisive military force of that time, the Royal Navy, to balance the continental powers. Able to control the European littoral, it could at any time blockade an adversary country and stage uncontested landings of armies led by a Marlborough or a Wellington on the side of the weaker state or alliance of states. An India that has been rendered incapable of ever achieving even 'notional parity' with China—a second tier nuclear weapon country—is unlikely to be able to countervail it. In the event, Subrahmanyam's concept of 'India as balancer' seems to be one of those abstractions that in the real world amount to nothing.

Subrahmanyam's case also hinged on his swallowing whole the US Secretary of State Condoleeza Rice's essentially self-serving view that Washington needs to help India attain 'major power' status, which Subrahmanyam has hailed as a revolutionary turn in American thinking. Read in conjunction with the ongoing non-proliferation thrust of US policy that prevents the continuous modernization and augmentation of the Indian deterrent, this turns out to be nothing more than a measure to strengthen India's conventional military in the hope that New Delhi can be persuaded to partake of President Bush's 'Global War On Terrorism' and democracy-building missions requiring 'boots on the ground' which the US and its closest European allies are growingly unwilling to supply. So, this it turns out, is only a ruse to farm out the military low-end, dirty, work to India.

But an apparently gullible Subrahmanyam is convinced that help rendered India to become a 'major power' will come without strings attached. And he has resorted to citing distorted history to prove the Rice-thesis right. Take. For example, his view that Britain of the last *fin de siecle* 'helped' Japan towards great power status in a bid to neutralize the imperial expansionism of Czarist Russia in Asia. This is nonsense. The facts are that by the late 19th century Britain and Japan were nearly equal powers in the Far East—they had about equal warship tonnage in the Far Eastern waters—and had developed huge financial, industrial and political stakes in China and Korea. The two countries came by these possessions, because Japan successfully prosecuted a war against China in 1894-95 and Britain because of its penetration of that country as a result of the Opium War and the 'open door' policy of the 1870s, which permitted the US and several West European countries to exploit a weak and enervated China.

To protect these investments from being contested by militarily strong Russia and France is why in January 1902 Japan and Britain agreed on a naval alliance. It obligated the signatories to remain neutral if one or the other side went to war but to come to the assistance of the country attacked by France or Russia. The naval treaty from the Japanese perspective was a preventive measure that ensured the Royal Navy did not expediently side with the Czar's Pacific Fleet based in Vladivostok, which the Japanese Admiralty had intended to crush and which the Japanese Imperial Navy accomplished in the 1905 Battle of the Tsushima Straits.

The other example Subrahmanyam repeatedly brought up was equally off the historical mark. He talked about US playing the 'China card' strategically to distract the Soviet Union in the Cold War and its help to Beijing to strengthen the Chinese economy by having it plug into the international economic system. In both instances, the necessary prior condition for cooperation between Japan and Britain in the first case and between the United States and China in the second case was that in these two cooperative dyads the countries involved were dealing with each other as near equals because of the existing deterrence between them.

Thus Britain was on par militarily and industrially with Japan, which after the Meiji restoration in 1867-68 had frenetically westernized itself and acquired a modern military, before re-discovering its nationalist roots in Confucianism and the Shinto religion. China, has firmed its Communist identity and by 1967 achieved long range nuclear missile deterrence *vis-a-vis* the United States and by conventional military means defeated the Soviet Union on the Ussuri River in 1969. In the event, Washington woke up to the heft that Beijing carried, and hence to the possibility of an informal Sino-American partnership discomfiting Moscow.

These two historical examples, in any case, have no relevance to the India-United States deal, considering India is nowhere near having an effective strategic deterrent against China, what to speak of the most powerful state, which alone will win it respect. After this analyst pointed out his flawed history ('George's Nuclear Durbar', *The Asian Age*, 1 March 2006), Subrahmanyam and his media cohort stopped using these cases to buttress their case for the N-deal. The more troubling nature of the public championing by Indian analysts of this N-deal is that it aims to exactly realize the 'intellectual barrier' against India's nuclear military advancement that Garwin had advocated be set up.

The only worthwhile lesson history teaches is that strength respects only strength, and that the political value of strategic military wherewithal—naval might in the 19th century-early 20th century and thermonuclearized ICBM forces in the nuclear age—is the decisive pivot for balancing interests. And it is the absence of this strategic wherewithal that conspicuously marks out India as a mere pretender to great power status. This is not because the Indian nuclear weapons and missile programmes cannot deliver on high yield thermonuclear weaponry and intercontinental ballistic missiles. But because the Indian government has deliberately disabled their capability by agreeing to this nuclear deal and thereby prevented them from doing so. The present set of Indian rulers, like their colonial-era counterparts, are verily the Calibans of a new age. They would rather be a cog in someone else's machine, and work to make India into a part of some other country's security architecture.

If the Manmohan Singh government were serious about making India a great power, it would articulate an Asia-girdling vision, an 'Indian Monroe Doctrine' for a start (which I had fleshed out as a more substantive version of Jawaharlal Nehru's impracticable 'Asian Monroe Doctrine' idea, over twelve years ago in my book *Future Imperilled: India's Security in the 1990s and Beyond*) to encompass the entire Indian Ocean basin on the seaward side and the landmass stretching from the Caspian, Central Asia to the Vietnamese littoral on the South China Sea and to provide the geopolitical justification for sizable Indian nuclear and conventional military forces.

Had the Manmohan Singh government this kind of geopolitical vision, the Indian negotiating team could have reasonably insisted that the CTBT-type restrictions and an imminent FMCT would be acceptable: (i) only after India had built up its WgPu holdings to the level of 75% of the mean of the estimated total fissile material stockpile figures for the US, China and Russia, and (ii) if the US, and by extension the other four NPT weapon states, agreed not to modernize or replace the current warheads/weapons in their inventories with new more innovative designs (see my 'Why the nuclear deal is a disaster', *The Asian Age*, 18 March 2006). The US would, of course, have rejected any such conditions. But it would have provided evidence to Washington that India cannot any more be trifled with.

But such a course of action would have required great power convictions on the part of Prime Minister Manmohan Singh, which he does not have. He would rather, it seems, wallow in the comfortable nonsense of riding piggyback on America to get somewhere, except that somewhere is a dependency station. Alas, it is a *denouement* that conforms with New Delhi's unwillingness to make the hard choices primarily because it sees India as a great power on its merits but as a form of social entitlement, like some backward caste seeking to go up in the world on the basis of a quota. But because international politics is not an exercise in social consciousness raising or charity, the chances of India's becoming a great power on the cheap are nil. This is ironical because in the early years of the 21st century India has growingly the resources. If only the Indian government had the confidence to articulate a rising nation's sense of itself, a matching grand strategic vision and, most crucially, the will to realize it.

(*Seminar*, April 2006, pp. 37-41)

5. The India-United States Rapprochement, the Nuclear Deal, and the Indian National Interest

"Nations have pursued self-interest more frequently than high-minded principle and have competed more than they have cooperated. There is little evidence to suggest that this age-old mode of behavior has changed, or that it is likely to change in the decades ahead."

Henry A. Kissinger, Diplomacy

Democracies, according to a popular thesis, are less likely to go to war against each other, in part, because extreme positions are supposedly eschewed by popularly-elected governments, whence the likelihood of compromise short of conflict.[1] While the empirical evidence for this belief is contested,[2] there is little doubt that, by and large, democratic countries share a certain community of interests and tend to conciliate differences. The fact of commonality of political systems and values do not, however, preclude a genuine clash of national interests which can lead to serious disaffection with each other, if not armed hostilities.

A potential clash is looming between India and the United States on the nuclear deal once its extremely adverse consequences begin to take effect and Indian governments down the road, reacting to popular sentiment, distance themselves from it, hold the Congress Party coalition government headed by Manmohan Singh responsible for this transaction, and blame a perfidious United States for the resulting strategic emasculation of the country. If the Indian government has stressed the deal as facilitating a speedy enlargement of the nuclear energy sector in the country with the help of imported enriched uranium-fueled reactors, the United States has all along had in mind the realization of its longstanding three-pronged non-proliferation objective of "capping", freezing" and "rolling back" the Indian nuclear weapons capability. As it has turned out, Washington has achieved the first two goals at the expense of India's strategic security, which the Manmohan Singh government has paid little attention to.

These negative aspects of the nuclear deal are bound, sooner or later, to boomerang on India's relations with the US. Should this happen, America, having incorporated India—the last major non-proliferation hold-out in the existing Non-Proliferation Treaty order as a *dejure* non-nuclear weapon state—is bound to be non-plussed by India's embittered attitude and begin to react adversely. And the bilateral relations will get locked into a downward spiral. From a "win-win", the situation will quickly become "lose-lose."

A Brief Historical Sketch of the India-US Rapprochement

In 2003, the Bharatiya Janata Party (BJP) prime minister Atal Bihari Vajpayee, when initiating the thaw in India-United States relations, described India and the United States as "natural allies". The somewhat quirky relationship between the largest democracy, one of the two fastest-growing economies in the world and, growingly, a "brain power" and (owing to the comparative skill and manpower cost advantages) manufacturer of choice to rival China in the world, on the one hand, and the richest democracy and, since World War Two, the driver of the global economy on the other hand, was always anomalous and bound, sooner or later, to be transformed into one of sustained, mutually beneficial, engagement.

Located on near opposite ends of the earth, there is no serious clash of geostrategic interests other than that potentially precipitated by a rising India's legitimate great power ambitions and "sphere of influence"—imperatives grating against the United States' *status-quo*-oriented geopolitics. The two countries are conservative by nature, by and large inclined to preserve the extant regional and international order, to which end, are prepared to join in cooperative security ventures in the extended region. Geopolitical logic and strategic expediency, in other words, naturally propel the two countries towards each other. Especially as an intimate India-US partnership has the capacity to contain China, stabilize Asia, restore order to endemically strife-ridden regions of the Gulf, Afghanistan and Central Asia, bring order to international energy politics centred on the oil-rich Gulf states, police the Indian Ocean basin, including the waters east of the Malacca Straits to prevent the threats of piracy and gun- and dope-running from becoming an uncontrolled menace and, generally, as the then Indian defence minister Franab Mukherjee (now minister for external affairs) put it, to meet the "security deficit" in the extended region.[3]

U.S. strategic stakes in such an arrangement are plain enough. But for three decades, 1950s-1980s, Washington's interest in South Asia was limited to beefing up Pakistan as a frontline state and "balancing" India in the subcontinent as part of its globe-girdling policy of defeating its ideological rival, the Soviet Union, in the Cold War. In the early years, this attitude coexisted with U.S. policies that perceived India as offering a political and economic development alternative to communist China for the developing states of the *tiers monde*. This dual-track policy meshed with Nehru's *sly realpolitik,* resulting in massive economic aid from the West, stealthy help from the U.S. and the United Kingdom to build up Nehru's personal prestige and credibility and that of the Non-Aligned Movement (NAM) he co-founded as a third bloc of nations able to act as the balancer in the larger East-West ideological conflict and able to draw the allegiance of the bulk of the Third World States away from the USSR and the Soviet-type authoritarian polity and statist economy. But Washington and London went much beyond this and provided India with overarching strategic military security against both internal Communist revolution and external aggression from the Soviet Union-aided Maoist China.[4] Indeed, it is still not sufficiently appreciated by Indian and foreign historians and strategic analysts just how much India was part of the Western security alliance system in the two decades following the end of the Second World War. A 1958 Pentagon plan, for instance, outlined the deployment of a massive expeditionary "task group" for "the defence of India" against communist subversion and the China threat, comprising two aircraft carrier task forces, Marine Expeditionary Groups with integral air, and US Airborne and Army Divisions.[5] Complementing this conventional military effort was the US-UK nuclear umbrella, which actually opened over India during the 1962 war with China.[6]

Sixties onwards, New Delhi discovered the political gains from balancing interests by plugging into the Russian military supply system. It led to the latest military armaments in the Indian order-of-battle purchased on easy credit, repayable at 2% interest over 17 years, some of it in kind. India, through a rupee-rouble arrangement, had a guaranteed market for its produce (foodstuffs, tobacco and other agricultural commodities) and light manufactures and cotton textiles. The downside was the Soviet Union's "short-reins"-policy of using the level of spares-support and servicing to upkeep its military hardware transferred to India as leverage over Indian politico-military decisions. But, even in its most dependent condition—and at the lowest point in India-US relations during the Richard Nixon presidency—when President Leonid Brezhnev sought New Delhi's support in 1972 for a Soviet-sponsored collective security system for Asia, prime minister Indira Gandhi countered with an "Asian security" system, demanding that both super powers get out and stay out of the continent.[7]

The strategic reappraisal of India by the United States began in the Ronald Reagan Administration when India was assessed as a potential strategic partner in the region and counterweight to China in Asia. An American policy expressly to cultivate India with offers of modern military equipment and advanced technology was mooted. U.S. Defence Secretary Casper Weinberger's visit to Delhi in 1985 along with his aides, in particular the sinologist Michael Pillsbury, was a path-breaking one in that it sought to snip off the military supply umbilical sustaining the India-USSR relations and to replace the USSR with the US as the main purveyor of capital military hardware, and thereby erode, in slow stages, the Soviet influence in India and the extended region while bolstering the American presence in the country and firming up a strong front against a militarily ambitious China. This American initiative did not go far in part because Washington was unable or unwilling to muster the necessary political will at a time when Pakistan and the Taliban cadres organized by the Pakistan Army's Inter-Services Intelligence, acting under Central Intelligence Agency's guidance, were proving to be an effective tool in frustrating Soviet occupation forces and in finally ending their stay in Afghanistan.[8] Under the circumstances, from the American point of view alienating Islamabad did not seem politically wise.

Updated Reaganite thinking is at the core of President George W. Bush's India policy. Except that India is a far more attractive "strategic partner" now than it was some 20 years ago owing to a stable, resolutely democratic, polity with a high economic growth rate over the last decade, and its emergence on the world scene as an Information Technology generator and "brain power" and increasingly a strong competitor with China as the preferred source of manufactures for the global market.[9] In military terms, moreover, India compensates for the manifest U.S. weaknesses in terms of strategic reach,[10] manpower,[11] and cultural affinity. India adjoins the Gulf and Central Asia— regions India has historically and culturally been closely connected with over the millennia, and an Indian military intervention in support of a friendly regime or to keep the peace, say, would be far less friction-full than any kind of interference by the United States. Also, India's military experience since Independence of conducting hard anti-guerilla operations but with a delicate touch (i.e., with minimum collateral damage and without radically alienating the local populations) against assorted insurgencies is in stark contrast to the American way of war let loose on unsuspecting peoples (like in Iraq, for instance), which is guaranteed to seed more strife and create enemies where none existed before. Most of these areas have traditionally constituted India's backyard and with whom cultural and religious ties (not always benign, because these regions also sourced many of the landward invasions into the subcontinent) go back at least half a millennium (in modern historical time). Indians and the Indian government instinctively know how to get along with the peoples and states in these parts, unlike Americans and the U.S. government.

With Washington always finding itself facing more trouble than it can handle, a strategic partner like India eases the situation immensely, especially if New Delhi joins in cooperative security and agrees to share in some compatible ventures. India's value as a fellow democracy and free market system, with an albeit colonial-era military history of keeping the peace in the entire Indian Ocean basin and, landwards, in the expanse from the Gulf and the Caspian to the Central Asian Republics, is at a premium. Thus, during the war to unseat Saddam Hussein in Iraq, Indian warships escorted US naval convoys through the Malacca Straits. And, responding to the pleadings by Washington, the BJP government in late 2003 almost agreed to send Indian army units to Iraq as part of the coalition forces active in that country.

Such military involvement by India, it was hoped, would, among other things, overcome the usual cultural disconnect between the U.S.-led coalition forces in Iraq and other possible Asian trouble spots, and the local peoples. Much as it might wish to, the United States simply cannot keep Asian order by itself. It has to have strong, like-minded, regional countries as members, of what General Colin Powell, Secretary of State during U.S. President George W. Bush's first term, in March 2003 called, a "coalition of the willing", a phrase first used by the UN Secretary General Kofi Annan on February 29, 2000 in relation to the peacekeeping operations in East Timor. Annan was reporting to the Security Council on his visit to South East Asia.[12] President Bush has since then amended the concept to the "coalition of the willing for freedom", thereby excluding authoritarian states, like China, and countries with unsatisfactory democratic systems, like Russia.[13]

The Indian Army and Air Force units have established a base in Ainee, Tajikistan, from where a watch is kept on the goings-on in the vicinity and training is imparted to the Tajikistan Air Force.[14] Besides complementing the U.S. military presence in Bishkek in Kazakhstan, such an outpost outflanks Pakistan and forms an air-bridge to enable India materially to assist the Hamid Karzai government in Afghanistan and friendly regimes in the Central Asian Republics, setting India up as a friendly in-region provider of security.[15] In fact, "military and naval diplomacy" is fast becoming a lynchpin of the country's relations with nations in the extended neighbourhood. Annual naval exercises, MILAN, hosted by the Indian Navy for the littoral navies, for instance, have had a particularly beneficial effect in changing the attitudes of the South East Asian militaries and governments towards India. At the higher level of military exchanges is the manifold increase in high level official dialogues, strengthening of military-to-military links with frequent joint and combined air, army, special forces and the annual naval 'Malabar' exercises.[16] The growing India-U.S. military intimacy was formalized with the 'New Framework for the U.S.-India Defence Relationship' agreed upon three weeks before the visiting Indian PM and President Bush initialed the 'Joint Statement' on July 18 (2005) for civilian nuclear cooperation.

The theoretical foundation for this approach was laid a few years earlier by Richard N. Haass, former Director, Policy Planning, at the U.S. State Department, who articulated the U.S. role in the post-Cold War era as one of "a reluctant sheriff compelled by the prevailing anarchy and by the unwillingness and/or inability of any other power to take on the burden of minding the global law and order business, to step up and do so. When international norms are conspicuously violated and, as a result, inter-state conflict with wider ramifications breaks out or some egregious peace-endangering act is committed, U.S.' brief, according to Haass, is to embark on strong punitive or preemptive action with the help of friendly countries to restore "normalcy", deter "rogue" nations, bring outlaw states to book, and, in the case of especially threatening states, to affect a "regime change".[17]

New Delhi's interest in such a strategic partnership is because, the Indian government believes, it legitimates the country's ambition and role beyond the subcontinent and establishes its strategic intent in the international arena, which hitherto was minimal. The more questionable basis for New Delhi's newly kindled desire for linking up with the U.S. is the thesis propounded by the Secretary of State Condoleeza Rice that America would help India become a "major power".[18] But, to what end? Presumably, to help the United States maintain its predominance. The thrust of the American approach in realizing this goal being primarily military, India's usefulness has to be established in this realm.

The increased frequency and technical complexity of military-to-military interactions in the form of army, special forces, air force and naval exercises involving the armed forces of the two states, serve this purpose. They have resulted in better appreciation of each other's capabilities, sharpened the professional skills of the participating combat arms, provided American forces with operational skill-sets required in different terrains and contingencies— the hallmark of the Indian Army, in particular, and obtained a measure of interoperability. All of which factors are expected to facilitate cooperative security ventures in the future to, for instance, neutralize the threat of international terrorism and, while formally disavowed, to achieve the objective of containing China. The Theatre Security Cooperation Plan unveiled by the Pentagon in 2005[19] and the third Quadrennial Defense Review published in early 2006[20] make these strategies clear. And these are implicit in the 'New Framework for the US-India Defence Relationship'.

The considerable convergence of Indian and US interests in the economic, political and military spheres as Washington sees it will not, however, be at the expense of its hoary policy of arming Pakistan with military hardware (F-16 aircraft, Harpoon anti-ship missiles, etc.) in order to maintain rough conventional military partly in the sub-continent.[21] And, it grows particularly thin in the policy realm where America's traditional nonproliferation concerns run smack into the natural growth path of India's nuclear arsenal as attribute of the country's great power aspirations. It is this latter divergence which is at the heart of the Deal that both the Indian and US governments have tried to paper over. Indeed, except in the harsh arena of inter-state relations where thermonuclear weapons and intercontinental ballistic missiles are the *ultima Thule*, the prospects are bright for mutually beneficial politico-military linkages of a close kind to emerge in the years to come. Then again, this last is what is imperiled by a skewed nuclear deal hurtful of Indian nuclear strategic interests, as the following sections will show.

The Dynamics of the Nuclear Deal

A nuclear weaponized India has always been hard for Washington to stomach. While the Indian scientific and technological capability to obtain nuclear weapons was never doubted by the U.S. government—Intelligence assessments since the late 1950s kept warning of the imminence of the Indian Bomb—Washington has been wary of another state joining the exclusive nuclear club and upsetting its own and the global strategic calculi. After a period of waffling up until the early 1960s when the emergence of a nuclear China gave Washington pause for thought, the U.S. finally settled on an antagonistic approach. It first sought to use the moral card, using India's moral pretensions against the country by-pointing to the immorality of nuclear weapons that sat ill with India's high moral posture. This was succeeded by arguments about nuclear weapons being unaffordable by a dirt-poor country, followed by sustained economic arm-twisting (at a time when India was in dire need of imported food grain and development grants-in-aid and assistance). Whence, America's infamous "ship-to-mouth" policy, which predicated continued US Public Law 480 food and development aid on India's cutting down its military expenditures generally, foregoing the Bomb and, after 1967, signing the Non-Proliferation Treaty, in particular. The aim was to keep India as a permanent nuclear threshold state. After the 1974 nuclear test, India faced the brunt of economic sanctions and technology denial. The Nuclear Suppliers' Group (NSG) and the Missile Technology Control Regime (MTCR) were bolted into place.

In the wake of the 1998 Shakti series of nuclear and thermonuclear tests, the immediate reaction was imposing economic sanctions, which were found by the U.S. to be counterproductive because other countries used the American absence from the scene to bolster their economic presence in India.[22] Whence a new, more nuanced, approach to tackling a now nuclear weapon possessing India was introduced. The Administration of President Bill Clinton had success in convincing the Bharatiya Janata Party-led coalition government, vide the 19 rounds of strategic dialogue between the Deputy Chairman of the Planning Commission and later Minister for External Affairs, Jaswant Singh, and the U.S. Deputy Secretary of State Strobe Talbott, in getting New Delhi to restrain the Indian strategic programmes, especially long range missile projects.[23] Thus, the Indian intercontinental ballistic missile project was put on ice and the nuclear-powered submarine project slowed down.[24]

But, cognizant of Washington's longstanding non-proliferation interest in getting India into the NPT net but desirous of a genuine rapprochement with the U.S., prime minister Atal Bihari Vajpayee forged a new policy. Believing that India needed advanced technology on a priority basis, the Vajpayee Administration concluded that civilian nuclear trade was "the key" to accessing advanced Western dual-use technologies.[25] The then National Security Adviser

Brajesh Mishra as a gambit offered to place "14 out of the 22" nuclear power plants operating or under construction under international safeguards. The U.S. government, espying the possibilities, approved of these developments and, to maintain momentum and, in return, for India's becoming part of the extant non-proliferation system, promised freer access and transfer of advanced technologies, including civilian nuclear technology and, in the economic field, a greater volume and faster flow of capital to finance and sustain India's economic growth, as *quo*.

While Mishra and the BJP leadership now claim that the deal they had in mind in no way "capped" or otherwise curtailed the qualitative and quantitative growth of the country's nuclear forces,[26] the fact is, they had placed India on a slippery slope. Once a great power espies perceives slippage, however small, on the part of a lesser state, the pressure on the latter to concede more and more becomes irresistible. Be that as it may, having wedged its foot in the Indian nuclear door, America was not about to ease up and let go of the opportunity. It used the promise of civilian nuclear technology to push India into the non-proliferation corner, only because the Vajpayee government made access to "advanced technology" the litmus test of good relations.[27] It eventuated in the so-called "New Strategic Steps for Partnership"—a series of measures (like changes in export control laws) taken mostly by New Delhi to prevent any leakage to third parties of such US technology as is bought or transferred to India. The successor Congress coalition regime not only tacked to the same wind but built hugely on it.

Prime Minister Manmohan Singh, using Mishra's nuclear plan-form, has justified the deal on two counts. One, that India will benefit from, not nuclear technologies *perse*—because India's primarily dual-use plutonium-oriented nuclear programme is in a different technology stream to the uranium-based economy the US and most other nuclear supplier countries subscribe to and, therefore, has very little to gain technology-wise from outside powers—but from the import of power reactors to meet dire energy shortfalls. And, more immediately, for India to procure enriched uranium fuel needed for the two American-origin light water reactors installed in Tarapur in the 1960s, and to buy natural uranium ore to run the indigenous Heavy Water moderated natural uranium-fueled CANDU/INDU reactors—the work horse of the Indian nuclear energy programme on the world market, from Namibia and Niger in Africa, and Canada and Australia.

The 18 July 2005 Joint Statement signed by Dr Manmohan Singh and George W. Bush in its operative part had the U.S. President stating that "as a responsible state with advanced nuclear technology"—which phrase has been crucially misinterpreted by the Indian government as formal acknowledgement of India's nuclear weapons status, leading to India "acquir[ing] the same benefits and advantages as other such states." Bush also undertook to "adjust U.S. laws and policies" and to "work with friends and allies to adjust international regimes, to enable full civilian nuclear energy cooperation and trade with India" and India's inclusion in the International Thermonuclear Experimental Reactor project and the Generation IV International Forum or the GNEP (Global Nuclear Energy Partnership) tasked to develop new, more efficient, but proliferation-resistant power reactors. In response, the Indian Prime Minister promised that "India would reciprocally agree. ... to assume the same responsibilities and practices and acquire the same benefits and advantages as other leading countries with advanced nuclear technology, such as the United States." Among the "responsibilities and practices" listed in the Joint Statement are "identifying and separating" military-use and civilian-use nuclear facilities and programmes, placing the civilian-use elements under the International Atomic Energy Agency safeguards, "adhering to an Additional Protocol" negotiated with IAEA, "continuing India's unilateral moratorium on nuclear testing, working with the United States for the conclusion of a multilateral Fissile Material Cutoff Treaty", taking steps to refrain from transferring uranium enrichment and plutonium reprocessing technologies and "adhering" to the export control system followed by the Nuclear Suppliers' Group and the Missile Control Technology Regime. The two sides also agreed to "undertake on a phased basis in the months ahead the necessary actions mentioned above to fulfil these commitments".[28]

Prime Minister Manmohan Singh justifying the nuclear deal emphasized in a *suo motu* statement in Parliament that the proposed steps would be based strictly on the "reciprocity" principle, that the choice of what to include in the list of civilian-use facilities would be entirely India's to make and, in reply to the criticism by the BJP that his government had fallen into the trap of agreeing to "cap" the Indian nuclear arsenal, referred to the "voluntary" nature of India's nuclear moratorium on testing, which qualifier, incidentally, is absent in the Joint Statement.[29] He also stated in Parliament on 29 July 2005 that India would be bound by the same safeguards system and Additional Protocol as followed by a nuclear weapon state such as the U.S., which permits the switching of civilian-use facilities to military use at will. But contrary to all these assurances, the actions of the two countries have, owing to prodding and pushing by-the U.S., got into a sequential mode rather than being in lockstep as the reciprocity principle mandates, which the Manmohan Singh government has accepted. And, the supposedly "India-specific" safeguards India will have to negotiate with the International Atomic Energy Agency (IAEA), it turns out, have to hew to the INFIRG (Information Circular) 66 rev 2 meant for nuclear non-weapon states under the NPT and the Additional Protocol will have to conform to the 1997 standard configured for nuclear non-weapon states.

In the event, first the reciprocity principle was over-turned and a sequencing method put in place requiring India to take the first substantive steps at every stage.[30] According to the original plan, India's deciding on a separation plan was to parallel the George W. Bush Administration move to amend the U.S. Atomic Energy Act, and the next step was to end in India negotiating an appropriate safeguards system and Additional Protocol with IAEA even as the U.S. government persuaded NSG members to reform their guidelines to treat India as an exception and facilitate nuclear trade with it.

The jettisoning of the reciprocity principle by the Manmohan Singh government, however, betrays its desperation to get this deal at any cost and hence its willingness to bend over backwards to accommodate the United States. Thus, New Delhi first produced a separation plan with a comprehensive list of nuclear science research organizations it meant to put in the "civilian" part of the programme, which included nearly 40 nuclear facilities and leading research institutions, like the Tata Institute of Fundamental Research and the Saha Institute of Nuclear Physics.[31] It did so without considering the adverse consequences of this action. Many scientists fear that international policing of the work done by these organizations would critically affect the nature and quality of research, in that remotely weapons-use projects would be shut down.[32] What the Indian government ought to have done was, as per the parity standard implied in the July 18 Statement, used the same criteria for separating its nuclear military and civilian facilities that the United States had used. Washington had in 1979 laid down four criteria for denoting a nuclear facility "civilian" for separation: that (1) it is not used for military purposes, (2) it is not co-located with military-use installations, (3) it is occasionally put to military use, and (4) its inclusion in the safeguards list poses no "incremental risk" to national security.[33] The Indian government has apparently used only the first criterion listed above when alighting on its separation plan. This plan, it is now evident, was expressly designed to adhere to the U.S. government strictures, which the U.S. Under Secretary of State for Arms Control and International Security Affairs Robert G. Joseph in Congressional testimony said needed to be "transparent, flexible and defensible", of course, as perceived by the U.S.

The sequential (rather than a genuinely reciprocal) mode the Indian government acquiesced in resulted in the U.S. Congress getting into a position to impose conditions on the deal not envisaged by the July 18 Joint Statement. The most worrying of these Congressional conditions codified in both the House and the Senate versions of the enabling legislation is an overarching demand that the President annually certify to the U.S. Congress that India is meeting all the conditions among which are the following: that India is making moves to end its production of fissile material, joining the U.S. in finalizing a Fissile Material Cutoff Treaty, not violating or planning to violate its "voluntary" test moratorium in any way, "harmonizing" its missile regime with MTCR, which may require India to ditch any plans for designing, testing and inducting into service IRBMs and ICBMs, and participating in the efforts to "isolate" Iran. In other words, India is required to get a "Good Housekeeping" certificate yearly in the form of a presidential "waiver" from the White House on the pain of the nuclear cooperation being instantly terminated if any of these and other Congressional conditions remain unmet.[34] Incomprehensibly, the Indian government appears fairly unconcerned by these stringent conditions in the proposed preamble to the amended Section 123 of the U.S. Atomic Energy Act.[35] The fact is the U.S. Congress is bent on holding India to the standards dictated by it, as Senator Richard Lugar has made clear.[36] Worse, accepting inappropriate safeguards and Additional Protocol has sealed India's status as a nuclear non-weapon state in international law and in the Non-proliferation Treaty (NPT)-driven global non-proliferation order, something New Delhi had fiercely resisted for over forty years.

The very adverse reaction in India to the skewed notion of reciprocity resulted in a slight modification. On the proffering of the Indian separation plan, it was agreed, the U.S. Congress would amend the 1954 Atomic Energy Act as emended in 1974. But the U.S. legislature's insistence on having a final say consequented in a cleaving of the agreed upon process for reforming the U.S. Atomic Energy Act. The Indian separation plan was to be succeeded by the first stage requiring changes in the language of the Act to permit nuclear commerce with India. This was to be followed by India's negotiating a safeguards system and Additional Protocol as a non-nuclear weapon state with the International Atomic Energy Agency (IAEA). These two documents were then to be the basis on which the U.S. Congress agreed, in the second stage, to stamp the deal with its approval and for the reformed U.S. law to come into force. As far as the second "parity of treatment"-principle implied in the July 18 Statement is concerned, the above narrative proves that India is in no way enjoying the "rights and obligations" of a nuclear weapon state, as Foreign Secretary Shyam Saran had confidently asserted in the wake of the Joint Statement.

The Downside of the Nuclear Deal

The biggest mistake made by prime minister Manmohan Singh was at the very beginning itself. First, by reiterating in the July 18 Joint Statement India's voluntary test moratorium prematurely announced by the previous Bharatiya Janata Party-led coalition government and, secondly, by committing to join the U.S. in negotiating a Fissile Material Cutoff Treaty (FMCT). These two undertakings, in the one case, prevents natural and continuous upgradation of the country's still technologically primitive, unreliable, unproven and unsafe nuclear weapons in line with what the five so-called NPT-recognized powers have been ceaselessly doing over the last forty years, which can only be realized by further testing. And, in the other instance, by acquiescing in the ending of production of weapon-grade plutonium (WgPu)—pursuant to its FMCT obligations—severely limit the size of the country's nuclear arsenal. In a move unanticipated by the Indian government, its American counterpart in May 2006 in a bid to preempt India's strategy of building up its WgPu stockpile even as an FMCT went through usual prolonged negotiating phase in the Commission on Disarmament (CD) in Geneva, introduced a draft FMCT in the Commission on Disarmament in Geneva for expeditious finalization. The traditionally long and pernickety negotiation was, by these means, sought to be short-circuited by Washington by its introducing a U.S. draft treaty in the CD. But this draft that Washington expects New Delhi to support has no verification clause, for instance, which India has all along demanded. And, it incorporates a mechanism to speed-up the treaty negotiating process. Article VI of the draft says that "This treaty shall enter into force on the date on which an instrument of ratification has been deposited" by all the five so-called NPT-recognized nuclear weapon states—P-5 (U.S., Russia, China, France and UK). With the common interest of the P-5 to restrict the size and quality of India's strategic forces, which could upset their individual and collective strategic calculi, these five states could quickly agree on the accord compelling India, on the basis of the India-US nuclear deal, to fall-in with this iniquitous treaty.[37] Plainly, such are the tactics the US has in mind to adopt. Considering how abjectly the Manmohan Singh government has given in to the flattery and cajolery by the George W. Bush Administration into sacrificing India's strategic security interests, Washington may be right in believing it will get what it wants on the FMCT as well.

As a result of this deal for "civilian nuclear cooperation", the U.S. will have achieved two of its three longstanding and premier non-proliferation goals: absorb India in the extant non-proliferation order and, more specifically, "freeze" the quality of the Indian arsenal (with a no-testing regime) and, by insisting India accept Fissile Material Cutoff Treaty restrictions, "cap" the size of the Indian WgPu stockpile and, prospectively, of the Indian deterrent. With the Indian strategic forces still in the initial build-up stage with first generation nuclear weapons, in reality, modernization-wise, the Indian N-weapons inventory is in a stand-still condition relative to the arsenals of the five so-called Non-Proliferation Treaty (NPT)-recognized nuclear weapon states—United States, Russia, China, France and the United Kingdom, who are continually enhancing their nuclear forces, US' third non-proliferation aim of "rolling-back" the Indian nuclear weapons programme becomes moot

This deal, moreover, will fetch the United States a commercial foothold in the Indian civil nuclear energy market. This will no doubt be achieved by Washington pressuring the Indian government into buying big from General Electric (now that the Westinghouse Company along with its leading nuclear reactor design, the AP 1000, has been bought by the Toshiba Corporation of Japan), the assemblies and sub-assemblies (like the turbine, heat-exchanger, etc.) it designs and manufactures. This is expected to translate into

(1) contracts in the next few decades worth as much as Rs. 300,000-400,000 crores for 1000 MWe (megawatt electric) capacity reactors producing a total of 30,000-40,000 MWe of power for the national grid, according to a former Chairman, Atomic Energy Regulatory Board, Dr A. Gopalakrishnan,[38] and, (2) as Secretary of State Condoleeza Rice informed the US Senate Foreign Relations Committee on April 5, 2006, 3,000-5,000 "new direct jobs ... and 10,000 to 15,000 indirect jobs in the United States".[39] The sale of reactors will be on the basis of a "closed loop" arrangement in which the exhausted uranium fuel bundles will be replaced with new ones periodically and the spent fuel shipped back to the reactor-supplying state. The prototype deal is the contract signed with Russia for the Koodankulum power plant with two VVER 1000 reactors. This will end up tying India to U.S.' fuel supply source and, as in the case of the contract for the Tarapur reactors, make it hostage to U.S. policy whims if things go wrong and an energy dependency, if they do not. As a complement to this situation and, for reasons that will be made clear later in this chapter, India will become a security dependency of the United States as well. It was a *denouement* predicted by this writer in August 2005.[40]

But, these up-front costs of imported reactors do not constitute the whole of the price India may have to pay. The U.S.-pleasing separation plan will require a number of critical facilities to be duplicated in the military sector and the bill for this may be as high as several thousands of crores of rupees. This will all be in addition to the higher costs of electricity per MWe produced by these imported reactors, even with a liberal depreciation period of 50 years now allowed the indigenously designed and built CANDU/INDU reactors.

Such an outcome will write *finis* to the visionary three stage plan (of natural uranium reactors being followed by plutonium breeder reactors which, in turn, were to be succeeded by thorium reactors to capitalize on the ample reserves of thorium in the country) articulated by Dr Homi J. Bhabha—the father of the Indian nuclear programme, which was designed by him to ensure energy security and independence for the country. Further, as a newly anointed member of the Global Nuclear Energy Programme (GNEP),[41] courtesy this agreement, India may have to part with its research and experimental data on breeder technology—in which it has the most experience of any country in the world.[42] Adequate compensation for use of India proprietary knowledge under Intellectual Property Rights regime may not be forthcoming. Worse, these Indian inputs will apparently assist the multilateral GNEP develop a proliferation-resistant plutonium breeder, which will be attempted to be sold back to India presumably at a premium.

Among other benefits of the deal, the government has ballyhooed is India's involvement in the ITER (International Thermonuclear Experimental Reactor) project. The consortium of countries working on ITER is supposed to concentrate its efforts to produce a commercially viable fusion reactor based on the "tokomak" principle. Tokomak, originally a Soviet Russian experimental concept, reproduced at the Princeton University in the US, uses high energy magnets to heat plasma to millions of degrees of centigrade to enable fusion of the heavy nuclei of hydrogen to generate power. ITER is unlikely to bear fruit in the next 50-60 years and should not have been taken into account. But it is high technology enough for the Manmohan Singh government to talk of as a prized benefit for India in order to befuddle the Indian public into accepting what, from this country's perspective, is quite simply a bad bargain.

What India should have Done

Assuming that commitments to end testing by, and halt fissile material production in, India were elements of the nuclear deal Washington insisted upon, and this deal was assessed by the Indian government to be absolutely essential to meet the energy deficit and spur fast-paced economic growth—a questionable thesis—Indian negotiators should have countered by sticking unflinchingly to two legitimate and fundamental positions. India should have undertaken to stop testing only after it had first repeatedly tested to obtain safe, proven and reliable array of nuclear and thermonuclear armaments as judged by the Indian military end-user and otherwise to reach the level of confidence that the P-5 militaries have in their respective nuclear arsenals.[43] And secondly, it should have flatly stated that there would be no end to production of WgPu short of India accumulating a stockpile (to cover all possible contingencies) of approximately 34,000 kg or three-quarters the size of the average estimated combined holdings of fissile material by the US, Russia, and China.[44] Calculated on the basis of 5 kg of fissile material per weapon in the operational and inactive weapons inventories of the Big Three, the United States has some 50,000 kg of fissile material, Russia some 80,000 kg, and China over 3000 kg.[45] Such a negotiating stance would have left New Delhi with lots of space and compelled Washington to accept an infinitely bigger fissile material stockpile than it has, by implication, conceded now. Because for many persuasive geopolitical, economic and strategic reasons, it is in the U.S.' national interest to have an India well disposed to it. An all-round stronger India in the future would be in a position to negotiate far better terms in the nuclear and other fields, and all New Delhi needed to do was wait and watch the technology denial regimes (NSG, Missile Technology Control Regime, Wassenar Agreement) come apart, considering that members of these consortia would be scrambling to sell even dual-use technologies to an economic powerhouse India on its terms, if New Delhi conditioned trade and economic relations on this factor.[46] This stance may, perhaps, have put paid to this particular nuclear deal, but it would have seeded tremendous respect for India in the US policy circles. And it is the respect for India that has always been missing and still is in the US' relations with this country.

Why is further testing necessary for India? Because the 1998 tests raised some grave doubts about the thermonuclear and "boosted fission" devices that were exploded.[47] These prototype weapon designs need to be reworked and tested and re-tested in order for them to acquire credibility as operational weapons which can perform reliably and with safety. And this is precisely what the nuclear deal prevents India from doing. An India, with its arsenal quality frozen at a relatively primitive level and with growingly close politico-military linkages, in the circumstances might look to the US for nuclear protection in dire strategic crises. After all, the likely outcome of a confrontation with, for instance, between this country armed with 20 kiloton "fire-crackers" and China with deployed standard warheads in the 1-3.3 megaton yield bracket riding atop their DF-31 IRBMs is entirely predictable. India will back down or seek US' assistance to neutralize the strategic imbalance created by the sheer disparity in the reach and clout of its deterrent compared with China's. In which case, India will slide, willy-nilly, to the status of a strategic nuclear protectorate and security dependency of the United States.

But the acquisition by India of unquestioned strategic might provided by high-yield, preferably megaton, thermonuclear weapons and intercontinental ballistic missiles (ICBMs), other than being able to obtain a strategic impasse with China, has other huge benefits in its train. It will flesh out India's status as a great power, help leverage a bigger say in international affairs, enhance its room for political and economic manoeuvre, legitimate a larger geopolitical footprint and sphere of influence or, to be more politically correct, "sphere of responsibility", define its vital national interests expansively, and preserve the country's strategic independence.[48] A consequential thermonuclear-ICBM force, moreover, will act as force-multiplier for the proven "soft power"[49] of the country.

For the maximum and enduring impact though, a deterrent with high yield weapons with long reach (and not the weak, minimal and ineffective "minimum deterrent" it currendy possesses) has to be coupled with a strategic vision. Such a vision requires enunciation of a grand strategy, say, an "Indian Monroe Doctrine", the ambit of which should cover the East African littoral, the Gulf, Central Asia, Tibet, South Asia and South East Asia, inclusive of Vietnam on the South China Sea. The geographic compass of the Indian Monroe Doctrine described above, incidentally, covers the regions that Governor General, Lord Minto, had included in the concept of "distant defence" he had articulated in the 1810s when British power in the subcontinent was on an upward curve.[50]

But even without such vision, at a minimum, strategic military muscle of the high yield, thermonuclear weapon-ICBM kind will establish the great power bonafides of a country. It is because it acquired such a strategic force at the expense of almost every other national attribute that China first won recognition as a great power from the United States. And, notwithstanding the enormous progress it has made in the economic sectors and as a trading nation since then, China continues to focus on beefing up its strategic military in order some day to surpass the United States in its military reach and clout.[51]

If India's enhanced strategic military power is yoked to a moderate political posture and proactive economic diplomacy to complement its newly confident military and naval diplomacy starting with countries in the immediate neighbourhood and the moving outward, soon an ever-widening circle of friendly but vulnerable countries will be co-opted into an Indian sphere of influence.[52] Thus, will be firmed up an architecture of genuine stability and peace in its "Monroe Doctrine" quadrant earlier delineated, with India at the centre as the fulcrum of security and engine of shared economic prosperity. India's ambitions are no secret. But the path that New Delhi has chosen with the nuclear deal to ride the US coat-tails, will only lead India into a subsidiary ally slot not the great power position it has rightly set its sights on.

NOTES

1. Edward D. Mansfield and Jack Snyder, "Democratization and the Danger of War", *International Security*, Summer 1995.
2. Henry S. Farber and Joanna Gowa, "Politics and Peace", *International Security*, Fall 1995.
3. Mukherjee was speaking in Singapore at the Annual 'Shangrila' Conference of Asian defence ministers hosted by the International Institute of Strategic Studies, London. See P.S. Suryanarayana, "India is a core state for Asian security: Pranab Mukherjee", *The Hindu*, 4 June 2006.
4. Karnad, *Nuclear Weapons and Indian Security: The Realist Foundations of Strategy*, 2nd ed. (New Delhi, Macmillan, 2002, 2005); pp. 74-132.
5. *Ibid*; pp. 132-46.
6. *Ibid*; pp. 146-53.
7. A.G. Noorani, *Brezhnev Plan for Asian Security* (Bombay, Jaico Publishing House, 1975); ch. VII.
8. Steve Coll, *The Ghost Wars: The Secret History of the CIA, Afghanistan, and Bin Laden, from the Soviet Invasion to September 10, 2001* (New York, The Penguin Press, 2004).
9. Anand Giridharadas, "In India, the next great industrial story", *International Herald Tribune*, May 21, 2006.
10. Major Kenneth E. Hickins, "Strategic Mobility: The U.S. Military's Weakest Link", *Commentary*, Nov/Dec. 2002.
11. Frederick Kagan, "The Military's Manpower Shortage", *Foreign Affairs*, July/August 2006.
12. See http://www.sourcewatch.org/index.php?title=Coalition_of_the_willing
13. Stephen Castle, "European Commission chief says Russia not a democracy", *(The Independent, London), The Statesman*, 14 July 2006.
14. Stephen Blank, "India: The new Central Asian player", Centre for Security Studies, Zurich, 29 June 2006 at http://www.isn.ethz.ch/news/sw/details.cfm?ID=16310

15. Lionel Beehner, "Asia: US Military Bases in Central Asia", Backgrounder, Council for Foreign Relations, July 26, 2005 at http://www.cfr.org/publication/8440/

16. Vijay Sakhuja, : Naval Diplomacy: Indian Initiatives" at http://www.bharat-rakshak.com/MONIYOR/lSSUES6-i/Sakliuja.html

17. Richard N. Haass, *The Reluctant Sheriff: The United States After the Cold War* (New York, Council on Foreign Relations, 1997).

18. Background Briefing by Administration Officials on US-South Asia Relations, US Department of State, Washington, DC, March 25, 2006, at http://state. gov/r/pa/prs/ps/2005/22853.htm

19. For the text of the QDR, see http://www.defenselink.mil/qdr/report20060203. pdf

20. For the testimony by C-in-C, US Pacific Command, Admiral William J. Fallon, before the US Senate Armed Services Committee on 7 March 2006 indicating how his Theater Plan may impact South Asia (which falls under PACOM), see http://wvw.pacom.mil/speeches/sst2006/DAR-FY07-Fallon%2003-07-06.pdf

21. Ajay Lele, "US Military Aid to Pakistan: Issues and Concerns", Article No. 75, Society for the Study of Peace and Conflict, June 30, 2006, at http://www. sspconline.org/article_details.asp?artd=art85

22. For the case that economic sanctions usually don't work, see Richard N. Haass, Economic Sanctions and American Diplomacy (New York, Council on Foreign Relations, 1998). For the then external affairs minister Jaswant Singh's take that the US sanctions failed, see his *Call To Honour: In Service of an Emergent India* (New Delhi, Rupa, 2006).

23. For Strobe Tatbott's and Jaswant Singh's accounts of these talks, see respectively, *Engaging India: Diplomacy, Democracy and the Bomb* (Delhi, Penguin-Viking, 2004) and Call to Honour; pp. 270-319.

24. Ashley J. Tellis has argued that it is to US advantage that the Indian N-force remain small, slow and short-legged and hinted that India, as a result of the Jaswant Singh-Strobe Talbott "dialogue", agreed to curb its long range missile development. See his "The Strategic Implications of a Nuclear India", *Orbis*, Vol. 26, No. 1, Winter 2002. External Affairs Minister Jaswant Singh however denies any such compromise was made. See his *Call to Honour;* p. 274.

25. See the speech by Foreign Secretary Shyam Saran on "India-US Joint Statement of July 2005: A Year Later" at the India Habitat Centre, New Delhi, July 14, 2006.

26. Ashley Tellis has indirectly suggested that while the Vajpayee government "did not offer much to the US in exchange for the agreement", "We got more from the government of Dr Manmohan Singh." See Tellis' interview—"Why Vajpayee didn't sign the nuclear deal", Rediffnews at http://ia.rediff.com/cms/print. jsp?docpath=//news/2006/jil/19interl.htm

27. *Ibid.*

28. The text of the 18 July 2005 Joint Statement at http://www.whitehouse.gov/ news/releases/2005/07/20050718-6.html

29. The text of the *suo motu* statement available at http://www.hinduonnet.com/thehindu/nic/suomotuu.htm

30. The US Assistant Secretary for South Asia Richard Boucher has admitted that the reciprocity principle was overthrown. See Seema Mustafa, "Boucher confirms nuke deal sequence change", *The Asian Age,* 19 July 2006.

31. For the details of the Indian separation plan, see the text of the document 'Implementation of the India-United States Joint Statement of July 18, 2005: India's

Separation Plan' tabled in parliament on 7 March 2006 at http://wwwthehindu.com/2006/03/08/stories/2006030808431100.htm

32. P.K. Iyengar and M. Gupta, "India-US deal will destroy nuclear research", *The Asian Age,* 15 April 2006.

33. This analyst had first revealed these American criteria for separation and advised India to use the same. See Bharat Karnad, "Do as the US Would", *The Asian Age,* 4 February 2006.

34. Bharat Karnad, "Why the nuclear deal is a disaster", *The Asian Age,* 18 March 2006.

35. Saran, "India-US Joint Statement of July 2005: A Year Later".

36. See Aziz Haniffa, "Don't nitpick N-bill: US Senator Lugar", Rediffnews at http://ia.rediff.com/news/2006/jul/1 gndeal.htm?q=tp&file=.htm

37. For the US draft FMCT text see http://geneva.mission.gov/Press2006/0518DraftFMCT.html

38. Dr A. Gopalakrishnan, "A Deal of broken assurances", *The Asian Age,* 7 July 2005.

39. See the Opening Remarks by Secretary Rice at the Hearing of the US Senate Foreign Relations Committee, April 5, soo6 at http://www.state.gov/secretary/ rm/2006/64136.htm

40. Bharat Karnad, "A Civilian Nuclear Dependency", *The Asian Age,* 13 August 2005.

41. For some details of the Generation III reactor options being developed by GNEP, see "UK nuclear power: The contenders", *BBC News,* at http://newsvote.bbc.uk/mpapps/pagetools/print/news.bbc.co.uk/shi/science/nature/5

42. Georges Vendryes, "father" of the French breeder reactor program, is of the view that India may become the most advanced country in breeder technology within a decade. See T.S. Subrahmaniam, "India surging ahead in FBR technology", *The Hindu,* July 19, 2006.

43. Bharat Karnad, "Turning India into a nuclear cripple", *The Asian Age,* 7 April 2006.

44. Refer Karnad, "Why the nuclear deal is a disaster".

45. Robert S. Norris and Hans Kristensen, "Global Nuclear Stockpiles, 1945-2006", *The Bulletin of Atomic Scientists,* August 2006; pp. 64-66.

46. I have made this point. See Bharat Karnad, "Blighted strategic future", Seminar, April 2006. Ashley Tellis, former adviser to the US Ambassador Robert Blackwill and brought in by US Under-Secretary of State Nicholas Burns to help push the deal with the Indians recently, while accepting this conclusion has merely inverted my slant, saying: "Reaching out to India and assisting it with nuclear cooperation at a time when it is relatively weak state geopolitically bequeaths the United States with greater dividends than would be the case if such cooperation were offered after India had already become a true great power and a repository of sophisticated nuclear technologies—when New Delhi presumably would have lesser need for such cooperation." See Ashley J. Tellis, *Atoms for War? US-India Civilian Nuclear Cooperation and India's Nuclear Arsenal* (Washington, DC, Carnegie Endowment for International Peace, June 26, 2006); p. 42.

47. For an analysis of the failed tests of the hydrogen bomb and "boosted fission" weapon design, see Karnad, *Nuclear Weapons and Indian Security,* 2nd ed.; pp. 412-420.

48. The costs, force-structuring and the policies attending on a thermonuclear deterrent with maximal strategic effect discussed at considerable length in Karnad, *Nuclear Weapons and Indian Security,* 2nd ed.; ch. V.

49. Joseph S. Nye, Jr. describes the "soft power" of a state as the ability to get what it wants by means of "attraction", not "coercion". See his *Soft Power: The Means to*

Success in World Politics (Cambridge, MA, Perseus Books, 2004).

50. This "Indian Monroe Doctrine" first articulated in Bharat Karnad, "India's Weak Geopolitics and What To do About It" in Bharat Karnad, ed., *Future Imperilled: India's Security in the 1990s and Beyond* (New Delhi, Viking, 1994).

51. Michael Pillsbury, "China's Strategic Outlook: A Case Study of Japan and India" in K. Santhanam and Srikanth Kondapalli (eds.), *Asian Security and China, 2000-2010* (Delhi, IDSA and Shipra Publications, 2004).

52. For a well argued case of the benefits to India from an ambitious economic diplomacy in Central Asia, see Dr Ibrokhim R. Mavlonov, "India's Economic Diplomacy, its Foreign Investment Policy and the Central Asian Nations", *Dialogue Quarterly*, April-June 2006. Dr Mavlonov is a senior official in the Foreign Ministry of Uzbekistan.

(Chapter in Prakash Nanda, ed., *Rising India: Friends and Foes*
[New Delhi & Olympia Fields, IL: Lancer, 2007], pp. 242-263)

6. Indo-US Nuclear Deal: A Debate

A.N. Prasad

As one who has dedicated the entire professional career towards development of nuclear energy in the country and having worked hands-on in some of the most technologically complex and strategically sensitive parts of the nuclear fuel cycle, I feel proud of the phenomenal achievements of the Indian nuclear establishment during the last five decades, practically starting from scratch, inspite of being challenged to work in isolation under international embargoes and restrictions in nuclear trade and cooperation for most of this period. I wish some of this accomplishment had drawn the attention of the media and the public at least a fraction of the way the currently debated Indo-US nuclear deal has caused awareness among almost all sections of society in the country and even beyond!!

Let me put the nuclear deal in some perspective very briefly.

Ever since the non-proliferation treaty (NPT) came into existence in 1970 with India opting out on grounds that it is a discriminatory treaty, dividing the states into 'haves' (nuclear weapons states) and 'have-nots' (non-nuclear weapon states), the US has been trying hard to use every opportunity to somehow bring India into the mainstream of global non-proliferation regime. In fact this has become an obsession with them. Creation of the 45 member Nuclear Suppliers' Group (NSG) led by the US in response to our 1974 nuclear test is one such measure to deny us access to nuclear market and any form of cooperation with the outside world in the nuclear field.

Undaunted, India stood up to the challenge and went on to develop a comprehensive capability not only in building nuclear power plants but also weapons capability. To cap it, India started building a prototype fast breeder reactor, an important step towards achieving utilization of abundant thorium reserves to meet our long-term objective for energy security.

Right from the word go, five decades ago, Dr. Homi Bhabha, the founding father of India's nuclear programme realizing the country's limited known reserves of uranium and vast resources of thorium had, with great vision, postulated the well known three stage programme for achieving energy independence and security in the long-run to be in place when once the conventional energy sources like coal get depleted. In fact this programme has been the guiding principle for our systematic development. It is estimated that the known uranium reserves which could generate a meager 10,000 MW of electricity, if properly managed as per the 3 stage programme envisaged, can generate in excess of 350,000 MW of electricity by thorium utilization. Of course there have been slip ups in uranium exploration and mining which have become bottle-necks in the short-term for nuclear energy production which need to be urgently addressed on a war footing politically as well as scientifically. Though imports could, on the face of it, appear attractive to get over short-term interests, the implications of the strings attached to the long-term interests of our energy security and independence need to be carefully assessed.

There is no doubt in my mind that India growing in strength to become a force to recon with in the nuclear field, far ahead of many of the economically advanced countries, has caught the eyes of the world. The world has realized that punitive measures to restrict determined India are not having the desired effect. In fact in the various international meetings I have attended India is treated with respect as an advanced country in the nuclear field. It may be in this context the US has taken the initiative to open up cooperation with India. Inherrent strength counts.

If you look at the joint statement issued by President Bush and Prime Minister Manmohan Singh on July 18, 2005 one can see the respect with which India has been addressed. There was recognition of India as a responsible state, technologically advanced and deserving to be treated at par with advanced countries like the US! Though there were some pin-pricks in the statement, the joint statement as a whole was welcomed by us hoping that there is at last a realization, though belated, of our strength and capability to play a global role as equal partner in the advancement of nuclear science and technology.

However as the subsequent development of this historic initiative unfolded it is evident that all the sweet words are only restricted to paper, that too the initial joint statement. Inspite of India, with even the Prime Minister expressing concerns about the change in goal posts, US has gone ahead and produced the voluminous Henry Hyde Act specifically giving prescriptions as to how we should behave if the bilateral cooperation has to survive spelling out repercussions if we decide to cross the lines they have drawn. A shameful and demeaning treatment meted out to tarnish our pride and self-respect.

As one goes deep into the details of the agreement it becomes quite clear that as far as the US is concerned, the deal is more to meet at least three objectives, viz. (1) bringing India into the mainstream of global non-proliferation agenda by taking all possible measures to cap and work for a roll back of its strategic programme, (2) exploit the Indian market for nuclear energy at the same time using our resources to revive their nuclear industry which is dormant since late 70's, and (3) make India a strategic partner in this part of the world in line with their foreign policy objectives. In essence, instead of India being treated as an equal partner, is made a client state subjected to periodic assessment and certification of good behavior!

The above may seem to be a harsh assessment of the intentions of the deal and the supporters including our government may play it down by saying that the deal will lift India out of isolation, help ending nuclear apartheid, gain access to global market and will ensure energy security. All these claims are debatable. The 123 agreement, the text of which is a fine work of craftsmanship in drafting and camouflaging the core issues by clever use of language is being touted as the main document governing the deal belittling the Hyde Act which has been formulated and passed as a legal US national document with great care specifically to fix the parameters of the deal exclusively for India. Essentially what the 123 document seems to ensure is, during the course of the operation of the deal, India will be given ample opportunities for consultations on any issue of divergence with the final decision resting with the US since their national laws being stringent and explicit with India having no leverage in the absence of any matching national laws. In fact there is no provision for arbitration if there is disagreement!

Let me briefly touch upon some of the major concerns not adequately addressed in the proposed agreement.

There is a systematic attempt on the part of the supporters of the deal to underplay the significance of the consequences if India were to conduct a nuclear test in supreme national interest. While there is nothing in the deal which legally prevents us from going in for a test if the situation so demands, the US law is very clear that the deal will be off and they reserve the right of return of all materials and equipment supplied. After investing billions of dollars in importing reactors and building huge infrastructure, which government in future will be able to take a decision in favour of tests and face economic catastrophe? For all practical purposes the option of testing will be as good as dead and remains only in theory. There may be strong views being expressed from influential quarters within the serving scientific community that weapon designs do not require actual testing but could be done by computer simulation. How reliable such an untested device, its quality, yield and effectiveness as a deterrent will all be questionable in view of the assumptions involved in computer simulation data. Certainly there will be a great compromise in maintaining truly effective deterrence with fast changing global situation and in particular in the region we are in with our neighbours having no such constraints. In fact the US perhaps would not have taken up this initiative of relaxing the nuclear cooperation norms if we had not conducted the tests in 1998. One should not undermine strength. While testing is a political decision, it is unfair to make the scientists responsible for producing an effectively deployable device without the option of testing. Effective, credible deterrence and testing are complimentary.

There is no unambiguous clarity in the deal about the assurances of supply of uranium while at the same time our commitments are to be in perpetuity regarding safeguards inspections. In fact shortage of uranium being the main trigger for us to go into this deal, this ought to be handled with great care. Our own experience in the past with the US on Tarapur agreement has been far from satisfactory. US will try to keep us in tenterhooks on this issue and prevent us from building a strategic reserve. Even if we are allowed to stock, in case of trouble they may invoke right of return. This is a serious area of concern which is also to be tied up with the IAEA safeguards agreement in terms of corrective measures we propose to take in case of disruption.

Another area of concern is, full civil nuclear cooperation. Though this has not been qualified in the initial joint statement of July 18, 2005, in all further documents right upto the final version this has been redefined leaving out major portions of the complex parts of the fuel cycle such as uranium enrichment, spent fuel reprocessing and heavy water production stating that these are sensitive technologies. By this, it is not full civil nuclear cooperation on offer but only a part which is of commercial interest, namely, supply of power reactors. We seem to be meekly surrendering to this serious change in their stand without even protesting. Added to this, while nothing is on offer as far as reprocessing is concerned, the 123 agreement stipulates all sorts of conditions for reprocessing spent fuel of imported uranium origin. This after we having 40 years of experience in this field. I see some deep rooted motive in putting hurdles on our reprocessing activity which is at the core of our 3 stage power programme. Here again we are still stuck with a bitter experience of stock-piling spent fuel from Tarapur reactors without any clearance from the US for reprocessing. The way the provision for reprocessing is worded in the 123 agreement, I suspect a trap to ultimately make the dedicated reprocessing we have agreed to build as a multinational facility or force it to come under international control.

If one were to take a holistic picture of the balance sheet of the plus and minus points, not all of which are quantifiable, the situation could be as follows. There could be respite in the short-term in gaining access to uranium to fuel the operating reactors and those under construction, getting foreign investments in building additional capacity in power generation though at much higher cost, and possible opportunity to interact with global nuclear community in certain areas.

On the flip side, by making us getting hooked on to the uranium fuelled reactors there could be less incentive to fund in a big way fast breeder reactor programme for power generation quoting resource crunch, and slow down the 3 stage programme affecting long-term energy independence using thorium and make us external uranium dependent.

The irony is, through this deal we are trying to achieve energy independence by becoming dependent on uranium imports with all the implications for national security! Though the percentage nuclear power contribution to the national power grid appears insignificant at present, the technological base has advanced to an extent that should help accelerating the pace of generation in the years to come. Even with imports the generation capacity is not expected to increase substantially. Need of the hour is patience and staying on course to redouble our efforts to reach the ultimate goal of thorium utilization which only can bring India real independent energy security. Short cuts like the one being contemplated through this deal could land us neither here nor there and may be left hanging.

(Paper presented at a Seminar on the Nuclear Deal at the Indian Institute of Management, Ahmedabad, Oct/Nov. 2007))

ANNEXURES

India-U.S. Joint Statement

Washington, DC
July 18, 2005

Prime Minister Manmohan Singh and President Bush today declare their resolve to transform the relationship between their countries and establish a global partnership. As leaders of nations committed to the values of human freedom, democracy and rule of law, the new relationship between India and the United States will promote stability, democracy, prosperity and peace throughout the world. It will enhance our ability to work together to provide global leadership in areas of mutual concern and interest.

Building on their common values and interests, the two leaders resolve:

- To create an international environment conducive to promotion of democratic values, and to strengthen democratic practices in societies which wish to become more open and pluralistic.
- To combat terrorism relentlessly. They applaud the active and vigorous counterterrorism cooperation between the two countries and support more international efforts in this direction. Terrorism is a .global scourge and the one we will fight everywhere. The two leaders strongly affirm their commitment to the conclusion by September of a UN comprehensive convention against international terrorism.

The Prime Minister's visit coincides with the completion of the Next Steps in Strategic Partnership (NSSP) initiative, launched in January 2004. The two leaders agree that this provides the basis for expanding bilateral activities and commerce in space, civil nuclear energy and dual-use technology.

Drawing on their mutual vision for the U.S.-India relationship, and our joint objectives as strong long-standing democracies, the two leaders agree on the following:

FOR THE ECONOMY

- Revitalize the U.S.-India Economic Dialogue and launch a CEO Forum to harness private sector energy and ideas to deepen the bilateral economic relationship.
- Support and accelerate economic growth in both countries through greater trade, investment, and technology collaboration.
- Promote modernization of India's infrastructure as a prerequisite for the continued growth of the Indian economy. As India enhances its investment climate, opportunities for investment will increase.

- Launch a U.S.-India Knowledge Initiative on Agriculture focused on promoting teaching, research, service and commercial linkages.

FOR ENERGY AND THE ENVIRONMENT

- Strengthen energy security and promote the development of stable and efficient energy markets in India with a view to ensuring adequate, affordable energy supplies and conscious of the need for sustainable development. These issues will be addressed through the U.S.-India Energy Dialogue.
- Agree on the need to promote the imperatives of development and safeguarding the environment, commit to developing and deploying cleaner, more efficient, affordable, and diversified energy technologies.

FOR DEMOCRACY AND DEVELOPMENT

- Develop and support, through the new U.S.-India Global Democracy Initiative in countries that seek such assistance, institutions and resources that strengthen the foundations that make democracies credible and effective. India and the U.S. will work together to strengthen democratic practices and capacities and contribute to the new U.N. Democracy Fund.
- Commit to strengthen cooperation and combat HIV/AIDs at a global level through an initiative that mobilizes private sector and government resources, knowledge, and expertise.

FOR NON-PROLIFERATION AND SECURITY

- Express satisfaction at the New Framework for the U.S.-India Defense Relationship as a basis for future cooperation, including in the field of defense technology.
- Commit to play a leading role in international efforts to prevent the proliferation of Weapons of Mass Destruction. The U.S. welcomed the adoption by India of legislation on WMD (Prevention of Unlawful Activities Bill).
- Launch a new U.S.-India Disaster Relief Initiative that builds on the experience of the Tsunami Core Group, to strengthen cooperation to prepare for and conduct disaster relief operations.

FOR HIGH-TECHNOLOGY AND SPACE

- Sign a Science and Technology Framework Agreement, building on the U.S.-India High-Technology Cooperation Group (HTCG), to provide for joint research and training, and the establishment of public-private partnerships.
- Build closer ties in space exploration, satellite navigation and launch, and in the commercial space arena through mechanisms such as the U.S.-India Working Group on Civil Space Cooperation.

- Building on the strengthened non-proliferation commitments undertaken in the NSSP, to remove certain Indian organizations from the Department of Commerce's Entity List.

Recognizing the significance of civilian nuclear energy for meeting growing global energy demands in a cleaner and more efficient manner, the two leaders discussed India's plans to develop its civilian nuclear energy program.

President Bush conveyed his appreciation to the Prime Minister over India's strong commitment to preventing WMD proliferation and stated that as a responsible state with advanced nuclear technology, India should acquire the same benefits and advantages as other such states. The President told the Prime Minister that he will work to achieve full civil nuclear energy cooperation with India as it realizes its goals of promoting nuclear power and achieving energy security. The President would also seek agreement from Congress to adjust U.S. laws and policies, and the United States will work with friends and allies to adjust international regimes to enable full civil nuclear energy cooperation and trade with India, including but not limited to expeditious consideration of fuel supplies for safeguarded nuclear reactors at Tarapur. In the meantime, the United States will encourage its partners to also consider this request expeditiously. India has expressed its interest in ITER and a willingness to contribute. The United States will consult with its partners considering India's participation. The United States will consult with the other participants in the Generation IV International Forum with a view toward India's inclusion.

The Prime Minister conveyed that for his part, India would reciprocally agree that it would be ready to assume the same responsibilities and practices and acquire the same benefits and advantages as other leading countries with advanced nuclear technology, such as the United States. These responsibilities and practices consist of identifying and separating civilian and military nuclear facilities and programs in a phased manner and filing a declaration regarding its civilians facilities with the International Atomic Energy Agency (IAEA); taking a decision to place voluntarily its civilian nuclear facilities under IAEA safeguards; signing and adhering to an Additional Protocol with respect to civilian nuclear facilities; continuing India's unilateral moratorium on nuclear testing; working with the United States for the conclusion of a multilateral Fissile Material Cut Off Treaty; refraining from transfer of enrichment and reprocessing technologies to states that do not have them and supporting international efforts to limit their spread; and ensuring that the necessary steps have been taken to secure nuclear materials and technology through comprehensive export control legislation and through harmonization and adherence to Missile Technology Control Regime (MTCR) and Nuclear Suppliers' Group (NSG) guidelines.

The President welcomed the Prime Minister's assurance. The two leaders agreed to establish a working group to undertake on a phased basis in the months ahead the necessary actions mentioned above to fulfil these commitments. The President and Prime Minister also agreed that they would review this progress when the President visits India in 2006.

The two leaders also reiterated their commitment that their countries would play a leading role in international efforts to prevent the proliferation of weapons of mass destruction, including nuclear, chemical, biological and radiological weapons.

In light of this closer relationship, and the recognition of India's growing role in enhancing regional and global security, the Prime Minister and the President agree that international institutions must fully reflect changes in the global scenario that have taken place since 1945. The President reiterated his view that international institutions are going to have to adapt to reflect India's central and growing role. The two leaders state their expectations that India and the United States will strengthen their cooperation in global forums.

Prime Minister Manmohan Singh thanks President Bush for the warmth of his reception and the generosity of his hospitality. He extends an invitation to President Bush to visit India at his convenience and the President accepts that invitation.

Henry J. Hyde United States-India Peaceful Atomic Energy Cooperation Act of 2006

Be it enacted by the Senate and House of Representatives of the United States of America in Congress assembled.

TITLE I—UNITED STATES AND INDIA NUCLEAR COOPERATION

SEC. 101. SHORT TITLE

This title may be cited as the "Henry J. Hyde United States-India Peaceful Atomic Energy Cooperation Act of 2006".

SEC. 102. SENSE OF CONGRESS

It is the sense of Congress that—

(1) preventing the proliferation of nuclear weapons, other weapons of mass destruction, the means to produce them, and the means to deliver them are critical objectives for United States foreign policy;

(2) sustaining the Nuclear Non-Proliferation Treaty (NPT) and strengthening its implementation, particularly its verification and compliance, is the keystone of United States non-proliferation policy;

(3) the NPT has been a significant success in preventing the acquisition of nuclear weapons capabilities and maintaining a stable international security situation;

(4) countries that have never become a party to the NPT and remain outside that treaty's legal regime pose a potential challenge to the achievement of the overall goals of global non-proliferation, because those countries have not undertaken the NPT obligation to prohibit the spread of nuclear weapons capabilities;

(5) it is in the interest of the United States to the fullest extent possible to ensure that those countries that are not States Party to the NPT are responsible in the disposition of any nuclear technology they develop;

(6) it is in the interest of the United States to enter into an agreement for nuclear cooperation arranged pursuant to section 123 of the Atomic Energy Act of 1954 (42 U.S.C. 2153) with a country that has never been a State Party to the NPT if—

(A) the country has demonstrated responsible behavior with respect to the non-proliferation of technology related to nuclear weapons and the means to deliver them;

(B)   the country has a functioning and uninterrupted democratic system
       of government, has a foreign policy that is congruent to that of the
       United States, and is working with the United States on key foreign
       policy initiatives related to non-proliferation;

(C)   such cooperation induces the country to promulgate and implement
       substantially improved protections against the proliferation of
       technology related to nuclear weapons and the means to deliver them,
       and to refrain from actions that would further the development of its
       nuclear weapons program; and

(D)   such cooperation will induce the country to give greater political and
       material support to the achievement of United States global and
       regional non-proliferation objectives, especially with respect to
       dissuading, isolating, and, if necessary, sanctioning and containing
       states that sponsor terrorism and terrorist groups that are seeking to
       acquire a nuclear weapons capability or other weapons of mass
       destruction capability and the means to deliver such weapons;

(7) the United States should continue its policy of engagement,
collaboration, and exchanges with and between India and Pakistan;

(8) strong bilateral relations with India are in the national interest of the
United States;

(9) the United States and India share common democratic values and the
potential for increasing and sustained economic engagement;

(10) commerce in civil nuclear energy with India by the United States and
other countries has the potential to benefit the people of all countries;

(11) such commerce also represents a significant change in United States
policy regarding commerce with countries that are not States Party to the
NPT, which remains the foundation of the international non-proliferation
regime;

(12) any commerce in civil nuclear energy with India by the United States
and other countries must be achieved in a manner that minimizes the risk of
nuclear proliferation or regional arms races and maximizes India's adherence
to international non-proliferation regimes, including, in particular, the
guidelines of the Nuclear Suppliers' Group (NSG); and

(13) the United States should not seek to facilitate or encourage the
continuation of nuclear exports to India by any other party if such exports
are terminated under United States law.

SEC. 103. STATEMENTS OF POLICY

(a) **In General.**—The following shall be the policies of the United States:

(1)   Oppose the development of a capability to produce nuclear weapons
       by any non-nuclear weapon state, within or outside of the NPT.

(2)   Encourage States Party to the NPT to interpret the right to "develop
       research, production and use of nuclear energy for peaceful purposes",
       as set forth in Article IV of the NPT, as being a right that applies only

to the extent that it is consistent with the object and purpose of the NPT to prevent the spread of nuclear weapons and nuclear weapons capabilities, including by refraining from all nuclear cooperation with any State Party that the International Atomic Energy Agency (IAEA) determines is not in full compliance with its NPT obligations, including its safeguards obligations.

(3) Act in a manner fully consistent with the Guidelines for Nuclear Transfers and the Guidelines for Transfers of Nuclear-Related Dual-Use Equipment, Materials, Software and Related Technology developed by the NSG, and decisions related to those guidelines, and the rules and practices regarding NSG decision-making.

(4) Strengthen the NSG guidelines and decisions concerning consultation by members regarding violations of supplier and recipient understandings by instituting the practice of a timely and coordinated response by NSG members to all such violations, including termination of nuclear transfers to an involved recipient, that discourages individual NSG members from continuing cooperation with such recipient until such time as a consensus regarding a coordinated response has been achieved.

(5) Given the special sensitivity of equipment and technologies related to the enrichment of uranium, the reprocessing of spent nuclear fuel, and the production of heavy water, work with members of the NSG, individually and collectively, to further restrict the transfers of such equipment and technologies, including to India.

(6) Seek to prevent the transfer to a country of nuclear equipment, materials, or technology from other participating governments in the NSG or from any other source if nuclear transfers to that country are suspended or terminated pursuant to this title, the Atomic Energy Act of 1954 (42 U.S.C. 2011 et seq.), or any other United States law.

(b) **With Respect to South Asia.**—The following shall be the policies of the United States with respect to South Asia:

(1) Achieve, at the earliest possible date, a moratorium on the production of fissile material for nuclear explosive purposes by India, Pakistan, and the People's Republic of China.

(2) Achieve, at the earliest possible date, the conclusion and implementation of a treaty banning the production of fissile material for nuclear weapons to which both the United States and India become parties.

(3) Secure India's—

    (A) full participation in the Proliferation Security Initiative;

    (B) formal commitment to the Statement of Interdiction Principles of such Initiative;

    (C) public announcement of its decision to conform its export control laws, regulations, and policies with the Australia Group and with the Guidelines, Procedures, Criteria, and Control Lists of the Wassenaar Arrangement;

(D) demonstration of satisfactory progress toward implementing the decision described in subparagraph (C); and

(E) ratification of or accession to the Convention on Supplementary Compensation for Nuclear Damage, done at Vienna on September 12, 1997.

(4) Secure India's full and active participation in United States efforts to dissuade, isolate, and, if necessary, sanction and contain Iran for its efforts to acquire weapons of mass destruction, including a nuclear weapons capability and the capability to enrich uranium or reprocess nuclear fuel, and the means to deliver weapons of mass destruction.

(5) Seek to halt the increase of nuclear weapon arsenals in South Asia and to promote their reduction and eventual elimination.

(6) Ensure that spent fuel generated in India's civilian nuclear power reactors is not transferred to the United States except pursuant to the Congressional review procedures required under section 131 f. of the Atomic Energy Act of 1954 (42 U.S.C. 2160 (f)).

(7) Pending implementation of the multilateral moratorium described in paragraph (1) or the treaty described in paragraph (2), encourage India not to increase its production of fissile material at unsafeguarded nuclear facilities.

(8) Ensure that any safeguards agreement or Additional Protocol to which India is a party with the IAEA can reliably safeguard any export or reexport to India of any nuclear materials and equipment.

(9) Ensure that the text and implementation of any agreement for cooperation with India arranged pursuant to section 123 of the Atomic Energy Act of 1954 (42 U.S.C. 2153) meet the requirements set forth in subsections a.(1) and a.(3) through a.(9) of such section.

(10) Any nuclear power reactor fuel reserve provided to the Government of India for use in safeguarded civilian nuclear facilities should be commensurate with reasonable reactor operating requirements.

SEC. 104. WAIVER AUTHORITY AND CONGRESSIONAL APPROVAL

(a) **In General.**—If the President makes the determination described in subsection (b), the President may—

(1) exempt a proposed agreement for cooperation with India arranged pursuant to section 123 of the Atomic Energy Act of 1954 (42 U.S.C. 2153) from the requirement of subsection a.(2) of such section;

(2) waive the application of section 128 of the Atomic Energy Act of 1954 (42 U.S.C. 2157) with respect to exports to India; and

(3) waive with respect to India the application of—

(A) section 129 a.(1)(D) of the Atomic Energy Act of 1954 (42 U.S.C. 2158(a)(1)(D)); and

(B) section 129 of such Act (42 U.S.C. 2158) regarding any actions that occurred before July 18, 2005.

(b) **Determination by the President.**—The determination referred to in subsection (a) is a determination by the President that the following actions have occurred:

(1)   India has provided the United States and the IAEA with a credible plan to separate civil and military nuclear facilities, materials, and programs, and has filed a declaration regarding its civil facilities and materials with the IAEA.

(2)   India and the IAEA have concluded all legal steps required prior to signature by the parties of an agreement requiring the application of IAEA safeguards in perpetuity in accordance with IAEA standards, principles, and practices (including IAEA Board of Governors Document GOV/1621 (1973)) to India's civil nuclear facilities, materials, and programs as declared in the plan described in paragraph (1), including materials used in or produced through the use of India's civil nuclear facilities.

(3)   India and the IAEA are making substantial progress toward concluding an Additional Protocol consistent with IAEA principles, practices, and policies that would apply to India's civil nuclear program.

(4)   India is working actively with the United States for the early conclusion of a multilateral treaty on the cessation of the production of fissile materials for use in nuclear weapons or other nuclear explosive devices.

(5)   India is working with and supporting United States and international efforts to prevent the spread of enrichment and reprocessing technology to any state that does not already possess full-scale, functioning enrichment or reprocessing plants.

(6)   India is taking the necessary steps to secure nuclear and other sensitive materials and technology, including through—

(A) the enactment and effective enforcement of comprehensive export control legislation and regulations;

(B) harmonization of its export control laws, regulations, policies, and practices with the guidelines and practices of the Missile Technology Control Regime (MTCR) and the NSG; and

(C) adherence to the MTCR and the NSG in accordance with the procedures of those regimes for unilateral adherence.

(7)   The NSG has decided by consensus to permit supply to India of nuclear items covered by the guidelines of the NSG.

(c) **Submission to Congress.**—

(1) IN GENERAL.—The President shall submit to the appropriate congressional committees the determination made pursuant to subsection (b), together with a report detailing the basis for the determination.

(2) INFORMATION TO BE INCLUDED.—To the fullest extent available to the United States, the report referred to in paragraph (1) shall include the following information:

(A) A summary of the plan provided by India to the United States and the IAEA to separate India's civil and military nuclear facilities, materials, and programs, and the declaration made by India to the IAEA identifying India's civil facilities to be placed under IAEA safeguards, including an analysis of the credibility of such plan and declaration, together with copies of the plan and declaration.

(B) A summary of the agreement that has been entered into between India and the IAEA requiring the application of safeguards in accordance with IAEA practices to India's civil nuclear facilities as declared in the plan described in subparagraph (A), together with a copy of the agreement, and a description of the progress toward its full implementation.

(C) A summary of the progress made toward conclusion and implementation of an Additional Protocol between India and the IAEA, including a description of the scope of such Additional Protocol.

(D) A description of the steps that India is taking to work with the United States for the conclusion of a multilateral treaty banning the production of fissile material for nuclear weapons, including a description of the steps that the United States has taken and will take to encourage India to identify and declare a date by which India would be willing to stop production of fissile material for nuclear weapons unilaterally or pursuant to a multilateral moratorium or treaty.

(E) A description of the steps India is taking to prevent the spread of nuclear-related technology, including enrichment and reprocessing technology or materials that can be used to acquire a nuclear weapons capability, as well as the support that India is providing to the United States to further United States objectives to restrict the spread of such technology.

(F) A description of the steps that India is taking to secure materials and technology applicable for the development, acquisition, or manufacture of weapons of mass destruction and the means to deliver such weapons through the application of comprehensive export control legislation and regulations, and through harmonization with and adherence to MTCR, NSG, Australia Group, and Wassenaar Arrangement guidelines, compliance with United Nations Security Council Resolution 1540, and participation in the Proliferation

Security Initiative.

(G) A description and assessment of the specific measures that India has taken to fully and actively participate in United States and international efforts to dissuade, isolate, and, if necessary, sanction and contain Iran for its efforts to acquire weapons of mass destruction, including a nuclear weapons capability and the capability to enrich uranium or reprocess nuclear fuel and the means to deliver weapons of mass destruction.

(H) A description of the decision of the NSG relating to nuclear cooperation with India, including whether nuclear cooperation by the United States under an agreement for cooperation arranged pursuant to section 123 of the Atomic Energy Act of 1954 (42 U.S.C. 2153) is consistent with the decision, practices, and policies of the NSG.

(I) A description of the scope of peaceful cooperation envisioned by the United States and India that will be implemented under the agreement for nuclear cooperation, including whether such cooperation will include the provision of enrichment and reprocessing technology.

(J) A description of the steps taken to ensure that proposed United States civil nuclear cooperation with India will not in any way assist India's nuclear weapons program.

(d) **Restrictions on Nuclear Transfers.—**

(1) IN GENERAL.—Pursuant to the obligations of the United States under Article I of the NPT, nothing in this title constitutes authority to carry out any civil nuclear cooperation between the United States and a country that is not a nuclear weapon State Party to the NPT that would in any way assist, encourage, or induce that country to manufacture or otherwise acquire nuclear weapons or nuclear explosive devices.

(2) NSG TRANSFER GUIDELINES.—Notwithstanding the entry into force of an agreement for cooperation with India arranged pursuant to section 123 of the Atomic Energy Act of 1954 (42 U.S.C. 2153) and pursuant to this title, no item subject to such agreement or subject to the transfer guidelines of the NSG, or to NSG decisions related thereto, may be transferred to India if such transfer would be inconsistent with the transfer guidelines of the NSG in effect on the date of the transfer.

(3) TERMINATION OF NUCLEAR TRANSFERS TO INDIA.—

(A) IN GENERAL.—Notwithstanding the entry into force of an agreement for cooperation with India arranged pursuant to section 123 of the Atomic Energy Act of 1954 (42 U.S.C. 2153) and pursuant to this title, and except as provided under subparagraph (B), exports of nuclear and nuclear-related material, equipment, or technology to India shall be terminated if there is any materially significant transfer by an Indian person of—

(i) nuclear or nuclear-related material, equipment, or technology that is not consistent with NSG guidelines or decisions, or

(ii) ballistic missiles or missile-related equipment or technology that is not consistent with MTCR guidelines,

unless the President determines that cessation of such exports would be seriously prejudicial to the achievement of United States non-proliferation objectives or otherwise jeopardize the common defense and security.

(B) EXCEPTION.—The President may choose not to terminate exports of nuclear and nuclear-related material, equipment, and technology to India under subparagraph (A) if—

(i) the transfer covered under such subparagraph was made without the knowledge of the Government of India;

(ii) at the time of the transfer, either the Government of India did not own, control, or direct the Indian person that made the transfer or the Indian person that made the transfer is a natural person who acted without the knowledge of any entity described in subparagraph (B) or (C) of section 110(5); and

(iii) the President certifies to the appropriate congressional committees that the Government of India has taken or is taking appropriate judicial or other enforcement actions against the Indian person with respect to such transfer.

(4) Exports, Reexports, Transfers, and Retransfers to India Related to Enrichment, Reprocessing, and Heavy Water Production.—

(A) IN GENERAL.—

(i) NUCLEAR REGULATORY COMMISSION.—The Nuclear Regulatory Commission may only issue licenses for the export or reexport to India of any equipment, components, or materials related to the enrichment of uranium, the reprocessing of spent nuclear fuel, or the production of heavy water if the requirements of subparagraph (B) are met.

(ii) SECRETARY OF ENERGY.—The Secretary of Energy may only issue authorizations for the transfer or retransfer to India of any equipment, materials, or technology related to the enrichment of uranium, the reprocessing of spent nuclear fuel, or the production of heavy water (including under the terms of a subsequent arrangement under section 131 of the Atomic Energy Act of 1954 (42 U.S.C. 2160)) if the requirements of subparagraph (B) are met.

(B) REQUIREMENTS FOR APPROVALS.—Exports, reexports, transfers, and retransfers referred to in subparagraph (A) may only be approved if—

(i) the end user—

(I) is a multinational facility participating in an IAEA-approved program to provide alternatives to national fuel cycle capabilities; or

    (II) is a facility participating in, and the export, reexport, transfer, or retransfer is associated with, a bilateral or multinational program to develop a proliferation-resistant fuel cycle;

  (ii) appropriate measures are in place at any facility referred to in clause (i) to ensure that no sensitive nuclear technology, as defined in section 4(5) of the Nuclear Non-proliferation Act of 1978 (22 U.S.C. 3203(5)), will be diverted to any person, site, facility, location, or program not under IAEA safeguards; and

  (iii) the President determines that the export, reexport, transfer, or retransfer will not assist in the manufacture or acquisition of nuclear explosive devices or the production of fissile material for military purposes.

(5) Nuclear Export Accountability Program.—

(A) IN GENERAL.—The President shall ensure that all appropriate measures are taken to maintain accountability with respect to nuclear materials, equipment, and technology sold, leased, exported, or reexported to India so as to ensure—

  (i) full implementation of the protections required under section 123 a.(1) of the Atomic Energy Act of 1954 (42 U.S.C. 2153 (a)(1)); and

  (ii) United States compliance with Article I of the NPT.

(B) MEASURES.—The measures taken pursuant to subparagraph (A) shall include the following:

  (i) Obtaining and implementing assurances and conditions pursuant to the export licensing authorities of the Nuclear Regulatory Commission and the Department of Commerce and the authorizing authorities of the Department of Energy, including, as appropriate, conditions regarding end-use monitoring.

  (ii) A detailed system of reporting and accounting for technology transfers, including any retransfers in India, authorized by the Department of Energy pursuant to section 57 b. of the Atomic Energy Act of 1954 (42 U.S.C. 2077(b)). Such system shall be capable of providing assurances that—

    (I) the identified recipients of the nuclear technology are authorized to receive the nuclear technology;

    (II) the nuclear technology identified for transfer will be used only for peaceful safeguarded nuclear activities and will not be used for any military or nuclear explosive purpose; and

    (III) the nuclear technology identified for transfer will not be retransferred without the prior consent of the United States, and facilities, equipment, or materials derived through the use of transferred technology will not be transferred without the prior consent of the United States.

(iii)   In the event the IAEA is unable to implement safeguards as required by an agreement for cooperation arranged pursuant to section 123 of the Atomic Energy Act of 1954 (42 U.S.C. 2153), appropriate assurance that arrangements will be put in place expeditiously that are consistent with the requirements of section 123 a.(1) of such Act (42 U.S.C. 2153(a)(1)) regarding the maintenance of safeguards as set forth in the agreement regardless of whether the agreement is terminated or suspended for any reason.

(C) IMPLEMENTATION.—The measures described in subparagraph (B) shall be implemented to provide reasonable assurances that the recipient is complying with the relevant requirements, terms, and conditions of any licenses issued by the United States regarding such exports, including those relating to the use, retransfer, safe handling, secure transit, and storage of such exports.

(e) JOINT RESOLUTION OF APPROVAL REQUIREMENT.—Section 123 d. of the Atomic Energy Act of 1954 (42 U.S.C. 2153(d)) is amended in the second proviso by inserting after "that subsection" the following: "or an agreement exempted pursuant to section 104(a)(1) of the Henry J. Hyde United States-India Peaceful Atomic Energy Cooperation Act of 2006."

(f) SUNSET.—The authority provided under subsection (a)(1) to exempt an agreement shall terminate upon the enactment of a joint resolution under section 123 d. of the Atomic Energy Act of 1954 (42 U.S.C. 2153(d)) approving such an agreement.

(g) REPORTING TO CONGRESS.—

(1)   INFORMATION ON NUCLEAR ACTIVITIES OF INDIA.—The President shall keep the appropriate congressional committees fully and currently informed of the facts and implications of any significant nuclear activities of India, including—

(A) any material non-compliance on the part of the Government of India with—

(i) the non-proliferation commitments undertaken in the Joint Statement of July 18, 2005, between the President of the United States and the Prime Minister of India;

(ii) the separation plan presented in the national parliament of India on March 7, 2006, and in greater detail on May 11, 2006;

(iii) a safeguards agreement between the Government of India and the IAEA;

(iv) an Additional Protocol between the Government of India and the IAEA;

(v) an agreement for cooperation between the Government of India and the United States Government arranged pursuant to section 123 of the Atomic Energy Act of 1954 (42 U.S.C. 2153) or any subsequent arrangement under section 131 of such Act (42 U.S.C. 2160);

(vi) the terms and conditions of any approved licenses regarding the export or reexport of nuclear material or dual-use material, equipment, or technology; and

(vii) United States laws and regulations regarding such licenses;

(B) the construction of a nuclear facility in India after the date of the enactment of this title;

(C) significant changes in the production by India of nuclear weapons or in the types or amounts of fissile material produced; and

(D) changes in the purpose or operational status of any unsafeguarded nuclear fuel cycle activities in India.

(2) IMPLEMENTATION AND COMPLIANCE REPORT.—Not later than 180 days after the date on which an agreement for cooperation with India arranged pursuant to section 123 of the Atomic Energy Act of 1954 (42 U.S.C. 2153) enters into force, and annually thereafter, the President shall submit to the appropriate congressional committees a report including—

(A) a description of any additional nuclear facilities and nuclear materials that the Government of India has placed or intends to place under IAEA safeguards;

(B) a comprehensive listing of—

(i) all licenses that have been approved by the Nuclear Regulatory Commission and the Secretary of Energy for exports and reexports to India under parts 110 and 810 of title 10, Code of Federal Regulations;

(ii) any licenses approved by the Department of Commerce for the export or reexport to India of commodities, related technology, and software which are controlled for nuclear non-proliferation reasons on the Nuclear Referral List of the Commerce Control List maintained under part 774 of title 15, Code of Federal Regulation, or any successor regulation;

(iii) any other United States authorizations for the export or reexport to India of nuclear materials and equipment; and

(iv) with respect to each such license or other form of authorization described in clauses (i), (ii), and (iii)—

(I) the number or other identifying information of each license or authorization;

(II) the name or names of the authorized end user or end users;

(III) the name of the site, facility, or location in India to which the export or reexport was made;

(IV) the terms and conditions included on such licenses and authorizations;

(V) any post-shipment verification procedures that will be applied to such exports or reexports; and

(VI) the term of validity of each such license or authorization;

(C) a description of any significant nuclear commerce between India and other countries, including any such trade that—

   (i) is not consistent with applicable guidelines or decisions of the NSG; or

   (ii) would not meet the standards applied to exports or reexports of such material, equipment, or technology of United States origin;

(D) either—

   (i) an assessment that India is in full compliance with the commitments and obligations contained in the agreements and other documents referenced in clauses (i) through (vi) of paragraph (1)(A); or

   (ii) an identification and analysis of all compliance issues arising with regard to the adherence by India to its commitments and obligations, including—

      (I) the measures the United States Government has taken to remedy or otherwise respond to such compliance issues;

      (II) the responses of the Government of India to such measures;

      (III) the measures the United States Government plans to take to this end in the coming year; and

      (IV) an assessment of the implications of any continued non-compliance, including whether nuclear commerce with India remains in the national security interest of the United States;

(E) (i) an assessment of whether India is fully and actively participating in United States and international efforts to dissuade, isolate, and, if necessary, sanction and contain Iran for its efforts to acquire weapons of mass destruction, including a nuclear weapons capability (including the capability to enrich uranium or reprocess nuclear fuel), and the means to deliver weapons of mass destruction, including a description of the specific measures that India has taken in this regard; and

   (ii) if India is not assessed to be fully and actively participating in such efforts, a description of—

      (I) the measures the United States Government has taken to secure India's full and active participation in such efforts;

(II) the responses of the Government of India to such measures; and

(III) the measures the United States Government plans to take in the coming year to secure India's full and active participation;

(F) an analysis of whether United States civil nuclear cooperation with India is in any way assisting India's nuclear weapons program, including through—

(i) the use of any United States equipment, technology, or nuclear material by India in an unsafeguarded nuclear facility or nuclear-weapons related complex;

(ii) the replication and subsequent use of any United States technology by India in an unsafeguarded nuclear facility or unsafeguarded nuclear weapons-related complex, or for any activity related to the research, development, testing, or manufacture of nuclear explosive devices; and

(iii) the provision of nuclear fuel in such a manner as to facilitate the increased production by India of highly enriched uranium or plutonium in unsafeguarded nuclear facilities;

(G) a detailed description of—

(i) United States efforts to promote national or regional progress by India and Pakistan in disclosing, securing, limiting, and reducing their fissile material stockpiles, including stockpiles for military purposes, pending creation of a worldwide fissile material cut-off regime, including the institution of a Fissile Material Cut-off Treaty;

(ii) the responses of India and Pakistan to such efforts; and

(iii) assistance that the United States is providing, or would be able to provide, to India and Pakistan to promote the objectives in clause (i), consistent with its obligations under international law and existing agreements;

(H) an estimate of—

(i) the amount of uranium mined and milled in India during the previous year;

(ii) the amount of such uranium that has likely been used or allocated for the production of nuclear explosive devices; and

(iii) the rate of production in India of—

(I) fissile material for nuclear explosive devices; and

(II) nuclear explosive devices;

(I) an estimate of the amount of electricity India's nuclear reactors produced for civil purposes during the previous year and the proportion of such production that can be attributed to India's declared civil reactors;

Strategic Sellout: Indian-U.S. Nuclear Deal

(J) an analysis as to whether imported uranium has affected the rate of production in India of nuclear explosive devices;

(K) a detailed description of efforts and progress made toward the achievement of India's—

    (i) full participation in the Proliferation Security Initiative;

    (ii) formal commitment to the Statement of Interdiction Principles of such Initiative;

    (iii) public announcement of its decision to conform its export control laws, regulations, and policies with the Australia Group and with the Guidelines, Procedures, Criteria, and Controls List of the Wassenaar Arrangement; and

    (iv) effective implementation of the decision described in clause (iii); and

(L) the disposal during the previous year of spent nuclear fuel from India's civilian nuclear program, and any plans or activities relating to future disposal of such spent nuclear fuel.

(3) Submittal with other Annual Reports.—

(A) REPORT ON PROLIFERATION PREVENTION.—Each annual report submitted under paragraph (2) after the initial report may be submitted together with the annual report on proliferation prevention required under section 601(a) of the Nuclear Non-Proliferation Act of 1978 (22 U.S.C. 3281(a)).

(B) REPORT ON PROGRESS TOWARD REGIONAL NON-PROLIFERATION.—

The information required to be submitted under paragraph (2)(F) after the initial report may be submitted together with the annual report on progress toward regional non-proliferation required under section 620F(c) of the Foreign Assistance Act of 1961 (22 U.S.C. 2376(c)).

(4) **Form.**—Each report submitted under this subsection shall be submitted in unclassified form, but may contain a classified annex.

SEC. 105. UNITED STATES COMPLIANCE WITH ITS NUCLEAR NON-PROLIFERATION TREATY OBLIGATIONS

Nothing in this title constitutes authority for any action in violation of an obligation of the United States under the NPT.

SEC. 106. INOPERABILITY OF DETERMINATION AND WAIVERS

A determination and any waiver under section 104 shall cease to be effective if the President determines that India has detonated a nuclear explosive device after the date of the enactment of this title.

SEC. 107. MTCR ADHERENT STATUS

Congress finds that India is not an MTCR adherent for the purposes of section 73 of the Arms Export Control Act (22 U.S.C. 2797b).

SEC. 108. TECHNICAL AMENDMENT

Section 1112(c)(4) of the Arms Control and Non-proliferation Act of 1999 (title XI of the Admiral James W. Nance and Meg Donovan Foreign Relations Authorization Act, Fiscal Years 2000 and 2001 (as enacted into law by section 1000(a)(7) of Public Law 106–113 and contained in appendix G of that Act; 113 Stat. 1501A–486)) is amended—

   (1)   in subparagraph (B), by striking "and" after the semicolon at the end;

   (2)   by redesignating subparagraph (C) as subparagraph (D); and

   (3)   by inserting after subparagraph (B) the following new subparagraph:
> "(C) so much of the reports required under section 104 of the Henry J. Hyde United States-India Peaceful Atomic Energy Cooperation Act of 2006 as relates to verification or compliance matters; and".

SEC. 109. UNITED STATES-INDIA SCIENTIFIC COOPERATIVE NUCLEAR NON-PROLIFERATION PROGRAM

(a) **Establishment.**—The Secretary of Energy, acting through the Administrator of the National Nuclear Security Administration, is authorized to establish a cooperative nuclear non-proliferation program to pursue jointly with scientists from the United States and India a program to further common nuclear non-proliferation goals, including scientific research and development efforts, with an emphasis on nuclear safeguards (in this section referred to as "the program").

(b) **Consultation.**—The program shall be carried out in consultation with the Secretary of State and the Secretary of Defense.

(c) **National Academies Recommendations.**—

(1) IN GENERAL.—The Secretary of Energy shall enter into an agreement with the National Academies to develop recommendations for the implementation of the program.

(2) RECOMMENDATIONS.—The agreement entered into under paragraph (1) shall provide for the preparation by qualified individuals with relevant expertise and knowledge and the communication to the Secretary of Energy each fiscal year of—

   (A)   recommendations for research and related programs designed to overcome existing technological barriers to nuclear non-proliferation; and

   (B)   an assessment of whether activities and programs funded under this section are achieving the goals of the activities and programs.

(3) PUBLIC AVAILABILITY.—The recommendations and assessments prepared under this subsection shall be made publicly available.

(d) **Consistency with Nuclear Non-proliferation Treaty.**— All United States activities related to the program shall be consistent with United States obligations under the Nuclear Non-Proliferation Treaty.

(e) **Authorization of Appropriations.**—There are authorized to be appropriated such sums as may be necessary to carry out this section for each of fiscal years 2007 through 2011.

SEC. 110. DEFINITIONS

In this title:

(1) The term "Additional Protocol" means a protocol additional to a safeguards agreement with the IAEA, as negotiated between a country and the IAEA based on a Model Additional Protocol as set forth in IAEA information circular (INFCIRC) 540.

(2) The term "appropriate congressional committees" means the Committee on Foreign Relations of the Senate and the Committee on International Relations of the House of Representatives.

(3) The term "dual-use material, equipment, or technology" means material, equipment, or technology that may be used in nuclear or non-nuclear applications.

(4) The term "IAEA safeguards" has the meaning given the term in section 830(3) of the Nuclear Proliferation Prevention Act of 1994 (22 U.S.C. 6305(3)).

(5) The term "Indian person" means—

    (A) a natural person that is a citizen of India or is subject to the jurisdiction of the Government of India;

    (B) a corporation, business association, partnership, society, trust, or any other non-governmental entity, organization, or group, that is organized under the laws of India or has its principal place of business in India; and

    (C) any Indian governmental entity, including any governmental entity operating as a business enterprise.

(6) The terms "Missile Technology Control Regime", "MTCR", and "MTCR adherent" have the meanings given the terms in section 74 of the Arms Export Control Act (22 U.S.C. 2797c).

(7) The term "nuclear materials and equipment" means source material, special nuclear material, production and utilization facilities and any components thereof, and any other items or materials that are determined to have significance for nuclear explosive purposes pursuant to subsection 109b. of the Atomic Energy Act of 1954 (42 U.S.C. 2139(b)).

(8) The terms "Nuclear Non-Proliferation Treaty" and "NPT" mean the Treaty on the Non-Proliferation of Nuclear Weapons, done at Washington, London, and Moscow July 1, 1968, and entered into force March 5, 1970 (21 UST 483).

(9) The terms "Nuclear Suppliers' Group" and "NSG" refer to a group, which met initially in 1975 and has met at least annually since 1992, of Participating Governments that have promulgated and agreed to adhere to Guidelines for Nuclear Transfers (currently IAEA INFCIRC/ 254/Rev.8/Part 1) and Guidelines for Transfers of Nuclear-Related Dual-Use Equipment, Materials, Software, and Related Technology

(currently IAEA INFCIRC/254/Rev.7/Part 2).

(10) The terms "nuclear weapon" and "nuclear explosive device" mean any device designed to produce an instantaneous release of an amount of nuclear energy from special nuclear material that is greater than the amount of energy that would be released from the detonation of one point of trinitrotoluene (TNT).

(11) The term "process" includes the term "reprocess".

(12) The terms "reprocessing" and "reprocess" refer to the separation of irradiated nuclear materials and fission products from spent nuclear fuel.

(13) The term "sensitive nuclear technology" means any information, including information incorporated in a production or utilization facility or important component part thereof, that is not available to the public and which is important to the design, construction, fabrication, operation, or maintenance of a uranium enrichment or nuclear fuel reprocessing facility or a facility for the production of heavy water.

(14) The term "source material" has the meaning given the term in section 11z. of the Atomic Energy Act of 1954 (42 U.S.C. 2014(z)).

(15) The term "special nuclear material" has the meaning given the term in section 11 aa. of the Atomic Energy Act of 1954 (42 U.S.C. 2014(aa)).

(16) The term "unsafeguarded nuclear fuel-cycle activity" means research on, or development, design, manufacture, construction, operation, or maintenance of—

(A) any existing or future reactor, critical facility, conversion plant, fabrication plant, reprocessing plant, plant for the separation of isotopes of source or special fissionable material, or separate storage installation with respect to which there is no obligation to accept IAEA safeguards at the relevant reactor, facility, plant, or installation that contains source or special fissionable material; or

(B) any existing or future heavy water production plant with respect to which there is no obligation to accept IAEA safeguards on any nuclear material produced by or used in connection with any heavy water produced therefrom.

TITLE II—UNITED STATES ADDITIONAL PROTOCOL IMPLEMENTATION

SEC. 201. SHORT TITLE.

This title may be cited as the "United States Additional Protocol Implementation Act".

SEC. 202. FINDINGS.

Congress makes the following findings:

(1) The proliferation of nuclear weapons and other nuclear explosive devices poses a grave threat to the national security of the United States and its vital national interests.

(2) The Nuclear Non-Proliferation Treaty has proven critical to limiting such proliferation.

(3) For the Nuclear Non-Proliferation Treaty to be effective, each of the non-nuclear-weapon State Parties must conclude a comprehensive safeguards agreement with the IAEA, and such agreements must be honored and enforced.

(4) Recent events emphasize the urgency of strengthening the effectiveness and improving the efficiency of the safeguards system. This can best be accomplished by providing IAEA inspectors with more information about, and broader access to, nuclear activities within the territory of non-nuclear-weapon State Parties.

(5) The proposed scope of such expanded information and access has been negotiated by the member states of the IAEA in the form of a Model Additional Protocol to its existing safeguards agreements, and universal acceptance of Additional Protocols by non-nuclear weapons states is essential to enhancing the effectiveness of the Nuclear Non-Proliferation Treaty.

(6) On June 12, 1998, the United States, as a nuclear weapon State Party, signed an Additional Protocol that is based on the Model Additional Protocol, but which also contains measures, consistent with its existing safeguards agreements with its members, that protect the right of the United States to exclude the application of IAEA safeguards to locations and activities with direct national security significance or to locations or information associated with such activities.

(7) Implementation of the Additional Protocol in the United States in a manner consistent with United States obligations under the Nuclear Non-Proliferation Treaty may encourage other parties to the Nuclear Non-Proliferation Treaty, especially non-nuclear-weapon State Parties, to conclude Additional Protocols and thereby strengthen the Nuclear Non-Proliferation Treaty safeguards system and help reduce the threat of nuclear proliferation, which is of direct and substantial benefit to the United States.

(8) Implementation of the Additional Protocol by the United States is not required and is completely voluntary given its status as a nuclear-weapon State Party, but the United States has acceded to the Additional Protocol to demonstrate its commitment to the nuclear non-proliferation regime and to make United States civil nuclear activities available to the same IAEA inspections as are applied in the

case of non-nuclear-weapon State Parties.

(9) In accordance with the national security exclusion contained in Article 1.b of its Additional Protocol, the United States will not allow any inspection activities, nor make any declaration of any information with respect to, locations, information, and activities of direct national security significance to the United States.

(10) Implementation of the Additional Protocol will conform to the principles set forth in the letter of April 30, 2002, from the United States Permanent Representative to the International Atomic Energy Agency and the Vienna Office of the United Nations to the Director General of the International Atomic Energy Agency.

SEC. 203. DEFINITIONS.

In this title:

(1) **Additional Protocol.**—The term "Additional Protocol", when used in the singular form, means the Protocol Additional to the Agreement between the United States of America and the International Atomic Energy Agency for the Application of Safeguards in the United States of America, with Annexes, signed at Vienna, June 12, 1998 (T. Doc. 107–7).

(2) **Appropriate Congressional Committees.**—The term "appropriate congressional committees" means the Committee on Armed Services, the Committee on Foreign Relations, and the Committee on Appropriations of the Senate and the Committee on Armed Services, the Committee on International Relations, the Committee on Science, and the Committee on Appropriations of the House of Representatives.

(3) **Complementary Access.**—The term "complementary access" means the exercise of the IAEA's access rights as set forth in Articles 4 to 6 of the Additional Protocol.

(4) **Executive Agency.**—The term "executive agency" has the meaning given such term in section 105 of title 5, United States Code.

(5) **Facility.**—The term "facility" has the meaning set forth in Article 18i. of the Additional Protocol.

(6) **IAEA.**—The term "IAEA" means the International Atomic Energy Agency.

(7) **Judge of the United States.**—The term "judge of the United States" means a United States district judge, or a United States magistrate judge appointed under the authority of chapter 43 of title 28, United States Code.

(8) **Location.**—The term "location" means any geographic point or area declared or identified by the United States or specified by the International Atomic Energy Agency.

(9) **Nuclear Non-proliferation Treaty.**—The term "Nuclear Non-Proliferation Treaty" means the Treaty on the Non-Proliferation of Nuclear Weapons, done at Washington, London, and Moscow, July 1, 1968, and entered into force March 5, 1970 (21 UST 483).

(10) **Nuclear-weapon State Party and Non-nuclear-weapon State Party.**—The terms "nuclear-weapon State Party" and "non-nuclear-weapon State Party" have the meanings given such terms in the Nuclear Non-Proliferation Treaty.

(11) **Person.**—The term "person", except as otherwise provided, means any individual, corporation, partnership, firm, association, trust, estate, public or private institution, any State or any political subdivision thereof, or any political entity within a State, any foreign government or nation or any agency, instrumentality, or political subdivision of any such government or nation, or other entity located in the United States.

(12) **Site.**—The term "site" has the meaning set forth in Article 18b. of the Additional Protocol.

(13) **United States.**—The term "United States", when used as a geographic reference, means the several States of the United States, the District of Columbia, and the commonwealths, territories, and possessions of the United States and includes all places under the jurisdiction or control of the United States, including—

(A) the territorial sea and the overlying airspace;

(B) any civil aircraft of the United States or public aircraft, as such terms are defined in paragraphs (17) and (41), respectively, of section 40102(a) of title 49, United States Code; and

(C) any vessel of the United States, as such term is defined in section 3(b) of the Maritime Drug Law Enforcement Act (46 U.S.C. App. 1903(b)).

(14) **Wide-area Environmental Sampling.**—The term "wide-area environmental sampling" has the meaning set forth in Article 18g. of the Additional Protocol.

SEC. 204. SEVERABILITY.

If any provision of this title, or the application of such provision to any person or circumstance, is held invalid, the remainder of this title, or the application of such provision to persons or circumstances other than those as to which it is held invalid, shall not be affected thereby.

Subtitle A—General Provisions

SEC. 211. AUTHORITY.

(a) **In General.**—The President is authorized to implement and carry out the provisions of this title and the Additional Protocol and shall designate through Executive order which executive agency or agencies of the United States, which may include but are not limited to the Department of State, the Department of Defense, the Department of Justice, the Department of Commerce, the Department of Energy, and the Nuclear Regulatory Commission, shall issue or amend and enforce regulations in order to implement this title and the provisions of the Additional Protocol.

(b) **Included Authority.**—For any executive agency designated under subsection (a) that does not currently possess the authority to conduct site vulnerability assessments and related activities, the authority provided in subsection (a) includes such authority.

(c) **Exception.**—The authority described in subsection (b) does not supersede or otherwise modify any existing authority of any Federal department or agency already having such authority.

Subtitle B—Complementary Access

SEC. 221. REQUIREMENT FOR AUTHORITY TO CONDUCT COMPLEMENTARY ACCESS.

(a) **Prohibition.**—No complementary access to any location in the United States shall take place pursuant to the Additional Protocol without the authorization of the United States Government in accordance with the requirements of this title.

(b) **Authority.**—

(1) IN GENERAL.—Complementary access to any location in the United States subject to access under the Additional Protocol is authorized in accordance with this title.

(2) UNITED STATES REPRESENTATIVES.—

(A) RESTRICTIONS.—In the event of complementary access to a privately owned or operated location, no employee of the Environmental Protection Agency or of the Mine Safety and Health Administration or the Occupational Safety and Health Administration of the Department of Labor may participate in the access.

(B) NUMBER.—The number of designated United States representatives accompanying IAEA inspectors shall be kept to the minimum necessary.

SEC. 222. PROCEDURES FOR COMPLEMENTARY ACCESS.

(a) **In General.**—Each instance of complementary access to a location in the United States under the Additional Protocol shall be conducted in accordance with this subtitle.

(b) **Notice.**—

(1) IN GENERAL.—Complementary access referred to in subsection (a) may occur only upon the issuance of an actual written notice by the United States Government to the owner, operator, occupant, or agent in

charge of the location to be subject to complementary access.

(2) TIME OF NOTIFICATION.—The notice under paragraph (1) shall be submitted to such owner, operator, occupant, or agent as soon as possible after the United States Government has received notification that the IAEA seeks complementary access. Notices may be posted prominently at the location if the United States Government is unable to provide actual written notice to such owner, operator, occupant, or agent.

(3) CONTENT OF NOTICE.—

(A) IN GENERAL.—The notice required by paragraph (1) shall specify—

(i) the purpose for the complementary access;

(ii) the basis for the selection of the facility, site, or other location for the complementary access sought;

(iii) the activities that will be carried out during the complementary access;

(iv) the time and date that the complementary access is expected to begin, and the anticipated period covered by the complementary access; and

(v) the names and titles of the inspectors.

(4) SEPARATE NOTICES REQUIRED.—A separate notice shall be provided each time that complementary access is sought by the IAEA.

(c) **Credentials.**—The complementary access team of the IAEA and representatives or designees of the United States Government shall display appropriate identifying credentials to the owner, operator, occupant, or agent in charge of the location before gaining entry in connection with complementary access.

(d) **Scope.**—

(1) IN GENERAL.—Except as provided in a warrant issued under section 223, and subject to the rights of the United States Government under the Additional Protocol to limit complementary access, complementary access to a location pursuant to this title may extend to all activities specifically permitted for such locations under Article 6 of the Additional Protocol.

(2) EXCEPTION.—Unless required by the Additional Protocol, no inspection under this title shall extend to—

(A) financial data (other than production data);

(B) sales and marketing data (other than shipment data);

(C) pricing data;

(D) personnel data;

(E) patent data;

(F) data maintained for compliance with environmental or occupational health and safety regulations; or

(G) research data.

(e) **Environment, Health, Safety, and Security.**—In carrying out their activities, members of the IAEA complementary access team and representatives or designees of the United States Government shall observe applicable environmental, health, safety, and security regulations established at the location subject to complementary access, including those for protection of controlled environments within a facility and for personal safety.

SEC. 223. CONSENTS, WARRANTS, AND COMPLEMENTARY ACCESS.

(a) **In General.**—

(1) PROCEDURE.—

(A) CONSENT.—Except as provided in paragraph (2), an appropriate official of the United States Government shall seek or have the consent of the owner, operator, occupant, or agent in charge of a location prior to entering that location in connection with complementary access pursuant to sections 221 and 222. The owner, operator, occupant, or agent in charge of the location may withhold consent for any reason or no reason.

(B) ADMINISTRATIVE SEARCH WARRANT.—In the absence of consent, the United States Government may seek an administrative search warrant from a judge of the United States under subsection (b). Proceedings regarding the issuance of an administrative search warrant shall be conducted *ex parte*, unless otherwise requested by the United States Government.

(2) EXPEDITED ACCESS.—For purposes of obtaining access to a location pursuant to Article 4b.(ii) of the Additional Protocol in order to satisfy United States obligations under the Additional Protocol when notice of two hours or less is required, the United States Government may gain entry to such location in connection with complementary access, to the extent such access is consistent with the Fourth Amendment to the United States Constitution, without obtaining either a warrant or consent.

(b) **Administrative Search Warrants for Complementary Access.**—

(1) OBTAINING ADMINISTRATIVE SEARCH WARRANTS.—For complementary access conducted in the United States pursuant to the Additional Protocol, and for which the acquisition of a warrant is required, the United States Government shall first obtain an administrative search warrant from a judge of the United States. The United States Government shall provide to such judge all appropriate information regarding the basis for the selection of the facility, site, or other location to which complementary access is sought.

(2) CONTENT OF AFFIDAVITS FOR ADMINISTRATIVE SEARCH WARRANTS.—

A judge of the United States shall promptly issue an administrative search warrant authorizing the requested complementary access upon an affidavit submitted by the United States Government—

(A) stating that the Additional Protocol is in force;

(B) stating that the designated facility, site, or other location is subject to complementary access under the Additional Protocol;

(C) stating that the purpose of the complementary access is consistent with Article 4 of the Additional Protocol;

(D) stating that the requested complementary access is in accordance with Article 4 of the Additional Protocol;

(E) containing assurances that the scope of the IAEA's complementary access, as well as what it may collect, shall be limited to the access provided for in Article 6 of the Additional Protocol;

(F) listing the items, documents, and areas to be searched and seized;

(G) stating the earliest commencement and the anticipated duration of the complementary access period, as well as the expected times of day during which such complementary access will take place; and

(H) stating that the location to which entry in connection with complementary access is sought was selected either—

(i) because there is probable cause, on the basis of specific evidence, to believe that information required to be reported regarding a location pursuant to regulations promulgated under this title is incorrect or incomplete, and that the location to be accessed contains evidence regarding that violation; or

(ii) pursuant to a reasonable general administrative plan based upon specific neutral criteria.

(3) CONTENT OF WARRANTS.—A warrant issued under paragraph (2) shall specify the same matters required of an affidavit under that paragraph. In addition, each warrant shall contain the identities of the representatives of the IAEA on the complementary access team and the identities of the representatives or designees of the United States Government required to display identifying credentials under section 222(c).

SEC. 224. PROHIBITED ACTS RELATING TO COMPLEMENTARY ACCESS.

It shall be unlawful for any person willfully to fail or refuse to permit, or to disrupt, delay, or otherwise impede, a complementary access authorized by this subtitle or an entry in connection with such access.

Subtitle C—Confidentiality of Information

SEC. 231. PROTECTION OF CONFIDENTIALITY OF INFORMATION.

Information reported to, or otherwise acquired by, the United States Government under this title or under the Additional Protocol shall be exempt from disclosure under section 552 of title 5, United States Code.

Subtitle D—Enforcement

SEC. 241. RECORDKEEPING VIOLATIONS.

It shall be unlawful for any person willfully to fail or refuse—
(1) to establish or maintain any record required by any regulation prescribed under this title;
(2) to submit any report, notice, or other information to the United States Government in accordance with any regulation prescribed under this title; or
(3) to permit access to or copying of any record by the United States Government in accordance with any regulation prescribed under this title.

SEC. 242. PENALTIES.

(a) **Civil.**—
    (1) PENALTY AMOUNTS.—Any person that is determined, in accordance with paragraph (2), to have violated section 224 or section 241 shall be required by order to pay a civil penalty in an amount not to exceed $25,000 for each violation. For the purposes of this paragraph, each day during which a violation of section 224 continues shall constitute a separate violation of that section.
    (2) NOTICE AND HEARING.—
        (A) IN GENERAL.—Before imposing a penalty against a person under paragraph (1), the head of an executive agency designated under section 211(a) shall provide the person with notice of the order. If, within 15 days after receiving the notice, the person requests a hearing, the head of the designated executive agency shall initiate a hearing on the violation.
        (B) CONDUCT OF HEARING.—Any hearing so requested shall be conducted before an administrative judge. The hearing shall be conducted in accordance with the requirements of section 554 of title 5, United States Code. If no hearing is so requested, the order imposed by the head of the designated agency shall constitute a final agency action.
        (C) ISSUANCE OF ORDERS.—If the administrative judge determines, upon the preponderance of the evidence received, that a person named in the complaint has violated section 224 or

section 241, the administrative judge shall state the findings of fact and conclusions of law, and issue and serve on such person an order described in paragraph (1).

(D) FACTORS FOR DETERMINATION OF PENALTY AMOUNTS.—In determining the amount of any civil penalty, the administrative judge or the head of the designated agency shall take into account the nature, circumstances, extent, and gravity of the violation or violations and, with respect to the violator, the ability to pay, effect on ability to continue to do business, any history of such violations, the degree of culpability, the existence of an internal compliance program, and such other matters as justice may require.

(E) CONTENT OF NOTICE.—For the purposes of this paragraph, notice shall be in writing and shall be verifiably served upon the person or persons subject to an order described in paragraph (1). In addition, the notice shall—

(i) set forth the time, date, and specific nature of the alleged violation or violations; and

(ii) specify the administrative and judicial remedies available to the person or persons subject to the order, including the availability of a hearing and subsequent appeal.

(3) ADMINISTRATIVE APPELLATE REVIEW.—The decision and order of an administrative judge shall be the recommended decision and order and shall be referred to the head of the designated executive agency for final decision and order. If, within 60 days, the head of the designated executive agency does not modify or vacate the decision and order, it shall become a final agency action under this subsection.

(4) JUDICIAL REVIEW.—A person adversely affected by a final order may, within 30 days after the date the final order is issued, file a petition in the Court of Appeals for the District of Columbia Circuit or in the Court of Appeals for the district in which the violation occurred.

(5) ENFORCEMENT OF FINAL ORDERS.—

(A) IN GENERAL.—If a person fails to comply with a final order issued against such person under this subsection and—

(i) the person has not filed a petition for judicial review of the order in accordance with paragraph (4), or

(ii) a court in an action brought under paragraph (4) has entered a final judgment in favor of the designated executive agency,

the head of the designated executive agency shall commence a civil action to seek compliance with the final order in any appropriate district court of the United States.

(B) NO REVIEW.—In any such civil action, the validity and appropriateness of the final order shall not be subject to review.

(C) INTEREST.—Payment of penalties assessed in a final order under this section shall include interest at currently prevailing rates calculated from the date of expiration of the 60-day period referred to in paragraph (3) or the date of such final order, as the case may be.

(b) **Criminal.**—Any person who violates section 224 or section 241 may, in addition to or in lieu of any civil penalty which may be imposed under subsection (a) for such violation, be fined under title 18, United States Code, imprisoned for not more than five years, or both.

SEC. 243. SPECIFIC ENFORCEMENT.

(a) **Jurisdiction.**—The district courts of the United States shall have jurisdiction over civil actions brought by the head of an executive agency designated under section 211(a)—

(1) to restrain any conduct in violation of section 224 or section 241; or

(2) to compel the taking of any action required by or under this title or the Additional Protocol.

(b) **Civil Actions.**—

(1) IN GENERAL.—A civil action described in subsection (a) may be brought—

(A) in the case of a civil action described in paragraph (1) of such subsection, in the United States district court for the judicial district in which any act, omission, or transaction constituting a violation of section 224 or section 241 occurred or in which the defendant is found or transacts business; or

(B) in the case of a civil action described in paragraph (2) of such subsection, in the United States district court for the judicial district in which the defendant is found or transacts business.

(2) SERVICE OF PROCESS.—In any such civil action, process shall be served on a defendant wherever the defendant may reside or may be found.

Subtitle E—Environmental Sampling

SEC. 251. NOTIFICATION TO CONGRESS OF IAEA BOARD APPROVAL OF WIDE-AREA ENVIRONMENTAL SAMPLING.

(a) **In General.**—Not later than 30 days after the date on which the Board of Governors of the IAEA approves wide-area environmental sampling for use as a safeguards verification tool, the President shall notify the appropriate congressional committees.

(b) **Content.**—The notification under subsection (a) shall contain—

    (1) a description of the specific methods and sampling techniques approved by the Board of Governors that are to be employed for purposes of wide-area sampling;

    (2) a statement as to whether or not such sampling may be conducted in the United States under the Additional Protocol; and

    (3) an assessment of the ability of the approved methods and sampling techniques to detect, identify, and determine the conduct, type, and nature of nuclear activities.

SEC. 252. APPLICATION OF NATIONAL SECURITY EXCLUSION TO WIDE-AREA ENVIRONMENTAL SAMPLING.

In accordance with Article 1(b) of the Additional Protocol, the United States shall not permit any wide-area environmental sampling proposed by the IAEA to be conducted at a specified location in the United States under Article 9 of the Additional Protocol unless the President has determined and reported to the appropriate congressional committees with respect to that proposed use of environmental sampling that—

    (1) the proposed use of wide-area environmental sampling is necessary to increase the capability of the IAEA to detect undeclared nuclear activities in the territory of a non-nuclear-weapon State Party;

    (2) the proposed use of wide-area environmental sampling will not result in access by the IAEA to locations, activities, or information of direct national security significance; and

    (3) the United States—

        (A) has been provided sufficient opportunity for consultation with the IAEA if the IAEA has requested complementary access involving wide-area environmental sampling; or

        (B) has requested under Article 8 of the Additional Protocol that the IAEA engage in complementary access in the United States that involves the use of wide-area environmental sampling.

SEC. 253. APPLICATION OF NATIONAL SECURITY EXCLUSION TO LOCATION-SPECIFIC ENVIRONMENTAL SAMPLING.

In accordance with Article 1(b) of the Additional Protocol, the United States shall not permit any location-specific environmental sampling in the United States under Article 5 of the Additional Protocol unless the President has determined and reported to the appropriate congressional committees with respect to that proposed use of environmental sampling that—

    (1) the proposed use of location-specific environmental sampling is necessary to increase the capability of the IAEA to detect undeclared nuclear activities in the territory of a non-nuclear-weapon State Party;

    (2) the proposed use of location-specific environmental sampling will

not result in access by the IAEA to locations, activities, or information of direct national security significance; and

(3) with respect to the proposed use of environmental sampling, the United States—

(A) has been provided sufficient opportunity for consultation with the IAEA if the IAEA has requested complementary access involving location-specific environmental sampling; or

(B) has requested under Article 8 of the Additional Protocol that the IAEA engage in complementary access in the United States that involves the use of location-specific environmental sampling.

SEC. 254. RULE OF CONSTRUCTION.

As used in this subtitle, the term "necessary to increase the capability of the IAEA to detect undeclared nuclear activities in the territory of a non-nuclear-weapon State Party" shall not be construed to encompass proposed uses of environmental sampling that might assist the IAEA in detecting undeclared nuclear activities in the territory of a non-nuclear-weapon State Party by—

(1) setting a good example of cooperation in the conduct of such sampling; or

(2) facilitating the formation of a political consensus or political support for such sampling in the territory of a non-nuclear-weapon State Party.

Subtitle F—Protection of National Security Information and Activities

SEC. 261. PROTECTION OF CERTAIN INFORMATION.

(a) **Locations and Facilities of Direct National Security Significance.**—No current or former Department of Defense or Department of Energy location, site, or facility of direct national security significance shall be declared or be subject to IAEA inspection under the Additional Protocol.

(b) **Information of Direct National Security Significance.**— No information of direct national security significance regarding any location, site, or facility associated with activities of the Department of Defense or the Department of Energy shall be provided under the Additional Protocol.

(c) **Restricted Data.**—Nothing in this title shall be construed to permit the communication or disclosure to the IAEA or IAEA employees of restricted data controlled by the provisions of the Atomic Energy Act of 1954 (42 U.S.C. 2011 et seq.), including in particular "Restricted Data" as defined under paragraph (1) of section 11y. of such Act (42 U.S.C. 2014(y)).

(d) **Classified Information.**—Nothing in this Act shall be construed to permit the communication or disclosure to the IAEA or IAEA employees of national security information and other classified information.

SEC. 262. IAEA INSPECTIONS AND VISITS.

(a) **Certain Individuals Prohibited from Obtaining Access**.— No national of a country designated by the Secretary of State under section 620A of the Foreign Assistance Act of 1961 (22 U.S.C. 2371) as a government supporting acts of international terrorism shall be permitted access to the United States to carry out an inspection activity under the Additional Protocol or a related safeguards agreement.

(b) **Presence of United States Government Personnel**.— IAEA inspectors shall be accompanied at all times by United States Government personnel when inspecting sites, locations, facilities, or activities in the United States under the Additional Protocol.

(c) **Vulnerability and Related Assessments**.—The President shall conduct vulnerability, counterintelligence, and related assessments not less than every 5 years to ensure that information of direct national security significance remains protected at all sites, locations, facilities, and activities in the United States that are subject to IAEA inspection under the Additional Protocol.

SUBTITLE G—REPORTS

SEC. 271. REPORT ON INITIAL UNITED STATES DECLARATION.

Not later than 60 days before submitting the initial United States declaration to the IAEA under the Additional Protocol, the President shall submit to Congress a list of the sites, locations, facilities, and activities in the United States that the President intends to declare to the IAEA, and a report thereon.

SEC. 272. REPORT ON REVISIONS TO INITIAL UNITED STATES DECLARATION.

Not later than 60 days before submitting to the IAEA any revisions to the United States declaration submitted under the Additional Protocol, the President shall submit to Congress a list of any sites, locations, facilities, or activities in the United States that the President intends to add to or remove from the declaration, and a report thereon.

SEC. 273. CONTENT OF REPORTS ON UNITED STATES DECLARATIONS.

The reports required under section 271 and section 272 shall present the reasons for each site, location, facility, and activity being declared or being removed from the declaration list and shall certify that—

(1) each site, location, facility, and activity included in the list has been examined by each agency with national security equities with respect to such site, location, facility, or activity; and

(2) appropriate measures have been taken to ensure that information of

direct national security significance will not be compromised at any such site, location, facility, or activity in connection with an IAEA inspection.

SEC. 274. REPORT ON EFFORTS TO PROMOTE THE IMPLEMENTATION OF ADDITIONAL PROTOCOLS.

Not later than 180 days after the entry into force of the Additional Protocol, the President shall submit to the appropriate congressional committees a report on—

(1) measures that have been or should be taken to achieve the adoption of additional protocols to existing safeguards agreements signed by non-nuclear-weapon State Parties; and

(2) assistance that has been or should be provided by the United States to the IAEA in order to promote the effective implementation of additional protocols to existing safeguards agreements signed by non-nuclear-weapon State Parties and the verification of the compliance of such parties with IAEA obligations, with a plan for providing any needed additional funding.

SEC. 275. NOTICE OF IAEA NOTIFICATIONS.

The President shall notify Congress of any notifications issued by the IAEA to the United States under Article 10 of the Additional Protocol.

Subtitle H—Authorization of Appropriations

SEC. 281. AUTHORIZATION OF APPROPRIATIONS.

There are authorized to be appropriated such sums as may be necessary to carry out this title.

Speaker of the House of Representatives.

Vice-President of the United States and
President of the Senate

Report Pursuant to Section 104(c) of the Hyde Act Regarding Civil Nuclear Cooperation with India

This report is submitted in accordance with Section 104(c) of the Henry J. Hyde United States-India Peaceful Atomic Energy Cooperation Act of 2006 (Public Law 109-401).

The U.S.-India Civil Nuclear Cooperation Initiative was announced in a Joint Statement by President Bush and Indian Prime Minister Manmohan Singh in Washington on July 18, 2005. On December 18, 2006, the President signed into law the Henry J. Hyde United States-India Peaceful Atomic Energy Cooperation Act of 2006 (the "Hyde Act"), to facilitate peaceful nuclear cooperation with India by authorizing the President to exempt the U.S.-India nuclear cooperation agreement and waive two provisions of the Atomic Energy Act of 1954 ("AEA") based on his determination that certain non-proliferation commitments have been met. Pursuant to Section 104(c) of the Hyde Act, the following report details the basis for the President's determinations and provides a available information on the areas listed in Section 104(c)(2).

Separation Plan and Declaration

Section 104(c)(2)(A) of the Hyde Act requires:

"A summary of the plan provided by India to the United States and the IAEA to separate India's civil and military nuclear facilities, materials, and programs, and the declaration made by India to the IAEA identifying India's civil facilities to be placed under IAEA safeguards, including an analysis of the credibility of such plan and declaration, together with copies of the plan and declaration."

The Government of India first made its Separation Plan public on March 7, 2006 and tabled the Separation Plan in Parliament on May 11. On July 25, 2008, the Government of India transmitted the Separation Plan to the Director-General of the IAEA to be distributed "to all Member-States of the Agency." The IAEA circulated the Separation Plan to Members as IAEA document INFCIRC/731.

The Separation Plan includes a list of facilities to be designated as civil, a general description of additional facilities to be designated civil in the future, and a description of India's rationale for civil *versus* military designations, including a statement that the overarching criterion would be a judgement whether subjecting a facility to IAEA safeguards would adversely impact India's national security. A copy of India's Separation Plan can be found at Tab 1. Designating a facility as civil marks it as not relevant to India's strategic nuclear program. The civil designation also ensures that after separation, these facilities will not be engaged in activities of strategic significance for India's military nuclear program. Facilities located in a larger hub of strategic significance, even if they do not normally engage in activities of strategic significance, will not be designated by India as civil. Also included in the Plan are dates specifying when each of the civil facilities are to be offered for safeguards according to a "phased" timeline.

The Separation Plan notes that "India has decided to place under safeguards all future civilian thermal power reactors and civilian breeder reactors, and the Government of India *retains the sole right to determine such reactors as civil*" (emphasis added). It also clarified that the "phasing of specific thermal power reactors being offered for safeguards would be indicated separately by India." And it explicitly described the distinct steps of (1) "filing a declaration regarding its civilian facilities with the IAEA", and (2) "taking a decision to place voluntarily its civilian facilities under IAEA safeguards." (See paragraph 3 of the Separation Plan).

The United States and other potential suppliers to India have international, and in many cases domestic, legal and policy requirements to ensure that items supplied under their agreements for peaceful nuclear cooperation serve exclusively the civil sector. All reactors supplied by the United States or by India's other international partners, and nuclear material used in such reactors, will be required to be designated as "civil" and subject to IAEA safeguards in perpetuity in accordance with IAEA practices. In addition, nuclear supplier nations will not be able to engage in nuclear cooperation, including fuel supply, with India's current reactors or future indigenous reactors unless they are designated as "civil" and subject to IAEA safeguards in perpetuity.

With these conditions in mind, the Plan's civil designations cover most of India's power reactors, raising the total installed thermal power capacity under safeguards from 19% to 65% by 2014.

India identifies 14 thermal reactors as civil, which according to the March 2006 Separation Plan were scheduled to be offered for safeguards between 2006 and 2014. These include the four existing foreign-supplied reactors (TAPS-1 and 2 (the U.S.-supplied Tarapur reactors), RAPS-1 and 2) and the two foreign-supplied reactors under construction (KK-1 and 2). These also include eight indigenous PHWRs, each with a generating capacity of 220 MWe: RAPS-3, 4, 5 and 6, KAPS-1 and 2, and NAPS-1 and 2. India further notes that safeguards will be applied in a phased manner consistent with its agreement with the IAEA. Eight indigenous PHWRs (TAPS-3 and 4, MAPS-1 and 2, Kaiga-1, 2, 3 and 4) are to remain outside of safeguards.

India opted to continue unsafeguarded operations at its operating fast breeder test reactor and also to exclude its prototype fast breeder reactor from safeguards. The fast breeder program is currently at the research and development stage and will take time to reach an advanced stage of development, according to India. India seeks to ensure that it does not face any external "encumbrances" in this process, and so chooses to exclude them from safeguards at this time. India and the United States would not be able to engage in the type of nuclear fuel cycle cooperation contemplated in the U.S.-India Agreement for Peaceful Nuclear Cooperation with regard to India's breeder reactors until India declared them "civil" and placed them under safeguards.

With regard to future reactors that India may operate, India states that it will place under IAEA safeguards "all future civilian thermal power reactors and civilian breeder reactors," retaining for itself the right to designate such reactors as civilian. While India retains the right to develop indigenous facilities for either civil or military purposes in the future, the United States expects the vast majority of future nuclear program growth to occur in India's civil sector. This expectation is based on discussions with the Government of India as well as India's need to obtain the maximum benefit from international cooperation in order to meet its enduring and expanding energy requirements.

Select research reactors and facilities are also included in the Separation Plan. India will permanently shut down the CIRUS plutonium production reactor in 2010. It will also place the foreign-supplied fuel core from the APSARA reactor under safeguards that year. India has not declared as civil the Dhruva research reactor, the Advanced Heavy Water Reactor, and activities relating to naval nuclear propulsion at Kalpakkam. India plans to declare as civil nine research facilities: the Tata Institute of Fundamental Research; the Variable Energy Cyclotron Centre; the Saha Institute of Nuclear Physics; the Institute for Plasma Research; the Institute of Mathematics Science; the Institute of Physics; the Tata Memorial Centre; the Board of Radiation and Isotope Technology; and the Harish Chandra Research Institute. India expects these civil facilities to play a "prominent role" in international cooperation. Other Indian nuclear and nuclear-related facilities—such as those in the Bhabha Atomic Research Center (BARC) or in the Indira Gandhi Center for Advanced Research (IGCAR)—were not declared as civil, presumably because they retain a military or strategic role. India has not declared as civil the Dhruva research reactor, the Advanced Heavy Water Reactor, and activities relating to naval nuclear propulsion at Kalpakkam.

The civil facilities covered under India's safeguards agreement also include all upstream and downstream facilities involved in India's civil nuclear fuel cycle. India designates as civil the following specific upstream facilities associated with the Nuclear Fuel Complex: the Uranium Oxide Plant (Block A); both the Palletizing and the Assembly Ceramic Fuel Fabrication Plants

(Block A); the Enriched Uranium Oxide Plant; the Enriched Fuel Fabrication Plant; and the Gadolinia Facility. The heavy water production plants at Thal, Tuticorin, and Hazira will also be designated as civil. While India does not consider them as "relevant for safeguards purposes," at a minimum India's Additional Protocol is expected to include them. India decided not to designate for civilian uses three additional heavy water production plants, as well as other select Nuclear Fuel Complex facilities.

India plans to continue the current policy of possible "campaign-mode" safeguards with respect to downstream facilities including the Tarapur Power Reactor Fuel Reprocessing Plant (PREFRE). Moreover, both the Tarapur and Rajasthan "Away from Reactor" spent fuel storage pools will be made available for safeguards. India decided not to declare as civil its other spent fuel reprocessing facilities, as well as its indigenous uranium enrichment capability. Subsequent to India's March 2006 separation plan, the Indian government decided to pursue development of a new civil facility dedicated to reprocessing material under safeguards. Development of this facility (and agreement with the United States on arrangements and procedures related thereto) will be required to bring into effect U.S. consent to reprocessing, pursuant to Article 6 of the Agreement.

Including upstream and downstream facilities under safeguards greatly enhances the ability to ensure that India is effectively separating its civilian and military facilities and programs, safeguarding the civil nuclear program, equipment, and materials, and that no diversion of international civil nuclear assistance is taking place to further military uses. By including both upstream and downstream facilities, India's Separation Plan covers every stage in the fuel cycle process from conversion and fuel fabrication, through the end of the nuclear fuel cycle into stages including spent fuel storage.

As a whole, the United States assesses India's plan to be credible, transparent, and defensible from a non-proliferation standpoint. When implemented, the total installed nuclear capacity under safeguards will rise from 19 percent today to 65 percent; a percentage that will increase to more than 80 percent as India further expands its civil infrastructure through foreign supply and indigenous development. Based on India's safeguards agreement with the IAEA (discussed below), appropriate safeguards will cover India's civil nuclear fuel cycle and provide strong assurances to supplier states that material and technology provided or generated through civil nuclear cooperation will not be diverted either to the military sphere or for unauthorized purposes. In addition, the total portion of India's spent fuel and plutonium stockpiles under safeguards will increase substantially over time (although the reprocessing consent in Article 6 of the U.S.-India Agreement for Peaceful Nuclear Cooperation, if and when the consent comes into effect, could increase modestly the quantity of separated civil plutonium stored in India).

With respect to India filing a declaration with the IAEA, as previously noted, on July 25, 2008, the Government of India transmitted the Separation Plan to the Director General of the IAEA to be distributed "to all Member-States of the Agency" (and the IAEA circulated the Separation Plan to Members as IAEA document INFCIRC/731). Paragraph 14 of the Separation Plan describes the "civil" elements of India's nuclear program, specifically naming the 14 reactors that will be declared "civil" and establishing a timetable for placing them under safeguards, as well as describing the treatment of other types of facilities (breeder reactors, research reactors, upstream facilities, downstream facilities, and research facilities). In a speech to the Indian Parliament on August 17, 2006, the Prime Minister confirmed that the "civil" facilities designated in the Separation Plan would be submitted to safeguards in a phased manner. He made similar statements to the Indian Parliament on August 13, 2007, after negotiations were completed on the 123 Agreement. In addition, in introducing the India-IAEA Safeguards Agreement, the Director-General of the IAEA specifically referred to the significance of the Separation Plan (which had been recently circulated within the IAEA), noting that it described the facilities envisages as coming under safeguards by 2014.

IAEA Safeguards

Section 104(c)(2)(B) of the Hyde Act requires:

"A summary of the agreement that has been entered into between India and the IAEA requiring the application of safeguards in accordance with IAEA practices to India's civil nuclear facilities as declared in the plan described in subparagraph (A), together with a copy of the agreement, and a description of the progress toward its full implementation."

India and the IAEA negotiated, in early 2008, a safeguards agreement, based on INFCIRC/66, the IAEA's approved safeguards system for states not party to the Treaty on the Non-Proliferation of Nuclear Weapons. A copy of India's safeguards agreement can be found at Tab 2. On August 1, 2008, the IAEA Board of Governors approved this agreement by consensus. Thus all legal steps required prior to signature of the safeguards agreement have been concluded. In his statement to the Board of Governors on August 1, 2008 Director-General El Baradei stated:

"The text before you is an INFCIRC/66-type safeguards agreement based on the Agency's standard safeguards practices and procedures. ... In the case of the draft before you, it is an "umbrella agreement", which provides for any facility notified by India to the Agency in the future to become subject to safeguards. .... The "umbrella" nature of this agreement provides a more efficient mechanism for ensuring that safeguards requirements can be met. It satisfies India's needs while maintaining all the Agency's legal requirements. ... As you can see from *India's Plan*, which has been circulated for the information of all IAEA Member States, a total of 14 reactors are envisaged to come under Agency safeguards by 2014. As with other safeguards agreements between the Agency and Member States, the agreement is of indefinite duration. There are no conditions for the discontinuation of safeguards other than those provided by the safeguards agreement itself. The termination provisions contained in the agreement are the same as for other 66-type agreements. Naturally - as with all safeguards agreements - this agreement is subject to the general rules of international law. Therefore, the agreement should be read as an integral whole. The preamble provides for contextual background and safeguards are implemented in accordance with the terms of the agreement."

Specifically, paragraph 11 of the safeguards agreement describes the items subject to safeguards:

"11. The items subject to this Agreement shall be:

    (a) Any facility listed in the Annex to this Agreement, as notified by India pursuant to paragraph 14(a) of this Agreement;

    (b) Any nuclear material, non-nuclear material, equipment and components supplied to India which are required to be safeguarded pursuant to a bilateral or multilateral arrangement to which India is a party;

    (c) Any nuclear material, including subsequent generations of special fissionable material, produced, processed or used in or by the use of a facility listed in the Annex or in or by the use of any nuclear material, non-nuclear material, equipment and components referred to in paragraph 11(b);

    (d) Any nuclear material substituted in accordance with paragraph 27 or 30(d) of this Agreement for nuclear material referred to in paragraph 11(b) or 11(c) of this Agreement;

    (e) Any heavy water substituted in accordance with paragraph 32 of this Agreement for heavy water subject to this Agreement;

    (f) Any facility other than a facility identified in paragraph 11(a) above, or any other location in India, while producing, processing, using, fabricating or storing any nuclear material, non-nuclear material, equipment or components referred to in paragraph 11(b), (c), (d), or (e) of this Agreement, as notified by India pursuant to paragraph 14(b) of this Agreement."

Paragraph 14(a) provides that India shall "notify the Agency in writing" of its decision to offer a facility for safeguards, after which that facility is included on the Annex to the safeguards agreement. This step of "notifying" the Agency of a facility offered for safeguards will be preceded by India's filing a "declaration" of civil facilities to be placed under safeguards in a phased manner; this filing will occur upon entry into force of the safeguards agreement.

Once a facility is listed in the Annex, safeguards will continue indefinitely unless "India and the Agency have jointly determined that the facility is no longer usable for any nuclear activity relevant from the point of view of safeguards" (paragraph 32). While there are a number of conditions for the termination of safeguards on materials (e.g., material is diluted to the point where it is no longer usable), these termination conditions, as noted by the El Baradei statement, are in accordance with standard IAEA practices, including INFICIRC/66. Thus, the facilities and materials subject to safeguards as described by paragraph 11(a)-(c) are under "safeguards in perpetuity in accordance with IAEA standards, principles, and practices."

India has indicated that it will submit facilities to safeguards under the India-IAEA safeguards agreement "as declared in" the Indian Separation Plan. As noted by the IAEA Director General, the "umbrella"-type safeguards agreement is well-suited for placing the facilities identified in the Separation Plan under safeguards in a phased manner. In addition, it is well-suited to adding future indigenous reactors that India may construct for civil purposes, as well as reactors that India may import from international suppliers.

Full implementation of the India-IAEA safeguards agreement will require signature of the agreement by both the IAEA and India. The agreement will enter into force once India informs the IAEA that India's domestic legal requirements for entry into force have been met. The Government of India's cover letter transmitting the Separation Plan to the IAEA contained a statement of its "intention to move forward in accordance with the provisions of the Safeguards Agreement after its entry into force." In the meantime, Indian discussions with the IAEA on implementation of the safeguards agreement are ongoing.

IAEA Additional Protocol

Section 104(c)(2c) of the Hyde Act requires:

"A summary of the progress made toward conclusion and implementation of an Additional Protocol between India and the IAEA, including a description of the scope of such Additional Protocol."

To further strengthen safeguards on India's civil nuclear facilities, consistent with its July 2005 Joint Statement commitment, India is in discussions and working closely with the IAEA to conclude an Additional Protocol that would give the IAEA expanded rights of access and additional information regarding India's civil nuclear facilities, including information on exports and imports of trigger list items. These activities, as well as others required to be reported and made available for access under an Additional Protocol, would not otherwise be subject to safeguards. Entry into force of an India-IAEA Additional Protocol could, therefore, provide even more transparency into India's civil nuclear activities.

Indian External Affairs Minister Pranab Mukherjee noted in his statement of September 5, 2008 that India was "working closely with the IAEA to ensure early conclusion of an Additional Protocol to the Safeguards Agreement." Indian officials have conveyed a letter to IAEA counterparts outlining the contours of a proposed Protocol, and the IAEA is currently reviewing India's proposal. The details included in this letter as well as substantive discussions between Indian officials and the IAEA prompted IAEA Director-General Mohammed El Baradei to conclude on September 10, 2008 that India has made substantial progress toward concluding an Additional Protocol consistent with IAEA principles, practices, and policies that would apply to India's civil nuclear program. We look forward to conclusion of this Additional Protocol at an early date.

Fissile Material Cut-Off Treaty

Section 104(c)(2)(D) of the Hyde Act requires:

"A description of the steps that India is taking to work with the United States for the conclusion of a multilateral treaty banning the production of fissile material for nuclear weapons, including a description of the steps that the United States has taken and will take to encourage India to identify and declare a date by which India would be willing to stop production of fissile material for nuclear weapons unilaterally or pursuant to a multilateral moratorium or treaty."

In August 2006, Indian Prime Minister Singh told the Indian Parliament that India was willing to join a "non-discriminatory, multilaterally negotiated and internationally verifiable FMCT... provided its security interests are fully addressed." Following this statement, India has publicly endorsed the negotiation of an FMCT in the Conference on Disarmament (CD) and has worked with the U.S. and its international partners to commence FMCT negotiations in that forum. In a 2007 session of the CD, although India initially posed procedural objections to the proposed Program of Work, which included among other items negotiations on an FMCT, India later dropped this objection and supported the measure after the U.S. decided to join consensus support of the Program. In a 2008 session of the CD, India was also supportive of U.S. efforts to realize an effective Program of Work for the CD; India made several constructive suggestions that were incorporated into the draft program of work presented in that session (CD/1840).

Despite the cooperative working relationship between the U.S., India, and some other countries in the CD, obstacles remain in securing consensus on a Program of Work in the CD that includes negotiations on an FMCT. Nevertheless, the U.S., India, and other like-minded states continue to seek a way forward. The U.S. has now given its support to work plan CD/1840 as the best, albeit not ideal, option available for forward movement on the FMCT.

In the March 2008 session of the CD, India made a statement expressing support for consensus on a program of work that took into account "the interests of all stake-holders." In July 2008, India told the U.S. that it's Ambassador in Geneva would, at a July 29 CD meeting, publicly declare broad support for an FMCT and efforts to reach consensus on a work plan. At that meeting, the Indian Ambassador repeated India's support for consensus on a program of work that takes into account "the interests of all stake-holders." India followed this with a statement in an informal session on July 31, where they reiterated their long-standing support for negotiating an FMCT in the CD.

On September 5, 2008, Indian External Affairs Minister Pranab Mukherjee stated, "We are committed to work with others towards the conclusion of a multilateral Fissile Material Cut-off Treaty in the Conference on Disarmament that is universal, non-discriminatory, and verifiable."

In addition to discussions at the CD on an FMCT, the U.S. remains willing to explore other intermediate options. We continue to encourage an early end to the production of fissile material production for weapons by all states. Toward that end we have urged India as part of our bilateral dialogue to put in place a moratorium on fissile material production, as we have done. India has rejected this notion in favor of working this issue at the CD.

Preventing the Spread of Enrichment and Reprocessing Technology

Section 104(c)(2)(E) of the Hyde Act requires:

"A description of the steps India is taking to prevent the spread of nuclear-related technology, including enrichment and reprocessing technology or materials that can be used to acquire a nuclear weapons capability, as well as the support that India is providing to the United States to further United States objectives to restrict the spread of such technology."

India has a solid non-proliferation record on enrichment and reprocessing (ENR) transfers; we are aware of no Indian transfers of ENR equipment or technologies to another state. India furthermore is supportive of international efforts to limit their spread to states that do not already posses ENR.

India has been supportive of U.S. efforts to work with other states to develop incentives to encourage states without ENR not to pursue these technologies. One such effort is the IAEA fuel bank initiative. Toward that end, India sent a letter dated 18 August 2008 to IAEA Director-General El Baradei indicating India's interest in participating as a supplier nation in the IAEA's effort to establish international fuel banks. In this letter, Dr. Anil Kakodkar, Chairman of India's Atomic Energy Commission, reaffirmed that "India will refrain from the transfer of enrichment and reprocessing technologies to States that do not have them, and support international efforts to limit their spread."

Indian External Affairs Minister Pranab Mukherjee reiterated that in a September 5, 2008 public statement that:

"India will not be the source of proliferation of sensitive technologies, including enrichment and reprocessing transfers. We stand for the strengthening of the non-proliferation regime. We support international efforts to limit the spread of ENR equipment or technologies to states that do not have them. We will work together with the international community to advance our common objective of non-proliferation. In this regard, India is interested in participating as a supplier nation, particularly for Thorium-based fuel and in establishment of international fuel banks, which also benefit India."

Export Controls

Section 104(c)(2)(F) of the Hyde Act requires:

"A description of the steps that India is taking to secure materials and technology applicable for the development, acquisition, or manufacture of weapons of mass destruction and the means to deliver such weapons through the application of comprehensive export control legislation and regulations, and through harmonization with and adherence to MTCR, NSG, Australia Group, and Wassenaar Arrangement guidelines, compliance with United Nations Security Council Resolution 1540, and participation in the Proliferation Security Initiative."

India committed under the July 18, 2005 Joint Statement, which launched the Civil Nuclear Cooperation Initiative, to harmonize its export controls with and unilaterally adhere to the Missile Technology Control Regime (MTCR) and NSG Guidelines. Through our various discussions since then, India has assured the United States that it has taken the necessary steps to have in place and fully implement effective and comprehensive export controls to deny unlawful access by states or non-state actors. Moreover, India has given assurances of a high-level political commitment to this effort.

India's June 2005 "Weapons of Mass Destruction (WMD) and their Delivery Systems (Prohibitions of Unlawful Activities) Act" and subsequent implementing regulations bring Indian export controls further in line with widely accepted export control standards for preventing WMD proliferation and are consistent with the kinds of measures that UN Security Council Resolution 1540 requires states to implement. The WMD Act, with its stronger "catch-all" provisions, considerably strengthens the government's regulatory ability to control transfers of otherwise uncontrolled items that could contribute to a WMD or missile program of concern.

To assist India in strengthening its export control system, the U.S. held two rounds of experts-level export control talks with India (October 15-16, 2007 and August 11-12, 2008). During these talks, the U.S. gained greater understanding of India's export control laws and regulations, their history, its Special Chemicals, Organisms, Materials, Equipment, and Technologies (SCOMET) list, and how its controls are implemented and enforced. As a result of our engagement with India on its export control system, India not only provided greater clarity on that system but also took specific steps such as issuing a revised SCOMET notification on September 7, 2007.

With respect to harmonization with the NSG and MTCR, in addition to issuing the revision to the SCOMET list in 2007, India explained how the Government of India sometimes uses broader terms than is utilized in the NSG or MTCR; this is done so as to exercise greater licensing oversight. India further explained that there are no substantial differences between its guidelines and those of the NSG and that the only linguistic differences flow from India's nonparticipation in the NSG. The U.S. assesses that India has harmonized with the MTCR and with the NSG up through the 2005 revisions, and has the means in place to make future updates to its guidelines and control lists if it chooses to do so. Furthermore, India's SCOMET list already captures some of the follow-on updates to the MTCR. We understand that this harmonization process will continue as an element of India's unilateral adherence to the NSG and MTCR. The Government of India has assured us that it has in place a process to make changes to the SCOMET list. Ongoing review and strengthening of India's export controls is built into the Indian system through regular inter-ministerial working groups as well as the Advisory Committees set-up in November 2006 under the WMD Act of 2005.

India stated its adherence to the NSG and its annexes in a letter dated September 8, 2008, to Dr. Mohammed El Baradei, the Director-General of the International Atomic Energy Agency. Likewise, India stated its adherence to the MTCR and its annex in a letter dated September 9, 2008, to Mr. Jacques Audibert, the MTCR Point of Contact in Paris. Taking into account these statements, the U.S. assesses that India has adhered to the guidelines and annexes of the NSG and the MTCR, and has done so in a manner consistent with the procedures and/or practices of those regimes.

As part of our strategic partnership, and in the course of a variety of dialogues, including annual non-proliferation talks, we discuss with India a wide range of non-proliferation and export control-related issues, including harmonization with and adherence to the Australia Group (AG) and Wassenaar Arrangement (WA), endorsement of the Proliferation Security Initiative, and implementation of UN Security Council Resolution 1540. We have discussed areas of differences between the SCOMET list and the AG as well as the process of adherence. With respect to the WA, India is in the process of developing a munitions list, and has welcomed outreach by the WA Chair. Discussions with India regarding PSI are ongoing. Since October 2007, India has attended as observers three PSI exercises and the PSI Fifth Anniversary Workshop for non-PSI partners. With respect to UNSCR 1540, India has submitted to the Committee established by UN Security Council Resolution 1540 its initial report as well as two subsequent reports on steps it has taken to meet its UN Security Council Resolution 1540 obligations, and continues to support the Committee's work.

Dissuading Iran from Acquiring WMD

Section 104(c)(2)(G) of the Hyde Act requires:

"A description and assessment of the specific measures that India has taken to fully and actively participate in United States and international efforts to dissuade, isolate, and, if necessary, sanction and contain Iran for its efforts to acquire weapons of mass destruction, including a nuclear weapons capability and the capability to enrich uranium or reprocess nuclear fuel and the means to deliver weapons of mass destruction."

The Government of India has taken several steps to support the U.S. in this regard and to bring Iran back into compliance with its international obligations, particularly those pertaining to its nuclear weapons program. As a member of the IAEA Board of Governors, India voted in favor of both the resolution that found Iran in non-compliance with its IAEA Safeguards Agreement in September 2005 and the resolution that reported Iran's non-compliance to the UN Security Council in February 2006. Responding to the adoption of three Chapter VII UN Security Council Resolutions (1737 in 2006, 1747 in 2007, and 183 in 2008), India reported that it is fully implementing their provisions, including those related to preventing Iran's acquisition of sensitive technology that could facilitate its uranium enrichment program or any future action to reprocess spent fuel.

India has also maintained a strong public line of support for P5+1 and U.S. diplomatic efforts to resolve international concerns with Iran's nuclear program. Furthermore, India has stressed that it does not favor the emergence of additional nuclear weapons states in the region and that all states must adhere to commitments under international treaties and be transparent in fulfilling these commitments. In this vein, India has called on Iran to cooperate fully with the IAEA on numerous occasions and delivered the same message to the Iranians during bilateral consultations.

Nuclear Suppliers' Group Exception

Section 104(c)(2)(H) of the Hyde Act requires:

"A description of the decision of the NSG relating to nuclear cooperation with India, including whether nuclear cooperation by the United States under an agreement for cooperation arranged pursuant to section 123 of the Atomic Energy Act of 1954 (42 U.S.C. 2153) is consistent with the decision, practices, and policies of the NSG.

On September 6, 2008, the Nuclear Suppliers' Group approved a policy statement by consensus excepting India from the Group's full-scope safeguards requirement for civil nuclear trade. This decision was made at the second of two Extraordinary Plenary sessions held August 21-22 and September 4-6, 2008. This historic decision by the NSG strengthens global non-proliferation principles while assisting India to meet its energy requirements in an environmentally friendly manner.

This exception involved intense scrutiny and debate by and among participating governments. On September 5, 2008, Indian External Affairs Minister (EAM) Pranab Mukherjee issued the following statement on the Civil Nuclear Cooperation Initiative, which was helpful in garnering additional momentum towards consensus:

Statement by External Affairs Minister of India
Shri Pranab Mukherjee on the Civil Nuclear Initiative

5 September 2008

To reiterate India's stand on disarmament and non-proliferation, EAM has made the following statement:

A Plenary meeting of the Nuclear Suppliers' Group to consider an exception for India from its guidelines to allow for full civil nuclear cooperation with India is being held in Vienna from September 4-5, 2008.

India has a long-standing and steadfast commitment to universal, non-discriminatory and total elimination of nuclear weapons. The vision of a world free of nuclear weapons which Shri Rajiv Gandhi put before the UN in 1988 still has universal resonance.

We approach our dialogue with the Nuclear Suppliers' Group and all its members in a spirit of cooperation that allows for an ongoing frank exchange of views on subjects of mutual interest and concern. Such a dialogue will strengthen our relationship in the years to come.

Our civil nuclear initiative will strengthen the international non-proliferation regime. India believes that the opening of full civil nuclear cooperation will be good for India and for the world. It will have a profound positive impact on global energy security and international efforts to combat climate change.

India has recently submitted a Working Paper on Nuclear Disarmament to the UN General Assembly, containing initiatives on nuclear disarmament. These include the reaffirmation of the unequivocal commitment of all nuclear weapon States to the goal of complete elimination of nuclear weapons; negotiation of a Convention on the complete prohibition of the use or threat of use of nuclear weapons; and negotiation of a Nuclear Weapons Convention prohibiting the development, production, stockpiling and use of nuclear weapons and on their destruction, leading to the global, non-discriminatory and verifiable elimination of nuclear weapons within a specified timeframe.

We remain committed to a voluntary, unilateral moratorium on nuclear testing. We do not subscribe to any arms race, including a nuclear arms race. We have always tempered the exercise of our strategic autonomy with a sense of global responsibility. We affirm our policy of no-first-use of nuclear weapons.

We are committed to work with others towards the conclusion of a multilateral Fissile Material Cut-off Treaty in the Conference on Disarmament that is universal, non-discriminatory and verifiable.

India has an impeccable non-proliferation record. We have in place an effective and comprehensive system of national export controls, which has been constantly updated to meet the highest international standards. This is manifested in the enactment of the Weapons of Mass Destruction and their Delivery Systems Act in 2005. India has taken the necessary steps to secure nuclear materials and technology through comprehensive export control legislation and through harmonization and committing to adhere to Missile Technology Control Regime and Nuclear Suppliers' Group guidelines.

India will not be the source of proliferation of sensitive technologies, including enrichment and reprocessing transfers. We stand for the strengthening of the non-proliferation regime. We support international efforts to limit the spread of ENR equipment or technologies to states that do not have them. We will work together with the international community to advance our common objective of non-proliferation. In this regard, India is interested in participating as a supplier nation, particularly for Thorium-based fuel and in establishment of international fuel banks, which also benefit India.

India places great value on the role played by the IAEA's nuclear safeguards system. We look forward to working with the IAEA in implementing the India-specific Safeguards Agreement concluded with the IAEA. In keeping with our commitment to sign and adhere to an Additional Protocol with respect to India's civil nuclear facilities, we are working closely with the IAEA to ensure early conclusion of an Additional Protocol to the Safeguards Agreement.

New Delhi
5th September 2008

With these assurances reaffirmed, NSG Participating Governments agreed by consensus on an exception for India on September 6, 2008. This decision is consistent with the cooperation envisioned under the U.S.-India peaceful nuclear cooperation agreement detailed below as well as with NSG practices and policies. This policy decision:

- exempts India from the NSG's full-scope safeguards requirement as a condition for transfer of Trigger List items for peaceful purposes and for use in IAEA safeguarded civil nuclear facilities, provided that the transfer satisfies all other provisions of the NSG Guidelines;
- contains an information exchange clause, which is consistent with current practice of the NSG;
- calls for intensified dialogue between the NSG Chair and India; this dialogue already exists. It is useful for it to be intensified not only as part of this decision, but also given India's decision to adhere to the NSG, which involves remaining abreast of and in line with changes to the NSG list and guidelines;
- addresses the desire expressed by some Participating Governments for an explicit review mechanism and/or for the ability to respond in the event that India abrogates its commitments, such as a nuclear explosive test or safeguards violation. This ability to consult in response to some problem is already provided for under Paragraph 16 of the Guidelines; any participating government may exercise this ability if they consider circumstances warrant;
- notes that Participating Governments will maintain contact and consult through regular channels to "consider" matters related to this decision consistent with the NSG's existing authority and practice; and
- provides for enhanced outreach between India and the NSG Chair following this decision and in light of India's decision to adhere to the NSG. This is consistent with enhanced outreach that we support with all adherents and is especially important in light of the civil nuclear trade with India to result from the NSG's decision.

Envisioned Scope of U.S.-India Peaceful Nuclear Cooperation

Section 104(c)(2i)

"A description of the scope of peaceful cooperation envisioned by the United States and India that will be implemented under the agreement for nuclear cooperation, including whether such cooperation will include the provision of enrichment and reprocessing technology."

Envisioned civil nuclear cooperation with India will include a number of activities, which are described in general terms in the *Proposed Agreement for Cooperation Between the Government of the United States of America and the Government of India Concerning Peaceful Uses of Nuclear Energy* Article 2(2). These activities are to take place in accordance with the provisions of the Agreement and each Party's applicable treaties, national laws, regulations, and license requirements and may include, but are not limited to the following areas:

- Advanced nuclear energy research and development in areas agreed to by the Parties;
- Nuclear safety matters;
- Facilitation of exchange of scientists for visits, meetings, symposia and collaborative research;
- Full civil nuclear cooperation activities covering nuclear reactors and aspects of the associated nuclear fuel cycle including technology transfer on an industrial or commercial scale between the Parties or authorized persons;
- Development of a strategic reserve to guard against any disruption of supply over the lifetime of India's reactors;
- Advanced research and development in nuclear sciences including biological research, medicine, agriculture and industry, environment and climate change;
- Supply between the Parties, whether for use by or for the benefit of the Parties or third countries, of nuclear material;
- Alteration in form or content of nuclear material as provided for in Article 6 of the Agreement;
- Supply between the Parties of equipment, whether for use by or for the benefit of the Parties or third countries;
- Controlled thermonuclear fusion including in multilateral projects; and
- Other areas of mutual interest as may be agreed by the Parties.

Article 2(3) of the Agreement specifically provides that the Parties may undertake transfers between themselves or their authorized persons of nuclear material, non-nuclear material, equipment, components and information.

In Article 2(4) of the Agreement, the U.S. and India further delimit the scope of cooperation by affirming that the purpose of the Agreement is to provide for peaceful nuclear cooperation and not to affect the unsafeguarded nuclear activities of either Party. Nothing in the Agreement is to be interpreted as affecting the rights of the Parties to use for their own purposes nuclear material, non-nuclear material, equipment, components, information or technology produced, acquired or developed by them independent of any nuclear material, non-nuclear material, equipment, components, information or technology transferred to them pursuant to the Agreement. The Agreement is to be implemented in a manner so as not to hinder or otherwise interfere with any other activities involving the use of nuclear material, non-nuclear material, equipment, components, information or technology and military nuclear facilities produced, acquired or developed by them independent of the Agreement for their own purposes.

Article 3(1) of the Agreement again specifically provides that *information* may be transferred between the Parties, and that such information may cover, but need not be limited to the following fields:

- Research, development, design, construction, operation, maintenance and use of reactors, reactor experiments, and decommissioning;
- The use of nuclear material in physical, chemical, radiological and biological research, medicine, agriculture and industry;
- Fuel cycle activities to meet future world-wide civil nuclear energy needs, including multilateral approaches to which they are parties for ensuring nuclear fuel supply and appropriate techniques for management of nuclear wastes;
- Advanced research and development in nuclear science and technology;
- Health, safety and environmental considerations related to the foregoing;
- Assessments of the role that nuclear power may play in national energy plans;
- Codes, regulations and standards for the nuclear industry;
- Research on controlled thermonuclear fusion including bilateral activities and contributions toward multilateral projects such as the International Thermonuclear Experimental Reactor (ITER); and
- Any other field mutually agreed to by the Parties.

Article 3(2) provides that the above cooperation may include training, exchange of personnel, meetings, exchange of samples, materials and instruments for experimental purposes and a balanced participation in joint studies and projects.

Article 3(3) states that the Agreement does not require the transfer of any information outside the scope of the Agreement, or information that the Parties are not permitted under their respective treaties, national laws or regulations to transfer.

Article 3(4) provides that Restricted Data, as defined by each Party, shall not be transferred under the Agreement.

Article 4(1) provides *inter alia* for the Parties to facilitate nuclear trade between themselves in the mutual interests of their respective industry, utilities and consumers and also, where appropriate, trade between either Party and a third country of items obligated to the other Party.

Article 4(2) provides *inter alia* that authorizations, including export and import licenses as well as authorizations or consents to third parties relating to trade, industrial operations or nuclear material movement, should be consistent with the sound and efficient administration of the Agreement and should not be used to restrict trade.

Article 5(1) provides that nuclear material, non-nuclear material, equipment and components may be transferred for applications consistent with the Agreement. However, any special fissionable material transferred shall be limited to low enriched uranium, except for "small quantities," which may be transferred pursuant to Article 5(5) for use as samples, standards, detectors and targets, and the accomplishment of other purposes as agreed by the Parties.

In considering the scope of civil nuclear cooperation with India, the issue of spreading sensitive technologies is often raised. The requirement of section 123a.(9) pertains to situations that may result when sensitive nuclear technology is transferred pursuant to a section 123 agreement for cooperation. Article 5(2) of the Agreement provides that sensitive nuclear technology shall only be transferred under the Agreement if provided for by an amendment to the Agreement, and Article 5(2) further provides that sensitive nuclear facilities and major critical components thereof shall only be transferred under the Agreement if provided for by an amendment to the Agreement. Accordingly, the requirement in section 123a.(9) is not relevant to the proposed Agreement, and the requirement in section 402(b) of the NNPA precluding the transfer of major critical components of facilities for uranium enrichment, nuclear fuel reprocessing, or heavy water production unless an agreement for cooperation "specifically designates such components as items to be exported pursuant to [such] agreement" is also satisfied.

Article 5(4) provides that the *quantity* of nuclear material transferred under the Agreement shall be consistent with any of the following purposes: use in reactor experiments or the loading of reactors, the efficient and continuous conduct of such reactor experiments or operation of reactors for their lifetime, use as samples, standards, detectors and targets, and other purposes as the Parties may agree.

Article 5(6) records verbatim certain political assurances relating to reliable supply of nuclear fuel given to India by the United States in March 2006. The Agreement language does not have the effect of converting these political assurances into legally binding commitments.

Articles 5(2), 6-10, and 14 address the specific requirements of section 123a. of the Atomic Energy Act of 1954 (AEA).

Article 11 provides that the Parties shall cooperate in following the best practices for minimizing the impact on the environment from any radioactive, chemical or thermal contamination arising from activities under the Agreement and in related matters of health and safety.

Article 12 contains additional provisions with regard to implementation of activities falling within the scope of the Agreement.

Article 13 provides for consultations at the request of either Party regarding implementation of the Agreement and the development of further cooperation in the field of peaceful uses of nuclear energy on a stable, reliable and predictable basis. It further provides that the Parties shall endeavor to avoid taking any action that adversely affects cooperation under Article 2, which is the general "Scope of Cooperation" article.

Article 15 provides for dispute settlement through negotiations between the Parties.

Article 16 provides for the Agreement to have an initial duration of 40 years and to continue in force for additional periods of 10 years each, subject to a proviso that either Party may terminate the Agreement by giving written notice to the other Party six months prior to the close of a period. It also provides for continuation in effect of key non-proliferation provisions of the Agreement in the event of its termination.

Ensuring Cooperation does not in any Way Assist India's Nuclear Weapons Program

Section 104(c)(2)(J) of the Hyde Act requires:

"A description of the steps taken to ensure that proposed United States civil nuclear cooperation with India will not in any way assist India's nuclear weapons program."

As previously described, India has developed a Separation Plan (INFCIR/731) to separate civil and military nuclear facilities. The India-IAEA safeguards agreement, which was unanimously approved by the IAEA Board of Governors on August 1, 2008, establishes procedures for applying safeguards to India's "civil" nuclear facilities in accordance with IAEA standards, principles, and practices. The stated purpose of the safeguards agreement is to ensure that no safeguarded item is "used for the manufacture of any nuclear weapon or to further any other military purpose and that such items are used exclusively for peaceful purposes." To this end, IAEA safeguards are designed to detect and prevent diversion from civil to military facilities, making the conclusion of this safeguards agreement the key to ensuring that civil nuclear cooperation could not be used to advance a nuclear weapons program. The U.S. does not in any way support India's nuclear weapons program.

Under the Safeguards Agreement, the IAEA will verify that all of India's current and future civil nuclear facilities and material, as well as certain upstream and downstream facilities, are used only for peaceful purposes. Once a reactor is under IAEA safeguards, those safeguards will remain in place on an unconditional basis until the reactor is jointly determined by the IAEA and India to be no longer usable for nuclear activities relevant from the point of view of safeguards. This Initiative will only allow for nuclear cooperation to proceed with facilities subject to IAEA safeguards, monitoring, and inspections to ensure that the civilian nature of the work therein is not compromised. This also provides an incentive for India to declare any future reactors as civil and thus bring them into this framework of nuclear cooperation; otherwise no foreign material and technology would be available for their construction and operation.

For dual-use nuclear exports administered by the Department of Commerce, there are several ways the U.S. is assured that exports are going to reliable recipients of U.S. origin items and have not been diverted to unauthorized end users or end uses. As part of the license application package, we require certification that the item(s) will not be used in any of the prohibited activities described in 744.2(a) of the Export Administration Regulations (EAR). Through the licensing process, the intelligence and enforcement communities provide information on the *bona fides* of prospective end-users. Commerce determines the *bona fides* of the transaction and suitability of the end-user through the use of pre-license checks. This information is then used to make licensing decisions. As part of the approval process, export licenses normally have conditions attached that prohibit re-export, retransfer, or use in sensitive nuclear, chemical, biological, or missile end uses. We require applicants to inform end-users of the licensing conditions. In addition, the U.S. has an end use assurance letter from the Government of India that commits it to ensure that items are not transferred from or through India for use in prohibited unsafeguarded nuclear, WMD, or WMD delivery programs. Also, through post-shipment verifications, the U.S. visits recipients of U.S.-origin items to ensure that the items have actually been delivered to the authorized ultimate consignee or end-user and those items are being used as stated on the export license application.

The transfer of nuclear fuel technology requires authorization by the Secretary of Energy under Section 57(b) of the Atomic Energy Act of 1954 as amended. The regulations that implement Section 57(b) are found in 10 CFR Part 810, which require that prior to such approval, government-to-government assurances outlining the controls/conditions that will be used for securing this technology must be in place. This includes the requirement that the transfer, anything derived from the transfer, and anything that is produced or modified in a facility constructed as a result of the transfer will be used for peaceful purposes. Further, the United States places additional conditions on an authorization to transfer the technology that limits access and prohibits the retransfer of the technology.

Conclusion

As great progress has been made in bringing the U.S.-India Civil Nuclear Cooperation Initiative to fruition, India has been brought closer to the non-proliferation mainstream. India has completed a Separation Plan, negotiated a safeguards agreement, and made substantial progress towards an Additional Protocol. India has greatly improved its export controls and pledged to maintain the highest international standards on restricting the transfer of sensitive technologies. The U.S.-India bilateral relationship has been revamped and has facilitated cooperation on many key regional and global issues, such as dissuading Iranian attempts to acquire WMD and completing an FMCT in the CD, and this close cooperation is expected to continue in the future, advancing U.S. strategic interests and increasing U.S. national security. Civil nuclear trade with India will increase global energy security and advance U.S. and Indian economic interests while at the same time strengthening the global non-proliferation regime. In meeting its non-proliferation commitments under the Hyde Act, India has made a great step forward in taking its place as a strategic partner for the U.S. now and in the future.

Attachments:

Tab 1   India Separation Plan.
Tab 2   Agreement Between the Government of India and the IAEA for the Application of Safeguards to Civilian Nuclear Facilities.

Communication (INFIRC 731] dated 25 July 2008 Received [by the International Atomic Energy Agency] from the Permanent Mission of India concerning a document entitled "Implementation of the India-United States Joint Statement of July 18, 2005: India's Separation Plan"

The resumption of full civilian nuclear energy cooperation between India and the United States arose in the context of India's requirement for adequate and affordable energy supplies to sustain its accelerating economic growth rate and as recognition of its growing technological prowess. It was preceded by discussions between the two Governments, particularly between President Bush and Prime Minister Manmohan Singh, of the global energy scenario and the long-term implications of increasing pressure on hydrocarbon resources and rising oil prices. These developments led to the announcement in April 2005 of an Indo-US Energy Dialogue that encompassed the entire spectrum of energy options ranging from oil and gas to coal, alternative fuels and civilian nuclear energy. Through the initiation of a sustained dialogue to address energy security concerns, the two countries sought to promote stable, efficient, predictable and cost effective solutions for India's growing requirements. At the same time, they also agreed on the need to develop and deploy cleaner, more efficient, affordable and diversified energy technologies to deal with the environmental implications of energy consumption. India had developed proven and wide ranging capabilities in the nuclear sector, including over the entire nuclear fuel cycle. It is internationally recognized that India has unique contributions to make to international efforts towards meeting these objectives. India has become a full partner in ITER, with the full support of the US and other partners. India also accepted the US invitation to join the initiative on Clean Development Partnership.

2. Noting the centrality of civilian nuclear energy to the twin challenges of energy security and safeguarding the environment, the two Governments agreed on 18 July 2005 to undertake reciprocal commitments and responsibilities that would create a framework for the resumption of full cooperation in this field. On its part, the United States undertook to:

- Seek agreement from the Congress to adjust US laws and policies to achieve full civil nuclear energy cooperation.

- Work with friends and allies to adjust international regimes to enable full civil nuclear energy cooperation and trade with India, including but not limited to expeditious consideration of fuel supplies for safeguarded nuclear reactors at Tarapur.
- In the meantime, encourage its partners to consider fuel supply to Tarapur expeditiously.
- To consult with its partners to consider India's participation in ITER.
- To consult with other participants in the Generation IV International Forum with a view towards India's inclusion.

3. India had conveyed its readiness to assume the same responsibilities and practices and acquire the same benefits and advantages as other leading countries with advanced nuclear technology, such as the United States. Accordingly, India for its part undertook the following commitments:

- Identifying and separating civilian and military nuclear facilities and programmes in a phased manner.
- Filing a declaration regarding its civilian facilities with the IAEA.
- Taking a decision to place voluntarily its civilian nuclear facilities under IAEA safeguards.
- Signing and adhering to an Additional Protocol with respect to civilian nuclear facilities.

4. Other commitments undertaken by India have already been fulfilled in the last year. Among them are:

- India's responsible non-proliferation record, recognized by the US, continues and is reflected in its policies and actions.
- The harmonization of India's export controls with NSG and MTCR Guidelines even though India is not a member of either group. These guidelines and control lists have been notified and are being implemented.
- A significant upgrading of India's non-proliferation regulations and export controls has taken place as a result of Weapons of Mass Destruction Act of May 2005. Inter-Ministerial consultations are ongoing to examine and amend other relevant Acts as well as framing appropriate rules and regulations.
- Refrain from transfer of enrichment and reprocessing technologies to states that do not have them and supporting international efforts to limit their spread. This has guided our policy on non-proliferation.
- Continued unilateral moratorium on nuclear testing.
- Willingness to work with the United States for the conclusion of a multilateral Fissile Material Cut-Off Treaty.

5. The Joint Statement of 18 July 2005, recognized that India is ready to assume the same responsibilities and practices as other leading countries with advanced nuclear technology, such as the United States. India has an impeccable record in non-proliferation. The Joint Statement acknowledges

that India's nuclear programme has both a military and a civilian component. Both sides had agreed that the purpose was not to constrain India's strategic programme but to enable resumption of full civil nuclear energy cooperation in order to enhance global energy and environmental security. Such cooperation was predicated on the assumption that any international civil nuclear energy cooperation (including by the US) offered to India in the civilian sector should, firstly, not be diverted away from civilian purposes, and secondly, should not be transferred from India to third countries without safeguards. These concepts will be reflected in the Safeguards Agreement to be negotiated by India with IAEA.

6. India's nuclear programme is unique as it is the only state with nuclear weapons not to have begun with a dedicated military programme. It must be appreciated that the strategic programme is an offshoot of research on nuclear power programme and consequently, it is embedded in a larger undifferentiated programme. Identification of purely civilian facilities and programmes that have no strategic implications poses a particular challenge. Therefore, facilities identified as civilian in the Separation Plan will be offered for safeguards in phases to be decided by India. The nature of the facility concerned, the activities undertaken in it, the national security significance of materials and the location of the facilities are factors taken into account in undertaking the separation process. This is solely an Indian determination.

7. The nuclear establishment in India not only built nuclear reactors but promoted the growth of a national industrial infrastructure. Nuclear power generation was envisaged as a three-stage programme with PHWRs chosen for deployment in the first stage. As indigenous reactors were set up, several innovative design improvements were carried out based on Indian R&D and a standardized design was evolved. The research and technology development spanned the entire spectrum of the nuclear fuel cycle including the front end and the back end. Success in the technologies for the back end of the fuel cycle allowed us to launch the second stage of the programme by constructing a Fast Breeder Test Reactor. This reactor has operated for 20 years based on a unique carbide fuel and has achieved all technology objectives. We have now proceeded further and are constructing a 500 MWe Prototype Fast Breeder Reactor. Simultaneously, we have launched design and development of reactors aimed at thorium utilization and incorporating inherent safety features.

8. Concepts such as grid connectivity are not relevant to the separation exercise. Issues related to fuel resource sustainability, technical design and economic viability, as well as smooth operation of reactors are relevant factors. This would necessitate grid connectivity irrespective of whether the reactor concerned is civilian or not civilian.

9. It must be recognized that the Indian nuclear programme still has a relatively narrow base and cannot be expected to adopt solutions that might

be deemed viable by much larger programmes. A comparison of the number of reactors and the total installed capacity between India and the P-5 brings this out graphically:

Country	Number of Reactors	Total Installed Capacity
India	15	3.04 GWe (2.8% of the total production)
USA	104 (103 operational)	99.21 GWe (19.9% of the total production)
France	59	63.36 GWe (78.1% of the total production)
UK	23	11.85 GWe (19.4% of the total production)
Russia	31	21.74 GWe (15.6% of the total production)
China	9	6.602 GWe (2.2% of the total production)

Source: Nuclear Energy Institute, Washington DC.

10. Another factor to be taken into account is the small capacity of the reactors produced indigenously by India, some of which would remain outside safeguards. Therefore, in assessing the extent of safeguards coverage, it would be important to look at both the number of reactors and the percentage of installed capacity covered. An average Indian reactor is of 220 MW and its output is significantly smaller than the standard reactor in a P-5 economy. The chart below illustrates this aspect:

Country	Most Common reactor	Number of such reactors
India	PHWRs 220 MWe	12
USA	69 PWRs and 34 BWRs.	Most plants are in the range of 1000-1250 MWe 51 Reactors in the range of 1000 MWe to 1250 MWe
France	PWRs of 900 MWe and 1300 MWe size	34 PWRs of 900 MWe and 20 PWRs of 1300 MWe
UK	No standard size. AGR is the most common in the range of 600-700 MWe	14 AGRs
Russia	3rd Generation VVER-1000 PWRs and RBMK 1000 Light Water Graphite Reactors	9 third Generation VVER 1000 PWRs and 11 RBMK 1000 Light Water Graphite Reactors
China	PWRs 984 MWe	Four

Source: Uranium Information Centre, Melbourne.

11. The complexity of the separation process is further enhanced by the limited resources that India has devoted to its nuclear programme as compared to P-5 nations. Moreover, as India expands international cooperation, the percentage of its thermal power reactor installed capacity under safeguards would rise significantly as fresh capacity is added through such cooperation.

12. India's approach to the separation of its civilian nuclear facilities is guided by the following principles:

- Credible, feasible, and implementable in a transparent manner;

- Consistent with the understandings of the 18 July Statement;
- Consistent with India's national security and R&D requirements as well as not prejudicial to the three-stage nuclear programme in India;
- Must be cost effective in its implementation; and
- Must be acceptable to Parliament and public opinion.

13. Based on these principles, India will:

- Include in the civilian list only those facilities offered for safeguards that, after separation, will no longer be engaged in activities of strategic significance.
- The overarching criterion would be a judgement whether subjecting a facility to IAEA safeguards would impact adversely on India's national security.
- However, a facility will be excluded from the civilian list if it is located in a larger hub of strategic significance, notwithstanding the fact that it may not be normally engaged in activities of strategic significance.
- A civilian facility would therefore, be one that India has determined not to be relevant to its strategic programme.

14. Taking the above into account, India, on the basis of reciprocal actions by the US, will adopt the following approach:

(i) **Thermal Power Reactors**: India will identify and offer for safeguards 14 thermal power reactors between 2006 and 2014. This will include the 4 presently safeguarded reactors (TAPS 1&2, RAPS 1&2) and in addition KK 1&2 that are under construction. 8 other PHWRs, each of a capacity of 220 MWe, will be offered. The overall plan will be as follows:

S.No.	Facility	Year offered for safeguards
1.	TAPS 1	2006
2.	TAPS 2	2006
3.	RAPS 1	2006
4.	RAPS 2	2006
5.	KK 1	2006
6.	KK 2	2006
7.	RAPS 5	2007
8.	RAPS 6	2008
9.	RAPS 3	2010
10.	RAPS 4	2010
11.	KAPS 1	2012
12.	KAPS 2	2012
13.	NAPS 1	2014
14.	NAPS 2	2014

The above offer would, in effect, cover 14 out of the 22 thermal power reactors in operation or currently under construction to be placed under safeguards, and would raise the total installed Thermal Power capacity by MWe under safeguards from the present 19% to 65% by 2014.

(ii) **Fast Breeder Reactors**: India is not in a position to accept safeguards on the Prototype Fast Breeder Reactor (PFBR) and the Fast Breeder Test Reactor (FBTR), both located at Kalpakkam. The Fast Breeder Programme is at the R&D stage and its technology will take time to mature and reach an advanced stage of development.

(iii) **Future Reactors**: India has decided to place under safeguards all future civilian thermal power reactors and civilian breeder reactors, and the Government of India retains the sole right to determine such reactors as civilian.

(iv) **Research Reactors**: India will permanently shut down the CIRUS reactor, in 2010. It will also be prepared to shift the fuel core of the APSARA reactor that was purchased from France outside BARC and make the fuel core available to be placed under safeguards in 2010.

(v) **Upstream facilities**: The following upstream facilities would be identified and separated as civilian:
  - List of specific facilities in the Nuclear Fuel Complex, Hyderabad which will be offered for safeguards by 2008 is give below:
    - Uranium Oxide Plant (Block A)
    - Ceramic Fuel Fabrication Plant (Palletizing) (Block A)
    - Ceramic Fuel Fabrication Plant (Assembly) (Block A)
    - Enriched Uranium Oxide Plant
    - Enriched Fuel Fabrication Plant
    - Gadolinia Facility
  - The Heavy Water Production plants at Thal, Tuticorin and Hazira are proposed to be designated for civilian use between 2006-2009. We do not consider these plants as relevant for safeguards purposes.

(vi) **Downstream facilities**: The following downstream facilities would be identified and separated as civilian:
    - India is willing to accept safeguards in the 'campaign' mode after 2010 in respect of the Tarapur Power Reactor Fuel Reprocessing Plant.
    - The Tarapur and Rajasthan 'Away From Reactors' spent fuel storage pools would be made available for safeguards with appropriate phasing between 2006-09.

(vii) **Research Facilities**: India will declare the following facilities as civilian:
    (a) Tata Institute of Fundamental research
    (b) Variable Energy Cyclotron Centre
    (c) Saha Institute of Nuclear Physics
    (d) Institute for Plasma Research
    (e) Institute of Mathematics Science
    (f) Institute of Physics
    (g) Tata Memorial Centre
    (h) Board of Radiation and Isotope Technology
    (i) Harish Chandra Research Institute

These facilities are safeguards-irrelevant. It is our expectation that they will play a prominent role in international cooperation.

15. **Safeguards**:

(a) The United States has conveyed its commitment to the reliable supply of fuel to India. Consistent with the July 18, 2005 Joint Statement, the United States has also reaffirmed its assurance to create the necessary conditions for India to have assured and full access to fuel for its reactors. As part of its implementation of the July 18, 2005 Joint Statement the United States is committed to seeking agreement from the U.S. Congress to amend its domestic laws and to work with friends and allies to adjust the practices of the Nuclear Suppliers' Group to create the necessary conditions for India to obtain full access to the international fuel market, including reliable, uninterrupted and continual access to fuel supplies from firms in several nations.

(b) To further guard against any disruption of fuel supplies, the United States is prepared to take the following additional steps:

  (i) The United States is willing to incorporate assurances regarding fuel supply in the bilateral U.S.-India agreement on peaceful uses of nuclear energy under Section 123 of the U.S. Atomic Energy Act, which would be submitted to the U.S. Congress.

  (ii) The United States will join India in seeking to negotiate with the IAEA an India-specific fuel supply agreement.

  (iii) The United States will support an Indian effort to develop a strategic reserve of nuclear fuel to guard against any disruption of supply over the lifetime of India's reactors.

  (iv) If despite these arrangements, a disruption of fuel supplies to India occurs, the United States and India would jointly convene a group of friendly supplier countries to include countries such as Russia, France and the United Kingdom to pursue such measures as would restore fuel supply to India.

(c) In light of the above understandings with the United States, an India-specific safeguards agreement will be negotiated between India and the IAEA providing for safeguards to guard against withdrawal of safeguarded nuclear material from civilian use at any time as well as providing for corrective measures that India may take to ensure uninterrupted operation of its civilian nuclear reactors in the event of disruption of foreign fuel supplies. Taking this into account, India will place its civilian nuclear facilities under India-specific safeguards in perpetuity and negotiate an appropriate safeguards agreement to this end with the IAEA.

16. This plan is in conformity with the commitments made to Parliament by the Government.

{Tabled in Parliament on May 11, 2006}

Agreement for Cooperation Between the government of the United States of America and the Government of India Concerning Peaceful Uses of Nuclear Energy [Agreed Text-123 Agreement], August 1, 2007, along with an accompanying letter from President George W. Bush to the US Congress

The Government of India and the Government of the United States of America, hereinafter referred to as the Parties,

RECOGNIZING the significance of civilian nuclear energy for meeting growing global energy demands in a cleaner and more efficient manner;

DESIRING to cooperate extensively in the full development and use of nuclear energy for peaceful purposes as a means of achieving energy security, on a stable, reliable and predictable basis;

WISHING to develop such cooperation on the basis of mutual respect for sovereignty, non-interference in each other's internal affairs, equality, mutual benefit, reciprocity and with due respect for each other's nuclear programmes;

DESIRING to establish the necessary legal framework and basis for cooperation concerning peaceful uses of nuclear energy;

AFFIRMING that cooperation under this Agreement is between two States possessing advanced nuclear technology, both Parties having the same benefits and advantages, both committed to preventing WMD proliferation;

NOTING the understandings expressed in the India-U.S. Joint Statement of July 18, 2005 to enable full civil nuclear energy cooperation with India covering aspects of the associated nuclear fuel cycle;

AFFIRMING their support for the objectives of the International Atomic Energy Agency (IAEA) and its safeguards system, as applicable to India and the United States of America, and its importance in ensuring that international cooperation in development and use of nuclear energy for peaceful purposes is carried out under arrangements that will not contribute to the proliferation of nuclear weapons or other nuclear explosive devices;

NOTING their respective commitments to safety and security of peaceful uses of nuclear energy, to adequate physical protection of nuclear material and effective national export controls;

MINDFUL that peaceful nuclear activities must be undertaken with a view to protecting the environment;

MINDFUL of their shared commitment to preventing the proliferation of weapons of mass destruction; and

DESIROUS of strengthening the strategic partnership between them;

Have agreed on the following:

ARTICLE 1 — DEFINITIONS

For the purposes of this Agreement:

(A) "By-product material" means any radioactive material (except special fissionable material) yielded in or made radioactive by exposure to the radiation incident to the process of producing or utilizing special fissionable material. By-product material shall not be subject to safeguards or any other form of verification under this Agreement, unless it has been decided otherwise by prior mutual agreement in writing between the two Parties.

(B) "Component" means a component part of equipment, or other item so designated by agreement of the Parties.

(C) "Conversion" means any of the normal operations in the nuclear fuel cycle, preceding fuel fabrication and excluding enrichment, by which uranium is transformed from one chemical form to another – for example, from uranium hexafluoride (UF6) to uranium dioxide (UO2) or from uranium oxide to metal.

(D) "Decommissioning" means the actions taken at the end of a facility's useful life to retire the facility from service in the manner that provides adequate protection for the health and safety of the decommissioning workers and the general public, and for the environment. These actions can range from closing down the facility and a minimal removal of nuclear material coupled with continuing maintenance and surveillance, to a complete removal of residual radioactivity in excess of levels acceptable for unrestricted use of the facility and its site.

(E) "Dual-Use Item" means a nuclear related item which has a technical use in both nuclear and non-nuclear applications.

(F) "Equipment" means any equipment in nuclear operation including reactor, reactor pressure vessel, reactor fuel charging and discharging equipment, reactor control rods, reactor pressure tubes, reactor primary coolant pumps, zirconium tubing, equipment for fuel fabrication and any other item so designated by the Parties.

(G) "High enriched uranium" means uranium enriched to twenty percent or greater in the isotope 235.

(H) "Information" means any information that is not in the public domain and is transferred in any form pursuant to this Agreement and so designated and documented in hard copy or digital form by mutual agreement by the Parties that it shall be subject to this Agreement, but will cease to be information whenever the Party transferring the information or any third party legitimately releases it into the public domain.

(I) "Low enriched uranium" means uranium enriched to less than twenty percent in the isotope 235.

(J) "Major critical component" means any part or group of parts essential to the operation of a sensitive nuclear facility or heavy water production facility.

(K) "Non-nuclear material" means heavy water, or any other material suitable for use in a reactor to slow down high velocity neutrons and increase the likelihood of further fission, as may be jointly designated by the appropriate authorities of the Parties.

(L) "Nuclear material" means (1) source material, and (2) special fissionable material. "Source material" means uranium containing the mixture of isotopes occurring in nature; uranium depleted in the isotope 235; thorium; any of the foregoing in the form of metal, alloy, chemical compound, or concentrate; any other material containing one or more of the foregoing in such concentration as the Board of Governors of the IAEA shall from time to time determine; and such other materials as the Board of Governors of the IAEA may determine or as may be agreed by the appropriate authorities of both Parties. "Special fissionable material" means plutonium, uranium-233, uranium enriched in the isotope 233 or 235, any substance containing one or more of the foregoing, and such other substances as the Board of Governors of the IAEA may determine or as may be agreed by the appropriate authorities of both Parties. "Special fissionable material" does not include "source material". Any determination by the Board of Governors of the IAEA under Article XX of that Agency's Statute or otherwise that amends the list of materials considered to be "source material" or "special fissionable material" shall only have effect under this Agreement when both Parties to this Agreement have informed each other in writing that they accept such amendment.

(M) "Peaceful purposes" include the use of information, nuclear material, equipment or components in such fields as research, power generation, medicine, agriculture and industry, but do not include use in, research on, or development of any nuclear explosive device or any other military purpose. Provision of power for a military base drawn from any power network, production of radioisotopes to be used for medical purposes in military environment for diagnostics, therapy and sterility assurance, and other similar purposes as may be mutually agreed by the Parties shall not be regarded as military purpose.

(N) "Person" means any individual or any entity subject to the territorial jurisdiction of either Party but does not include the Parties.

(O) "Reactor" means any apparatus, other than a nuclear weapon or other nuclear explosive device, in which a self-sustaining fission chain reaction is maintained by utilizing uranium, plutonium, or thorium or any combination thereof.

(P) "Sensitive nuclear facility" means any facility designed or used primarily for uranium enrichment, reprocessing of nuclear fuel, or fabrication of nuclear fuel containing plutonium.

(Q) "Sensitive nuclear technology" means any information that is not in the public domain and that is important to the design, construction, fabrication, operation, or maintenance of any sensitive nuclear facility, or other such information that may be so designated by agreement of the parties.

ARTICLE 2 – SCOPE OF COOPERATION

1. The Parties shall cooperate in the use of nuclear energy for peaceful purposes in accordance with the provisions of this Agreement. Each Party shall implement this Agreement in accordance with its respective applicable treaties, national laws, regulations, and license requirements concerning the use of nuclear energy for peaceful purposes.

2. The purpose of the Agreement being to enable full civil nuclear energy cooperation between the Parties, the Parties may pursue cooperation in all relevant areas to include, but not limited to, the following:

   a. Advanced nuclear energy research and development in such areas as may be agreed between the Parties;

   b. Nuclear safety matters of mutual interest and competence, as set out in Article 3;

   c. Facilitation of exchange of scientists for visits, meetings, symposia and collaborative research;

   d. Full civil nuclear cooperation activities covering nuclear reactors and aspects of the associated nuclear fuel cycle including technology transfer on an industrial or commercial scale between the Parties or authorized persons;

   e. Development of a strategic reserve of nuclear fuel to guard against any disruption of supply over the lifetime of India's reactors;

   f. Advanced research and development in nuclear sciences including but not limited to biological research, medicine, agriculture and industry, environment and climate change;

g. Supply between the Parties, whether for use by or for the benefit of the Parties or third countries, of nuclear material;

h. Alteration in form or content of nuclear material as provided for in Article 6;

i. Supply between the Parties of equipment, whether for use by or for the benefit of the Parties or third countries;

j. Controlled thermonuclear fusion including in multilateral projects; and

k. Other areas of mutual interest as may be agreed by the Parties.

3. Transfer of nuclear material, non-nuclear material, equipment, components and information under this Agreement may be undertaken directly between the Parties or through authorized persons. Such transfers shall be subject to this Agreement and to such additional terms and conditions as may be agreed by the Parties. Nuclear material, non-nuclear material, equipment, components and information transferred from the territory of one Party to the territory of the other Party, whether directly or through a third country, will be regarded as having been transferred pursuant to this Agreement only upon confirmation, by the appropriate authority of the recipient Party to the appropriate authority of the supplier Party that such items both will be subject to the Agreement and have been received by the recipient Party.

4. The Parties affirm that the purpose of this Agreement is to provide for peaceful nuclear cooperation and not to affect the unsafeguarded nuclear activities of either Party. Accordingly, nothing in this Agreement shall be interpreted as affecting the rights of the Parties to use for their own purposes nuclear material, non-nuclear material, equipment, components, information or technology produced, acquired or developed by them independent of any nuclear material, non-nuclear material, equipment, components, information or technology transferred to them pursuant to this agreement. This Agreement shall be implemented in a manner so as not to hinder or otherwise interfere with any other activities involving the use of nuclear material, non-nuclear material, equipment, components, information or technology and military nuclear facilities produced, acquired or developed by them independent of this Agreement for their own purposes.

ARTICLE 3 – TRANSFER OF INFORMATION

1. Information concerning the use of nuclear energy for peaceful purposes may be transferred between the Parties. Transfers of information may be accomplished through reports, data banks and computer programs and any other means mutually agreed to by the Parties. Fields that may be covered include, but shall not be limited to, the following:

a. Research, development, design, construction, operation, maintenance and use of reactors, reactor experiments, and decommissioning;

b. The use of nuclear material in physical, chemical, radiological and biological research, medicine, agriculture and industry;

c. Fuel cycle activities to meet future world-wide civil nuclear energy needs, including multilateral approaches to which they are parties for ensuring nuclear fuel supply and appropriate techniques for management of nuclear wastes;

d. Advanced research and development in nuclear science and technology;

e. Health, safety, and environmental considerations related to the foregoing;

f. Assessments of the role nuclear power may play in national energy plans;

g. Codes, regulations and standards for the nuclear industry;

h. Research on controlled thermonuclear fusion including bilateral activities and contributions toward multilateral projects such as the International Thermonuclear Experimental Reactor (ITER); and

i. Any other field mutually agreed to by the Parties.

2. Cooperation pursuant to this Article may include, but is not limited to, training, exchange of personnel, meetings, exchange of samples, materials and instruments for experimental purposes and a balanced participation in joint studies and projects.

3. This Agreement does not require the transfer of any information regarding matters outside the scope of this Agreement, or information that the Parties are not permitted under their respective treaties, national laws, or regulations to transfer.

4. Restricted Data, as defined by each Party, shall not be transferred under this Agreement.

ARTICLE 4 – NUCLEAR TRADE

1. The Parties shall facilitate nuclear trade between themselves in the mutual interests of their respective industry, utilities and consumers and also, where appropriate, trade between third countries and either Party of items obligated to the other party. The Parties recognize that reliability of supplies is essential to ensure smooth and uninterrupted operation of nuclear facilities and that industry in both the Parties needs continuing reassurance that deliveries can be made on time in order to plan for the efficient operation of nuclear installations.

2. Authorizations, including export and import licenses as well as authorizations or consents to third parties, relating to trade, industrial operations or nuclear material movement should be consistent with the sound and efficient administration of this Agreement and should not be used to restrict trade. It is further agreed that if the relevant authority of the concerned Party considers that an application cannot be processed within a two month

period it shall immediately, upon request, provide reasoned information to the submitting Party. In the event of a refusal to authorize an application or a delay exceeding four months from the date of the first application the Party of the submitting persons or undertakings may call for urgent consultations under Article 13 of this Agreement, which shall take place at the earliest opportunity and in any case not later than 30 days after such a request.

ARTICLE 5— TRANSFER OF NUCLEAR MATERIAL, NON-NUCLEAR MATERIAL, EQUIPMENT, COMPONENTS AND RELATED TECHNOLOGY

1. Nuclear material, non-nuclear material, equipment and components may be transferred for applications, consistent with this Agreement. Any special fissionable material transferred under this Agreement shall be low enriched uranium, except as provided in paragraph 5.

2. Sensitive nuclear technology, heavy water production technology, sensitive nuclear facilities, heavy water production facilities and major critical components of such facilities may be transferred under this Agreement pursuant to an amendment to this Agreement. Transfers of dual-use items that could be used in enrichment, reprocessing or heavy water production facilities will be subject to the Parties' respective applicable laws, regulations and license policies.

3. Natural or low enriched uranium may be transferred for use as fuel in reactor experiments and in reactors, for conversion or fabrication, or for such other purposes as may be agreed to by the Parties.

4. The quantity of nuclear material transferred under this Agreement shall be consistent with any of the following purposes: use in reactor experiments or the loading of reactors, the efficient and continuous conduct of such reactor experiments or operation of reactors for their lifetime, use as samples, standards, detectors, and targets and the accomplishment of other purposes as may be agreed by the Parties.

5. Small quantities of special fissionable material may be transferred for use as samples, standards, detectors, and targets, and for such other purposes as the Parties may agree.

6. (a) The United States has conveyed its commitment to the reliable supply of fuel to India. Consistent with the July 18, 2005, Joint Statement, the United States has also reaffirmed its assurance to create the necessary conditions for India to have assured and full access to fuel for its reactors. As part of its implementation of the July 18, 2005, Joint Statement the United States is committed to seeking agreement from the U.S. Congress to amend its domestic laws and to work with friends and allies to adjust the practices of the Nuclear Suppliers' Group to create the necessary conditions for India to obtain full access to the international fuel

market, including reliable, uninterrupted and continual access to fuel supplies from firms in several nations.

(b) To further guard against any disruption of fuel supplies, the United States is prepared to take the following additional steps:

   (i) The United States is willing to incorporate assurances regarding fuel supply in the bilateral U.S. – India agreement on peaceful uses of nuclear energy under Section 123 of the U.S. Atomic Energy Act, which would be submitted to the U.S. Congress.

   (ii) The United States will join India in seeking to negotiate with the IAEA an India-specific fuel supply agreement.

   (iii) The United States will support an Indian effort to develop a strategic reserve of nuclear fuel to guard against any disruption of supply over the lifetime of India's reactors.

   (iv) If despite these arrangements, a disruption of fuel supplies to India occurs, the United States and India would jointly convene a group of friendly supplier countries to include countries such as Russia, France and the United Kingdom to pursue such measures as would restore fuel supply to India.

(c) In light of the above understandings with the United States, an India specific safeguards agreement will be negotiated between India and the IAEA providing for safeguards to guard against withdrawal of safeguarded nuclear material from civilian use at any time as well as providing for corrective measures that India may take to ensure uninterrupted operation of its civilian nuclear reactors in the event of disruption of foreign fuel supplies. Taking this into account, India will place its civilian nuclear facilities under India-specific safeguards in perpetuity and negotiate an appropriate safeguards agreement to this end with the IAEA.

ARTICLE 6 – NUCLEAR FUEL CYCLE ACTIVITIES

In keeping with their commitment to full civil nuclear cooperation, both Parties, as they do with other states with advanced nuclear technology, may carry out the following nuclear fuel cycle activities:

   (i) Within the territorial jurisdiction of either Party, enrichment up to twenty percent in the isotope 235 of uranium transferred pursuant to this Agreement, as well as of uranium used in or produced through the use of equipment so transferred, may be carried out.

   (ii) Irradiation within the territorial jurisdiction of either Party of plutonium, uranium-233, high enriched uranium and irradiated nuclear material transferred pursuant to this Agreement or used in or produced through the use of non-nuclear material, nuclear material or equipment so transferred may be carried out.

(iii) With a view to implementing full civil nuclear cooperation as envisioned in the Joint Statement of the Parties of July 18, 2005, the Parties grant each other consent to reprocess or otherwise alter in form or content nuclear material transferred pursuant to this Agreement and nuclear material and by-product material used in or produced through the use of nuclear material, non-nuclear material, or equipment so transferred. To bring these rights into effect, India will establish a new national reprocessing facility dedicated to reprocessing safeguarded nuclear material under IAEA safeguards and the Parties will agree on arrangements and procedures under which such reprocessing or other alteration in form or content will take place in this new facility. Consultations on arrangements and procedures will begin within six months of a request by either Party and will be concluded within one year. The Parties agree on the application of IAEA safeguards to all facilities concerned with the above activities. These arrangements and procedures shall include provisions with respect to physical protection standards set out in Article 8, storage standards set out in Article 7, and environmental protections set forth in Article 11 of this Agreement, and such other provisions as may be agreed by the Parties. Any special fissionable material that may be separated may only be utilized in national facilities under IAEA safeguards.

(iv) Post-irradiation examination involving chemical dissolution or separation of irradiated nuclear material transferred pursuant to this Agreement or irradiated nuclear material used in or produced through the use of non-nuclear material, nuclear material or equipment so transferred may be carried out.

ARTICLE 7 – STORAGE AND RETRANSFERS

1. Plutonium and uranium 233 (except as either may be contained in irradiated fuel elements), and high enriched uranium, transferred pursuant to this Agreement or used in or produced through the use of material or equipment so transferred, may be stored in facilities that are at all times subject, as a minimum, to the levels of physical protection that are set out in IAEA document INFCIRC 225/Rev 4 as it may be revised and accepted by the Parties. Each Party shall record such facilities on a list, made available to the other Party. A Party's list shall be held confidential if that Party so requests. Either Party may make changes to its list by notifying the other Party in writing and receiving a written acknowledgement. Such acknowledgement shall be given no later than thirty days after the receipt of the notification and shall be limited to a statement that the notification has been received. If there are grounds to believe that the provisions of this sub-Article are not being fully complied with, immediate consultations may be called for.

Following upon such consultations, each Party shall ensure by means of such consultations that necessary remedial measures are taken immediately. Such measures shall be sufficient to restore the levels of physical protection referred to above at the facility in question. However, if the Party on whose territory the nuclear material in question is stored determines that such measures are not feasible, it will shift the nuclear material to another appropriate, listed facility it identifies.

2. Nuclear material, non-nuclear material, equipment, components, and information transferred pursuant to this Agreement and any special fissionable material produced through the use of nuclear material, non-nuclear material or equipment so transferred shall not be transferred or re-transferred to unauthorized persons or, unless the Parties agree, beyond the recipient Party's territorial jurisdiction.

ARTICLE 8 – PHYSICAL PROTECTION

1. Adequate physical protection shall be maintained with respect to nuclear material and equipment transferred pursuant to this Agreement and nuclear material used in or produced through the use of nuclear material, non-nuclear material or equipment so transferred.

2. To fulfil the requirement in paragraph 1, each Party shall apply measures in accordance with (i) levels of physical protection at least equivalent to the recommendations published in IAEA document INFCIRC/225/Rev. 4 entitled "The Physical Protection of Nuclear Material and Nuclear Facilities." And in any subsequent revisions of that document agreed to by the Parties, and (ii) the provisions of the 1980 Convention on the Physical Protection of Nuclear Material and any amendments to the Convention that enter into force for both Parties.

3. The Parties will keep each other informed through diplomatic channels of those agencies or authorities having responsibility for ensuring that levels of physical protection for nuclear material in their territory or under their jurisdiction or control are adequately met and having responsibility for coordinating response and recovery operations in the event of unauthorized use or handling of material subject to this Article. The Parties will also keep each other informed through diplomatic channels of the designated points of contact within their national authorities to cooperate on matters of out-of-country transportation and other matters of mutual concern.

4. The provisions of this Article shall be implemented in such a manner as to avoid undue interference in the Parties' peaceful nuclear activities and so as to be consistent with prudent management practices required for the safe and economic conduct of their peaceful nuclear programs.

ARTICLE 9 – PEACEFUL USE

Nuclear material, equipment and components transferred pursuant to this

Agreement and nuclear material and by-product material used in or produced through the use of any nuclear material, equipment, and components so transferred shall not be used by the recipient Party for any nuclear explosive device, for research on or development of any nuclear explosive device or for any military purpose.

ARTICLE 10 – IAEA SAFEGUARDS

1. Safeguards will be maintained with respect to all nuclear materials and equipment transferred pursuant to this Agreement, and with respect to all special fissionable material used in or produced through the use of such nuclear materials and equipment, so long as the material or equipment remains under the jurisdiction or control of the cooperating Party.

2. Taking into account Article 5.6 of this Agreement, India agrees that nuclear material and equipment transferred to India by the United States of America pursuant to this Agreement and any nuclear material used in or produced through the use of nuclear material, non-nuclear material, equipment or components so transferred shall be subject to safeguards in perpetuity in accordance with the India-specific Safeguards Agreement between India and the IAEA (*identifying data*) and an Additional Protocol, when in force.

3. Nuclear material and equipment transferred to the United States of America pursuant to this Agreement and any nuclear material used in or produced through the use of any nuclear material, non-nuclear material, equipment, or components so transferred shall be subject to the Agreement between the United States of America and the IAEA for the application of safeguards in the United States of America, done at Vienna, November 18, 1977, which entered into force on December 9, 1980, and an Additional Protocol, when in force.

4. If the IAEA decides that the application of IAEA safeguards is no longer possible, the supplier and recipient should consult and agree on appropriate verification measures.

5. Each Party shall take such measures as are necessary to maintain and facilitate the application of IAEA safeguards in its respective territory provided for under this Article.

6. Each Party shall establish and maintain a system of accounting for and control of nuclear material transferred pursuant to this Agreement and nuclear material used in or produced through the use of any material, equipment, or components so transferred. The procedures applicable to India shall be those set forth in the India-specific Safeguards Agreement referred to in Paragraph 2 of this Article.

7. Upon the request of either Party, the other Party shall report or permit the IAEA to report to the requesting Party on the status of all inventories of material subject to this Agreement.

8. The provisions of this Article shall be implemented in such a manner as to avoid hampering delay, or undue interference in the Parties' peaceful nuclear activities and so as to be consistent with prudent management practices required for the safe and economic conduct of their peaceful nuclear programs.

ARTICLE 11 - ENVIRONMENTAL PROTECTION

The Parties shall cooperate in following the best practices for minimizing the impact on the environment from any radioactive, chemical or thermal contamination arising from peaceful nuclear activities under this Agreement and in related matters of health and safety.

ARTICLE 12 – IMPLEMENTATION OF THE AGREEMENT

1. This Agreement shall be implemented in a manner designed:
   (a) to avoid hampering or delaying the nuclear activities in the territory of either Party;
   (b) to avoid interference in such activities;
   (c) to be consistent with prudent management practices required for the safe conduct of such activities; and
   (d) to take full account of the long-term requirements of the nuclear energy programs of the Parties.
2. The provisions of this Agreement shall not be used to:
   (a) secure unfair commercial or industrial advantages or to restrict trade to the disadvantage of persons and undertakings of either Party or hamper their commercial or industrial interests, whether international or domestic;
   (b) interfere with the nuclear policy or programs for the promotion of the peaceful uses of nuclear energy including research and development; or
   (c) impede the free movement of nuclear material, non-nuclear material and equipment supplied under this Agreement within the territory of the Parties.
3. When execution of an agreement or contract pursuant to this Agreement between Indian and United States organizations requires exchanges of experts, the Parties shall facilitate entry of the experts to their territories and their stay therein consistent with national laws, regulations and practices. When other cooperation pursuant to this Agreement requires visits of experts, the Parties shall facilitate entry of the experts to their territory and their stay therein consistent with national laws, regulations and practices.

ARTICLE 13 – CONSULTATIONS

1. The Parties undertake to consult at the request of either Party regarding the implementation of this Agreement and the development of further

cooperation in the field of peaceful uses of nuclear energy on a stable, reliable and predictable basis. The Parties recognize that such consultations are between two States with advanced nuclear technology, which have agreed to assume the same responsibilities and practices and acquire the same benefits and advantages as other leading countries with advanced nuclear technology.

2. Each Party shall endeavor to avoid taking any action that adversely affects cooperation envisaged under Article 2 of this Agreement. If either Party at any time following the entry into force of this Agreement does not comply with the provisions of this Agreement, the Parties shall promptly hold consultations with a view to resolving the matter in a way that protects the legitimate interests of both Parties, it being understood that rights of either Party under Article 16.2 remain unaffected.

3. Consultations under this Article may be carried out by a Joint Committee specifically established for this purpose. A Joint Technical Working Group reporting to the Joint Committee will be set up to ensure the fulfilment of the requirements of the Administrative Arrangements referred to in Article 17.

ARTICLE 14 —TERMINATION AND CESSATION OF COOPERATION

1. Either Party shall have the right to terminate this Agreement prior to its expiration on one year's written notice to the other Party. A Party giving notice of termination shall provide the reasons for seeking such termination. The Agreement shall terminate one year from the date of the written notice, unless the notice has been withdrawn by the providing Party in writing prior to the date of termination.

2. Before this Agreement is terminated pursuant to paragraph 1 of this Article, the Parties shall consider the relevant circumstances and promptly hold consultations, as provided in Article 13, to address the reasons cited by the Party seeking termination. The Party seeking termination has the right to cease further cooperation under this Agreement if it determines that a mutually acceptable resolution of outstanding issues has not been possible or cannot be achieved through consultations. The Parties agree to consider carefully the circumstances that may lead to termination or cessation of cooperation. They further agree to take into account whether the circumstances that may lead to termination or cessation resulted from a Party's serious concern about a changed security environment or as a response to similar actions by other States which could impact national security.

3. If a Party seeking termination cites a violation of this Agreement as the reason for notice for seeking termination, the Parties shall consider whether the action was caused inadvertently or otherwise and whether the violation could be considered as material. No violation may be considered as being material unless corresponding to the definition of material violation or breach in the Vienna Convention on the Law of Treaties. If a Party seeking termination

cites a violation of an IAEA safeguards agreement as the reason for notice for seeking termination, a crucial factor will be whether the IAEA Board of Governors has made a finding of non-compliance.

4. Following the cessation of cooperation under this Agreement, either Party shall have the right to require the return by the other Party of any nuclear material, equipment, non-nuclear material or components transferred under this Agreement and any special fissionable material produced through their use. A notice by a Party that is invoking the right of return shall be delivered to the other Party on or before the date of termination of this Agreement. The notice shall contain a statement of the items subject to this Agreement as to which the Party is requesting return. Except as provided in provisions of Article 16.3, all other legal obligations pertaining to this Agreement shall cease to apply with respect to the nuclear items remaining on the territory of the Party concerned upon termination of this Agreement.

5. The two Parties recognize that exercising the right of return would have profound implications for their relations. If either Party seeks to exercise its right pursuant to paragraph 4 of this Article, it shall, prior to the removal from the territory or from the control of the other Party of any nuclear items mentioned in paragraph 4, undertake consultations with the other Party. Such consultations shall give special consideration to the importance of uninterrupted operation of nuclear reactors of the Party concerned with respect to the availability of nuclear energy for peaceful purposes as a means of achieving energy security. Both Parties shall take into account the potential negative consequences of such termination on the on-going contracts and projects initiated under this Agreement of significance for the respective nuclear programmes of either Party.

6. If either Party exercises its right of return pursuant to paragraph 4 of this Article, it shall, prior to the removal from the territory or from the control of the other Party, compensate promptly that Party for the fair market value thereof and for the costs incurred as a consequence of such removal. If the return of nuclear items is required, the Parties shall agree on methods and arrangements for the return of the items, the relevant quantity of the items to be returned, and the amount of compensation that would have to be paid by the Party exercising the right to the other Party.

7. Prior to return of nuclear items, the Parties shall satisfy themselves that full safety, radiological and physical protection measures have been ensured in accordance with their existing national regulations and that the transfers pose no unreasonable risk to either Party, countries through which the nuclear items may transit and to the global environment and are in accordance with existing international regulations.

8. The Party seeking the return of nuclear items shall ensure that the timing, methods and arrangements for return of nuclear items are in accordance with paragraphs 5, 6 and 7. Accordingly, the consultations between

the Parties shall address mutual commitments as contained in Article 5.6. It is not the purpose of the provisions of this Article regarding cessation of cooperation and right of return to derogate from the rights of the Parties under Article 5.6.

9. The arrangements and procedures concluded pursuant to Article 6(iii) shall be subject to suspension by either Party in exceptional circumstances, as defined by the Parties, after consultations have been held between the Parties aimed at reaching mutually acceptable resolution of outstanding issues, while taking into account the effects of such suspension on other aspects of cooperation under this Agreement.

ARTICLE 15 – SETTLEMENT OF DISPUTES

Any dispute concerning the interpretation or implementation of the provisions of this Agreement shall be promptly negotiated by the Parties with a view to resolving that dispute.

ARTICLE 16 – ENTRY INTO FORCE AND DURATION

1. This Agreement shall enter into force on the date on which the Parties exchange diplomatic notes informing each other that they have completed all applicable requirements for its entry into force.

2. This Agreement shall remain in force for a period of 40 years. It shall continue in force thereafter for additional periods of 10 years each. Each Party may, by giving 6 months written notice to the other Party, terminate this Agreement at the end of the initial 40 year period or at the end of any subsequent 10 year period.

3. Notwithstanding the termination or expiration of this Agreement or withdrawal of a Party from this Agreement, Articles 5.6 (c), 6, 7, 8, 9, 10 and 15 shall continue in effect so long as any nuclear material, non-nuclear material, by-product material, equipment or components subject to these articles remains in the territory of the Party concerned or under its jurisdiction or control anywhere, or until such time as the Parties agree that such nuclear material is no longer usable for any nuclear activity relevant from the point of view of safeguards.

4. This Agreement shall be implemented in good faith and in accordance with the principles of international law.

5. The Parties may consult, at the request of either Party, on possible amendments to this Agreement. This Agreement may be amended if the Parties so agree. Any amendment shall enter into force on the date on which the Parties exchange diplomatic notes informing each other that their respective internal legal procedures necessary for the entry into force have been completed.

ARTICLE 17—ADMINISTRATIVE ARRANGEMENT

1. The appropriate authorities of the Parties shall establish an Administrative Arrangement in order to provide for the effective implementation of the provisions of this Agreement.

2. The principles of fungibility and equivalence shall apply to nuclear material and non-nuclear material subject to this Agreement. Detailed provisions for applying these principles shall be set forth in the Administrative Arrangement.

3. The Administrative Arrangement established pursuant to this Article may be amended by agreement of the appropriate authorities of the Parties.

IN WITNESS WHEREOF the undersigned, being duly authorized, have signed this Agreement.

DONE at _____, this _____ day of _____, 2000, in duplicate.

FOR THE GOVERNMENT OF THE   FOR THE GOVERNMENT
UNITED STATES OF AMERICA   OF INDIA

AGREEMENT MINUTE

During the negotiation of the Agreement for Cooperation Between the Government of India and the Government of the United States of America concerning Peaceful Uses of Nuclear Energy ("the Agreement") signed today, the following understandings, which shall be an integral part of the Agreement, were reached.

Proportionality

For the purposes of implementing the rights specified in Articles 6 and 7 of the Agreement with respect to special fissionable material and by-product material produced through the use of nuclear material and non-nuclear material, respectively, transferred pursuant to the Agreement and not used in or produced through the use of equipment transferred pursuant to the Agreement, such rights shall in practice be applied to that proportion of special fissionable material and by-product material produced that represents the ratio of transferred nuclear material and non-nuclear material respectively, used in the production of the special fissionable material and by-product material to the total amount of nuclear material and non-nuclear material so used, and similarly for subsequent generations.

By-product material

The Parties agree that reporting and exchanges of information on by-product material subject to the Agreement will be limited to the following:

(1) Both Parties would comply with the provisions as contained in the IAEA document GOV/1999/19/Rev. 2, with regard to by-product material subject to the Agreement.

(2) With regard to tritium subject to the Agreement, the Parties will exchange annually information pertaining to its disposition for peaceful purposes consistent with Article 9 of this Agreement.

FOR THE GOVERNMENT OF THE   FOR THE GOVERNMENT
UNITED STATES OF AMERICA   OF INDIA

Questions for the Record Submitted to Assistant Secretary for Legislative Affairs, Jeffrey T. Bergner by Chairman Tom Lantos, US Congress, House Committee on Foreign Affairs, Oct. 5, 2007 – Clarification by the US Department of State about Provisions in the 123 Agreement

Question 1: What is the Administration's expectation regarding the likely economic benefits of this partnership, including India's purchase of U.S. nuclear fuel, reactors, and technology?

Answer: We are confident that this initiative will yield important economic benefits to the private sector in the United States. India currently has 15 operating thermal power reactors with seven under construction, but it intends to increase this number significantly. Meeting this ramp-up in demand for civil nuclear reactors, technology, fuel, and support services holds the promise of opening new markets for the United States. Indian officials indicate they plan to import at least eight 1000-megawatt power reactors by 2012, as well as additional reactors in the years ahead. Studies suggest that if American vendors win just two of these reactor contracts, it could add 3,000-5,000 new direct jobs and 10,000-15,000 indirect jobs in the United States. The Indian government has conveyed to us its commitment to enable full U.S. participation in India's civil nuclear growth and modernization. At least 15 nuclear-related U.S. firms, including General Electric and Westinghouse, participated in a business delegation led by the Commerce Department in December 2006.

In addition, participation in India's market will help make the American nuclear power industry globally competitive, thereby benefiting our own domestic nuclear power sector. This initiative will permit U.S. companies to enter the lucrative and growing Indian market—something they are currently prohibited from doing. In addition, access to Indian nuclear infrastructure will allow U.S. companies to build reactors more competitively here and in the rest of the world—not just India.

Question 2: What scientific and technical benefits does the U.S. expect as a result of this agreement?

Answer: A successfully implemented civil nuclear cooperation initiative with India will allow scientists from both our nations to work together in making nuclear energy safer, less expensive, more proliferation-resistant, and more efficient. Newly forged partnerships in this area may also facilitate scientific advancement in the many facets of nuclear energy technology. Indian involvement in international fora such as the International Thermonuclear Experimental Reactor and the Generation-IV Forum can expand the potential for innovation in the future of nuclear energy, as well as the stake of emerging countries in developing cheaper sources of energy.

In addition, we could choose to allow India to participate in the future in the Department of Energy's Global Nuclear Energy Partnership and collaborate with other countries with advanced nuclear technology in developing new proliferation-resistant nuclear technology. Such interaction could only be contemplated subsequent to the completion of the civil nuclear cooperation initiative.

Question 3: Does the Administration believe that the nuclear cooperation agreement with India overrides the Hyde Act regarding any apparent conflicts, discrepancies, or inconsistencies? Does this include provisions in the Hyde Act which do not appear in the nuclear cooperation agreement?

Answer: In his September 19 statement, Assistant Secretary Boucher twice made clear that "we think [the proposed 123 Agreement with India] is in full conformity with the Hyde Act." Indeed, the Administration is confident that the proposed agreement is consistent with the legal requirements of both the Hyde Act and the Atomic Energy Act. The proposed agreement satisfies the particular requirements of Section 123 of the Atomic Energy Act with the exception of the requirement for full-scope safeguards, which the President is expected to exempt prior to the submission of the agreement to Congress for its approval, as provided for in section 104 of the Hyde Act. The agreement is also fully consistent with the legal requirements of the Hyde Act.

Question 4: Why are dual-use items for use in sensitive nuclear facilities mentioned in the proposed U.S.-Indian nuclear cooperation agreement, when such items are not transferred pursuant to an agreement for cooperation?

Answer: The Agreement provides for such transfers, consistent with the "full" cooperation envisaged by the July 18, 2005 Joint Statement. Article 5(2) of the 123 Agreement provides for such transfers by the Parties, however, only "subject to their respective applicable laws, regulations and license policies." It is not unusual for U.S. agreements for peaceful nuclear cooperation to provide for transfers of items that would in fact be transferred outside the agreement, if they are to be transferred at all. For example, many U.S. agreements, including the proposed U.S.-India Agreement, cover transfers of "components" and "information," even though such transfers would normally take place outside the agreement. Most importantly, it should be noted that while the proposed U.S.-India Agreement provides for transfer of the items in question, as a framework agreement it does not compel any such transfers; and as a matter of policy the United States does not transfer dual-use items for use in sensitive nuclear facilities.

Question 5: Is it the intention of the U.S. government to assist India in the design, construction, or operation of sensitive nuclear technologies through the transfer of dual-use items outside the agreement? If so, how is this consistent with longstanding U.S. policy to discourage the spread of sensitive nuclear technology and with Section 103(a)(5) of the Hyde Act? Has the U.S. transferred such dual-use items to sensitive nuclear facilities in other cooperating parties and, if so, to which countries?

Answer: Consistent with standing U.S. policy, the U.S. government will not assist India in the design, construction, or operation of sensitive nuclear technologies through the transfer of dual-use items, whether under the Agreement or outside the Agreement. The United States rarely transfers dual-use items for sensitive nuclear activities to any cooperating party and no such transfers are currently pending.

Question 6: Does the Administration have any plan or intention to negotiate an amendment to the proposed U.S.-India agreement to transfer to India sensitive nuclear facilities or critical components of such facilities? If so, how would such transfers be consistent with the above-cited provision of the Hyde Act and the long-standing U.S. policy to discourage the spread of such technologies?

Answer: The Administration does not plan to negotiate an amendment to the proposed U.S.-India Agreement to transfer to India sensitive nuclear facilities or critical components of such facilities.

Question 7: Is it the intention of the Administration to transfer or allow the transfer of sensitive nuclear technology outside of the U.S.-India nuclear cooperation agreement? If so, how would such transfers be consistent with the Hyde Act and the long-standing U.S. policy to discourage the spread of such technologies?

Answer: Although the Hyde Act allows for transfers of sensitive nuclear technology under certain circumstances, it is not the intention of the Administration to transfer or allow the transfer of sensitive nuclear technology to India outside the U.S.-India Agreement for peaceful nuclear cooperation.

Question 8: What is the State Department's position regarding the manner by which an amendment to the proposed U.S.-India nuclear cooperation agreement would be submitted to the Congress? Because it would be an amendment to an exempted agreement, does the Administration agree that it would require a Joint Resolution of Approval before entering into force?

Answer: We would look at any future amendment on a case-by-case basis. Regarding the specific example discussed in the question, the Administration has no plan or intention to negotiate an amendment to the proposed U.S.-India agreement to transfer to India sensitive nuclear facilities or critical components of such facilities.

Question 9: Would the U.S. limit any transfer of dual-use technology to India's enrichment and reprocessing facilities to those that were participants in a bilateral or multinational program to develop proliferation-resistant fuel cycle technologies?

Answer: As previously stated, it is not the intention of the U.S. government to assist India in the design, construction, or operation of sensitive nuclear technologies through the transfer of dual-use items, whether under the Agreement or outside the Agreement. India does not have any facilities that participate in a bilateral or multinational program to develop proliferation-resistant fuel cycle technologies. If India were to develop such facilities, potential dual-use transfers could be considered only under the exceptions granted in the Hyde Act.

Question 10: Why does Paragraph 4 of Article 10 of the U.S.-India agreement rely on an IAEA decision regarding the impossibility of applying safeguards rather than either party's judgment that the Agency is not or will not be applying safeguards? Would this permit a situation to arise in which there were a period of time during which safeguards might not be applied but the IAEA had not reached a conclusion that the application of safeguards was no longer possible?

Answer: Paragraph 4 of Article 10 addresses one situation—the same situation as is addressed in paragraph 4(a) of the Nuclear Suppliers' Group Guidelines—in which fall-back safeguards would be required because the International Atomic Energy Agency has decided that the application of Agency safeguards is no longer possible. It does not, however, constitute the fundamental basis provided by the Agreement for the application, if needed, of fall-back safeguards. That basis is provided by Paragraph 1 of Article 10 which states categorically that "[s]afeguards will be maintained with respect to all nuclear materials and equipment transferred pursuant to this Agreement, and with respect to all special fissionable material used in or produced through the use of such nuclear materials and equipment, so long as the material or equipment remains under the jurisdiction or control of the cooperating Party."

This guarantee follows the formula prescribed by section 123(a)(1) of the U.S. Atomic Energy Act of 1954, as amended. Taken together with paragraph 3 of Article 16 of the Agreement, it provides that safeguards in some form—International Atomic Energy Agency or other—must *always* be maintained with respect to all nuclear items in India subject to the Agreement so long as they remain under the jurisdiction or control of India irrespective of the duration of other provisions in the Agreement or whether the Agreement is terminated or suspended for any reason, precisely as section 123(a)(1) of the Atomic Energy Act requires.

Regarding the second part of the question, for the reasons just given, Paragraph 1 of Article 10 precludes there arising such a situation.

Question 11: Why does the provision not call for rectifying measures, as in the Japan agreement? Why does it not call for the parties to immediately enter into arrangements which conform to safeguards principles and procedures of the Agency?

Answer: Different approaches to fall-back safeguards are possible, consistent with the requirement of section 123(a)(1) of the Atomic Energy Act. If for some reason International Atomic Energy Agency safeguards fail to be applied to nuclear items in India subject to the U.S.-India Agreement, the Parties of necessity must enter into arrangements for alternative measures to fulfil the requirement of paragraph 1 of Article 10.

Question 12: Have "appropriate verification measures" been discussed, defined, or otherwise outlined with Indian officials? If Indian officials have shared their views on appropriate verification measures, what are those views? Do U.S. and Indian views diverge and if so, how?

Answer: The United States has not discussed in detail with India what form "appropriate verification measures" might take if the International Atomic Energy Agency decides that it is no longer possible for it to apply safeguards as provided for by paragraph 2 of Article 10 of the U.S.-India Agreement. The United States has expressed its view to India that acceptable alternative measures in that case might range from an alternative safeguards arrangement with the International Atomic Energy Agency, to some other form of international verification. The Government of India has expressed its view that for purposes of implementing the U.S.-India Agreement Agency safeguards can and should be regarded as being "in perpetuity." At the same time it fully appreciates that paragraph 1 of Article 10 of the Agreement does not limit the safeguards required by the Agreement to Agency safeguards.

Question 13: In the U.S. view, how would potential appropriate verification measures provide effectiveness and coverage equivalent to that intended to be provided by safeguards in paragraph 1 of Article 10?

Answer: The "appropriate verification measures" referred to in paragraph 4 of Article 10 would be an alternative to International Atomic Energy Agency safeguards applied pursuant to the India-Agency safeguards agreement referenced in paragraph 2 of Article 10, the implementation of which in the normal course of events would satisfy the safeguards requirement of paragraph 1 of Article 10 with respect to India. If it were no longer possible for the Agency to apply safeguards to nuclear items subject to the U.S.-India Agreement in India, alternative verification measures agreed by the Parties would need to be carried out on some other international basis to maintain continuity of safeguards as required by paragraph 1 of Article 10. The United States would expect such measures to provide effectiveness and coverage equivalent to that intended to be provided by the India-Agency safeguards agreement referenced in paragraph 2 of Article 10, albeit without a necessary role for the International Atomic Energy Agency in their application.

Question 14: Which of the commitments that the United States made in Article 5 are of a binding legal character? Does the Indian Government agree?

Answer: The question quotes paragraph 6 of article 5, which contains certain fuel supply assurances that were repeated verbatim from the March

2006 separation plan. These are important Presidential commitments that the U.S. intends to uphold, consistent with U.S. law.

Question 15: What is the definition of "disruption of supply" as used in Article 5? Do the U.S. and Indian governments agree on this definition?

Answer: It is the understanding of the United States that the use of the phrase "disruption of fuel supplies" in Article 5.6 of the 123 Agreement is meant to refer to disruptions in supply to India that may result through no fault of its own. Examples of such a disruption include (but are not limited to): a trade war resulting in the cut-off of supply; market disruptions in the global supply of fuel; and the potential failure of an American company to fulfil any fuel supply contracts it may have signed with India. We believe the Indian government shares our understanding of this provision.

Question 16: Would any of these commitments continue to apply if India detonated a nuclear explosive device? If so, under what circumstances?

Answer: As outlined in Article 14 of the 123 Agreement, should India detonate a nuclear explosive device, the United States has the right to cease all nuclear cooperation with India immediately, including the supply of fuel, as well as to request the return of any items transferred from the United States, including fresh fuel. In addition, the United States has the right to terminate the agreement on one year's written notice. (Notice of termination has to precede cessation of cooperation pursuant to Article 14). In case of termination, the commitments in Article 5.6 would no longer apply.

Question 17: Do the assurances in Article 5 require the United States to assist India in finding foreign sources of nuclear fuel in the event that the United States ceases nuclear cooperation with India?

Answer: Ceasing nuclear cooperation with India would be a serious step. The United States would not take such a serious step without careful consideration of the circumstances necessitating such action and the effects and impacts it would entail. Such circumstances would include, for example, detonation of a nuclear weapon, material violation of the 123 Agreement, or termination, abrogation, or material violation of International Atomic Energy Agency safeguards. The provisions in article 14 on termination of the agreement and cessation of cooperation would be available in such circumstances, and their exercise would render article 5.6 inapplicable. Moreover, such circumstances would likely be inconsistent with the political underpinnings of the U.S.-India Initiative upon which the commitments in article 5.6 were based.

Question 18: How is this fuel supply assurance consistent with Section 103(a)(6) of the Hyde Act which states that it is U.S. policy to: "Seek to prevent the transfer to any country of nuclear equipment, materials, or technology from other participating governments in the Nuclear Suppliers' Group or from any other source if nuclear transfers to that country are suspended or terminated pursuant to this title, the Atomic Energy Act, or any other United States law"?

Answer: There is no inconsistency between the fuel supply assurances contained in Article 5 of the U.S.-India Agreement and section 103(a)(6) of the Hyde Act. Paragraph 6 of Article 5 of the U.S.-India Agreement records assurances given by the United States to India in March 2006. In particular, the United States conveyed its commitment "..... to work with friends and allies to adjust the practices of the Nuclear Suppliers' Group to create the necessary conditions for India to obtain full access to the international fuel market, including reliable, uninterrupted and continual access to fuel supplies from firms in several nations," and "[i]f despite these arrangements a disruption of fuel supplies to India occurs, the United States and India would jointly convene a group of friendly countries ... to pursue such measures as would restore fuel supply to India."

These fuel supply assurances are intended to guard against disruptions of fuel supply to India that might occur through no fault of India's own. Instances of such a disruption might include, for example, a trade war resulting in the cut-off of supply, market disruptions in the global supply of fuel, or the failure of a company to fulfil a fuel supply contract it may have signed with India. In such circumstances the United States would be prepared to encourage transfers of nuclear fuel to India by other Nuclear Suppliers' Group members. The fuel supply assurances are not, however, meant to insulate India against the consequences of a nuclear explosive test or a violation of non-proliferation commitments. The language of Article 5.6(b), particularly in the context of Article 14, does not provide for any such insulation.

Question 19: How are these provisions regarding a life-time strategic reserve for the operating life of India's safeguarded reactors consistent with subparagraph (10) of paragraph (a) of Section 103 of the Hyde Act, which states that: "Any nuclear power reactor fuel reserve provided to the Government of India for use in safeguarded civilian nuclear facilities should be commensurate with reasonable operating requirements?"

Answer: We do not read these provisions to be inconsistent. The parameters of the proposed "strategic reserve" and of India's capacity to acquire nuclear fuel for its reactors will be developed over time. Thus, it is premature to conclude that the strategic reserve will develop in a manner inconsistent with the Hyde Act.

Question 20: Do the U.S. and India agree on the definition of reasonable reactor operating requirements for Indian reactors? If yes, what is it? If not, how do they disagree? Does the U.S. have an assessment of how much nuclear material would be required for a life-time strategic reserve for each safeguarded Indian power reactor that could receive fuel pursuant to the proposed agreement?

Answer: The U.S.-India Agreement does not define "reasonable operating requirements," and the two governments have not discussed a definition. Any definition would have to take into account among other things the physical characteristics of the reactors, their expected operating cycles, their expected time in service, the likelihood of fuel supply disruptions over decades of operation, and many similar factors that are difficult to quantify in the abstract. We would expect that the actual amount of fuel put in the reserve would depend not only on the factors just mentioned, but also on such factors as availability of fuel in the market, price, Indian storage capacity, costs of storage, and similar practical considerations. The Agreement itself establishes neither a minimum nor a maximum quantity of nuclear material to be placed in India's reserve.

Question 21: How are these assurances consistent with subparagraph (6) of paragraph (a) of Section 103 of the Hyde Act which states that it is U.S. policy to: "Seek to prevent the transfer to a country of nuclear equipment, materials, or technology from other participating governments in the Nuclear Suppliers' Group or from any other source if nuclear transfers to that country are suspended or terminated pursuant to this title, the Atomic Energy Act of 1954 (42 U.S.C. 2011 et seq.), or any other United States law"?

Answer: Please see the response to Question 18.

Question 22: What impact will these U.S. commitments of nuclear fuel supply to India have on the U.S. initiatives to discourage the spread of enrichment and reprocessing facilities?

Answer: We do not foresee any negative impact on these initiatives. India already possesses both types of facilities. We do not believe that the provision of fuel assurances to India will have any effect on our efforts to offer reliable access to nuclear fuel to persuade countries aspiring to develop civil nuclear energy to forgo enrichment and reprocessing capabilities of their own.

Question 23: Have the Indians explained to the U.S. or to the International Atomic Energy Agency their definition of the term "an India-specific safeguards agreement?" If so, what is it?

Answer: The Indian government has not yet explained to the United States what it means by the term "India-specific" safeguards agreement. The Indian government has been in discussions with the IAEA regarding its safeguards agreement. However, these discussions have not concluded. The United States remains confident that the safeguards agreement to be negotiated between India and the IAEA will address all of the concerns associated with the term "India-specific."

Question 24: Which provisions of INFCIRC/66/Rev.2 agreements provide for safeguards in perpetuity? Would these apply to civil nuclear reactors that a country such as India requests the IAEA to safeguard?

Answer: INFCIRC/66/Rev.2 is not a "model agreement" as is INFCIRC/153 (the basis for NPT safeguards agreements)—INFCIRC/66-type agreements are not as rigidly determined as Nuclear Non-proliferation Treaty safeguards agreements. Because INFCIRC/66-type agreements do not involve fullscope safeguards (safeguards applied to all nuclear material in a state), but have been aimed at the application of safeguard to specific supplied materials or facilities, the scope of safeguards application is delineated uniquely in each agreement.

This is generally done through the mechanism of a dynamic list of inventory items to which the agreement stipulates that safeguards must be applied. The main part of the inventory list contains facilities and material that are permanently under safeguards. The subsidiary part of the inventory list contains facilities that are temporarily under safeguards due to the presence of safeguarded material. There is a third section of the list that contains nuclear material on which safeguards are suspended or exempted (e.g., because the material has been diluted to the point where it is no longer usable, has been transferred out of the state, etc.). We would expect that the Indian safeguards agreement will be based on this general structure, and that the nuclear facilities India declares to be "civil" will be placed in the main (permanent safeguards) part of the inventory list. Also in the main part of the inventory would be nuclear material exported to India, and any nuclear material generated through the use of that material.

Consistent with International Atomic Energy Agency Board Document GOV/1621 (which is referenced in the Hyde Act, Sec. 104(b)2), the safeguards agreement should also contain language that ensures that: (1) the duration of the agreement is related to the period of actual use of the items in the recipient state; and (2) the rights and obligations with respect to safeguarded nuclear material shall apply until such time as the International Atomic Energy Agency terminates safeguards pursuant to the agreement (e.g. the material is no longer usable or has been transferred from the recipient state).

Question 25: Has the Indian government provided U.S. officials with a definition of "corrective measures"? If so, what is it? Does it involve removing IAEA-safeguarded material from such safeguards in certain circumstances? If so, does the U.S. support the conclusion of an Indian agreement with the IAEA that provides for perpetuity of safeguards while at the same time making such perpetuity contingent on the invocation of "corrective measures?"

Answer: The Indian government has not provided the United States with a definition of "corrective measures." Until a safeguards agreement is completed between India and the International Atomic Energy Agency and the issue of "corrective measures" is clarified, we cannot comment on the appropriateness of the agreement. However, we expect that the Indian government will implement in letter and in spirit its commitment to "safeguards in perpetuity," to which it agreed on March 2, 2006. As Secretary Rice stated during her testimony before the Senate Foreign Relations Committee on April 5, 2006, "We've been very clear with the Indians that the permanence of safeguards is the permanence of safeguards without condition."

Question 26: Since India is not a party to the Nuclear Non-Proliferation Treaty (NPT) and does not accept full-scope safeguards, does this long-term consent for reprocessing for India change U.S. policy for granting long-term consent to reprocessing and the use of plutonium? If so, what criteria will the U.S. now use to consider requests for reprocessing and the use of plutonium either on a case-by-case basis or for long-term advance programmatic arrangements?

Answer: The consent to reprocessing is contingent upon the construction of a new, dedicated reprocessing facility that will be under International Atomic Energy Agency safeguards. The criteria applied by the United States in considering the Indian request were the same as those applied in the earlier instances (EURATOM and Japan). They are that (1) the reprocessing will not be inimical to the common defense and security, and (2) the reprocessing will not result in a significant increase in the risk of proliferation beyond that which exists at the time the approval is requested, giving foremost consideration to whether the reprocessing will take place under conditions that will ensure timely warning to the United States of any diversion well in advance of the time at which the diverted materiel could be transformed into a nuclear explosive device. These are the criteria for granting approval for reprocessing established by section 131 of the Atomic Energy Act.

Article 6(iii) of the Agreement provides that India and the United States must agree on "arrangements and procedures" under which the reprocessing will take place before India can physically reprocess any material subject to the Agreement. The Administration will ensure that the safeguards, physical protection and other measures to be set forth in the agreed "arrangements and procedures" will be both rigorous and consistent with the criteria described above.

Question 27: What special challenges will the International Atomic Energy Agency (IAEA) face in safeguarding a reprocessing plant in a non-NPT state that does not have full-scope safeguards?

Answer: Assuming that, consistent with the terms of the 123 Agreement, India builds a new reprocessing plant dedicated to the processing of material under International Atomic Energy Agency safeguards, there would be little, if any, difference in the technical challenge of applying safeguards to such a facility as opposed to a comparable facility in a State with a comprehensive safeguards agreement. There are some differences under an INFCIRC/66 agreement in the state's record-keeping and material accounting report requirements, but these should not have an impact on safeguards effectiveness. The technical objectives and technical measures applied in the two cases would not differ in any significant way. In each case the International Atomic Energy Agency would seek to provide assurance that the declared material was not diverted, and that the facility was operated in the manner declared. The facility would be under uninterrupted safeguards, and the material entering, exiting, and resident in the facility would all be subject to safeguards. In the case of India, the Agency's safeguards conclusions would have to be limited to the civil facilities and materials under safeguards, and could not be extrapolated to apply to the nuclear program as a whole.

Question 28: Will the U.S. insist that the safeguards agreement for the planned Indian reprocessing plant include all the safeguards procedure and approaches that the IAEA applies to the Rokkasho reprocessing facility in Japan, including state-of-the-art, near-real-time accountancy and containment and surveillance?

Answer: U.S. policy is that safeguards should be applied to meet established technical standards of effectiveness, as efficiently as possible; that is the policy we pursue in the context of our bilateral agreements with other states such as Japan, and we would continue to pursue such a policy in discussions with India in connection with arrangements for reprocessing. The safeguards methods employed at the Rokkasho Reprocessing Plant are consistent with both International Atomic Energy Agency safeguards criteria, and with the results of a lengthy international cooperative effort to address the technical problems of safeguarding large reprocessing plants. We would expect the same approaches to apply to a new Indian reprocessing plant dedicated to processing safeguarded material. However, we cannot yet speculate that safeguards would be carried out in exactly the same manner, although containment, surveillance, and some sort of continuous material monitoring would certainly be involved. A new reprocessing plant may well be many years off, and safeguards technology constantly moves forward; by the time a new Indian plant is in operation, there will almost certainly be a new generation of surveillance and radiation measurement devices available, and lessons learned from Rokkasho safeguards.

Question 29: Will the Administration submit any consent arrangements for Indian reprocessing to Congress as an amendment to the U.S.-India agreement for cooperation so that Congress will have a full 90 days to give adequate time to review its provisions? Or will the Administration submit these only as a subsequent arrangement under section 131 of the Atomic Energy Act, thereby allowing Congress only 15 days of continuous session for review of this complex issue?

Answer: Section 131 of the Atomic Energy Act provides explicitly for review and execution of subsequent arrangements related to the reprocessing of U.S. origin material. However, if proposed "arrangements and procedures" for reprocessing involved changes to provisions in the U.S.-India 123 Agreement, an amendment to the agreement would be required.

Question 30: Why are the programmatic consent arrangements that the U.S. is proposing to India, a non-NPT signatory, much less specific and rigorous than the procedures that the U.S. required of EURATOM and Japan?

Answer: The advance, long-term consent accorded to India in the U.S.-India Agreement by Article 6(iii) centers on a new Indian national reprocessing facility that has not yet been designed, let alone built. Many relevant non-proliferation considerations that could readily be dealt with in the texts of the U.S.-Japan and U.S.-EURATOM agreements (or in related documents) could not be dealt with immediately in the U.S.-India Agreement.

Nevertheless, the U.S.-India Agreement establishes as fundamental criteria that a new national reprocessing facility must be dedicated to reprocessing safeguarded nuclear material under International Atomic Energy Agency safeguards, and that any special fissionable material (i.e., plutonium) separated by the facility may only be utilized in national facilities under International Atomic Energy Agency safeguards. Further, it provides that the consent does not become effective until the United States and India consult and agree on arrangements and procedures under which activities at the new facility will take place.

Finally, Article 6(iii) provides that the arrangements and procedures must address non-proliferation considerations identical to those addressed in the procedures relating to the U.S.-Japan and U.S.-EURATOM agreements (e.g. safeguards, physical protection, storage, environmental protection), as well as "such other provisions as may be agreed by the Parties." At the appropriate time the United States will consult with India for the purpose of agreeing on the requisite arrangements and procedures and will ensure that they are no less rigorous than those governing the U.S. consent arrangements with Japan and with EURATOM.

Question 31: Why are there no notification procedures for adding new Indian facilities to the list of facilities that may use plutonium derived from U.S.-supplied fuel?

Answer: The procedures established by Article 7.1 of the U.S.-India Agreement whereby each Party records all facilities storing separated plutonium subject to the Agreement on a list and makes its list available to the other Party serve equally to notify to the other Party all facilities utilizing (or potentially utilizing) plutonium subject to the Agreement, since the plutonium-bearing fuel must first be located at the facility before it can be utilized. A similar approach is taken in the U.S.-EURATOM Agreement, where facilities formally notified as being added to a party's "Delineated Program" (Annex A) do not include utilization facilities; the latter are notified, as appropriate, when they are added to a "Storage" list as provided for by Article 8.3.

Question 32: Will the United States insist that any plutonium and uranium recovered from-the reprocessing of U.S.-origin fuel at the proposed dedicated Indian reprocessing facility be subject to IAEA safeguards and peaceful, non-explosive use assurances in perpetuity, including any such material recycled in Indian reactors?

Answer: Yes. Article 9, Article 10, and Article 16 of the U.S.-India Agreement guarantee this coverage.

Question 33: Will the U.S. insist that any uranium or plutonium used in or produced through the use of U.S.-supplied material be subject to safeguards in perpetuity if such material is used in India's breeder reactors?

Answer: Yes. Article 10 of the U.S.-India Agreement guarantees this coverage.

Question 34: If India decides at some point in the future to reprocess spent breeder reactor fuel that contains U.S.-origin material, how will the U.S. ensure that it is subject to all the non-proliferation conditions and controls in the proposed agreement, including safeguards and consent rights?

Answer: Article 10.6 of the U.S.-India Agreement provides that "[e]ach Party shall establish and maintain a system of accounting for and control of nuclear material transferred pursuant to this Agreement and nuclear material used in or produced through the use of any material, equipment, or components so transferred." Article 10.7 provides that [u]pon the request of either Party, the other Party shall report or permit the IAEA to report to the requesting Party on the status of all inventories of material subject to this Agreement." Thus, the United States will be able to track all clear material in India subject to the Agreement, including at India's breeder reactors (which would have to be brought under International Atomic Energy Agency safeguards before U.S.-obligated nuclear material could be introduced to them), at India's new dedicated reprocessing facility (when built), and at any other Indian facility where U.S.-obligated plutonium may be located. In tracking this material the United States will be able to ensure that all conditions and controls required by the Agreement, including International Atomic Energy Agency safeguards, are in fact being maintained.

Question 35: In light of these requirements of U.S. law, why doesn't the proposed U.S.-Indian peaceful nuclear cooperation agreement contain an explicit reference to the actions that would give the U.S. the right to terminate nuclear cooperation and to require the return of equipment and materials subject to the agreement, if India detonates a nuclear explosive device?

Answer: Article 14 of the proposed U.S.-India agreement for cooperation provides for a clear right for the U.S. to terminate nuclear cooperation and a right to require the return of equipment and materials subject to the agreement in all of the circumstances required under the Atomic Energy Act, including if India detonated a nuclear explosive device or terminated or abrogated safeguards (per section 123(a)(4) of the Act). Thus, it fully satisfies the relevant requirements of the Act.

Question 36: Does the U.S. possess the right under Article 14, without any precondition or consent by India, to take back any and all U.S.-origin nuclear material or equipment provided to India pursuant to the nuclear cooperation agreement?

Answer: Under Article 14 of the proposed agreement, the U.S. would be able to exercise the right to require the return of material and equipment subject to the agreement after (1) giving written notice of termination of the agreement, and (2) ceasing cooperation, based on a determination that "a mutually acceptable resolution of outstanding issues has not been possible or cannot be achieved through consultations." Thus, both of the actions that must be taken to exercise the right of return would be within the discretion of the U.S. Government, and both actions could be taken at once in the unlikely case that the U.S. believed that a resolution of the problem could not be achieved through consultations.

Article 14 does not require that the other party consent to the exercise of the right to terminate the agreement, the right to cease cooperation, or the right of return. Prior to the actual removal of items pursuant to the right of return, the parties would engage in consultations regarding, *inter alia*, the quantity of items to be returned, the amount of compensation due, and the methods and arrangements for removal. These consultations are a standard feature of right of return provisions and are included in all 123 agreements that the United States has signed with other cooperating parties.

Question 37: Under what circumstances does the termination provision allow the United States to terminate cooperation with India? Does the U.S. have the unconditional right to cease cooperation immediately upon its determination that India has taken action that the U.S. believes constitutes grounds for termination of cooperation?

Answer: Like all other U.S. agreements for nuclear cooperation, the proposed U.S.-India agreement is a framework agreement and does not compel any specific cooperation. Thus, a cessation of cooperation would not be inconsistent with the provisions of the agreement. Also, as in other agreements for cooperation, the proposed U.S.-India agreement provides specifically (in article 14) for a right to cease cooperation. Article 14 makes clear that the U.S. would have the right to cease cooperation immediately if it determined that India had taken actions that constituted grounds for such cessation and that a resolution of the problem created by India's actions could not be achieved through consultations. This is a reciprocal right that India enjoys as well. Article 14 does not elaborate the specific circumstances that might bring about such a formal cessation of cooperation. However, the provisions of article 14 underscore the expectation of both parties that termination of the agreement, cessation of cooperation, and exercise of the right of return would be serious measures not to be undertaken lightly.

Question 38: Could the U.S. terminate cooperation pursuant to Article 14 of the nuclear cooperation agreement for reasons other than India's detonation of a nuclear explosive device or abrogating or violating a nuclear safeguards agreement? Does the government of India agree?

Answer: As noted in the previous answer, Article 14 of the U.S.-India Agreement does not elaborate the specific circumstances that might trigger a cessation of cooperation pursuant to that article. As explained in the answer to question 17, the circumstances for possible termination would include, for example, detonation of a nuclear weapon, material violation of the 123 Agreement, or termination, abrogation, or material violation of a safeguards agreement. The provisions of Article 14 underscore the expectation of both parties that termination of the agreement, cessation of cooperation, and exercise of the right of return would be serious measures not to be undertaken lightly. We believe the language establishing these rights is clear and well understood by both countries.

Question 39: Do the non-proliferation assurances and conditions in the proposed new agreement apply to the nuclear materials and equipment that the U.S. supplied for the Tarapur reactors, as well as the spent fuel from those reactors? If not, why?

Answer: The proposed U.S.-India Agreement would not apply retroactively to the spent fuel from the Tarapur reactors. The Atomic Energy Act does not require such retroactive application, but it does impose certain conditions with respect to previously exported material before embarking on new cooperation (see section 127). The Administration believes it will be able to satisfy these requirements of the Atomic Energy Act.

Question 40: Does the U.S. continue to hold the position that India legally obligated to adhere to the non-proliferation assurances and controls, including peaceful-use assurances, safeguards, consent to reprocessing and retransfer to their countries with respect to the nuclear equipment and materials that were subject to the expired 1963 agreement for cooperation? Does the Indian Government share the U.S. views?

Answer: The U.S. and India have maintained differing legal positions on the question of residual conditions and controls on nuclear material subject to the 1963 agreement following expiration of the agreement in 1993. However, India has agreed with the International Atomic Energy Agency on the application of safeguards to nuclear material from the Tarapur reactors. Moreover, the material is subject to the INFCIRC/66 Agreement. And the U.S. is confident that there would be consultations between the U.S. and India before any change in the status of the nuclear material (e.g., reprocessing).

Question 41: Will the Indian Government have any legal right to suspend or eliminate safeguards, reprocess U.S.-origin material, or otherwise take any action that would be prohibited under the proposed agreement after the termination by either party of the proposed?

Answer: Article 16 of the proposed U.S.-India Agreement expressly provides for the survival of essential rights and conditions on items subject to the agreement even after termination or expiration of the agreement, including *inter alia* with respect to the application of safeguards (article 10), reprocessing consent (article 6), and peaceful use (article 9).

Question 42: Does the Administration agree with Prime Minister Singh that there will be no derogation of India's right to take corrective measure in the event of fuel supply interruption? Will any corrective measure that India might take involve any derogation of the U.S. non-proliferation assurances, rights, and controls that are set out in articles 5.6(c), 6, 7, 8, 9, and 10?

Answer: The language of article 16 clearly provides for the applicability of the referenced provisions to items subject to the proposed agreement even after termination or expiration of the agreement. Until India has completed its safeguards agreement with the International Atomic Energy Agency and the parameters of "corrective measures" are known, we will not be in a position to speak definitively to the potential effect on other provisions of the proposed agreement. That said, it would not be consistent with the proposed agreement text for such corrective measures to extract from the applicability of the provisions referenced in article 16 to items subject to the proposed agreement, including after termination or expiration of the agreement.

Question 43: What are the explicit linkages and interlocking rights and commitments that Prime Minister Singh was referring to? Do the U.S. and India governments agree on the definition of these linkages and interlocking rights and commitments? If not, how do they differ?

Answer: International agreements, by their nature, typically involve interlocking rights and commitments, and this is the case with our agreements for nuclear cooperation. The creation of a framework for nuclear cooperation is predicated on a set of rights and conditions that serve essential non-proliferation purposes. Beyond that, we can only say that the quoted statement is at a high level of generality, and we are not in a position to speak for the Indian government as to whether anything more specific was intended by these words.

Question 44: What is the Administration's understanding of the Prime Minister's statement that India's reprocessing rights are "permanent"? Specifically, does it mean that the U.S. will not have the right to withdraw its consent to India's reprocessing of U.S.-obligated nuclear material, even if the U.S. determines that the continuation of such activities would pose a serious threat to our national security or non-proliferation?

Answer: The U.S. has agreed to the reprocessing of U.S.-origin materials, to come into effect when the parties agree on "arrangements and procedures" and India establishes a new national reprocessing facility dedicated to reprocessing safeguarded material under IAEA safeguards. As with the arrangements governing reprocessing consents granted by the U.S. in connection with the Japan and EURATOM agreements, the proposed arrangements and procedures with India will provide for withdrawal of reprocessing consent. Such a right is also included in Article 14.9 of the U.S.-India Agreement.

Question 45: In the conference report of the Hyde Act, Congress stated that it intended for the United States to "seek agreement among Nuclear Suppliers' Group members that violations by one country of an agreement with any Nuclear Suppliers' Group member should result in joint action by all members, including, as appropriate, the termination of nuclear exports." Will the administration be seeking such a commitment when it proposes that the Nuclear Suppliers' Group provide a nuclear trade rule exemption for India? If not, why not?

Answer: Paragraph 16 of the Nuclear Suppliers' Group Guidelines for Nuclear Transfers (INFCIRC/254/Rev.8/Part 1) provides that suppliers should (1) consult if, *inter alia*, one or more suppliers believe there has been a violation of a supplier/recipient understanding; (2) avoid acting in a manner that could prejudice measures that may be adopted in response to such a violation; and (3) agree on "an appropriate response and possible action, which could include the termination of nuclear transfers to that recipient." Assuming the Nuclear Suppliers' Group agrees by consensus to an exception for India, this guideline would apply in the case of any nuclear transfers by a Nuclear Suppliers. Group supplier to India. The Administration believes that the existing provisions of paragraph 16 of the Guidelines serve the Congressional concerns expressed in the conference report on the Hyde Act, and therefore no further elaboration is needed in connection with the proposed exception for India.

Nuclear Cooperation Assessment Statement: Pursuant to Section 123 (a) of the Atomic Energy Act of 1954, as Amended, with Respect to the Proposed Agreement for Cooperation Between The Government of the United States of America and The Government of India Concerning Peaceful Uses of Nuclear Energy

This Nuclear Proliferation Assessment Statement ("NPAS") relates to the proposed Agreement for Cooperation Between the Government of the United States of America and the Government of India Concerning Peaceful Uses of Nuclear Energy (the "Agreement"). The Agreement is being submitted to the President jointly by the Secretary of State and the Secretary of Energy for his approval.

Section 123a. of the Atomic Energy Act, as amended (the "Atomic Energy Act" or "the AEA"), provides that an NPAS be submitted by the Secretary of State to the President on each new or amended agreement for cooperation concluded pursuant to that section. Pursuant to section 123a. the NPAS must analyze the consistency of the text of the proposed agreement with all the requirements of the AEA, with specific attention to whether the proposed agreement is consistent with each of the criteria set forth in that subsection, and address the adequacy of the safeguards and other control mechanisms and the peaceful use assurances contained in the agreement for cooperation to ensure that any assistance furnished thereunder will not be used to further any military or nuclear explosive purpose.

With this statutory mandate in mind, this NPAS: (a) provides background information on India's civil nuclear program and the military nuclear program from which it is being separated (Part I); (b) describes the nature and scope of the cooperation contemplated in the proposed Agreement (Part II); (c) reviews the applicable substantive requirements of the AEA and the Nuclear Non-Proliferation Act of 1978 ("NNPA") and details how they are met by the proposed Agreement (Part III); (d) addresses additional relevant policy issues (Part IV); and (e) sets forth the net assessment, conclusions, views and recommendations of the Department of State as contemplated by section 123a. of the AEA (Part V).

INTRODUCTION: THE U.S.-INDIA CIVIL NUCLEAR COOPERATION INITIATIVE

The U.S.-India Civil Nuclear Cooperation Initiative, of which the proposed U.S.-India Agreement for Peaceful Nuclear Cooperation is the central element, was announced in a Joint Statement by President Bush and Indian Prime Minister Manmohan Singh in Washington on July 18, 2005 "Joint Statement"). For the United States the Initiative is premised on its contribution to U.S. national security interests by establishing a broad strategic partnership with India that encourages India's emergence as a positive force on the world scene. India is a rising global power and an important democratic partner for the United States. The United States and India are bound together by a strong congruence of interests and values. For example, the United States is seeking to work with India to win the Global War on Terrorism, to prevent the spread of weapons of mass destruction and the missiles that could deliver them, to enhance peace and stability in Asia, and to advance the spread of democracy. In the context of this growing partnership, the United States and India issued a landmark Joint Statement in July 2005 to work toward full civil nuclear cooperation while at the same time strengthening global non-proliferation efforts.

India believes, and the United States agrees, that it needs nuclear power to sustain dynamic economic growth and to address its growing energy requirements in an affordable and environmentally-responsible manner. The U.S. goal—in the context of the Joint Statement—is to provide India access to the technology it needs to build a safe, modern and efficient infrastructure that will provide clean, peaceful nuclear energy.

At the same time, India has clearly demonstrated over the past several years its desire to work with the United States and the international community to fight the spread of sensitive nuclear and other technologies. As part of an effort launched with India during the Administration's first term—the Next Steps in Strategic Partnership—India took a number of significant steps to strengthen export controls and to ensure that Indian companies would not be a source of future proliferation. Not only did India pledge to bring its export control laws, regulations, and enforcement practices in line with international export control standards, but it also passed an extensive export control law and issued an upgraded national control list that will help it achieve this goal. India is a signatory to the Biological and Toxin Weapons Convention and the Chemical Weapons Convention, and reports annually to the UN Register of Conventional Arms. In addition, India has become a party to the Convention on the Physical Protection of Nuclear Material, ratified the International Convention for the Suppression of Acts of Nuclear Terrorism, and supports the IAEA Code of Conduct on Safety and Security of Radioactive Sources. India is also a partner in the Global Initiative to Combat Nuclear Terrorism. With respect to its UNSCR 1540 obligations, India has submitted a national report and two addenda to the Committee and currently is represented on the UNSCR 1540 Experts Committee.

With respect to strategic trade enforcement, India has bilateral customs cooperation agreements in place with a number of countries, including with the United States, and has announced its intent to join the Department of Homeland Security's Container Security Initiative. In addition, India participates in the Department of Energy's Megaports Initiative radiation portal monitor program and has deployed advanced scanners at seaports to screen container cargo for arms, explosives, WMD, and other contraband. India also has participated as an official observer of Proliferation Security Initiative regional interdiction exercises.

The additional non-proliferation commitments India has made as part of the Joint Statement go even further and will bring it into closer conformity with international nuclear non-proliferation standards and practices. While the United States will continue to work with India to encourage it to do more over time, India's implementation of its commitments will, on balance, enhance global non-proliferation efforts. The United States expects that the international nuclear non-proliferation regime will emerge stronger as a result.

Through the Joint Statement, India publicly committed to take the following important non-proliferation steps:

- Identify and separate its civilian and military nuclear facilities and programs and file a declaration with the International Atomic Energy Agency (IAEA) regarding its civilian facilities;
- Place voluntarily its civilian nuclear facilities under IAEA safeguards;
- Sign and adhere to an Additional Protocol with the IAEA with respect to its civilian nuclear facilities;
- Continue its unilateral moratorium on nuclear testing;
- Work with the United States for the conclusion of a multilateral Fissile Material Cut-Off Treaty (FMCT) to halt production of fissile material for nuclear weapons;
- Refrain from the transfer of enrichment and reprocessing technologies to states that do not have them, and support efforts to limit their spread; and
- Secure nuclear and missile materials and technologies through comprehensive export control legislation and through harmonization and adherence to the Missile Technology Control Regime (MTCR) and the Nuclear Suppliers' Group (NSG) guidelines.

India's commitment to separate its civil and military facilities and place its civil facilities and activities under IAEA safeguards demonstrates its willingness to assume full responsibility for preventing proliferation from its civil nuclear program. It will also help protect against diversion of nuclear material and technologies to India's nuclear weapon program.

By adopting an Additional Protocol with the IAEA, India will commit to reporting to the IAEA on exports of all NSG Trigger List items. This will help the IAEA track potential proliferation elsewhere, and bolster U.S. efforts to encourage all states to adopt an Additional Protocol as a condition of supply.

By committing to adopt strong and effective export controls, including adherence to NSG and MTCR Guidelines, India will help ensure that its companies do not transfer sensitive weapons of mass destruction and missile-related technologies to countries of concern.

In July 2005, India took an important step by harmonizing its national control list with the NSG Guidelines and by adding many items that appear on the MTCR Annex.

India has also committed to work with the United States toward the conclusion of a multilateral FMCT, which, if successfully negotiated and ratified, will ban the production of fissile material for use in nuclear weapons or other nuclear explosive devices.

India's pledge to maintain its nuclear testing moratorium contributes to non-proliferation efforts by making its ending of nuclear explosive tests one of the conditions of full civil nuclear cooperation. Since to date Pakistan has test-exploded nuclear weapons only in response to Indian nuclear tests, this commitment may help diminish the prospects for future nuclear testing in South Asia.

By committing not to export enrichment and reprocessing technology to states that do not already have such fully-functioning capabilities, India will help the United States achieve its goal of preventing the further spread of such proliferation sensitive equipment and technology.

Each of these steps is significant. Together, they constitute a substantial shift in moving India into closer conformity with international non-proliferation standards and practices. Their successful implementation will help to strengthen the global non-proliferation regime.

On a reciprocal basis with India's commitments, the United States committed to work to achieve full civil nuclear cooperation with India. The proposed U.S.-India Agreement for Peaceful Nuclear Cooperation constitutes a core element of that commitment.

I. INDIA'S NUCLEAR PROGRAMS AND POLICIES

India's Energy Needs

India, a nation of more than one billion people today, with an economy growing in the range of 8 percent per year, faces real and growing energy needs. Substantial population growth, expanding industrial production, economic development, urbanization, and growth in transportation sector energy consumption are all driving strong energy demand. Between 1980 and 2001, demand increased by 208 percent. By contrast, China, often thought of as the world's next big energy consumer, saw a 130 percent increase over the same period. In 2003, India was the sixth largest consumer of energy in the world behind only the United States, China, Russia, Japan, and Germany.

To meet these growing demands, the Indian Government plans to double its capacity to produce electricity within the next seven years. At present, almost 55 percent of India's 127 gigawatt (GW) total installed energy generating capacity is derived from coal; roughly 26 percent from hydro-electric power; 11 percent from natural gas; and almost 5 percent from renewable sources. Just 3 percent of India's total power generation comes from nuclear energy.

Indian energy officials project that by 2031-32, roughly a quarter century from now, India will have a total energy requirement of 700 GW, of which the nuclear component is expected to comprise 63 GW, or approximately nine percent. India will also require large-scale infrastructure investments and upgrades, including transmission and distribution, as a result of a five-fold increase in electrical power consumption.

Nuclear Energy in India

India has a substantial and growing nuclear infrastructure. Its current capabilities span the nuclear fuel cycle. Indian nuclear facilities include various uranium processing capabilities (uranium mining and milling, copper mine tailing extraction, uranium conversion, fuel fabrication, enrichment); thermal and breeder reactors; research reactors; heavy water production facilities; and spent fuel reprocessing facilities. As of early 2007, the Nuclear Power Corporation of India, Ltd. (NPCIL) operated 16 power reactors, and an additional six are currently under construction. Bharatiya Nabhikiya Vidyut Nigam, Ltd. (Bhavini) operates a 40 MWe fast breeder test reactor and is currently building a 500 MWe prototype fast breeder reactor.

India's operating civil nuclear power plants currently have approximately 3,900 megawatts (MWe) of installed electricity generation capacity, based on the 14 pressurized heavy water reactors (PHWRs) and two boiling water reactors (BWRs) currently on-line. An additional four PHWRs, two light water reactors (LWRs), and the prototype fast breeder reactor (FBR) currently under construction should add an additional 3,380 MWe when operational, bringing the total installed nuclear energy generating capacity to approximately 7,280 MWe. Indian officials have stated their intent to increase the installed nuclear capacity to 20,000 MWe by 2020—a five-fold increase over present output and a goal that cannot be obtained absent substantial foreign assistance.

Over time, the Indian Government intends to increase the nuclear component of its energy output to approximately 20 percent of India's total energy production, thus significantly decreasing the growth in its reliance on fossil fuels. Senior officials in India's atomic energy establishment have indicated their desire to exceed the 20,000 MWe target through the accelerated import of high-unit capacity foreign reactors.

To this end, Indian officials have begun to discuss their long-term plans with American, Russian, French, and other potential vendors. In early 2007, India and Russia announced a statement of intent to field an additional four LWRs at Kudankulam, one of three planned "nuclear parks" set aside for international supply. While Russia is already supplying two LWRs at Kudankulam—a "grandfathered" arrangement dating to a time prior to establishment of the Nuclear Suppliers' Group (NSG) full-scope safeguards export guideline—the expanded deal is predicated on positive NSG action to enable civil nuclear cooperation with India. American companies would similarly like the chance to compete, on a level playing field, to supply India's civil nuclear program. The recent NSG decision by consensus to except India from the full-scope safeguards export condition is a principal enabling step for potential suppliers. Positive Congressional action on the proposed U.S.-India Agreement for Peaceful Nuclear Cooperation is an additional step necessary to open the Indian civil nuclear market to U.S. industry.

India's Three-Stage (Thorium) Program

India has long sought to implement a three-stage nuclear power program to meet its growing energy needs. The Department of Atomic Energy (DAE) argues that in the context of India's "modest" uranium reserves but substantial thorium reserves, large scale deployment of nuclear energy is best realized through eventual use of thorium. According to a report issued by the IAEA, India has limited uranium reserves, consisting of approximately 54,636 tons of "reasonably assured resources," 25,245 tons of "estimated additional resources," 15,488 tons of "undiscovered conventional resources," and 17,000 tons of "speculative" resources.

India's known and recoverable uranium resources are insufficient to generate, on a sustainable basis, a capable civil nuclear energy program. According to NPCIL, India's uranium reserves are sufficient to generate perhaps 10,000 MW of electricity for 40 years. Together with India's current installed capacity, once the seven reactors currently under construction come on-line India's total installed nuclear capacity will rise to more than 70 percent of this sum. This is inadequate to meet India's energy requirements.

By contrast, India has roughly one-third of the world's known thorium reserves. Natural uranium is a source material that can be used in a nuclear reactor to produce energy through nuclear fission. Thorium must first be converted to a fissile material, uranium-233, in a reactor. For more than four decades DAE has sought to develop the capability to use thorium, based on a closed nuclear fuel cycle, for large-scale nuclear energy production. The three-stage program it has sought to implement involves: (1) natural uranium-fueled pressurized heavy water reactors (PHWRs); (2) fast breeder reactors using plutonium-based fuel; and (3) advanced nuclear power systems based on a thorium-uranium-233 cycle. In theory, DAE argues, breeder reactors, using plutonium produced through domestic uranium sources, could generate perhaps 500 GW of electricity.

Despite years of effort, however, India's three-stage program has advanced slowly. India's Atomic Energy Commission projected in 1954 that India would achieve a target of 3 GWe by 1975 and 8 GWe by 1980; instead it hit 540 MWe through 1980, and produces roughly 3 GWe today. As noted above, India is also far short of achieving its goal of 20 GWe of installed capacity by 2020 or its projections that upwardly revise this target. While Indian officials continue to seek the long-term energy independence that, in principle, could be achieved through successful implementation of its three-stage nuclear program, in practice it is clear that India must import fuel, reactors, and other technologies that it has been denied for more than three decades under international export control policies to meet its nuclear electricity-generating targets. With the NSG decision to enable supply of Trigger List items to India, prospective international suppliers now have the ability to supply nuclear-related items to India for peaceful uses.

Civil vs. Military

India's existing nuclear infrastructure is today largely unsafeguarded: only four (rising to six, once Kudankulam-1 and 2 come on-line) power reactors and related nuclear material are currently under International Atomic Energy Agency safeguards. This accounts for approximately 19 percent of India's total current nuclear energy output. India's existing nuclear infrastructure is today fundamentally intertwined, serving both civil and military or strategic purposes; the Indian government states that its strategic program is an "offshoot" of its research on civil nuclear power, and consequently "it is embedded in a larger undifferentiated programme." In the July 2005 U.S.-India Joint Statement, India committed to identify and separate its civil and military nuclear facilities and programs in a phased manner, placing the civil aspects under safeguards and an Additional Protocol with the IAEA. In this context, India has undertaken to ensure that any international civil nuclear cooperation would not be diverted from civil purposes or transferred to third countries without safeguards or on an otherwise unauthorized basis.

Overview of India's Separation Plan

The Indian government released its plan to separate India's civil and military nuclear facilities on March 7, 2006; it updated this document on May 11, 2006 and asked the IAEA to circulate it to Member States on July 25, 2008 (IAEA document INFCIRC/731). Because India's existing nuclear infrastructure is intertwined, identification of purely civil facilities and programs that have no strategic implications proved a significant challenge. As its plan developed, the Indian government decided that the nature of the facility concerned, the activities undertaken in it, the national security significance of materials, and the location of the facilities were critical factors in determining what to declare as civilian. (In this context, India did not define or distinguish "military" from "strategic" facilities. The latter may include those having a military role, but also those having a role in India's three stage nuclear energy program.) Similarly, issues relating to fuel resource sustainability, technical design, economic viability, and smooth reactor operation were notable Indian decision criteria. The final plan released by the Indian government notes that India's approach to the separation of its facilities would be guided by the following principles:

- Credible, feasible, and implementable in a transparent manner;
- Consistent with the understandings of the July 18, 2005 Joint Statement;
- Consistent with India's national security and research and development requirements, as well as not prejudicial to India's three-stage nuclear program;
- Must be cost-effective in its implementation; and
- Must be acceptable to India's Parliament and public opinion.

Derived from these principles, India's plan:

- Includes in the civilian list "only those facilities to be offered for safeguards that, after separation, will no longer be engaged in activities of strategic significance";
- Requires a judgment on the overarching criterion of whether subjecting a facility to IAEA safeguards would impact adversely India's national security;
- Excludes a facility from the civilian list if it is located in a larger hub of strategic significance, even if it does not engage in activities of strategic significance; and accordingly
- Identifies only those facilities that India has determined not to be relevant to its strategic program.

Specifically, India passes its existing and developmental nuclear infrastructure as follows:

- *Thermal reactors:* India identifies as civil 14 thermal reactors, which according to the March 2006 Separation Plan were scheduled to be offered for safeguards between 2006 and 2014. These include the four existing foreign-supplied reactors (TAPS-1 and 2 (the U.S.-supplied Tarapur reactors), RAPS-1 and 2) and the two foreign-supplied reactors under construction (KK-1 and 2). These also include eight indigenous PHWRs, each with a generating capacity of 220 MWe: RAPS-3, 4, 5 and 6, KAPS-1 and 2, and NAPS-1 and 2. India further notes that safeguards will be applied in a phased manner consistent with its agreement with the IAEA. Eight indigenous PHWRs (TAPS-3 and 4, MAPS-1 and 2, Kaiga-1, 2, 3 and 4) are to remain outside of safeguards.

- *Fast breeder reactors:* India opted to continue unsafeguarded operations at its operating fast breeder test reactor and also to exclude its prototype fast breeder reactor from safeguards. The fast breeder program is currently at the research and development stage and will take time to reach an advanced stage of development, according to India. India seeks to ensure that it does not face any external "encumbrances" in this process, and so chooses to exclude them from safeguards at this time. India and the United States could not engage in the type of nuclear fuel cycle cooperation authorized by the Hyde Act, the Atomic Energy Act, and the U.S.-India Agreement for Peaceful Nuclear Cooperation with regard to India's breeder reactors until India declared them "civil" and placed them under safeguards.
- *Future reactors:* India states that it will place under IAEA safeguards "all future civilian thermal power reactors and civilian breeder reactors," retaining for itself the right to determine such reactors as civilian. The United States and other potential suppliers to India have international, and in many cases domestic, legal and policy requirements to ensure that the types of items supplied under their agreements for peaceful nuclear cooperation serve exclusively the civil sector. All reactors, and the material that passes through them, supplied by the United States or by India's other international partners will by definition be "civil" and be subject to IAEA safeguards in perpetuity. While India retains the right to develop indigenous facilities for either civil or military purposes in the future, the separation plan notes that all future thermal and breeder reactors declared "civil" will also be placed under safeguards. Because India seeks the maximum benefit from international cooperation, as a result of India's enduring and expanding energy requirements, and based on bilateral discussions, the United States expects the vast majority of future nuclear program growth to occur in India's civil sector.
- *Research reactors:* India will permanently shut down the CIRUS plutonium production reactor in 2010. It will also place the foreign-supplied fuel core from the APSARA reactor under safeguards in 2010. India has not declared as civil the Dhruva research reactor, the Advanced Heavy Water Reactor, and activities relating to naval nuclear propulsion at Kalpakkam.
- *Upstream facilities:* India's separation plan designates as civil the following specific facilities associated with the Nuclear Fuel Complex: the Uranium Oxide Plant (Block A); both the Palletizing and the Assembly Ceramic Fuel Fabrication Plants (Block A); the Enriched Uranium Oxide Plant; the Enriched Fuel Fabrication Plant; and the Gadolina Facility. The heavy water production plants at Thal,

Tuticorin, and Hazira will also be designated as civil. While India does not consider them as "relevant for safeguards purposes," at a minimum India's Additional Protocol is expected to include them. India decided not to designate for civilian uses three additional heavy water production plants, as well as other Nuclear Fuel Complex facilities.

- *Downstream facilities:* India plans to continue the current policy of possible "campaign-mode" safeguards with respect to the Tarapur Power Reactor Fuel Reprocessing Plant (PREFRE). Moreover, both the Tarapur and Rajasthan "Away from Reactor" spent fuel storage pools will be made available for safeguards. India decided not to declare as civil its other spent fuel reprocessing facilities, as well as its indigenous uranium enrichment capability. Subsequent to India's March 2006 separation plan, the Indian government decided to pursue development of a new civil facility dedicated to reprocessing material under safeguards. Development of this facility (and agreement with the United States on arrangements and procedures related thereto) will be required to bring into effect the "programmatic consent" in Article 6 of the Agreement.

- *Research facilities:* Finally, India plans to declare as civil nine research facilities: the Tata Institute of Fundamental Research; the Variable Energy Cyclotron Centre; the Saha Institute of Nuclear Physics; the Institute for Plasma Research; the Institute of Mathematics Science; the Institute of Physics; the Tata Memorial Centre; the Board of Radiation and Isotope Technology; and the Harish Chandra Research Institute. India expects these civil facilities to play a "prominent role" in international cooperation. Other Indian nuclear and nuclear-related facilities—such as those in the Bhabha Atomic Research Center (BARC) or in the Indira Gandhi Center for Advanced Research (IGCAR)—were not declared as civil, presumably because they retain a military or strategic role.

The United States assesses India's plan to be credible, transparent, and defensible from a non-proliferation standpoint. When implemented, the total installed nuclear capacity under safeguards will rise from 19 percent today to 65 percent, a percentage that will increase to more than 80 percent as India further expands its civil infrastructure through foreign supply and indigenous development. Based on India's safeguards agreement with the IAEA (discussed below), appropriate safeguards will cover India's civil nuclear fuel cycle and provide strong assurances to supplier states that material and technology provided or generated through civil nuclear cooperation will not be diverted either to the military sphere or for unauthorized purposes. In addition, the total portion of India's spent fuel and plutonium stockpiles under safeguards will rise substantially over time (although the reprocessing consent in Article

6 of the U.S.-India Agreement for Peaceful Nuclear Cooperation, if and when the consent comes into effect, could increase modestly the quantity of separated civil plutonium stored in India).

II. NATURE AND SCOPE OF THE COOPERATION CONTEMPLATED BY THE PROPOSED AGREEMENT

Article 2(2) of the Proposed Agreement describes in general terms the kinds of cooperative activities envisaged. These are to take place in accordance with the provisions of the Agreement and each Party's applicable treaties, national laws, regulations, and license requirements and may include, but are not limited to, the following areas:

- Advanced nuclear energy research and development in areas agreed by the Parties;
- Nuclear safety matters;
- Facilitation of exchange of scientists for visits, meetings, symposia and collaborative research;
- Full civil nuclear cooperation activities covering nuclear reactors and aspects of the associated nuclear fuel cycle including technology transfer on an industrial or commercial scale between the Parties or authorized persons;
- Development of a strategic reserve to guard against any disruption of supply over the lifetime of India's reactors;
- Advanced research and development in nuclear sciences including biological research, medicine, agriculture and industry, environment and climate change;
- Supply between the Parties, whether for use by or for the benefit of the Parties or third countries, of nuclear material;
- Alteration in form or content of nuclear material as provided for in Article 6 of the Agreement;
- Supply between the Parties of equipment, whether for use by or for the benefit of the Parties or third countries;
- Controlled thermonuclear fusion including in multilateral projects; and
- Other areas of mutual interest as may be agreed by the Parties.

In Article 2(4) of the Agreement the Parties further delimit the scope of cooperation by affirming that the purpose of the Agreement is to provide for peaceful nuclear cooperation and not to affect the unsafeguarded nuclear activities of either Party. Nothing in the Agreement is to be interpreted as affecting the rights of the Parties to use for their own purposes nuclear material, non-nuclear material, equipment, components, information or technology produced, acquired or developed by them independent of any nuclear material, non-nuclear material, equipment, components, information or technology transferred to them pursuant to the Agreement. The Agreement is to be implemented in a manner so as not to hinder or otherwise interfere with any other activities involving the use of nuclear material, non-nuclear material, equipment, components, information or technology and military nuclear facilities produced, acquired or developed by them independent of the Agreement for their own purposes.

Article 2(3) of the Agreement specifically provides that the Parties may undertake transfers between themselves or their authorized persons of nuclear material, non-nuclear material, equipment, components and information.

Article 3(1) of the Agreement again specifically provides that *information* may be transferred between the Parties, and that such information may cover, but need not be limited to, the following fields:

- Research, development, design, construction, operation, maintenance and use of reactors, reactor experiments, and decommissioning;
- The use of nuclear material in physical, chemical, radiological and biological research, medicine, agriculture and industry;
- Fuel cycle activities to meet future world-wide civil nuclear energy needs, including multilateral approaches to which they are parties for ensuring nuclear fuel supply and appropriate techniques for management of nuclear wastes;
- Advanced research and development in nuclear science and technology;
- Health, safety and environmental considerations related to the foregoing;
- Assessments of the role that nuclear power may play in national energy plans;
- Codes, regulations and standards for the nuclear industry;
- Research on controlled thermonuclear fusion including bilateral activities and contributions toward multilateral projects such as the International Thermonuclear Experimental Reactor (ITER); and
- Any other field mutually agreed by the Parties.

Article 3(2) provides that the above cooperation may include training, exchange of personnel, meetings, exchange of samples, materials and instruments for experimental purposes and a balanced participation in joint studies and projects.

Article 3(3) states that the Agreement does not require the transfer of any information outside the scope of the Agreement, or information that the Parties are not permitted under their respective treaties, national laws or regulations to transfer.

Article 3(4) provides that Restricted Data, as defined by each Party, shall not be transferred under the Agreement.

Article 4(1) provides *inter alia* for the Parties to facilitate nuclear trade between themselves in the mutual interests of their respective industry, utilities and consumers and also, where appropriate, trade between either Party and a third country of items obligated to the other Party.

Article 4(2) provides *inter alia* that authorizations, including export and import licenses as well as authorizations or consents to third parties relating to trade, industrial operations or nuclear material movement, should be consistent with the sound and efficient administration of the Agreement and should not be used to restrict trade.

Article 5(1) provides that nuclear material, non-nuclear material, equipment and components may be transferred for applications consistent with the Agreement. Article 5(3) provides that natural or low enriched uranium may be transferred for use as fuel in reactor experiments and in reactors, for conversion or fabrication, and for other purposes as may be agreed to by the Parties. Article 5(1) provides also that any special fissionable material transferred shall be limited to low enriched uranium, except for "small quantities," which may be transferred pursuant to Article 5(5) for use as samples, standards, detectors and targets, and the accomplishment of other purposes as agreed by the Parties.

Article 5(4) provides that the *quantity* of nuclear material transferred under the Agreement shall be consistent with any of the following purposes: use in reactor experiments or the loading of reactors, the efficient and continuous conduct of such reactor experiments or operation of reactors for their lifetime, use as samples, standards, detectors and targets, and other purposes as the Parties may agree.

Article 5(6) records verbatim certain political assurances relating to reliable supply of nuclear fuel given to India by the United States in March 2006. The Agreement language does not have the effect of converting these political assurances into legally binding commitments because the Agreement, like other U.S. agreements of its type, is intended as a framework agreement that does not compel specific exports.

Articles 5(2), 6-10, and 14 address the specific requirements of section 123a. of the AEA and are discussed in detail in part III below.

Article 11 provides that the Parties shall cooperate in following the best practices for minimizing the impact on the environment from any radioactive, chemical or thermal contamination arising from activities under the Agreement and in related matters of health and safety.

Article 12 contains additional provisions with regard to implementation of activities falling within the scope of the Agreement.

Article 13 provides for consultations at the request of either Party regarding implementation of the Agreement and the development of further cooperation in the field of peaceful uses of nuclear energy on a stable, reliable and predictable basis. It further provides that the Parties shall endeavor to avoid taking any action that adversely affects cooperation under Article 2, which is the general "Scope of Cooperation" Article.

Article 15 provides for dispute settlement through negotiations between the Parties.

Article 16 provides for the Agreement to have an initial duration of 40 years and to continue in force for additional periods of 10 years each, subject to a proviso that either Party may terminate the Agreement by giving written notice to the other Party six months prior to the close of a period. It also provides for continuation in effect of key non-proliferation provisions of the Agreement in the event of its termination.

Article 17 provides for the establishment of agreed-upon procedures to implement the terms of the Agreement.

The statutorily mandated non-proliferation conditions and controls contained in the Agreement are detailed and analyzed in the following section.

III. SUBSTANTIVE CONDITIONS

The proposed Agreement meets the applicable requirements of the Atomic Energy Act and the NNPA. Section 123a. of the Atomic Energy Act sets forth nine specific requirements that must be met in agreements for cooperation. Sections 402 and 407 of the NNPA set forth supplementary requirements. The provisions contained in the proposed Agreement satisfy those requirements as follows:

(1) Application of Safeguards

Section 123a.(1) requires a guaranty from the cooperating party that safeguards as set forth in the agreement for cooperation will be maintained with respect to all nuclear materials and equipment transferred pursuant thereto and with respect to all special nuclear material used in or produced through the use of such transferred nuclear materials and equipment, so long as the material or equipment remains under the jurisdiction or control of the cooperating party, irrespective of the duration of the other provisions in the agreement or whether the agreement is terminated or suspended for any reason.

This requirement is satisfied by Articles 10 and 16(3) of the Agreement. Safeguards are mandated by Article 10(1) on "all nuclear material and equipment transferred pursuant to this Agreement and with respect to special fissionable material used in or produced through the use of such nuclear material and equipment, so long as the material or equipment remains under the jurisdiction or control of the cooperating party." Article 10(2) provides that nuclear material and equipment transferred from the U.S. to India and "any nuclear material used in or produced through the use of nuclear material, non-nuclear material, equipment or components so transferred shall be subject to safeguards *in perpetuity* in accordance with" the India-IAEA safeguards agreement, which was recently approved by the IAEA Board of Governors.

Article 16(3) provides the assurance that, notwithstanding the termination or expiration of the Agreement or the withdrawal of a Party from the Agreement, the safeguards required under Article 10 shall "continue in effect so long as any nuclear material, non-nuclear material, by-product material, equipment or components subject to [Article 10] remains in the territory of the Party concerned or under its jurisdiction or control anywhere, or until such time as the Parties agree that such nuclear material is no longer usable for any nuclear activity relevant from the point of view of safeguards." In addition, Article 10(4) provides that both countries shall consult regarding appropriate verification measures in the event that the application of IAEA safeguards is no longer possible.

(2) Full-Scope Safeguards

The requirement for full-scope safeguards as a condition of cooperation mandated by section 123a.(2) is to be exempted pursuant to section 104 of the Hyde Act (the Henry J. Hyde United States-India Peaceful Atomic Energy Cooperation Act of 2006, Public Law 109-401).

(3) Peaceful Use

The requirement of section 123a.(3) of the AEA for a guaranty against explosive or military uses of nuclear materials and equipment transferred and special nuclear material produced through the use of such items is met by Article 9 of the Agreement, which provides that:

> Nuclear material, equipment and components transferred pursuant to this Agreement and nuclear material and by-product material used or produced through the use of any nuclear material, equipment, and components so transferred shall not be used by the recipient Party for any nuclear explosive device, for research on or development of any nuclear explosive device or for any military purpose.

(4) Right of Return

Section 123a.(4) of the AEA requires a stipulation that, in the event of a nuclear detonation by a non-nuclear weapon state cooperating party or termination or abrogation of an IAEA safeguards agreement by such a party, the United States shall have a right to the return of any nuclear materials and equipment transferred pursuant to the agreement for cooperation and any special nuclear material produced through the use of such transferred items. This requirement is met by Article 14 of the Agreement, which provides a right of return regarding "any nuclear material, equipment, non-nuclear material or components transferred under this Agreement and any special fissionable material produced through their use" (Article 14(4)). The procedure for exercising this right of return is as follows:

- Pursuant to Article 14(1), either Party has the right to terminate the Agreement on one year's written notice to the other Party;

- The Party seeking termination has the right to cease further cooperation if it determines that "a mutually acceptable resolution of outstanding issues has not been possible or cannot be achieved through consultations" (Article 14(2));
- Either party may exercise the right of return "following the cessation of cooperation" as provided for in Article 14(2) and "on or before the date of termination" as provided for in Article 14(1).

Thus, the right of return provided for in Article 14 of the Agreement fully satisfies the requirements of section 123a.(4) in terms of the items subject to the right of return and the circumstances under which it may be exercised.

(5) Retransfer Consent

Section 123a.(5) of the AEA requires a guaranty by the cooperating party that any material, Restricted Data, and production or utilization facility transferred pursuant to the agreement "or any special nuclear material produced through the use of any such [facility or material] will not be transferred to unauthorized persons or beyond the jurisdiction or control of the cooperating party" without prior U.S. consent. This requirement is met by Article 7(2) of the Agreement. (The transfer of Restricted Data is precluded by Article 3(4) of the Agreement.)

(6) Physical Security

The requirement of section 123a.(6) of the AEA for a guaranty that adequate physical security will be maintained with respect to any nuclear material transferred pursuant to an agreement of cooperation and any special nuclear material used in or produced through the use of nuclear material, production facility or utilization facility transferred pursuant to the agreement is met by Article 8 of the Agreement.

(7) Enrichment/Reprocessing/Alteration Consent Right

Section 123a.(7) of the AEA requires a guaranty that "no material transferred pursuant to the agreement for cooperation and no material used in or produced through the use of any material, production facility, or utilization facility transferred pursuant to the agreement will be reprocessed, enriched or (in the case of plutonium, uranium 233, or uranium enriched to greater than 20 per cent in the isotope 235, or other nuclear materials which have been irradiated) otherwise altered in form or content without the prior approval of the United States."

In Article 6, the Parties provide mutual consent for enrichment up to 20 percent in the isotope 235 of uranium subject to the Agreement. The Parties also provide mutual consent to reprocessing and alteration in form or content of nuclear material subject to the Agreement, except that to bring this right into effect in the case of India, India must establish a new national reprocessing facility dedicated to reprocessing safeguarded nuclear material under IAEA safeguards *and* both Parties must agree on arrangements and procedures under which the reprocessing or other alteration in form or content will take place in the new facility, including provisions with respect to the application of IAEA safeguards to *all* facilities concerned with these activities, as well as provisions relating to physical protection, storage, environmental protection, and use of any separated special fissionable material only in national facilities under IAEA safeguards. Article 14(9) provides that the above "arrangements and procedures" are subject to suspension by either Party in exceptional circumstances, as defined by the Parties, after consultations as specified in that paragraph. (Since Article 14 is not among those continuing in effect if the Agreement as a whole were to be terminated (Article 16(3)), a Party intending to suspend the "arrangements and procedures" under Article 6 would need to do so prior to termination of the Agreement itself.)

Article 6 also satisfies section 402(a) of the NNPA, which states that, except as specifically provided in any agreement for cooperation, no source or special nuclear material exported from the United States after the date of the NNPA may be enriched after export without the prior approval of the United States for such enrichment.

(8) Storage Consent Right

The requirement of section 123a.(8) of the AEA for a guaranty of a right of prior U.S. approval over facilities for the storage of specified nuclear materials is met by Article 7(1).

(9) Sensitive Nuclear Technology

The requirement of section 123a.(9) pertains to situations that may result when sensitive nuclear technology is transferred pursuant to a section 123 agreement for cooperation. Article 5(2) of the Agreement provides that sensitive nuclear technology shall only be transferred under the Agreement if provided for by an amendment to the Agreement, and Article 5(2) further provides that sensitive nuclear facilities and major critical components thereof shall only be transferred under the Agreement if provided for by an amendment to the Agreement. Accordingly, the requirement in section 123a.(9) is not relevant to the proposed Agreement, and the requirement in section 402(b) of the NNPA precluding the transfer of major critical components of facilities for uranium enrichment, nuclear fuel reprocessing, or heavy water production unless an agreement for cooperation "specifically designates such components as items to be exported pursuant to [such] agreement" is also satisfied.

Environmental: Article 11 of the proposed Agreement provides that the Parties "shall follow the best practices for minimizing the impact on the environment from any radioactive, chemical or thermal contamination arising from peaceful activities under this Agreement," thereby satisfying section 407 of the NNPA.

Proportionality: For the purpose of implementing rights specified in Articles 6 and 7 of the proposed Agreement, "produced" special nuclear material is defined in terms of proportionality in the Agreed Minute to the Agreement. Thus, if U.S. nuclear material is used in a non-U.S. reactor, the special nuclear material produced will be attributed to the U.S. in the proportion of the U.S. nuclear material to the total amount of nuclear material used, and similarly for subsequent generations. It has been our consistent view that sections 123 and 127 of the AEA allow this concept of proportionality to be used in determining the reasonable application of U.S. consent rights. Indeed, all of the agreements negotiated since the enactment of the NNPA in 1978 contain a similar proportionality provision.

The proposed Agreement thus satisfies all the substantive requirements specified for agreements for cooperation by the AEA and the NNPA, with the exception of section 123a.(2), from which it is to be exempted.

IV. OTHER NONPROLIFERATION POLICY ISSUES

1. Safeguards

Full-Scope versus INFCIRC/66 safeguards

A non-nuclear weapons state party to the NPT is required to have in place a "full-scope" safeguards agreement, applicable to all nuclear material and activities in the state. Such an agreement, based on IAEA document INFCIRC/153, has historically been considered the gold standard of safeguards. Such full-scope safeguards, in conjunction with an assessment that a state's political situation was consistent with adherence to non-proliferation norms, was seen as meeting the safeguards standard for the NPAS. More recently, the United States and others have indicated that they consider that the new safeguards standard should be a full-scope safeguards agreement with an Additional Protocol. Whereas the 153-based safeguards agreement focuses on declared material and facilities, the Additional Protocol provides the IAEA with additional information and access, to provide increased assurance of the absence of *undeclared* activities.

For a non-nuclear weapon state party to the NPT, safeguards are required to be able to detect in a timely manner, and thereby deter, the diversion of one weapons-quantity (called by the IAEA a "significant quantity") of nuclear material from declared facilities. Clearly, the diversion of even one weapons-quantity of material by a NNWS NPT party would have very serious implications, both in terms of regional stability and damage to the non-proliferation regime. The IAEA has therefore adopted standards for timeliness of detection consistent with the detection of one weapons-quantity of material within a time approximately equal to that needed to convert that material into weapons-usable form; this was deemed to provide time for political action. There are no such quantitative standards for implementation of the Additional

Protocol, as activities related to detecting undeclared activities do not lend themselves to quantification and are somewhat dependent on external sources of information.

Because India is not an NPT signatory, the Indian safeguards agreement is not based on INFCIRC/153, but on another document, INFCIRC/66, discussed further below. The context in which safeguards will be applied in India differs importantly from that of a NNWS NPT signatory. India has already acquired nuclear weapons, has a fully capable nuclear weapons complex, all of the technical expertise necessary to produce weapons-grade materials, and a large stockpile of nuclear material that is outside of the safeguards agreement. The facilities retained by India outside the agreement constitute the full nuclear fuel cycle, including heavy water reactors, advanced reactors, uranium and plutonium fuel fabrication plants, and reprocessing plants.

In short, India's non-civil facilities already include every capability likely to exist among the facilities declared as civil; indeed, it is unlikely that India would chose to offer a facility as civil if it were needed for military purposes. India thus would have no apparent incentive to divert material, equipment, or technology from its declared civil sector to military uses. Its non-civil sector already possesses the necessary capabilities, and a diversion would risk a strong reaction from the U.S. and other nuclear cooperation partners.

India has committed to negotiating an Additional Protocol "with respect to its civilian facilities" with the IAEA. The IAEA's standard "Model Additional Protocol" (INFCIRC/540) was designed as an enhancement of an INFCIRC/ 153-type safeguards agreement, and to apply to the state as a whole. Thus there are bound to be important differences between the Indian AP and the Model AP. It is not clear yet what the provisions of the Indian AP will be, but it will probably provide some additional information or access to the facilities declared as civil, enhancing somewhat the effectiveness of safeguards at civil facilities. Because India will obviously have undeclared activities that are outside the scope of the safeguards agreement, the primary function of its Additional Protocol will not in general be the same as that of the Model Additional Protocol (that of detecting undeclared nuclear activities).

The safeguards agreement between India and the IAEA is based on INFCIRC/66, the Agency's approved safeguards system for states not party to the NPT. INFCIRC/66 predated the NPT and is entitled "the Agency's Safeguards System." It is not, like INFCIRC/153, a model safeguards agreement, but contains language that 66-based safeguards agreements draw on, either verbatim or by reference. These agreements can be seen as comprising two components.

One component includes the sections on the mechanics of safeguards such as procedures, reports, inspections, exemptions, termination, transfers, and procedures for various facility types. These are generally drawn from INFCIRC/

66 itself; this is the case with the Indian agreement. The technical safeguards methods provided for under an INFCIRC/66-based agreement are based on this standard language, and will be no different than those used in other safeguards agreements. We would expect that safeguards would be applied to an Indian heavy water reactor, for example, using the same technology and techniques applied to a heavy water reactor elsewhere. Some states, including Canada and Japan, are under the regime the IAEA calls "integrated safeguards" because they have an Additional Protocol in force, and because the IAEA has drawn a formal conclusion regarding the absence of undeclared activities in those states. Integrated safeguards allow the IAEA some additional flexibility in its safeguards activities, and some reductions in the intensity of inspections. We do not anticipate that such integrated safeguards would be applicable to India, because the IAEA will not be in a position to draw the relevant conclusion regarding undeclared activities. In particular, safeguards goals for timeliness and significant quantity described above are expected to apply to India, with no reductions in the frequency or extensiveness of inspections.

Safeguards on Facilities

There are also sections in the safeguards agreement identifying the scope of application of safeguards: what items the IAEA will actually inspect. This section is necessarily unique to each INFCIRC/66-based agreement; generally it names specific facilities being offered for safeguards, and describes how safeguards obligations follow material and subsequent generations of material used in or produced by that facility. In the case of the Indian safeguards agreement, no facilities or materials are offered for safeguards initially. The agreement provides that India will place a facility under safeguards in a two-step process:

- First, after entry into force of the agreement, India must "file with the Agency a Declaration, based on its sovereign decision to place voluntarily its civilian nuclear facilities under Agency safeguards in a phased manner" (para. 13); and
- Second, "India, on the basis of its sole determination, shall notify the Agency in writing of its decision to offer for Agency safeguards a facility identified by India in the Declaration referred to in paragraph 13, or any other facility to be determined by India. Any facility so notified by India to the Agency will be included in the Annex" (para. 14).

In the first step, the facilities in the declaration are expected to be those in the Indian Separation Plan, circulated to the IAEA Board of Governors as INFCIRC/731. The Separation Plan indicates that India will identify and offer for safeguards in a phased manner a number of facilities, including 14 power reactors and other facilities listed in the document. The declaration under paragraph 13 does not allow the Agency to start inspections. This can only happen after a subsequent notification under paragraph 14.

Once such a facility is notified and placed in the Annex, safeguards cannot terminate on it without a joint determination by the IAEA and India (para. 32):

> "Safeguards shall be terminated on a facility listed in the Annex after India and the Agency have jointly determined that the facility is no longer usable for any nuclear activity relevant from the point of view of safeguards."

Although the safeguards agreement includes preambular language noting India's ability to take "corrective measures" to ensure uninterrupted operation of India reactors, both the U.S. and the IAEA have concluded that the preambular language establishes the historical context of the agreement and does not affect the obligations quoted above, which are contained in the agreement's operational provisions.

The safeguards agreement allows for the possibility that safeguards could be temporarily placed on a facility not on the Annex by virtue of the fact that safeguarded material was placed in the facility (para. 11f). This is foreseen in the Indian separation plan, which indicates that an Indian reprocessing plant could be safeguarded "in campaign mode." The proposed U.S.-India agreement for cooperation stipulates that reprocessing of U.S.-obligated material will take place only in a new reprocessing facility dedicated to processing material under IAEA safeguards, subject to "arrangements and procedures" that must be agreed upon by the United States; such a facility would have to be subject to safeguards in perpetuity. It is U.S. policy not to allow export to facilities temporarily under safeguards.

Safeguards on Material

The safeguards agreement requires safeguards on material as provided for in paragraph 11:

> "11. The items subject to this Agreement shall be:
> (a) Any facility listed in the Annex to this Agreement ...
> (b) Any nuclear material, non-nuclear material, equipment and components supplied to India which are required to be safeguarded pursuant to a bilateral or multilateral arrangement to which India is a party;
> (c) Any nuclear material, including subsequent generations of special fissionable material, produced, processed or used in or by the use of a facility listed in the Annex or in or by the use of any nuclear material, non-nuclear material, equipment and components referred to in paragraph 11(b); ...."

As in all safeguards agreements, there is standard termination and suspension language that allows for material to cease being safeguarded under certain conditions; for example, if it has been diluted in a way that makes it no longer usable. The termination provision includes standard language (paragraph 30(d)) that would allow India to remove from safeguards the *Indian indigenous* uranium in spent fuel that had been used to fuel a reactor that was under safeguards in the Annex. In order to do so, India would have to separate out (by reprocessing) the plutonium in the spent fuel, which *would* remain subject to safeguards because it was produced in a reactor listed in the Annex (11(c) above). The uranium remaining after irradiation and reprocessing would be lower in U-235 than the fresh fuel that went into the reactor to begin with, and thus less attractive for any nuclear purpose. It is unlikely that India would go to such extraordinary lengths to remove from safeguards material less attractive than what it voluntarily placed under safeguards in the first place. India's ability to withdraw such material in the situation described is, however, in accordance with Agency standards, principles, and practices.

Other Safeguards Considerations

One difference between a full-scope safeguards agreement under INFCIRC/153 and an INFCIRC/66-based agreement is that substitution of non-subject material for subject material by India is allowed (paras. 11(d), 27, 30(d)), provided the Agency agrees, and provided the amount and quality of the substituted material is at least equivalent to that of the material being substituted for. The obligations on the original material transfer to the substituted material, so there is no net impact from a non-proliferation perspective. Substitution provisions are a standard element of INFCIRC/66 and substitution is widely used in nuclear commerce.

A second difference is that the agreement allows for, but does not require, safeguards on heavy water and pieces of equipment. Such safeguards are not part of INFCIRC/153 safeguards at all; heavy water is not a "nuclear material." They are needed in this safeguards agreement because existing safeguards agreements for facilities in India have such requirements. In addition, this agreement permits, but does not require, these existing safeguards agreements to be suspended in favor of the new agreement.

2. Potential for Increase in Availability of Indian Indigenous Nuclear Material for Military Use as a Result of Transfers to India for Civil Use

It has been suggested that supplying nuclear fuel to India for civil purposes could assist India's nuclear weapon program by allowing India to use more of its limited domestic supply of uranium exclusively for weapon purposes. The Executive Branch has no evidence indicating that India plans to use additional domestic uranium resources in its nuclear weapons program as a consequence of implementing the Civil Nuclear Cooperation Initiative.

Moreover, the amount of fissile material available for potential weapons use is a function not just of the amount of natural uranium available, but also of factors such as overall fuel cycle capabilities, including the capacity to produce plutonium in reactors and to separate the plutonium through reprocessing. In this regard, under the Civil Nuclear Cooperation Initiative several indigenous Indian reactors, which in theory have been available to support military programs, will be placed under safeguards and no longer be available for this purpose.

As previously noted, India has substantial, albeit limited, domestic uranium reserves, estimated by the IAEA to be about 95,000 metric tons*, a complete functioning fuel cycle, and demonstrated competence with nuclear technologies. Limits on India's capacity to process uranium ore currently constrain domestic uranium production, but new capacity should be on line in the next several years. In short, India is capable of maintaining and expanding its existing nuclear arsenal within the limits of its indigenous resources and capabilities. This will be the situation whether or not India is supplied externally with fuel for civil nuclear power.

Finally, India's stated policies indicate a posture of restraint rather than a Cold War-style, unconstrained build up of its nuclear stockpile and forces. India has long indicated that it seeks a so-called "credible minimum deterrent," and it has articulated a no-first-use policy for nuclear weapons. India has also committed to work with the United States to achieve a multilateral Fissile Material Cut-Off Treaty that would cap material available for weapons. On March 30, 2006, then Foreign Secretary Saran publicly reiterated that India "remains committed to a credible minimum deterrent. If our posture so far has been one of restraint and responsibility—not disputed even by our critics —there is no reason why we should suddenly change now." The United States will continue to urge India to maintain a posture of strategic restraint and to further strengthen its non-proliferation commitments within the context of the U.S.-India strategic partnership.

3. Physical Protection and Safety

India has been a member of the International Convention on the Physical Protection of Nuclear Materials since March 12, 2002; a member of the International Convention on Nuclear Safety since March 31, 2005; and a member of the International Convention on the Suppression of Acts of Nuclear Terrorism since it entered into force on July 7, 2007. It has thus undertaken a legal obligation to adhere to the terms of all three of these conventions. There are no cases known to the Executive Branch of fissile material being lost, diverted, or stolen in India.

---

* IAEA-TECDOC-1463, Sep. 2005. IAEA estimate included uranium in RAR, EAR-I and EAR-II categories.

4. Previous U.S.-India Peaceful Nuclear Cooperation (Tarapur)

An earlier U.S.-India agreement for peaceful nuclear cooperation, signed at Washington, August 8, 1963, entered into force October 25, 1963, and expired by its terms October 25, 1993. Under that agreement, known informally as the "Tarapur Agreement," the United States initially supplied reactor units one and two at India's Tarapur site, together with low enriched uranium (LEU) fuel to operate them. (Whereas other U.S. nuclear cooperation agreements have been "framework" agreements requiring no specific transfers, the Tarapur Agreement required the supply of these items.) U.S. cooperation under the 1963 Agreement became problematic following passage of the 1978 NNPA, which among other things established full-scope IAEA safeguards (FSS) as a requirement for continued U.S. supply of nuclear material to non-nuclear-weapon States. The NNPA provided for certain transitional arrangements for supply to India. Under these, the President in 1980 approved two further transfers of LEU fuel after the NRC determined that it could not make the findings necessary under the AEA to license the exports. One shipment was completed. The second, by mutual agreement of the Administration and Congress, was not sent. To avoid a breach of the Agreement, the United States instead engaged France as a surrogate supplier under the Tarapur Agreement. A decade later, France adopted its own FSS export policy and ended its supply for Tarapur. After expiration of the U.S.-India Agreement for Cooperation in 1993, China (which did not then have an FSS export policy) stepped in as a supplier. Later Russia stepped in as a supplier, invoking a "safety" exception in the NSG Guidelines, despite objections by the United States and most other NSG members. Russian supply is continuing.

The United States maintains, and has formally advised the Indian Government on several occasions, that certain U.S. "vested rights" have survived expiration of the 1963 Agreement, including a U.S. right to approve reprocessing of the fuel used in Tarapur reactor units one and two. India has consistently disputed the U.S. position, although it did agree "voluntarily" to maintain IAEA safeguards on the two reactors after the 1963 Agreement expired. The proposed new Agreement with India does not apply retroactively to the U.S.-supplied Tarapur reactors or their fuel. However, the Administration regards the current non-proliferation status of the Tarapur reactors and fuel as acceptable and sustainable so long as they remain under safeguards. Moreover, the Government of India has included the Tarapur reactors among the facilities to be safeguarded as part of its "civil" nuclear program; once the reactors are subject to the new safeguards agreement, they cannot be removed from safeguards unless India and the IAEA jointly determine that they are "no longer usable for any nuclear activity relevant from the point of view of safeguards" (India-IAEA Safeguards Agreement, paragraph 31).

V. CONCLUSION

Entry-into-force of the proposed U.S.-India Agreement will put in place a framework for mutually beneficial civil nuclear cooperation between the two countries and provide a foundation for continued collaboration on achieving nuclear non-proliferation goals.

On the basis of the analysis in this NPAS and all pertinent information of which it is aware, the Department of State has arrived at the following assessment, conclusions, views and recommendations:

1. The safeguards and other control mechanisms and the peaceful use assurances in the proposed Agreement are adequate to ensure that any assistance furnished under it will not be used to further any military or nuclear explosive purpose.

2. The Agreement meets all the legal requirements of the AEA and the NNPA, except section 123a.(2) of the AEA, which is to be exempted pursuant to section 104 of the Hyde Act.

3. Execution of the proposed Agreement would be compatible with the non-proliferation program, policy, and objectives of the United States.

4. Therefore, it is recommended that the President determine that the performance of the proposed Agreement will promote, and will not constitute an unreasonable risk to, the common defense and security, that he approve the Agreement and authorize its execution, and that he submit it to Congress for its approval.

Letter from President George W. Bush to the US Congress

I am pleased to transmit to the Congress, pursuant to section 123 of the Atomic Energy Act of 1954, as amended (42 U.S.C. 2153) (AEA), the text of a proposed Agreement for Cooperation Between the Government of the United States of America and the Government of India Concerning Peaceful Uses of Nuclear Energy. I am also pleased to transmit my written determination concerning the Agreement, including my approval of the Agreement and my authorization to execute the Agreement, and an unclassified Nuclear Proliferation Assessment Statement (NPAS) concerning the Agreement. (In accordance with section 123 of the AEA, as amended by title XII of the Foreign Affairs Reform and Restructuring Act of 1998 (Public Law 105-277), a classified annex to the NPAS, prepared by the Secretary of State in consultation with the Director of National Intelligence, summarizing relevant classified information, will be submitted to the Congress separately.) The joint memorandum submitted to me by the Secretary of State and the Secretary of Energy and a letter from the Chairman of the Nuclear Regulatory Commission stating the views of the Commission are also enclosed.

The proposed Agreement has been negotiated in accordance with the AEA and other applicable law. In my judgment, it meets all applicable statutory requirements except for section 123 a.(2) of the AEA, from which I have exempted it as described below.

The proposed Agreement provides a comprehensive framework for U.S. peaceful nuclear cooperation with India. It permits the transfer of information, non-nuclear material, nuclear material, equipment (including reactors) and components for nuclear research and nuclear power production. It does not permit transfers of any restricted data. Sensitive nuclear technology, heavy-water production technology and production facilities, sensitive nuclear facilities, and major critical components of such facilities may not be transferred under the Agreement unless the Agreement is amended. The Agreement permits the enrichment of uranium subject to it up to 20 percent in the isotope 235. It permits reprocessing and other alterations in form or content of nuclear material subject to it; however, in the case of such activities in India, these rights will not come into effect until India establishes a new national reprocessing facility dedicated to reprocessing under IAEA safeguards and both parties agree on arrangements and procedures under which the reprocessing or other alteration in form or content will take place.

In Article 5(6) the Agreement records certain political commitments concerning reliable supply of nuclear fuel given to India by the United States in March 2006. The text of the Agreement does not, however, transform these political commitments into legally binding commitments because the Agreement, like other U.S. agreements of its type, is intended as a framework agreement.

The Agreement will remain in force for a period of 40 years and will continue in force thereafter for additional periods of 10 years each unless either party gives notice to terminate it 6 months before the end of a period. Moreover, either party has the right to terminate the Agreement prior to its expiration on 1 year's written notice to the other party. A party seeking early termination of the Agreement has the right immediately to cease cooperation under the Agreement, prior to termination, if it determines that a mutually acceptable resolution of outstanding issues cannot be achieved through consultations. In any case the Agreement, as noted, is a framework or enabling agreement that does not compel any specific nuclear cooperative activity. In the event of termination of the Agreement, key non-proliferation conditions and controls would continue with respect to material and equipment subject to the Agreement.

An extensive discussion of India's civil nuclear program, military nuclear program, and nuclear non-proliferation policies and practices is provided in the Nuclear Proliferation Assessment Statement (NPAS) and in a classified annex to the NPAS submitted to the Congress separately.

The AEA establishes the requirements for agreements for nuclear cooperation, some of which apply only to non-nuclear-weapon states (see AEA, section 123 a.). The AEA incorporates the definition of "nuclear-weapon state" from the Treaty on the Non-Proliferation of Nuclear Weapons (NPT), which defines it to mean a state that has manufactured and exploded a nuclear weapon or other nuclear explosive device prior to January 1, 1967. Therefore, India is a non-nuclear-weapon state for NPT and AEA purposes, even though it possesses nuclear weapons. The Agreement satisfies all requirements set forth in section 123 a. of the AEA except the requirement of section 123 a.(2) that, as a condition of continued U.S. nuclear supply under the Agreement, IAEA safeguards be maintained in India with respect to all nuclear materials in all peaceful nuclear activities within its territory, under its jurisdiction, or carried out under its control anywhere (i.e., "full-scope" or "comprehensive" safeguards).

The Henry J. Hyde United States-India Peaceful Atomic Energy Cooperation Act of 2006 (the "Hyde Act") established authority to exempt the Agreement from the full-scope safeguards requirement of section 123 a.(2) of the AEA, as well as certain other provisions of the AEA relating to supply under such an agreement, provided that the President makes certain determinations and transmits them to the Congress together with a report detailing the basis for the determinations. I have made those determinations, and I am submitting them together with the required report as an enclosure to this transmittal.

Approval of the Agreement, followed by its signature and entry into force, will permit the United States and India to move forward on the U.S.-India Civil Nuclear Cooperation Initiative, which Indian Prime Minister Manmohan Singh and I announced on July 18, 2005, and reaffirmed on March 2, 2006. Civil nuclear cooperation between the United States and India pursuant to the Agreement will offer major strategic and economic benefits to both countries, including enhanced energy security, an ability to rely more extensively on an environmentally friendly energy source, greater economic opportunities, and more robust non-proliferation efforts.

The Agreement will reinforce the growing bilateral relationship between two vibrant democracies. The United States is committed to a strategic partnership with India, the Agreement promises to be a major milestone in achieving and sustaining that goal.

In reviewing the proposed Agreement I have considered the views and recommendations of interested agencies. I have determined that its performance will promote, and will not, constitute an unreasonable risk to, the common defense and security. Accordingly, I have approved it and I urge that the Congress also approve it this year.

Text of the Letter dated September 10, 2008 from President George W. Bush to the Secretary of State and the Secretary of Energy exempting India from strictures on nuclear commerce and trade with non-signatory states to the Non-Proliferation Treaty

Presidential Determination No. 2008-26

Memorandum For The Secretary of State
The Secretary of Energy

Subject: Proposed Agreement for Cooperation Between the Government of the United States of America and the Government of India Concerning Peaceful Uses of Nuclear Energy

I have considered the proposed Agreement for Cooperation Between the Government of the United States of America and the Government of India Concerning Peaceful Uses of Nuclear Energy, along with the views, recommendations, and statements of interested agencies.

I have determined that the performance of the Agreement will promote, and will not constitute an unreasonable risk to the common defense and security. Pursuant to section 123b. of the Atomic Energy Act of 1954, as amended (42 U.S.C. 2153(b)), I hereby approve the proposed Agreement and authorize the Secretary of State to arrange for its execution.

In addition, pursuant to the authority vested in me by the Constitution and the laws of the United States of America, including the Henry J. Hyde United States-India Peaceful Atomic Energy Cooperation Act of 2006 (Public Law 109-401), I hereby determine that:

1. India has provided the United States and the IAEA with a credible plan to separate civil and military nuclear facilities, materials, and programs, and has filed a declaration regarding its civil facilities and materials with the IAEA;

2. India and the IAEA have concluded all legal steps required prior to signature by the parties of an agreement requiring the application of IAEA safeguards in perpetuity in accordance with IAEA standards, principles, and practices (including IAEA Board of Governors

Document GOV/1621 (1973)) to India's civil nuclear facilities, materials, and programs as declared in the plan described in paragraph (1), including materials used in or produced through the use of India's civil nuclear facilities;

3. India and the IAEA are making substantial progress toward concluding an Additional Protocol consistent with IAEA principles, practices, and policies that would apply to India's civil nuclear program;

4. India is working actively with the United States for the early conclusion of a multilateral treaty on the cessation of the production of fissile materials for use in nuclear weapons or other nuclear explosive devices;

5. India is working with and supporting United States and international efforts to prevent the spread of enrichment and reprocessing technology to any state that does not already possess full-scale, functioning enrichment or reprocessing plants;

6. India is taking the necessary steps to secure nuclear and other sensitive materials and technology, including through (A) the enactment and effective enforcement of comprehensive export control legislation and regulations; (B) harmonization of its export control laws, regulations, policies, and practices with the guidelines and practices of the Missile Technology Control Regime (MTCR) and the Nuclear Suppliers' Group (NSG); and (C) adherence to the MTCR and the NSG in accordance with the procedures of those regimes for unilateral adherence; and

7. The NSG has decided by consensus to permit supply to India of nuclear items covered by the guidelines of the NSG.

I therefore hereby (1) exempt the proposed Agreement for Cooperation Between the Government of the United States of America and the Government of India Concerning Peaceful Uses of Nuclear Energy arranged pursuant to section 123 of the Atomic Energy Act of 1954 (42 U.S.C. 2153) from the requirement of subsection 123a.(2) of such section; (2) waive the application of section 128 of the Atomic Energy Act of 1954 (42 U.S.C. 2157) with respect to exports to India; and (3) waive with respect to India the application of:

(A) subsection 129a.(1)(D) of the Atomic Energy Act of 1954 (42 U.S.C. 2158(a)(1)(D)); and

(B) section 129 of the Atomic Energy Act of 1954 (42 U.S.C. 2158) regarding any actions that occurred before July 18, 2005.

The Secretary of State is authorized and directed to publish this determination in the *Federal Register*.

Index